Ruth Rendell

THE CROCODILE BIRD

SIMISOLA

This edition published in 2000 by Cresset Editions,
an imprint of The Random House Group Ltd,
20 Vauxhall Bridge Road, London SW1V 2SA

The Crocodile Bird first published in 1993 by Hutchinson
Simisola first published in 1994 by Hutchinson

Printed and bound in Germany

ISBN 0 09186 962 5

THE CROCODILE BIRD

To Don, Simon,
Donna and Phillip

Chapter One

The world began to fall apart at nine in the evening. Not at five when it happened, nor at half-past six when the policemen came and Eve said to go into the little castle and not show herself, but at nine when all was quiet again and it was dark outside.

Liza hoped it was all over. She watched the car go down the lane towards the bridge and then she went back to the gate-house and upstairs to watch it from her bedroom window, the red lights on its tail as it went over the bridge and its white lights when it faced her again as the road climbed and twisted among the hills. Only when she could see its lights no longer, could see no lights anywhere but a red moon and a handful of stars, did she feel they were saved.

Downstairs she found Eve, calmly waiting for her. They would talk now, but of course about other things, or read or listen to music. Eve smiled a very little, then composed her face. There was no book in her lap or piece of sewing in her hands. Liza saw that Eve's hands were shaking, and this frightened her. The first real fear she felt came from the sight of those small, normally steady hands, faintly trembling.

Eve said, 'I have something very serious to say to you.'

Liza knew what it was. It was Sean. Eve had found out about Sean and didn't like it. With a sense of shock she thought about what Eve did to men she didn't like or who interfered in her plans. An attempt would be made to separate her from Sean and if that failed, what would Eve do? She herself was safe, she always was, she was the bird who pecked at the jaws of death, but Sean was vulnerable and Sean, she saw quite clearly, might be the next candidate. She waited, tense.

It was about something quite different. 'I know it'll be hard for you, Liza, but you're going to have to go away from here.'

Again Liza got it wrong. She thought Eve meant both of them. After all, that particular threat had been hanging over them for days. This was a battle Eve hadn't been able to win, a conquest she couldn't make.

'When will we have to leave?'

'Not we. You. I've told the police you don't live here. They think you just come sometimes to visit me. I've given them your address.' Eve looked hard at Liza. 'Your address in London.'

The falling apart of things started then, and the real fear. Liza understood that she had never really known what fear was until that moment, a minute or two after nine on an evening in late August. She saw that Eve's hands had stopped shaking. They lay limp in her lap. She clenched her own.

'I haven't got an address in London.'

'You have now.'

Liza said in a jerky voice, 'I don't understand.'

'If they think you live here they'll ask you about what you saw and what you heard and perhaps – perhaps about the past. It's not only that I can't trust you – ' Eve offered a grim little smile '– to tell lies as well as I can. It's for your own protection.'

If Liza hadn't been so afraid she would have laughed. Hadn't Eve told her that saying things were for people's own protection was one way totalitarians

2

justified secret police and lying propaganda? But she was too frightened, so frightened that she forgot she had been calling Eve by her first name for years and reverted to the childhood usage.

'I can't go away alone, Mother.'

Eve noticed. She noticed everything. She winced as if that name had brought her a twinge of pain. 'Yes, you can. You must. You'll be all right with Heather.'

So that's whose address it was. 'I can stay here. I can hide if they come back.' Like a child, not someone of nearly seventeen. And then, 'They won't come back.' A sharp indrawing of breath, the voice not hers but a baby's. 'Will they?'

'I think so. No, I know so. This time they will. In the morning probably.'

Liza knew Eve wasn't going to explain anything, and she didn't want an explanation. She preferred her own knowledge to the horror of naked confession, admission, perhaps excuse. She said again, 'I can't go.'

'You must. And tonight, preferably.' Eve looked at the dark out there. 'Tomorrow morning, first thing.' She closed her eyes for a moment, screwed them up and made a face of agony. 'I know I haven't brought you up for this, Lizzie. Perhaps I've been wrong. I can only say I had the best intentions.'

Don't let her say that about my own protection again, Liza prayed. She whispered, 'I'm scared to go.'

'I know – oh, I know.' A voice caressing yet wretched, a voice that somehow yearned, Eve's large dark eyes full of compassion. 'But listen, it won't be too hard if you do exactly what I say, and then you'll be with Heather. You always do what I say, don't you, Lizzie.'

I don't. I used to once. Her fear held her rigid and silent.

3

'Heather lives in London. I've written the address down, this is the address. You must walk to where the bus stops. You know where that is, on the way to the village, between the bridge and the village, and when the bus comes – the first one comes at seven-thirty – you must get on it and tell the driver where you want to go. It's written down here. You must hold out your money and say, "The station, please." The bus will take you to the station, it stops outside the station, and you must go to the place where it says "tickets" and buy a single ticket to London. "A single to London," is what you say. It's written down here: Paddington, London.

'I can't get in touch with Heather to say you're coming. If I go to the house to use the phone Matt will see. Anyway, the police may be there. But Heather works at home, she'll be at home. At Paddington station you must go to where it says "taxis" and take a taxi to her house. You can show the taxi driver the piece of paper with her address on. You can do all that, Lizzie, can't you?'

'Why can't you come with me?'

Eve was silent for a moment. She wasn't looking at Liza but at Bruno's painting on the wall, Shrove at sunset, purple and gold and dark bluish-green. 'They told me not to go anywhere. "You aren't planning on going anywhere, I hope," is what they said.' She lifted her shoulders in that characteristic way, a tiny shrug. 'You have to go alone, Liza. I'm going to give you some money.'

Liza knew she would get it from the little castle. When Eve had gone she thought of the ordeal before her. It would be impossible. She saw herself lost as she sometimes was in dreams. Those were the kind of dreams she had, of wandering abandoned in a strange place, and weren't all places strange to her? She would be alone in some grey desolation of

4

concrete and buildings, of empty tunnels and high windowless walls. Her imagination created it out of well-remembered Victorian fiction and half-forgotten monochrome television scenes, a rats' alley from Dickens or a film studio. But it was impossible. She would die first.

The money was a hundred pounds in notes and some more in coins. Eve put it into her hands, closing her fingers around it, thinking no doubt that Liza had never touched money before, not knowing that she had done so once when she found the iron box.

The coins were for the bus, the exact fare. What would she say to the driver? How would she ask? Eve began explaining. She sat beside Liza and went through the instructions she had written down.

Liza said, 'What's going to happen to you?'

'Perhaps nothing and then you can come back and everything will be like it used to be. But, we must face it, the chances are they'll arrest me and I'll have to appear in the magistrates' court and then – and then a bigger court. Even then, it may not be too bad, it may only be a year or two. They aren't like they used to be about these things, not like – ' even now she could be reassuring, jokey ' – in the history books. No torture, Lizzie, no dungeons, no shutting up in a cell for ever. But we have to face it, it may be – for a while.'

'You haven't taught me to face anything,' Liza said.

It was as if she had slapped Eve's face. Eve winced, though Liza had spoken gently, had spoken despairingly.

'I know. I did it for the best. I never thought it would come to this.'

'What did you think?' Liza asked, but she didn't wait for an answer. She went upstairs to her room.

*

5

Eve came in to say good night.

She was cheerful as if nothing had happened. She was smiling and at ease. These mood swings made Liza more frightened than ever. She thought it likely Eve would fall asleep at once and sleep soundly. Eve kissed her good night and said to be off in the morning early, to take a few things with her but not to bother too much, Heather had cupboards full of clothes. Smiling radiantly, she said it sounded terrible to say it but in a strange way she felt free at last.

'The worst has happened, you see, Lizzie, it's rather liberating.'

The last thing Liza noticed before her mother left the room was that she was wearing Bruno's gold earrings.

She had meant not to sleep at all but she was young and sleep came. The sound of a train woke her. She sat up in the dark, understanding at once it had been a dream. No train had run along the valley for years, not since she was a child. Without the trains the silence had been deeper than ever.

Fear came back before the memory of what there was to be afraid of. A vague unformulated terror loomed, a great black cloud, that split into the constituents of her dread, the initial departure, the bus – suppose it didn't come? – the terrible train, in her mind a hundred times the size of the valley train with its toy engine, Heather whom she recalled as tall, strange, remote and full of secrets to be whispered to Eve behind a guarding hand.

In all of it Liza had forgotten Sean. How could she let Sean know? The load of bewilderment and despair cast her down among the bedclothes again and she lay there with her face buried and her ears covered. But the birds' singing wouldn't let her lie quiet. The birds were sometimes the only things

6

down here to make a sound from morning till night. The dawn chorus broke with a whistling call, then came a single trill and soon a hundred birds were singing in as many trees.

She sat up fully this time. The gate-house was silent. Outside all but the birds seemed quiet, for the wind had dropped. The curtains at the window were wide apart as they always were, since the only lights ever to be seen were those of Shrove. She knelt up on the bed in front of the window.

Some demarcation was visible between the brow of the high wooded hills and the dark but clear and glowing sky. There, in the east, a line of red would appear, a gleaming red sash of light unravelled. Meanwhile, something could be seen, the outline of the house, a single light in the stable block, a dense black shapelessness of woodland.

Knowledge of what was out there began to give the prospect form or else the cold glow that comes just before dawn had started to lift the countryside out of darkness into morning twilight. The water meadows showed themselves pale as clouds and the double line of alders on either side of the river seemed to step out of the surrounding dark. Now Liza could see the shape of the high hills beyond, though not yet their greenness, nor the road that banded them halfway up like a white belt.

She got off the bed, opened the door very quietly and listened. Eve, who never rested by day, who was always alert, attentive, watchful, uncannily obser-vant, slept by night like the dead. She was going to be arrested today but still she slept. The uneasy feeling came to Liza, as it had come before, that her mother was strange, was odd inside her head, but how would she really know? She had no standard of comparison.

If she didn't think about what she was going to do

7

but kept her mind on practical things, if she didn't *think*, it wasn't so bad. These moments had to be lived through, not the future. She went downstairs to the bathroom, came back and dressed. She wasn't hungry, she thought she would never eat again. The thought of food, of eating a piece of bread, of drinking milk, make her feel sick. She put on the cotton trousers Eve had made, a tee shirt from the reject shop, her trainers, Eve's old brown parka, the hundred pounds divided between its two pockets.

Did Eve mean her to say goodbye?

Opening her mother's door, she thought how this was the first time she had done so without knocking while Eve was inside, since Bruno came, or earlier even, since the first Jonathan days. Eve lay asleep on her back. She wore a decorous white nightdress, high at the neck, and her thick dark brown hair was spread all over the pillows. In her deep sleep she was smiling as if she dreamed of lovely pleasurable things. That smile made Liza shiver and she shut the door quickly.

It was no longer dark. Clouds were lifting away from the thin red girdle that lay along the tops of trees, dark blue feathers of cloud being drawn away up into a brightening sky. Birdsong filled up past silence with its loud yet strangely remote music. Liza was thinking again, she couldn't help it. Opening the front door and going outside and closing it behind her was the hardest thing she had ever done. It exhausted her and she leaned on the gate for a moment. Perhaps nothing would seem so hard again. She had taken her key with her, why she couldn't tell.

The chill of daybreak touched her face like a cool damp hand. It brought back the feeling of sickness and she breathed deeply. Where would she be this time tomorrow? Better not think of it. She began to walk along the lane, slowly at first, then faster, trying to calculate the time. Neither she nor Eve had ever possessed a watch. It must be somewhere between six-thirty and seven.

Too light for cars to have their lights on, yet these had, two of them that she could see in the far distance coming along the winding road towards the bridge. She sensed that they were together because both had lights, one following the other, aiming for a certain goal.

By now she was in that part of the lane that was the approach to the bridge and where no tall trees grew. She could see the flash the morning light made on the river and see too the tunnel mouth on the other side where once the train had plunged into the hillside. Suddenly the car lights were switched off, both sets. Liza couldn't even see the cars any more, but she knew they were coming this way. There was nowhere else for them to go.

If she got on to the bridge they would have to pass her, only they wouldn't pass her, they would stop. She climbed up the bank and hid herself among the late summer tangle of hawthorn and bramble and wayfarer's tree. The cars glided up silently. One of them had a blue lamp on its roof, but the lamp wasn't lit.

Liza had been holding her breath all the time and now she expelled it in a long sigh. They would come back – they would bring Eve back – and in doing so pass the bus stop. She scrambled down the bank and ran on to the bridge. The river was wide and deep and glassy, not gulping at boulders and rippling between them until much farther up. On the bridge Liza did what it was unwise to do, she stopped and turned and looked back.

It might be that she would never see it again, any of it. She would never return, so she stopped and looked back like the woman in the picture at Shrove had done, the tall sad woman in white draperies that Eve told her was Lot's wife and her forsaken home the Cities of the Plain. But instead of those desolate and wicked places, she saw between the trees that rose out of the misty water meadows, the alders and the balsams and the lombardy poplars, the gracious outlines of Shrove House.

The sun that had risen in a golden dazzlement shed a pale amber light on its stone façade, the central pediment which held a coat of arms of unknown provenance, its broad terrace approached by flights of steps on both sides, its narrow door below and wide noble door above. This was the garden front, identical to the front that faced the gates in all but that aspect's gracious portico. All its windows were blanked by this light that lay on them like a skin. The house looked as immovable as the landscape in which it rested, as natural and as serene.

From nowhere else could you see Shrove as from here. Trees hid it from spectators on the high hills. They knew how to conceal their homes from view, those old builders of great houses, Eve had said. Liza said a silent goodbye to it, ran across the bridge and out on to the road. The place where the bus stopped was a couple of hundred yards up on the left. Whatever Eve might think, she knew it well, she had often walked this way, had seen the bus, a green bus that she had never once been tempted to board.

What time was it now? A quarter past seven? When would the next bus come if she missed this one? In an hour? Two hours? Insurmountable difficulties once more built themselves up before her. Ramparts of difficulties reared up in her path, impossible to scale. She couldn't wait for that bus out in the open and risk the police cars passing her.

10

For all that, she kept on walking towards the bus stop, shifting the bag on to her other shoulder, now wondering about the train. There might not be another train to London for a long time. The train that had once run along the valley had passed quite seldom, only four times a day in each direction. How would she know anyway if the train she got into was the one for London?

The sound of a car made her turn but it wasn't one of their cars. It was red with a top made of cloth and it rattled. As it passed it left behind a smell she wasn't used to, metallic, acrid, smoky.

One other person waited at the stop. An old woman. Liza had no idea who she was or where she came from. There were no houses until the village was reached. She felt vulnerable, exposed, the focus of invisible watching eyes as she came up to the stop. The woman looked at her and quickly looked away as if angry or disgusted.

It took only one more car to pass for Liza to know she couldn't wait there, she couldn't stand on the verge and wait for the bus. What was she to do there? Stand and stare? Think of what? She couldn't bear her thoughts and her fear was like a mouthful of something too hot to swallow. If she waited here by the old woman with the downcast eyes she would fall down or scream or cast herself on to the grassy bank and weep.

An impulse to run came to her and she obeyed it. Without looking to see if anything was coming, she ran across the road and plunged in among the trees on the other side. The old woman stared after her. Liza hung on to the trunk of a tree. She hugged it, laying her face against the cool smooth bark. Why hadn't she thought of this before? It had come to her on a sudden what she must do. If she had thought of this last evening how happy the night would have

11

been! Except that if she had she would have left last night, gone when Eve first told her to go, fled in the darkness across the fields.

A footpath ran close by here and through the pass. You couldn't really call it a pass, a pass was for mountains, but she had read the word and liked it. First of all she had to scramble up a hundred yards of hillside. The rumble of the bus, whose engine made a different noise from cars, made her look down. Somehow she guessed it had arrived exactly on time. The old woman got on it and the bus moved off. Liza went on climbing. She didn't want to be there still when the cars came by. The footpath signpost found, she climbed the stile and took the path that ran close under the hedge. The sun was up now and feeling warm.

It was a relief to be far from the road, to know that when they came back they would be down there below her. When the path came to an end she would find herself in a web of lanes, buried in banks, sheltered by hedges, far from thoroughfares that went anywhere. The nearest town was seven miles off. It ought not to take her more than half an hour from here and she would be with him soon after eight. She wouldn't let herself think he might have gone, he might have moved on, that angry with her, he had abandoned her and fled.

The birds had stopped singing. All was still and silent, her own footfalls soundless on the sandy track. The white and gold faces of camomile flowers had appeared everywhere among the grass and the old man's beard that had been clematis clung to the hedges in cascades of curly grey hair. She encountered her first animals, half a dozen red cows and two grey donkeys cropping the lush grass. A ginger cat, going home from a night's hunting, gave her a suspicious look. She had seen few cats, most of them in pictures, and the sight of this one was as pleasing as that of some exotic wild creature might be.

With the bright morning and her marvellous decision, fear was fast ebbing away. She had only one isolated fear left, that he wouldn't be there. The path came to an end with another stile and she was out in a lane so narrow that if she had lain down and stretched her arms beyond her head, her hands might have touched one side and her feet the other. A small car could have got along it, tunnelling between the steep, almost vertical, banks, green ramparts hung with the long leaves of plants whose flowers had bloomed and faded. The tree branches met and closed overhead.

It was flat, even a little downhill, and she began to run. She ran from youth and an increasing sense of freedom but from hope and anxiety too. If he had gone, meaning to let her know tomorrow or the next day . . . Her hands in her pockets closed over and crushed the notes, two thin fistfuls – a lot or a little?

She ran on through the green tunnel and a rabbit ran across ahead of her. A cock pheasant squawked and flapped, teetered across the lane, a poor walker and a worse flier, its two hens following it, scrabbling for the shelter of the bank. She knew about things like that, knew far better, she suspected, than most people, but would it suffice? Would it do until she could learn about the other things?

The lane met another and another at a fork with a tiny triangle of green in the midst of it. She took the right-hand branch where the land began to fall still further but she had to go past one bend and then another before she saw the caravan below her. Her heart leapt. It was all right. He was there.

It was parked, as it had been for the past few weeks, since midsummer, on a sandy space from which a bridlepath opened and followed the

13

boundary between field and wood. Horses were supposed to use it but Liza had never seen a horse or a rider on that path. She had never seen anyone there but Sean. His old Triumph Dolomite, like a car from a 'sixties film, was parked where it always was. The curtains were drawn at the caravan windows. He only got up early for work. She had been running but she walked this last bit, she walked quite slowly up to the caravan, mounted the two steps, and taking her right hand from her pocket and the notes it had still been enclosing, brought it to the smooth surface of the door.

Her hand poised, she hesitated. She drew in her breath. Knowing nothing but natural history and scraps of information from Victorian books, she nevertheless knew that love is unreliable, love is chancy, love lets you down. It came to her, this knowledge, from romantic dramas and love poetry, the sighs of the forsaken, the bitterness of the rejected, but from instinct too. Innocence is never ignorant of this except in those nineteenth-century novels and then only sometimes. She thought of how he could kill her with the wrong word or the abstracted look and then she expelled her breath and knocked on the door.

His voice came from in there. 'Yes? Who is it?'

'Sean, it's me.'

'Liza?'

Only amazed, only incredulous. He had the door open very quickly. He was naked, a blanket from the bed tied round him. Blinking at the light, he stared at her. If she saw a sign of dismay in his eyes, if he asked her what she was doing there she would die, it would kill her.

He said nothing. He took hold of her and pulled her inside, into the stuffy warm interior that smelt of man, and put his arms round her. It wasn't an ordinary hug but an all-enveloping embrace. He folded himself around her and held her inside himself as a hand might enfold a fruit or a cone, softly but intensely, sensuously appreciating.

She had been going to explain everything and had foreseen herself telling her long tale, culminating in what had happened yesterday. It was a justification she had had in mind and a defence. But he gave her no chance to speak. Somehow, without words, he had made plain to her his great happiness at her untoward unexpected arrival and that he wanted her without explanation. As his arms relaxed their hold she lifted up her face to him, to look at his beautiful face, the eyes that changed his whole appearance when they grew soft with desire. But she was deprived of that too by his kiss, by his bringing his mouth to hers, so sweet-tasting and warm, blinding and silencing her.

When the bed was pulled down out of the wall the caravan was all bed. Her face still joined to his, she wriggled out of her clothes, dropped her clothes garment by garment on to the floor, stepped out of the cotton trousers, kicked off her trainers. She put her arms up again to hold him as he had held her. He let her pull him down on to the bed. It was warm where he had left it. They lay side by side, her breasts soft and full against his chest, hip to hip, their legs entwined. He began to kiss her with the tip of his tongue, lightly, quickly. She laughed, turned her face.

'I've run away! I've come to you for good.'

'You're a marvel,' he said. 'You're the greatest,' and then, 'What about her?'

'I don't know. The police came, they came in two cars, they'll have taken her away.' She appreciated his look of amazement, his interest. 'I'd gone by then. Are you pleased?'

15

'Am I *pleased*? I'm over the moon. But what d'you mean, the police? What police?'

'I don't know. The police from the town.'

'What's she done?'

She put her lips close to his ear. 'Shall I tell you about it?'

'Tell me the lot but not now.'

He ran his hands down her body, down her back in a long slow sweep and drew it close to him in a delicate arch. Without looking she sensed him viewing her, appreciating her smoothness, her whiteness, her warmth. His hip touched hers, his thigh pressed against hers, warmth to warmth and skin to skin.

'Don't talk now, sweetheart,' he said. 'Let's have this now.'

Chapter Two

She slept for a long time. She was very tired. Relief had come too and a reprieve. When she woke up Sean was sitting on the bed, looking down at her. She put out her hand and took hold of his, clutching it tightly.

Sean was wonderful to look at. She hadn't much to judge by, the painted man at Shrove, grainy mono-chrome images of actors in old movies, the postman, the oilman, Jonathan and Bruno, Matt and a few others. His face was pale, the shape of the features sharply cut, his nose straight, his mouth red and full for a man's, dark eyes where she fancied she saw dreams and hopes, and eyebrows like the strokes of a Chinese painter's brush. She had seen a painting in the drawing room at Shrove with willow leaves and pink-breasted birds, a strange flower Eve said was a lotus, and letters made up of black curves like Sean's eyebrows. His hair was black as coal. Liza had read that, for as far as she knew she had never seen coal.

'You've been asleep for five hours.' He said it admiringly, as one acclaiming another for some particular prowess.

'For a minute, when I woke up, I didn't know where I was. I've never been to sleep anywhere but in the gate-house.'

'You're kidding,' he said.

'No, why would I? I've never slept away from home.' She marvelled at it. 'This is my home now.'

'You're the greatest,' he said. 'I'm lucky to have you, don't think I don't know it. I never thought you'd come, I thought, she'll never come and stay and *be* with me, she'll go and I'll lose her. Don't laugh, I know I'm a fool.'

'I wouldn't laugh, Sean. I love you. Do you love me?'

'You know I do.'

'Say it, then.'

'I love you. There, is that OK? Haven't I proved I love you? I'd like to prove it all the time. Let me come in there with you, love, let's do it again, shall we? D'you know what I'd like best? To do it to you all the time, we wouldn't eat or sleep or watch TV or any of those things, we'd just do it for ever and ever till we died. Wouldn't that be a lovely death?'

For answer she jumped up, eluding his grasp, and shifted to the far corner of the bed. He had laid her clothes there, the garments shaken and carefully placed side by side, like Eve might. Quickly she pushed her legs into the trousers, pulled the tee shirt over her head.

She said gravely, 'I don't want to die. Not that way or any other.' A thought came that she had never considered before. 'You wouldn't ever do it to me without me wanting it, would you, Sean?'

He was angry for a moment. 'Why d'you say things like that? Why did you ask me that? I don't understand you sometimes.'

'Never mind. It was just an idea. Don't you ever have nasty ideas?'

He shrugged, the light and the desire gone out of his face. 'I'm going to make us a cup of tea. Or d'you fancy a Coke? I've got Coke and that's about all I have got. I haven't got nothing to eat, we shall have to go down the shop.'

'Anything', she thought. 'I haven't got anything to

eat.' She wouldn't tell him this time. 'Sean,' she said, up in the corner, her back to the wall, 'Sean, we'll have to *go*. I mean, leave here. We ought to put a good many miles between us and her.'

'Your Mum?'

'Why do you think the police came? I told you they came.' As she spoke she knew he hadn't thought, he hadn't listened. Probably he hadn't heard her say that about the police. He had been consumed by desire, mad for her, closed to everything else. She knew how that felt, to be nothing but a deaf, blind, senseless *thing*, swollen and thick with it, breathless and faint. 'I told you the police came.'

'Did you? I don't know. What did they come for?'

'Can I have that Coke?' She hesitated and made the hesitation long. 'I'm supposed to have gone to her friend Heather. That's where she thought she'd sent me. But I came to you.'

'Tell me what she's done.'

His expression was a bit incredulous and a bit – well, indulgent, she thought the word was. He was going to get a surprise. It wasn't going to be what he thought – she searched her imagination – stealing something or doing things against the law with money. He sat down where he had sat before and became intent on her. That pleased her, his total absorption.

'She killed someone,' she said. 'The day before yesterday. That's why they came and took her away and I'm afraid they'll want me, they'll want me to be a witness or something. They'll want to ask me questions and then maybe they'll try and put me somewhere to have people look after me. I've heard about that. I'm so young, I won't be seventeen till January.'

She had been wrong about his absorption. He hadn't been listening. Again he hadn't heard her, but for a different reason. He was staring at her with his mouth slightly open. As she noted this he curled his upper lip as people do when confronted by a horror.

'What did you say?'

'About what? My age? Being a witness?'

He hesitated, seemed to swallow. 'About her killing someone.'

'It was yesterday, after I came back from meeting you in the wood. Or I think so. I mean I didn't actually see it but I know she killed him.'

'Come on, love.' An awkward grin. 'I don't believe you.'

It left her helpless, she had no idea how to respond to this. She drank a few mouthfuls out of the open triangle in the top of the can. Eve had once told her that when a cat is in doubt how to act it waves the tip of its tail. She felt like a cat but with no tail to wave. He must make the next move, for she couldn't.

He got up and took a few steps away. The caravan was too small for more than a few steps to be taken. She drank some more of her Coke, watching him.

'Why did you say that,' he said, 'about her killing somebody? Was you kidding? Was you trying to be funny?'

'It's true.'

'It *can't* be.'

'Look, Sean, I didn't make it up. It's why I came away, I didn't want them to take me and shut me up, make me live somewhere. I knew they'd come this time. This time they'd find out and it wouldn't take long. I was expecting them all night.'

His naturally pale face had gone whiter. She noticed and wondered why. 'You mean she killed someone by accident, don't you?'

'I don't understand what that means.' It was a sentence she was often obliged to utter since she had been with him.

20

'She was shooting birds and shot someone by mistake, is that it? You told me she wouldn't never kill birds or rabbits, you told me that when we first met.'

Only the last five words really registered with her. They made her smile, remembering. She slithered down the bed, jumped off and put her arms round him. 'Wasn't it lovely that I met you and you met me? It was the best thing that ever happened to me.'

This time it was he who pulled away from the embrace. 'Yes, love, OK, it was great. But you've got to tell me. About this killing, this is serious, right? What happened? Was it some guy poaching?'

'No,' she said, 'no, you don't understand.'

'Too bloody right I don't and I won't if you don't tell me.'

'I'll try.' She sat down and he sat down and she held his hand. 'She murdered him, Sean. People do do that, you know.' It seemed a wild and curious statement for her to be making. 'She murdered him because she wanted to be rid of him. She wanted him out of the way, it doesn't matter why, it's not important now.'

This time he didn't say he disbelieved her but, 'I *can't* credit it.'

What had Eve said? 'Then you must just accept.'

'Who did she murder?' She could tell from his tone that he still thought she was lying.

'It doesn't matter.' That made her impatient. 'A man. No one you know. Sean, it's the truth, you have to believe me.' She was learning truths of her own. 'I can't be with someone who thinks I'm telling him lies.' From delighted laughter, she was near to tears. She sought for a way out. 'I can't prove it. What can I do to make you believe it?'

He said in a low voice, 'I sort of do believe you – now.'

21

'I'll tell you all about it.' She was eager. She took hold of his shoulders and brought her face close up to his. 'I'll tell you everything, if you like, from when I was small, from when I can first remember.'

He kissed her. When her face was as close to his as that he couldn't resist kissing her. His tongue tasted of the caramel sweetness of Coke as she supposed hers must. They were on the bed, that was where you sat in the caravan, and her body grew soft, sliding backwards, sinking into the mattress, she was wanting him as much as she had when she first arrived that morning. He pulled her up, grasping her hands.

'I want you to tell me, Liza, I want to know everything about you. But not now. Now tell me what your Mum did.'

Being frustrated made her sulky. 'What's the good? You won't believe it.'

'I will, I've said so.'

'I think we ought to leave, we ought to be on our way, not sitting here talking.'

'Don't you worry yourself about that, I'll see to all that. You tell me about your Mum and this man.' She saw it in his eyes as the idea came to him. 'Did he try raping her, was that it?'

'He was teaching her to shoot pigeons with a shotgun. He was out there shooting and she said, "show me how".'

'You've got to be joking.'

'It's the truth. If you're going to say that, I won't tell you.'

'Right, then. Go on.'

'I hate shooting birds. I hate people shooting anything, rabbits, squirrels, anything, it's *wrong*. And I thought Eve – my Mother – I thought she did. She said so, she taught me to think like that. But she told him the pigeons were eating her vegetables and she asked him to show her how and he said he

22

would. You see, I think he'd have done anything she asked, Sean.'

'She's an attractive woman.'

'More attractive than I am?'

'Don't be bloody ridiculous. Was you watching all this?'

'I'd been in the wood with you,' Liza said. 'They didn't see me. I came up through the garden and they were on the grass where the new trees are. Sound carries terrific distances there, you know. Even when people are speaking softly you can hear them. I saw the two of them with just the one gun and I thought she must be telling him not to shoot the pigeons. He was allowed to, you know, because though pheasant shooting doesn't start till October you can shoot pigeons when you like. Poor things! What did it matter to him, he wasn't a farmer, they weren't his cabbages they were eating and if they were, the pigeons have got to live, haven't they?

'I thought, good for her, she's going to stop him, but she didn't. She was out there with him for a shooting lesson. I'd heard her talking about it with him but I didn't think she was serious. When I saw them I asked myself, what on earth is she doing? He started showing her things about the gun and she was looking and then he handed it to her.

'I didn't want to see the birds killed. I started to go back towards the gate-house. Then the shot came and immediately afterwards this screaming choking noise. So I turned round and ran across the lawn and there she was looking at him where he lay. She wasn't holding the gun, she'd dropped it, she was looking down at him and all the blood on him.'

Sean had put up his hand to cover his mouth. His eyes had grown very big. He took his hand away, pushing at his cheek in a curious wiping movement. 'What did you do?' he said in a small voice.

23

'I didn't do anything. I went home. She didn't tell the police and I didn't, so I think Matt must have. You know Matt?'

'Of course I do.'

'He was there, up by the house. Only I don't think he saw any more than I did. He guessed.'

'But you said the police had only just come, they were coming when you left – when? A couple of hours ago?'

'They came last evening. They didn't see me. You see, they didn't come to the gate-house, not then. First of all cars came and a black van to take away the body. I watched it all from my bedroom window. Eve told me to stay there and not come out, not to let anyone see me. I didn't want them to see me. She went up to Shrove and I think the policemen talked to her there. They talked to her and they talked to Matt and Matt's wife.

'She knew they'd come back, so she said I must go. For my own protection, she said. I ran away to you. That's it.'

'That's all of it?'

'Not *all*, Sean. It'll take me a long time to tell you all of it.'

'I'll get the van fixed up to the tow bar,' he said.

She went outside with him. The day was warm and sultry, two in the afternoon, and the sun a puddle of light in a white sky. Watching him, she picked blackberries off the hedge and ate them by the handful. She was enormously hungry.

The battered Dolomite shifted the caravan with the slow weary competence of an old carthorse. It groaned a bit and expelled a lot of black exhaust. Liza got into the passenger seat and banged the door. Car and caravan lurched off the grass verge on to the harder surface of the lane.

'Where shall we go?'

24

'We have to go where they'll let me park the van. Before you come I was thinking of trying Vanner's, they're wanting pickers for the Coxes, we could both of us do that.'

'Coxes won't be ready till the third week of September,' she said, always glad to show off something she knew and he might not. 'Anyway, how far is it?'

'Twenty-five miles, thirty. Far enough for you?'

'I don't know. What else can you do?'

He laughed. 'Electrical work, sort of, put washers on taps, grind knives, I'm halfway to a motor mechanic, wash your car, do your garden – as *you* should know – clean windows, most things, you name it.'

'Why apples then?'

'Apples make a change. I reckon I always do pick apples in September and cherries in July.'

'I'm hungry,' she said, 'I'm so *bloody* hungry.'

'Don't swear, Liza.'

'You do. Who d'you think I got it from?'

'It's different for me. You're a woman. I don't like to hear a woman swear.'

She lifted her shoulders, the way Eve did. 'I'm tremendously hungry. Can we buy some food?'

'Yeah, we can get takeaway.' He looked at her, remembered and explained, 'Stuff they've cooked for you in a shop, right? Or we'll find a caff, maybe a Little Chef if there's one on the A road.'

She was no longer afraid. Fear might not be cancelled but it was postponed. The prospect of going into a café excited her. And she'd be with Sean. Shops she had been in, one or two over the years, but a real restaurant, if that was the word, that was very different. She remembered what she had taken with her when she left the gate-house.

'I've got money. I've got a hundred pounds.'

25

'For Christ's sake,' he said.

'It's in the van, in my coat.'

'Did you nick it?' His tone was stern.

'Of course not. Eve gave it to me.'

He said nothing. She looked out of the window at the passing countryside, all of it new, all uncharted for her. They drove through a village as the church clock struck three and ten minutes later were in a sizeable town with parking in the marketplace.

On either side of the car park the roads which enclosed it were lined with shops. She had seen something like this before, though not here, the dry cleaner's, the building society, the estate agent, the Chinese restaurant, the Oxfam shop, the sandwich bar, the building society, the insurance company, the Tandoori House, the bank, the pub, the card shop, the estate agent. An arch, in pink glass and gold metal, led into a deserted hall of shops. Perhaps all towns were like this, all the same inside, perhaps it was a rule.

Sean's practised eye quickly summed up the situation. 'The caffs are closed, it's too late. Pubs are meant to stay open till all hours but they don't never seem to. I can go get us pie and chips or whatever.'

Her hunger was greater than her disappointment. 'Whatever you like. Do you want some money?'

She said it cheerfully, trying to strike the right note, having never said it before. Yet for some reason he was offended. 'I hope I'll never see the day when I've got to live off my girlfriend.'

Once he had gone she got out of the car. She stretched her arms above her head, tasting freedom. It was heady stuff, for something was making her shiver and it couldn't be the day, which was as warm as high summer. She had never felt like this before, dizzy, faint was perhaps the word, as if she might fall.

She opened the door of the caravan and clambered up inside. Five minutes' sitting down and a few deep breaths and she felt better. The bed was stowed away in the wall, the sheets and blankets folded and the table down ready for a meal by the time Sean came back. The packages he was carrying had grease seeping through the wrapping paper and gave off a pungent smell of deep frying.

She had been so hungry and the smell from the chips and Cornish pasties he unwrapped was so enticing but she couldn't help herself. Without warning to herself or him she burst into violent tears. He held her in his arms close to him, stroking her hair while she sobbed. Her body shook and her heart was pounding.

'It's all right, it's all right, sweetheart. You've had a shock, it's delayed shock, you'll be OK. I'll look after you.'

He soothed her. He stroked her hair and when she was just crying, not sobbing and shrieking any more, wiped her eyes with his fingers, as gently as a woman, as gently as Eve when she was being gentle. As she quietened he did something she loved him to do, began combing her hair with his own comb that had thick blunt teeth. The comb ran smoothly through the length of her long dark hair, from crown to tip, and as he paused she felt his fingers just touch and then linger on her neck and the lobe of her ear. She shivered, not this time from shock or strangeness.

'Give us a kiss,' he said.

It was more enthusiastic than he had bargained for, a deep sensuous kiss full of controlled energy now released. He laughed at her. 'Let's eat. I thought you was hungry.'

'Oh, I am. I'm starving.'

'You could've fooled me.'

This was her first Cornish pasty. She had no means of knowing whether it was a good one or passable or bad, but she liked it. In the past she had never been allowed to eat with her fingers. There had been many gently enforced rules and much benevolent constraint.

'When we get wherever we're going,' she said, 'I'll tell you the story of my life.'

'Right.'

'I don't *know* but I don't think there've been many lives like mine.'

'You've got a long way to go with it yet, like maybe seventy years.'

'Can I have the last chip? I'll tell you from back as far as I can remember. That's when I was four and that's when she killed the first one.'

She pulled a length from the toilet roll he kept by the bed to use as tissues and wiped her mouth. When she turned back to him to say she was ready, they could be off as soon as he liked, she saw that he was staring at her and the look on his face was aghast.

Chapter Three

One of the first things she could remember was the train. It was summer and she and Mother had gone for a walk in the fields when they heard the train whistle. The single track ran down there in the valley between the river and lower slopes of the high hills. It was a small branch line and later on, when she was older, Mother told her it was the most beautiful train journey in the British Isles. Her eyes shone when she said it.

But on that afternoon when Liza was four there were not many passengers and those there were can't have been looking out to appreciate the view, or else they were all looking out the other side at the high hills, for when Mother waved and she waved no one waved back. The train jogged along not very fast and disappeared into the round black tunnel that pierced the hillside.

Liza suspected that she and Mother hadn't been there very long the day she saw her first train. If they had been she would have seen a train before. It was possible they had been at the gate-house for only a few days. Where they had come from before that she had had no idea then nor for a long time to come. But she could remember nothing from before that day, not a face nor a place, a voice nor a touch.

There was only Mother.

There was only the gate-house where they lived and the arched gateway with the tiny one-roomed house on the other side and Shrove House in the distance. It was half-concealed by tall and beautiful trees, its walls glimpsed mysteriously and enticingly between their trunks. When Mother read stories to her and there was a palace in them as there often was, she would say, 'Like Shrove, that's what a palace is, a house like Shrove.' But all Liza had seen of the real Shrove until she was nearly five and the leaves had turned brown and blown off the trees, were a dreamy greyness, a sheet of glittering glass, a gleam of sun-touched slate.

Later on she saw it in its entirety, the stone baluster that crowned it, broken by a crest-filled pediment, the many windows, the soaring steps and the statues that stood in its alcoves. She was aware even then of the way it seemed to bask, to sit and smile as if pleased with itself, to recline smiling in the sun.

Nearly every day Mother went up to the house that was like a palace in a fairy tale, sometimes for several hours, sometimes for no more than ten minutes, and when she went she locked Liza up in her bedroom.

The gate-house was the Lodge of Shrove House. Later on, when Liza was older, Mother told her it was built in the Gothic style and not nearly so old as the house itself. It was supposed to look as if dating from the Middle Ages and had a turret with crenellations round its top and a tall peaked gable. Out of the side of the gable came the arch which went over the top of a pair of gates and came down on the other side to join up with the little house that looked like a miniature castle with its slit windows and studded door.

The gates were of iron, were always kept open and had Shrove House written on them in curly letters. The gate-house and the arch and the little castle were made of small red bricks, the dark russet colour of rosehips. Liza and Mother had two bedrooms upstairs, a living room and a kitchen downstairs and an outside lavatory. That was all. Liza's was the bedroom in the turret with a view over their garden and the wood and Shrove park and everything beyond. She disliked being locked in her bedroom but she wasn't frightened and as far as she could remember she didn't protest.

Mother gave her things to do. She had started teaching Liza to read, so she gave her rag books with big letters printed on the cloth pages. She also gave her paper and two pencils and a book to rest on. Liza had a baby bottle with orange juice in it because if she had had a glass or a cup she would have spilt the juice on the floor. Sometimes she had two biscuits, just two, or an apple.

Liza didn't know then what Mother did in Shrove House but later on she found out because Mother began taking her too and she was no longer locked in her bedroom – or only when Mother went shopping. But that was more than six months later, after it had all happened and the winter had come, when snow covered the hillsides and the only trees to keep their leaves were the huge blue cedars and the tall black firs.

Before that, in the summertime, the dogs came. Except in pictures Liza had never seen a dog or a cat or a horse or any animals but wild ones. She thought these two came the day after she and Mother had walked in the fields and seen the first train but it might have been some other day, a week or even a month later. It wasn't easy to remember time spans from so far back.

The dogs belonged to Mr Tobias. It wasn't he who brought them but another man. Liza had never seen Mr Tobias but only heard about him, and she wasn't to see him for a long long time. The man who brought the dogs came in a kind of small truck with a barrier like a white wire fence across the back inside to keep the dogs off the front scats. His name was Matt. He was a short, squarish man with big shoulders who looked very strong and his hair grew up from his broad red forehead like the bristles on a brush.

'They are Doberman pinschers,' Mother said. She always explained everything slowly and carefully. 'In Germany, which is another country a long way away, they used to be trained as police dogs. But these are pets.' She said to Matt, who was staring at her in a strange way, 'What are their names?'

'This one's Heidi and he's Rudi.'

'Are they nice friendly dogs?'

'They'll be OK with you and the kiddy. They'll never attack women, they've been trained that way. I'd be up the nearest tree myself if someone called out "Kill!" when they're around.'

'Really? Mr Tobias didn't say.'

'Thought you might say no to looking after them, I daresay.' He gazed around him, stared at the high hills beyond the valley as if they were the Himalayas. 'Bit isolated down here, aren't you? Not what you'd call much life going on.'

'It's what I like.'

'It takes all sorts, I suppose, though I'd have thought a smashing-looking girl like yourself'd want something a bit more lively. Bright lights, eh, bit of dancing and the movies? You wouldn't have such a thing as a cup of tea going, I daresay?'

'No, I wouldn't,' said Mother and she took the dog leashes in one hand and Liza's hand in the other, went into the gate-house and shut the door. The man outside on the step said something Liza couldn't catch but which Mother said was a dirty word and never to say it. They heard his van start up with a roar as if it was angry.

The dogs started licking Liza, they licked her

hands and when she stroked them, they licked her face. Their coats felt like nothing she had ever touched before, shiny as leather, soft as fur, smooth as the crown of her own head when Mother had just washed her hair.

She said to Mother, 'Heidi and Rudi are black lined with brown,' and Mother had laughed and said that was right, that was just how they looked.

'You can't remember all those things your Mum and him said word for word, can you?' said Sean.

'Not really. But it was *like* that. I know all the kinds of things she says and ever could say. I know her so well, you see, it's as if I know her perfectly because I don't know anyone else.'

'How about me? You know me.'

She could tell she had hurt him and tried to make amends. 'I know you *now*. I didn't then.'

'Go on then. What happened with the dogs?'

'Eve was looking after them for Mr Tobias. He had to go away, he went to see his mother in France, and he couldn't take the dogs for some reason.'

'Quarantine.'

'What?'

'When he come back in he'd have to put the pair of them in quarantine for six months, that means they'd be in like kennels. It's the law.'

'I expect that was it.'

'Why couldn't this Matt look after him wherever it was he lived?'

'In the Lake District. He had a job, he was working all day. He couldn't take them out for exercise – or wouldn't. Anyway, Eve wanted to do this for Mr Tobias, she wanted to please him.

'We were supposed to have them for two or three weeks, I can't exactly remember. I loved them, I wanted us to have a dog after they'd gone back but Eve wouldn't. She said Mr Tobias wouldn't like it.'

'So it wasn't them she killed?'
'I told you, it was a person, a man.'

Liza never knew who he was or what it was he had
tried to do. Now that twelve years had passed and
she was grown-up, doing the thing that grown-ups
did herself, she could guess.

It was she who saw him first. Mother was down at
Shrove and Liza was locked up in her bedroom.
Where the dogs were she didn't know. Probably in
the little castle where they slept at night or even at
Shrove, for in a sort of way it was *their* house. It
belonged to Mr Tobias who owned them.

Mother had been gone a long time. Who could say
now how long those long times actually were? It's
different when you're four. Half an hour? An hour?
Or only ten minutes? She had read the letters in the
rag book and made them into words, 'dog', 'cat',
'bed', 'cot'. The baby bottle had been sucked dry and
the pencil had scribbled over every single sheet of
paper.

She climbed up on the bed and crawled on all fours
over to the window. The room had six sides and
three windows but was too small for the bed to be
anywhere but pushed against the wall with the
window that had the best view. The sun was shining,
sparkling on the river, and the wind was blowing the
clouds and making their shadows run across the
slopes of the high hills. A train whistled from
somewhere out of sight and came into her view from
out of the tunnel. She climbed on to a chair to look
out of the window that overlooked the gateway and
the little castle.

There was never anyone there. There was never
anyone to be seen but Mother, the milkman and the
postman in the morning, and Mr Frost on his tractor
on certain afternoons. Sometimes a car came down

on its way to the bridge. Mostly the lane was empty and all that showed its face in the barn on the other side was the white owl, so seeing the man made her jump. He was holding on to one of the gates and looking towards Shrove, a tall man in trousers Mother called jeans and brown leather jacket and with a canvas bag on his back.

Suddenly he looked up in the direction of her window and saw her there between the curtains. She knew he saw her and it frightened her. She couldn't have said why it did but it was something to do with his face, not a nice face, not the kind she had ever seen before, masked in yellow-brown hair, great bushes of curly hair from which eyes stared and the nose poked out. Later she wondered if she had thought the face not nice because of the beard which was new to her. She never saw another until the day Bruno and Mother took her shopping in the town.

She was afraid he was coming to the gate-house and would get in and come to get her. Ducking down from the window and wriggling across the floor and hiding under the bed couldn't stop that and she knew it. She knew it even then. Under the bed she didn't feel safe, only a bit safer and she thought it might be a little while before he found her. Mother had locked the door of her room and the front door of the gate-house, but that didn't make Liza think the man wouldn't be able to find her.

A long time went by and Mother came back. She pulled Liza out and hugged her and said she hadn't seen any man and if there was one he was probably harmless. If he wasn't she'd set Heidi and Rudi on him.

'How will you know?' Liza said.

'I know everything.'

Liza believed that was true.

Late that afternoon there was a knock at the front

door and when Mother went to answer it the man with the beard was on the step, asking for a glass of water. Liza thought Mother would say no, she hung on to Mother's skirt, peering round her until Mother said to let go, not to be so stupid. The man said he hoped he wasn't a nuisance.

'Go and fetch some water, please, Liza,' Mother said. 'Not a glass, a mug. You know how to do it.'

Liza knew. In some ways Mother had brought her up to be independent. Only in some ways, of course. For a long while she had fetched her own water when she wanted a drink, climbing up on to the chair by the sink, taking a mug from the shelf, turning on the tap and filling the mug and then being very careful to turn the tap off again. She did this now, filling the mug that had a picture on it of a lady in a crown, and carrying it back to the front door. Some of it spilt on the way but she couldn't help that.

The man drank the water. She saw so few people she noticed everything about the ones she did see. He held the mug in his left hand, not his right like Liza and Mother did, and on the third finger of that hand was a wide gold ring. That was the first time she had ever seen a ring on anyone's hand, for Mother wore none.

He said to Liza, 'Thank you, darling,' and gave her back the mug. 'Is there anywhere round here doing B and B?' he said to Mother.

'Doing what?'

'B and B. Bed and breakfast.'

'There's nowhere round here doing anything,' said Mother, sounding glad to say it. She took a step outside, making him step backwards, and spread out her arms. 'What you see is what you get.'

'Best press on then.'

Mother made no answer. She did what Liza didn't like her doing to *her*. It was a way she had of lifting

36

her shoulders and dropping them again while looking hard into the other person's eyes, but not smiling or showing anything. Until then Liza hadn't seen her do it to anyone but herself.

From an upstairs window, the one in Mother's room in the gable which overlooked the lane this time, they watched the man go. It was only from here that you could see where the lane ran along past the wood on its way to the bridge in one direction, and in the other to peter out into first a track and then a footpath. The man walked slowly, as if his pack felt heavier with each step he took. At the point where the lane wound and narrowed he paused and looked back in the direction of Shrove or perhaps just at the high hills.

They lost him among the trees but they went on watching and after a little while saw him again, by now a small figure plodding along the footpath under the maple hedge. After that it became a game between the two of them, each claiming to be able to see him still. But when Liza got excited Mother lifted her down from the window and they went downstairs to get on with Liza's reading lesson. An hour every afternoon was spent on teaching her to read and an hour every morning teaching her writing. The lessons were soon to get much longer, with sums as well as drawing, but at the time the man with the beard came they lasted just two hours each day.

Every morning very early, long before the writing lesson, they took the dogs out. Heidi and Rudi had been used to living indoors, so couldn't have kennels outside which Mother would have thought best, but slept in the little castle. Liza had never been in there before the dogs came but Mother had a key and took her in with her and she saw a room shaped like her bedroom with six sides and narrow windows with arched tops, only these had no glass in them. The floor was of stone with straw on it and two old blankets and two old cushions for the dogs. Rudi and Heidi bounded about and nuzzled her and licked her face, making noises of relief and bliss at being released.

Liza had thought how horrible it would be if they met the man with the beard while they were out in the water meadows. But they met no one, they hardly ever did, only a vixen going home with a rabbit in her mouth. Mother ordered the dogs to sit, to be still, and they obeyed her. She told Liza about foxes, how they lived and raised their young in earths, how people hunted them and that this was wrong.

That might have been the morning she saw her first kingfisher. It was about that time, she couldn't be sure. Mother said kingfishers were not common and when you saw one you should phone up and tell the County Kingfisher Trust. So it must have been that morning, for after they got home and the dogs were back in the house next door, Mother locked her in her bedroom and went over to Shrove to phone.

Liza read the words in the rag book and drew a picture of Mother on one of the sheets of paper. It might have been another day she did that but she thought it was the Day of the Kingfisher. From about that time she got it into her head that all men had fair hair and all women dark. The man who delivered the oil was fair and so were the postman and Matt and the man with the beard, but Mother and she were dark. She drew a picture of Mother with her long dark hair down her back and her long coloured skirt and her sandals.

It was just finished when Mother unlocked the door and let her out. There was something different in the living room, Liza spotted it at once. It was hanging up on the wall over the fireplace, a long dark brown tube with a wooden handle. She had never seen anything like it before but she knew Mother must have brought it back from Shrove.

'It was a gun,' said Sean.

'A shotgun. There were a lot of guns at Shrove. I began thinking about it later -- I mean years later – and I think that man had really frightened her. Frightened is probably not the word, she doesn't get frightened. Let's say, alerted her to danger.'

'Yeah, maybe she reckoned she should never have said that about what you see is what you get. I mean, like, you know, not being no one else around for miles.'

'I expect so.'

'But he'd gone, hadn't he?'

'He came back.'

It stayed light in the evenings until nearly ten but Liza was put to bed at seven. She had her tea, always wholemeal bread with an egg or a piece of cheese. Cake and sweets were not allowed and years passed before she found out what they were. After the bread she had fruit, as much as she wanted, and a glass of milk. The milkman came three times a week, another man with fair hair.

Mother read her a story when tea was over: Hans Andersen or Charles Kingsley, books borrowed from the library at Shrove. Then came her bath. They had a bath in the kitchen with a wooden lid on it. She wasn't locked in her bedroom at night, she was never locked in except when Mother went to Shrove or shopping in the town. When Liza couldn't get to sleep she knew it was useless calling out or crying, for Mother took no notice and if she came downstairs Mother would shrug at her and give her one of those wordless looks before taking her back up again.

So all she could do was wander about upstairs, looking out of the windows, hoping to see something, though she hardly ever did. If Mother knew Liza went into her room and played with her things, she gave no sign of it. Mother read books in the evenings, Liza knew that, or listened to music coming into her ears through wires from a little square black box.

In Mother's room she opened the cupboard door and examined all the long bright-coloured skirts that Mother wore and the other things she never wore, long scarves, a couple of big straw hats, a yellow gown with a flounce round the hem. She looked in her jewel case which was kept in the dressing table drawer and could have told anyone precisely what the case held: a long string of green beads, a hair comb made of brown mottled stuff with brilliant shiny bits set in it, a brooch of carved wood and another of mother-of-pearl. Mother had told her that was what it was when she wore the brooch just as she told her the beads were jade and the two pairs of earrings made of gold.

That evening the green beads and one pair of earrings were missing because Mother was wearing them. Liza closed the box, went back to her own room and knelt up on the bed, looking out of the window. The gate-house garden, in which Mother later on grew peas and beans and lettuces, soft fruit on bushes and strawberries under nets, was mostly bare earth at that time. Mother had been working on it that day, digging it over with a fork. There was just one tree, a single cherry tree, growing out of the soft red-brown soil, and two long grass paths.

Liza shifted her gaze upwards, waiting for the last south-bound train which would go through a bit after eight-thirty. She hadn't known about north and south and eight-thirty then, though Mother was teaching her to tell the time and to understand a map, but she knew the last train would come out from the tunnel while it was still light but after sunset. The sky was red all over, though you couldn't see where the sun went down from her room. Once it had set, the high hills went grey and the woods changed from green to a soft dark blue.

The train whistled at the tunnel mouth and came chugging down. Lights were on inside, though there was a lot of light outside still. It would stop at the station, at Ring Valley Halt, but you couldn't see the station from here. In the distance, the train grew very small, long and wriggling like one of the millipedes that lived near the back door. After it was gone there would be nothing more to be seen from this window. Liza scrambled off the bed and went on tip-toe back across the landing to Mother's room.

From here, you could see the bats that lived in the barn roof on the other side of the lane and swooped after moths and gnats. Sometimes she saw the great cream-coloured owl with a face like a cat's in a book. She had never seen a real cat. It was a little too early for owls this evening. Down below her, in the little patch of front garden, as twilight came, the colour began to fade from the red and pink geraniums and the tobacco flowers began to gleam more whitely. If the window had been open she could have smelt them, for their scent came out at dusk.

Just as Liza was thinking nothing would happen, it would get dark without anything happening, the front door opened and Mother came out in her green and purple and blue skirt and purple top, her green beads and gold earrings, with a black shawl wrapped round her. She opened the gate in the wall that ran round the garden, unlocked the door of the little castle and the dogs came rushing out. Mother said, 'Quiet. Sit,' and they sat, though trembling and quivering, Liza could see, hating this enforced stillness.

41

Mother said, 'Off you go,' and the pair of them began gambolling about, jumping up and trying to lick her, leaving off when she didn't respond. She walked round the side of the gate-house out of sight, the dogs following, but Liza knew she wouldn't go far because she never did in the evenings.

Liza ran back into her own bedroom, climbed on to the bed and pressed her face against the window. Outside a bat swooped, so close that she jerked her face back, though she knew the glass was there. Rudi and Heidi were in the back garden playing, grappling with each other and making mock growling noises and rolling over and over. Mother wasn't with them, Mother must have come back into the house.

Back on the landing, Liza listened, but she couldn't hear Mother down there. She ran into Mother's room and up to the window. Mother was sitting on the wall, listening to the music coming out of the band round her head and holding the little black box in her hands.

Where were the dogs? No longer in the back garden, she discovered as she bounced back on to her own bed. They must have gone out through the opening in the fence and into the wood, as they sometimes did. But they were well-trained, they always came back at a call.

It would get dull now if nothing more happened than Mother sitting on the wall, waiting for the dogs to finish their play. Liza never considered getting back into bed and trying to sleep as an alternative to this roving from room to room. Either she fell asleep when she happened to be on her own bed or Mother found her asleep on the landing floor or in the chair by the front bedroom window. She always woke in her own bed in the mornings. But she didn't want to be there now, she wasn't tired.

Perhaps Mother had decided to do something different. Liza ran back to check. Mother was still there, still listening. It was nearly dark but not too dark to see the man with the beard come along the lane from the bridge direction. The man looked just the same except that this time he hadn't got his backpack with him.

His footsteps made no sound on the sandy floor. Mother wouldn't have heard them if they had with that thing on her head and the music that was called Wagner flowing into her ears. Liza began to be frightened. Mother had said the dogs would protect them but the dogs weren't there, the dogs were a long way away in the wood.

Liza couldn't look.

Why hadn't she banged on the window to warn Mother? She hadn't thought of that till afterwards. The first time the man came she had got under the bed, the second time she had fetched him a drink of water. This time she put her hands over her eyes. They were talking, she could hear their voices but not what they said. Very cautiously she parted her fingers and peeped through them but they had gone, Mother and the man, they had come too near the gate-house for her to see or else they had walked round the back. She ran to the back and as she jumped on her bed, Mother screamed.

'What was he doing to her?' Sean said.

'She never told me, she never said a word about it, not then and not later. I know now, of course I do. When she screamed I was so frightened I covered up my ears but I could still hear, the window was open. I thought the man would catch her and – oh, make her his prisoner or something, and then come and get me.'

'You were only a little kid.'

'And there was no one else for miles and miles.

You know that. There never was. If there had been it couldn't have happened, none of it could.'

It wasn't dark but the beginning of the long midsummer twilight. When Mother's scream died away she heard the man laugh but she couldn't hear what it was he whispered. She looked out of the window, she had to look, and Mother was on the grass path and the man was on top of her. He was trying to hold her there with one hand and with the other he was undoing his jeans.

Liza was so frightened she couldn't make a sound or do anything. But Mother could. Mother twisted her head round under the man's arm that pinned her neck and bit his hand. He jumped and pulled up his hand, shouting that word Matt'd used on the doorstep, and Mother screamed out, 'Heidi, Rudi! Kill! Kill!'

The dogs came out of the wood. They came running as if they had been waiting for the summons, as if they had been sitting among the trees listening for just that command. In the half-dark they no longer looked like nice friendly dogs that licked your face but hounds of hell, though that was before Liza had ever heard of hounds of hell.

They didn't jump at the man, they flew at him. All eight powerful black legs took off and they were airborne. Their mouths gaped open and Liza could see their white shining teeth. The man had started to get to his feet but he fell over on his back when the dogs came at him. He covered his face with his hands and rolled this way and that. Heidi had half his great yellow beard in her jaws and Rudi was on him biting his neck. The dogs made a noise, a rough, grumbling, snorting sound.

Mother jumped up lightly as if nothing had happened and dusted down her skirt with her hands. She stood in that way she had with her hands

44

on her hips, the shawl hanging loose from her shoulders, and she watched them calmly, the dogs savaging the man and the man screaming and cursing.

Then, after a little while, she said, 'All right, dogs, that'll do. Quiet now. Still.'

They obeyed her at once. It was clever the way they stopped the moment she spoke. Rudi had some of the man's blood on his face and Heidi a mouthful of beard. The man rolled over again, his head on his arms, but he had stopped screaming, he didn't make a sound. Mother bent over him, looking closely, she didn't touch him with her hands but prodded him with one small delicate foot.

Liza made a little sound to herself up in her bedroom, a whimper like a dog whining behind a closed door.

Sean said hoarsely, 'Was he dead?'

'Oh, no, he wasn't *dead*.'

'What did she do?'

'Nothing. She just looked at him.'

'Didn't she get help? There was a phone in Shrove House, you said.'

'Of course she didn't get help,' Liza said impatiently.

Mother took hold of the dogs by their collars and put them in the little castle for the night. Liza saw her do that from the other window and heard her come into their own house and shut the front door after her. She went out on to the landing and listened. In the sitting room Mother was moving a chair about and it sounded as if she had climbed on the chair and jumped off it. Liza scrambled across the bed to have another look at the man on the grass. He was still there but not lying face-downwards any more.

It was really dark now, too dark to see much but the shape of the man sitting there with his head on his knees and his arms up round his head. Soon he would get up and go away and leave them and they'd be safe. She peered out through the dark, hoping for that to happen.

Suddenly she could see the man very clearly in a big oblong of light. The back door was open and light was coming from the kitchen. She wrinkled up her nose and made a face because the man's face and beard were a mass of blood. Her knees had looked like that when she fell over and hurt herself on the gravel.

Mother walked out into the light and pointed something she had in her arms and there was a tremendous explosion. The man tumbled over backwards and jerked a bit and shuddered and lay still. In the little castle the dogs set up a wild barking. Mother came back into the house and shut the door and the light went out.

Chapter Four

In the late afternoon, going by the lanes instead of the A road, Sean and Liza reached Vanner's fruit farm. This was orchard country, acre after acre of close-pruned stubby apple trees in long lines and then acre after acre of Comice pears and Louise Bonnes. The big wooden crates that would take the apples were stacked on top of each other in the corners of orchards. Liza saw women mounted on steps picking the big green Comice. Very few of the pears had been left to fall but the apple crop, Discovery and Jonagold, had been a heavy one and under the trees the ground was scarlet with abandoned fruit.

Sean took the left-hand turn into Vanner's land. He had been there before and knew where to go. The long straight macadamed roadway was bounded on either side by lines of alders, neat quick-growing trees to make high hedges. He had to pull in to let a car with its soft top down go past in the other direction, coming from the farm shop. A woman was driving. She had shiny blonde hair and red lipstick on, gold earrings and red varnish on her nails and Liza stared at her, fascinated.

'You're not still thinking women are all dark and men are all fair, are you, love?'

'Of course I'm not. I was only *four*.'

'Because there's other ways of telling the difference.' He put his hand in her lap and moved the fingers into her crotch. 'Bet you can't talk while I'm doing that. Go on, try. I bet you can't.'

'I can do that too,' said Liza, reaching for him. 'It'll be worse for you, you won't be able to drive.'

He laughed and gasped and grabbed her hand. 'Better leave off till we get there or I'll have to stop the van and we'll cause an obstruction.'

The parking place for caravans was in a remote spot where the orchards ended and the strawberry fields began. The strawberries were long over, the people who came to pick their own departed, and the fields a desolate waste of brown tendrils and dying leaves. A line of extremely tall lombardy poplars on a high bank divided these fields from the Discovery orchard and under the shadow of the poplars, on a rutted area of dried mud and scrubby grass, stood a sign which said: *Pickers' vans park here.* Beside the sign was a water tap and an arrow paint-sprayed on cardboard pointed to the waste disposal.

Other pickers there might be but there was only one caravan. It was parked at the far end up against the bank and looked as if no one was living in it or had lived in it for a long time. Its door and windows were shut and its blinds down. Just the same, Sean parked his car and van as far away from it as he could.

He didn't uncouple the van from the car or get the generator going or fill the water tanks. He and Liza, without a word, with scarcely an exchanged glance, got out of the car, went into the van and made love. They delayed for just the time it took to pull the bed down.

'I tell you what,' said Sean, when it was finished and she was lying in his arms, warm and damp and sighing with pleasure, 'now we're here and got a base you can get yourself to the family planning or whatever and go on the pill. Then I won't have to keep on using these things, I hate them.'

48

She looked up at him, uncomprehending. When he had explained she said, 'You'll have to come with me then. I won't know what to do.'

'Haven't you never been to the doctor's?'

He would be hurt if she said, 'Haven't you *ever* been,' so she didn't say it. 'Eve took me a couple of times. It's lucky I'm healthy. She said I had my injections when I was a baby.'

'Yeah, OK, but injections won't stop you getting yourself pregnant.'

'*You* getting me pregnant,' she said.

He laughed. He liked her being a bit sharp with him. Hugging her tight, he said, 'D'you mind talking about it or is this the wrong time? I mean, you know, what happened after your mum shot the guy with the beard.'

'Why would I mind?'

She couldn't see why she would. Eve said people liked talking about themselves better than anything and now, savouring the pleasure of it for the first time, she understood this was right. Thinking about it, going over it all, picking the bits to tell him and the bits not to, she enjoyed very much. It was her life and she was beginning to see what an extraordinary one it had so far been.

'I started crying, I couldn't help it. I lay on the bed sobbing and screaming.'

'I'm not surprised.'

'No, well, Eve came up and hugged me. She got me a drink of water and told me not to cry, not to worry, everything was going to be all right. The man had gone away, she'd blown him away.'

'Christ.'

'She didn't mean me to think she'd killed him. She didn't know I'd been watching. I didn't tell her. I was only four but somehow I knew not to tell her. All she knew was that I'd seen the man come and heard the

49

shot. She got into bed with me and I liked that. I was always wanting to sleep in the same bed with her but she'd never let me. She was so nice and warm and *young*. D'you know how old she is now?'

'About thirty-five?'

'She's thirty-eight. But that's young, isn't it? I mean, it's not young to us but people would call it young, wouldn't they?'

'I reckon,' said Sean, who was twenty-one. 'How did she come to have a funny name like Eve?'

'It's Eva really. It's German. Her father was German. I didn't know what her name was till I heard Mr Tobias call her Eve. She was just Mother. And then when Bruno was always calling her Eve I started doing it too and she didn't mind.'

'Who's Bruno?'

'Just a man. He doesn't come into it for years and years. I'll tell you about him when we get there. We'd got this other man lying dead on our grass, or Eve had, it wasn't really much to do with me. The thing was no one ever came near us then, no one at all but the milkman and the oilman, and the man who read the electric meter at the cottage and at Shrove. And they didn't go in the back garden or ask any questions.

'The milkman was strange. I noticed more when I was older. I never knew any children so I don't know if he talked like a child but Eve said he had a mental age of eight. He used to say things about the weather and the trains and that was all he ever said. "Here comes the train," he'd say and, "We're in for a cloudburst." He never noticed things. That man's dead body could have been lying on our doorstep and he'd have just stepped over it.'

'What about it then,' said Sean, 'the dead body?'

She didn't know exactly. Real events got mixed up with dreams at this point. She'd had awful dreams that night, had woken screaming and found Eve gone, back to her own bed. But she had come and comforted her and stayed, as far as Liza knew for the rest of the night.

But she can't have done, Liza realised that later, for in the morning when she looked out of the window, the man was gone. What does death mean to a child of four? It hadn't really registered with her the night before, that the man wouldn't ever get up again, wouldn't ever speak again or laugh or walk about. She had just been terribly frightened. When he was gone she thought he had gone of his own volition. He had mended and got well and walked away.

It was years afterwards when she was much older, piecing memories together and comparing them with similar contemporary events, that she understood he was dead and Eve had killed him with Mr Tobias's shotgun. Not only had Eve killed him but had taken his body away.

Eve was a small woman with a tiny waist and slender elegant legs. She had small hands with long tapering fingers. Her face was wide at the cheekbones and narrow at the chin, her forehead high, her upper lip short and her mouth full and lovely. Slightly tilted, her pretty nose was a little too small for her face. She had large hazel-green eyes and black eyebrows like Chinese brush-strokes, not unlike Sean's, and her thick shiny dark hair reached to the middle of her back. But she was very small, no more than five feet or five feet one at best. Liza didn't know her weight, they had no scales, but when she was sixteen Eve estimated seven and a half stone for herself and eight stone and a bit for Liza and that was probably right. Yet this tiny woman had somehow moved a man one and a half times her weight and nearly six feet tall.

And put him where? Somewhere in the wood, Liza

decided when she thought about it around that sixteenth birthday. She put the body in the wheelbarrow and took it through the gap in the fence and buried it in the wood. During the night while Liza slept and before she woke up screaming. Or after she had held her and soothed her and she had slept again, Mother had gone down and worked silently in the dark.

The first thing she saw from the window that morning – even before she saw the man was gone – was Matt opening the door of the little castle and letting the dogs out. He wasn't due till mid-morning, Mother said, running into the room. She sounded cross and upset. Liza went to the other window. The dogs had made straight for the place where the man had lain and ran about sniffing the grass in a frenzied way and pushing their noses into the earth.

'There's something fascinating them,' Matt said when Liza and Mother went outside, 'they been burying bones?'

'Do you know what time it is?' Mother said. 'It's six-thirty in the morning.'

'So it is. Dear, oh, dear. I'd some business down this way yesterday so I stopped the night and come over here first thing. Not got you girls out of bed, I hope.'

Mother ignored this. 'Has Mr Tobias come back from France?'

'Coming back tonight. He wants his dogs there when he gets home. They're all the company he's got, I reckon. It wouldn't suit me, I like a bit of action myself, but it takes all sorts to make a world.'

'It certainly does,' said Mother, not very pleasantly.

'You'd think he'd get himself a girl – well, he does but nothing permanent.' Matt spoke as if Mother didn't know it all already. 'Of course he's loaded, got his own place and this here and the London one and there's girls falling over themselves to get him but to be perfectly honest with you he's just not interested.' He winked incomprehensibly at Liza. 'Not in settling down, I mean.'

In spite of what had happened, Liza wasn't afraid to put her arms round each dog's neck and place a tender kiss on each glossy black skull. She cried a bit when they had gone. She asked Mother if they could have a dog of their own.

'No, absolutely not. Don't ask me.'

'Why couldn't we, Mother, why couldn't we? I do want a dog, I love Heidi and Rudi, I do want one of my own.'

'Then you must want.' Mother smiled when she said it, she wasn't angry, and she called Liza Lizzie which she sometimes did when she was pleased with her or not too disappointed in her. 'Listen, Lizzie, suppose Mr Tobias came to live at Shrove? He might, it's his house – one of his houses. Then Heidi and Rudi would come with him and what would happen to our dog? They don't like other dogs, they'd attack it. They'd hurt it.'

Like they hurt the man, Liza felt like saying but she didn't say it. Instead, she said, 'Is he going to come? I'd like him to come because then we'd have *his* dogs and we wouldn't have to have our own. Is he going to come?'

Mother said nothing for a moment. Then she put her arm round Liza and pulled her close against her skirts and said, 'I hope so, Lizzie, I hope he will,' but she wasn't smiling and she gave a heavy sigh.

Next day was Mother's day for going shopping. She went once a fortnight to get the things the milkman wouldn't bring. He brought butter and eggs and porridge oats and orange juice and bread and yogurt as well as milk but he never brought meat or fish. Until they grew their own, Mother had to buy vegetables. She had to buy fruit and cheese. The bus that went to the shops, to town that is, ran four times a day and Mother had to walk down the lane and go over the river bridge and a hundred yards along the road to the bus stop. When Mother went to town she never took Liza with her. Liza was locked up in her bedroom.

She was used to it and she accepted, but not this time. At first she gave in, sat on the bed with the rag book and the pencils, sucked at her orange juice bottle. Mother had given her an apple as well for a treat, a Golden Delicious because there were no English ones in July. She knelt on the bed and watched Mother go along the lane towards the main road. Then she shifted her gaze from the distance to the foreground and saw where the man had been and the dogs and the explosion had happened. She began to scream.

Probably she couldn't have screamed for the whole hour and a half Mother was away. Halfway through she may have fallen asleep. But she was screaming when Mother came back. Mother said, 'I won't leave you again,' and she didn't for a long while but of course she did again one day.

It might have been that evening or an evening days or weeks later, at any rate it was after the dogs had gone, that Liza was playing her roving-between-the-bedrooms game after bed-time. She tried on Mother's straw hats, the golden one with the white band and the brown one with the cream scarf tied round it, and she stroked Mother's suede shoes, that had things inexplicably called trees thrust into them. When she was tired of that she looked inside the jewel case.

Mother was wearing one set of earrings and the mother-of-pearl brooch, so of course those things weren't in there. Liza hung the jade beads round her own neck, put the comb with the shiny bits on it into her hair and admired the result in the mirror. She picked up the wooden brooch and found lying underneath it a gold ring.

Whose could it be? She had never seen it before, she had never seen any ring on Mother's hand. Examining it with great interest, she saw that there was some writing on the inside of the ring but she was only four then and she couldn't read very well. Nor did she at that time connect the ring with the man with the beard.

'It was his ring?' said Sean.

'It must have been. I looked at it again later, when I could read. The writing said: TMH and BHH, 3 March 1974. I didn't know what it meant then but now I think it was his wedding ring. Victoria had a wedding ring. Do men have them?'

'I reckon there's some as do.'

'Those were his initials and his wife's and that was the date they got married, don't you think?'

'She must have took it off him, off his hand,' said Sean, making a face.

'I don't know why she did unless she thought she might sell it one day. Or maybe she thought if she buried it with him someone might dig it up.'

'Why did she do it?'

'Do what? Shoot that man?'

'Why didn't she get an ambulance, have him taken to hospital? You said he could sit up, he'd have got all right. It wasn't her fault, no one'd have put the blame on her, not if she said he'd been going to rape her.'

'I never knew quite why,' Liza said, 'but it might have been something like this. Later on someone told me a story about a child being attacked by dogs and I put two and two together. It was Bruno, as a matter of fact, he told me. You see, the man would have told them at the hospital and they'd have told the police. About the dogs, I mean. And the dogs would have been killed.'

'Destroyed.'

'Yes, I expect that's the word. The dogs would have been destroyed like the ones in Bruno's story. Mr Tobias loved his dogs and he'd have blamed Eve and given her the sack and turned us out of the gate-house. Or that's what she thought. Maybe he would and maybe he wouldn't but she thought he would and that was the important thing. She couldn't leave Shrove, you see, she couldn't, that was the most important thing in the world to her, Shrove, more important even than me. Well, Mr Tobias was important to her too but only in a special sort of way.'

Sean was looking bewildered. 'You've lost me.'

'Never mind. That's really all there was to it. If the dogs had killed the man she wouldn't have had to kill him. I expect that's the way she thought. But they hadn't killed him, so she had to, or else he'd have told the police. She shut the dogs up and went into the house and got the gun and shot him.'

'Just for that? Just so Tobias wouldn't get mad at her?'

Liza looked at him doubtfully. 'I don't know. Now you put it like that, I really don't know. Perhaps there was more to it. Perhaps she had some other reason, something to make her hate him, but we're never going to know that, are we?'

She watched Sean as he got up and washed at the sink. He put his jeans back on again and found himself a clean tee shirt. It occurred to her that she hadn't any clothes except the ones lying in a heap on the floor. She'd have to wear his, or those of his which would fit her, and when she'd made some money picking apples . . . The hundred pounds, she had forgotten the hundred pounds.

56

'I want to drive into town, wherever that is,' she said, 'and go and eat in a real restaurant. Can we?'

'Course we can. Why not? We can go and have a Chinese.'

Liza washed her knickers and her socks at the sink. She had to put her jeans on over nothing but that didn't much matter. Her jeans were a cause of great pride, not least because it had been such a struggle getting Eve to let her have them. She'd managed to get two pairs, these and a pair she'd left behind. Eve hated trousers and had never worn jeans in all her life. Liza borrowed a long-sleeved check shirt with a collar from Sean and thought a little about Eve, wondering where she was now and what was happening to her.

Sean had been thinking the same thing. 'We ought to get a paper tomorrow. You haven't never seen a paper, I suppose? A newspaper, I mean.'

'Oh, yes, I have.' She was a bit huffy. Once, in a magazine rack at Shrove, she had found a newspaper called *The Times* and the date on it the year before she was born. Eve had taken it away before she could read much of it. 'What we ought to get is television.'

'Now there's something you've never seen, telly, I bet.'

She answered him in quite a lofty way. 'I used to watch it at Shrove every single day. Eve never knew, she'd have stopped it but I didn't tell her. It was a secret thing I did.'

'Like me,' said Sean.

'Not really like you. You're much better. But I didn't know you then. I watched it for *years* till the set broke and Jonathan wouldn't have it mended.' The expression on his face made her laugh. 'Could we have one in here? Would your generator work it?'

'Hopefully,' he said. 'Course it would.'

'Then I'm going to buy one.' A thought struck her.

'Only, I don't know – is a hundred pounds a lot of money, Sean?'

He said rather bitterly, 'It's a lot for us, love,' and then, 'Hopefully it'd buy a little portable telly but I don't know about colour.'

Her eyes grew wide. 'Does it come in colour? Does it really?'

When they went outside to the car they saw that the other van, the camper, wasn't unoccupied as they had at first thought. A light was on inside it and the blind was raised in the window nearest to the roadway. They had to pass it to get out. Inside, a fiercer bluer glow than the overhead lamp indicated the presence of a television screen and as they passed within a few feet Liza saw the little rectangle filled with dazzling colour, emerald green grass, yellow spotted leaves and an orange and black tiger prowling.

'What a lot I've got to catch up with,' she said.

Life at the gate-house had been of the simplest. Much of it would seem dull to Sean, incredible. There was a good deal she wouldn't tell him but keep locked in her memory. For instance, how, because Eve wouldn't leave her alone in the cottage any more even with the doors locked, couldn't bring herself to do that when she screamed so piteously, she had been obliged to take Liza with her.

And that was how she came to enter Shrove House for the first time. The palace, the house of pictures and secrets, dolls and keys, books and shadows. Sean would never see it quite like that, no one would but herself and Eve. Most of all Eve.

Chapter Five

They walked up the drive between the trees, the horn-beams that were nearly round in shape and the larches that were pointed, the silver birches whose leaves trembled in the breeze and the swamp cypresses that came from Louisiana but grew happily here because it was damp by the river. There were giant cedars and even taller Douglas firs and Wellingtonias taller than that, black trees you saw as dark green only when you were close up underneath them. The trees parted and she saw the house for the first time and to her then it was no more than a big house with an enormous lot of windows.

A man was mowing the grass, sitting up in a high chair on wheels. She had seen him once or twice before and was often to see him again. His name was Mr Frost; he wasn't a young man but had wrinkles and white hair, and he came on his bicycle from the village on the other side of the river. White hair was only another kind of fair hair and his confirmed Liza's belief. He raised one hand to Mother and Mother nodded but they didn't speak.

Steps went up one side to the front door of Shrove and then there was a kind of platform before the stairs ran down the other side. The stairs had railings like theirs at the gate-house but the rails here were made of stone with a broad stone shelf running along the tops of them. On the shelf were stone vases from which ivy hung and between the vases stone people stood looking towards the trees.

Liza and Mother went up the flight on the left and Liza held on to the stone railings. Everything was very large and this made her feel smaller than usual. She looked up, as Mother told her, to see the coat of arms, the sword, the shield, the lions. The house towered, its windows shiny sheets, its roof lost in the sky. Mother unlocked the front door and they went in.

'You will not rush about, Liza,' Mother said, 'and you will not climb on the furniture. Do you understand? Let me see your hands.'

Liza held them out. They were very clean because Mother had made her wash them before they came out and she had held Mother's hand all the way.

'All right. You can't get them dirty in here. Now, remember, *walk*, don't run.'

The carpets were soft and thick underfoot and the ceilings were very high. None of the ceilings were white but done in gold and black squares or painted like a blue sky with white clouds and people with wings flying across it, trailing scarves and ribbons and bunches of flowers. The lamps were like raindrops when it is raining very hard and some of the walls had things like thin carpets hanging on them. A huge painting covered one entire wall. Mother called it 'The Birthday of Achilles' and it showed a lot of men in helmets and women in white robes all rushing to pick up a golden apple while a woman in green with flowers stood by holding a fat naked baby.

Mother took her through the drawing room and showed her the fireplace with the lady's face on it, the screen painted with flowers and the tables which were of shiny wood with shiny metal bits on it and some with mother-of-pearl on like Mother's brooch.

The tall glass doors were framed in mahogany, Mother said, and they were more than two hundred years old but as good as new. Liza and Mother went through the doorway out on to the terrace at the back, and when Liza ran down the steps and stood on the lawn and looked up at Mother, she was frightened for a moment because the back of the house was the same as the front, the same coat of arms, sword, shield and lion, the same railing round the roof and up the stairs, the same windows and the same statues standing in the alcoves.

Mother called out to her that it was all right, it was supposed to be that way, but that if she looked closely she would see it wasn't quite the same. The statues were women, not men, there was no front door, and instead of ivy, small dark pointed trees grew in the stone urns on the terrace.

So Liza ran up again and she and Mother made their way to the kitchen. Mother unhooked an apron from behind a cupboard door, a big ugly brown apron, and wrapped it round herself, covering up her white cotton blouse and her long full green and blue skirt. She took a clean yellow duster from a pile and tied her head up so that you couldn't see her hair, she trundled out a vacuum cleaner and found a large deep tin of mauve polish that smelt of lavender.

For the next three hours they remained in Shrove House while Mother cleaned the carpets with the vacuum cleaner, dusted the surfaces and the ornaments and polished the tables. She couldn't get it all done today, she said, and she explained to Liza how she did a bit one day and another bit two days later and so on, but she hadn't been in there for two weeks because, as she put it, of one thing and another. She had been afraid of Liza being a nuisance or of breaking something but Liza had been as good as gold.

Remembering not to run, she had walked through all the rooms, looking at everything, at a table with a glass top and little oval pictures in frames inside, at a small green statue of a man on a horse, at a green jar with black birds and pink flowers on it that was taller than she was. One room was full of books, they were all over the walls where other rooms had paint or panelling. Another, instead of books, had those things hanging up like the one Mother had that made the explosion. She didn't stay in there for long.

A cabinet in one room was full of dolls in different dresses and she would have loved to touch, to get them out, she *longed* to, but she did what Mother told her, or if she didn't she made sure Mother couldn't find out. But mostly she did as she was told because as well as loving Mother so much, she was afraid of her.

The door to a room opening out of that one was shut. Liza tried the handle and it turned but the door wouldn't open. It was locked as her bedroom door used to be locked when Mother went out, and the key gone. Of course she very much wanted to get into that room, as much as anything because the door was locked. She rattled the handle, which did no good.

There were three staircases. By this time she had learnt to count up to three – well, to six, in fact. She went up the biggest staircase and down the smallest, having been in every bedroom and climbed on to one of the window seats – Mother wouldn't find out, the vacuum cleaner could be heard howling downstairs – and looked across the flat green valley floor to watch a train go by.

If not, then, conscious of beauty, she was aware of light, of how radiantly light the house was everywhere inside. There wasn't a dark corner or a dim passage. Even when the sun wasn't shining, as it wasn't that day, a clear pearly light lit every room and the things inside the rooms gleamed, the glass and the porcelain, the silver and brass and the gilt on the mouldings and cornices. The biggest staircase had flowers and fruit carved on the wood on each side of it and the carving gleamed with a deep rich glow, but all she could think of then was how much she would like to slide down the polished banister.

They left at four o'clock, in time to get home for Liza's reading lesson.

'Doesn't Mr Tobias ever live there?' she asked, taking Mother's hand.

'He never has. His mother did for a while and his grandfather lived there all the time, it was his only home.' She gave Liza a thoughtful glance, as if she was pondering whether the time had come to tell her. 'My mother, who was your grandmother, was his housekeeper. And then his nurse. We lived in the gate-house ourselves, my mother, my father and I.' Mother squeezed Liza's hand. 'You're too young for this, Lizzie. Look up in the ash tree, see the green woodpecker? On the trunk, picking insects out with his beak?' So if the day the man with the beard came was called the Day of the Kingfisher, this was the Day of the Woodpecker, the day of the first visit to Shrove.

After that Liza always went with Mother to Shrove and now, when Mother went to town on the bus, instead of locking Liza in her bedroom in the cottage, she put her in one of the Shrove bedrooms. Mostly it was the one called the Venetian Room because the four-poster bed had its posts made out of the poles used by gondoliers in Venice, Mother said. Liza could read quite well by the time she was five and had a real book in the room with her. She wasn't in the least frightened of being shut up in the Venetian Room at Shrove, she wouldn't have been frightened of being in her own room any more, but she did ask Mother why Shrove and not at home.

'Because Shrove has central heating and we don't. I can be sure you're warm enough. They have to keep the heating on all winter because of the damp even though no one lives there. If it was allowed to get damp the furniture might be spoiled.'

'Why is the little room next to the morning room always locked up?'

'Is it?' said Mother. 'I seem to have mislaid the key.'

Shrove was to become her library and her picture gallery. More than that, for the paintings were a guide to her and a catalogue of people's faces. To them she ran when she needed to identify a new person or when confirmation was required. They were her standard of comparison and her second-hand portrait of the outside world. This was how other people looked, this what they wore, these the chairs they sat on, the other countries they lived in, the things their eyes saw.

In the cold depths of winter, a very cold one when the river froze over and the water meadows disappeared under snow for a whole month, a black car with chains on its tyres slid slowly down the lane and parked in the deep snow outside the gate-house. There were two men inside. One stayed in the car and the other one came to the front door and rang the bell. He was a fat man with no hair at all but for a fairish fringe surrounding the great shiny pale egg that was his head.

By chance, Liza and Mother had been sitting side by side at Mother's bedroom window, watching the birds feeding from the nut feeders they had hung on the branches of the balsam tree. They saw the car come and the man come to the door.

'If he talks to you you are not to say anything but "I don't know",' said Mother, 'and you can cry a bit if you like. You might like that, it might amuse you.'

Liza never found out who the man was. Of course she guessed later on. He said he was looking for a missing person, a man called Hugh something. She had forgotten his other name but Hugh she remembered.

Hugh came from Swansea, was around these parts last July on a walking holiday but left the B and B he was stopping at without paying for his two nights. The fat man talked a lot more about Hugh and why they were looking for him and what was making them look six months later, but Liza didn't understand any of it. He described Hugh, which she did understand, she remembered his fair beard, she remembered tufts of it in Rudi's mouth.

'We are very quiet down here, Inspector,' Mother said. 'We see hardly anyone.'

'A lonely life.'

'It depends what suits you.'

'And you never saw this man?' He showed Mother something in the palm of his hand and Mother looked at it, shaking her head. 'You didn't see him in the lane or walking the footpath?'

'I'm afraid not.'

Mother lifted her face and looked deep into the fat man's eyes when she said this. Although it meant nothing at the time, when she was older, thinking back and comparing her own personal experience, Liza understood how Mother's look must have affected him. Her full red lips were slightly parted, her eyes large and lustrous, her skin creamy and her expression oh, so winsome and trusting. About her shoulders her glorious hair, a rich dark shining brown, hung like a silk cape. She had one small white finger pressed against her lower lip.

'It was just a possibility,' the fat man said, unable to take his eyes off her, but having to, having to drag his eyes away and speak to Liza. 'I don't suppose this young lady saw him?'

She was shown the photograph. Apart from prints on the fronts of Mother's books, it was the first she had ever seen, but she didn't say so. She looked at the face which had frightened her and which Heidi and Rudi had ruined with their teeth, looked at it and said, 'I don't know.'

This made him eager, 'So you might have?'

'I don't know.'

'Have another look, my love, look closely and try to remember.'

Liza was growing frightened. She was letting Mother down, she was obeying Mother but letting her down just the same. The man's face was horrible, the bearded man called Hugh, cruel and sneering, and who knew what he would have done if Mother hadn't . . .

She didn't have to pretend to cry. 'I don't know, I don't know, I don't know,' she screamed and burst into tears.

The fat man went away, apologising to Mother, shaking hands with her and holding her hand a long time, and when he had gone Mother roared with laughter. She said Liza had been excellent, quite excellent, and she hugged her, laughing into her hair. For all that she loved Liza and cared for her, she hadn't understood that she had been really frightened, really shy of people, really bewildered.

It took the driver a long time to get the car started and an even longer time to pull it out of the snow without its wheels spinning. Liza calmed down and began to enjoy herself. She and Mother watched the driver's struggles from the bedroom window with great interest.

66

The snow went away and the spring came. Most of the trees which were coniferous looked just the same, always the same greenish-black or light smoky blue, but the larches and the swamp cypresses grew new leaves like clumps of fur of an exquisite pale and delicate green. Mother explained that larches too were deciduous conifers and the only ones native to the British Isles.

Primroses with sunny round faces appeared under the hedges and clusters of velvety purple violets close by the boles of trees. Wood anemones, that were also called windflowers and had petals like tissue paper, grew in the clearings of the wood. Mother told Liza to be careful never to pronounce them an-en-omies, as so many people did who ought to know better. Liza hardly talked to anyone but Mother, so was unlikely to hear the wrong pronunciation.

Except the postman, though they didn't discuss botany. And the milkman who noticed nothing but the trains and the signs of changes in the weather, and the oilman who came to fill Shrove's heating tank in March, and Mr Frost the gardener who mowed the grass and trimmed the hedges and sometimes pulled out the weeds.

Mr Frost went on never speaking. They saw him ride past the gate-house on his bicycle and if he saw them he waved. He waved from his mowing machine if he happened to be there when they walked up the drive to Shrove. The oilman only came twice a year, in September and again in March. Liza had never talked to him, though Mother did for about five minutes, or listened rather, and listened impatiently, while he told her about his flat in Spain and how he had found a cut-rate flight to Malaga that was so reasonable you wouldn't believe. Liza didn't know what that meant, so Mother explained how he went across the sea in one of those things that flew overhead sometimes and made a buzzing noise about it, unlike birds.

The milkman said, 'It feels like spring,' which was silly because it *was* spring, and 'Here comes the train,' that he needn't have bothered to say because anyone could see and hear it.

They got very few letters. Liza never got any. Letters came for Mother sometimes, from someone called her aunt, though she never explained what an aunt was, from her friend Heather in London, and one regularly once a month from Mr Tobias. This one had a piece of pink paper in it which Mother said was a cheque. When next she went to the shops she took the pink paper with her and took it to a bank and they turned it into money. Like a good fairy waving a wand, suggested Liza who was much into fairy tales at that time, but Mother said, no, not like that, and explained that this was money which she had earned for cleaning Mr Tobias's house and looking after it and seeing it came to no harm.

In April the dogs came again to stay. Matt brought them and told Mother that Mr Tobias had gone to somewhere called the Caribbean this time, not France. Liza hugged Heidi and Rudi, who knew her at once and were overjoyed to see her. Had they forgotten the man with the beard called Hugh? Had they forgotten how they attacked him? Liza wondered if they would attack Matt if she called out, 'Kill!'

'Why doesn't Mr Tobias ever come himself?' Liza asked Mother while they were out in the meadows with the dogs.

'I don't know, Lizzie,' Mother said and she sighed.

'Doesn't he like it here?'

'He seems to like it better in Sri Lanka and

68

Mozambique and Montagu Square and the horrible old Lake District,' said Mother incomprehensibly. 'But perhaps he will come one day. Of course he'll come one day, you'll see.'

Instead of coming himself, he sent a postcard. It had a picture on it of silver sand and palm trees and a blue blue sea. On the back Mr Tobias had written: *This is a wonderful place. It's good to get away from cold grey England in the cruellest month, though I hardly suppose you would agree. Say hallo to Heidi and Rudi for me and to your daughter, of course. Ever, J.T.*

Liza couldn't read joined-up writing, even the beautiful curvy large kind like Mr Tobias's, so Mother read it to her. Mother made a face and said she didn't like him putting his dogs before her daughter but Liza didn't mind.

'I know what T's for,' she said, 'but what's his name that starts with J?'

'Jonathan,' said Mother.

By the time the summer came Liza could read Beatrix Potter and the Andrew Lang Fairy Books if the print was large enough. She could write her name and address and simple sentences, printing of course, and she could tell the time and count to twenty and add up easy sums. Mother took her into the library at Shrove and said that when she was older she would be welcome to read all the books in there she wanted. Mr Tobias had told *her* to help herself to any books she fancied reading, he knew she loved reading, and of course that invitation extended to her daughter.

'Jonathan,' said Liza.

'Yes, Jonathan, but you must call him Mr Tobias.'

There were history books and geography books and books about languages and philosophy and religion. Liza noted the words without understanding their meaning. Mother said there were also a great many books that were stories, which meant made-up things not things that had really happened, they were novels. Most of them had been written a long time ago, more than a hundred years ago, which wasn't surprising since they had belonged to Mr Tobias's grandfather's father who had bought the house when he got rich in eighteen hundred and sixty-two. The books were rather old-fashioned now, Mother said, but perhaps that was no bad thing, and she looked at Liza with her head on one side.

It grew hot that summer and one day Liza went with Mother to a part of the river that was very deep, a pool below the rapids that came rushing over the stones, and Mother began teaching her to swim. Mother was a good strong swimmer and Liza felt safe with her even where the water was so deep that Mother's feet couldn't touch the bottom. The second or third time they had been down there they were coming back up the lane – Mother said afterwards she wished they'd come through the Shrove grounds as they usually did – when they had to flatten themselves against the hedge to let a car go by. It didn't go by, it stopped, and a lady put her head out of the window.

That was when Liza had to revise her ideas on her hair colour-sex-linkage theory, for the lady's hair was blonde. It was not otherwise much like hair at all but seemed to be carved out of some pale yellow translucent substance, a kind of lemon jelly perhaps, and then varnished. The lady had a face like the monkey in the illustrations to Liza's *Jungle Book* and hands with ropes under the skin on the backs of them and a brown paper dress Mother said afterwards was called linen and made from a plant with blue flowers that grew in the fields like grass.

The lady said, 'Oh, my dear, I haven't seen you for an age. Don't you ever come down to the village any more? I must say I've expected to see you in church. Your mother was such a regular at St Philip's.'

'I am not my mother,' said Mother, very coldly.

'No, of *course* not. And this is your little girl?'

'This is Eliza, yes.'

'She will be going to school soon, I suppose. I don't know how you're going to get her there with no car but I suppose the school bus will come. At least it will come to where the lane joins the main road.'

Mother said in the voice that frightened Liza when it was used to her, which was seldom, 'Eliza will be educated privately,' and she walked away without waiting for the lady to put her head in and her window up.

That was the first time Liza heard school mentioned. She didn't know what it was. At that time no school or schoolchildren figured in the books she read. But she didn't ask Mother, only what the name of the lady was and Mother said Mrs Hayden, Diana Hayden, that Liza would probably never have to see her again.

They had the dogs back for a fortnight in October and again six months later. When the time came for Matt to come with the van to collect them he didn't turn up. Something must have gone wrong, Mother said, there was no means of letting her know as they had no phone and it was impossible to send telegrams any more.

But when he didn't come on the following day she got it into her head this was because Mr Tobias would come himself. He had told the man to leave it to him this time, he would collect the dogs when he got back. But he wasn't due back till today. After he had had a good night's sleep and got over his jet lag he would get in his car, or more likely the estate car, and drive down here from Ullswater where he lived but had no one willing to look after his dogs. Mother was sure he would come. She and Liza went over to Shrove early in the morning and Mother gave it a special clean.

71

At home she had a bath in their kitchen bath and washed her hair. That was the next day, in the morning. She put on one of her long bright coloured skirts and her tight black top, the green beads round her neck and the gold hoops in her ears. It took her half an hour to plait her hair in the special way she had and pin it to the back of her head. And she did all this because Mr Tobias was coming.

He didn't come. Matt did. He drove up in the afternoon and pushed past Mother into the gatehouse before she could stop him.

'I've been down with one of them viruses that's going about,' he said, 'or I'd have been here before.'

'Where is Mr Tobias?'

'He rung up from Mozam-whatsit, said he'd be home today. Didn't he never let you know? Dear, oh, dear. Never mind, there's no harm done, is there?'

No harm done! Mother went up to her bedroom after Matt had gone and lay on her bed and cried. Liza heard her crying and went up and got in bed with her and hugged her and said to stop, not to cry, it was going to be all right.

And so it was. In the month of June, when all the wild roses were out and flowers were on the elder trees and the nightingales sang in the wood, Mr Tobias came to Shrove in his dark green shiny Range Rover and, with the dogs at his heels, ran up the cottage garden path and banged on their door, calling, 'Eve, Eve, where are you?'

That was how Liza learned what Mother's first name was.

She called the day gone by the Day of the Nightingale because the nightingales had sung from morning till night and beyond. People who didn't know, Mother said, believed nightingales only sang by night but that was false, for they sang all round the clock.

Chapter Six

'My real name's Eliza. I've sometimes thought she called me after Eliza Doolittle in *Pygmalion*.'

'Come again?' said Sean.

'Because she intended to do the same thing with me as Pygmalion did with Galatea and as Professor Higgins did with Eliza Doolittle, he re-made her to be the way he wanted her, or let's say he had an ideal and he tried to turn her into that.'

Sean frowned while he concentrated. 'Sounds like *My Fair Lady* to me.'

'She said she didn't, anyway, when I asked her. She just liked the name.' Liza finished her strawberry milkshake and wiped her mouth. 'Sean, can I have a burger? D'you know I've never had one.'

'Course you can. We'll both have a burger and chips.'

'Isn't it funny? I was so afraid to leave the gatehouse and *her*, I thought I'd die of fright.'

'You're always dying of something, you are.'

'Only I never do really, do I? I was so frightened and now I'm out in the world – that's how I see it, out in the world – I really like it. Or perhaps it's just you I like. I wouldn't have liked Heather.'

'You might've. You don't know her.'

'Oh, yes, I do. I *did*. She came to stay. But not then, not till after Mr Tobias had been.'

They were in the town, Liza wary of the crowded pavements but liking the shops and the big green with a few old people sitting on wooden seats and children feeding ducks on a pond. Sean wouldn't take her money, he had a bit saved up, and when they had had lunch he bought two bottles of wine and sixty cigarettes, something else she had never tried before. Sean lit a cigarette as soon as he was in the car.

'Eve said they kill you.'

'She's not the only one says that. But I reckon it's just the same old thing, them trying to stop you having a bit of pleasure. I mean, look at it this way, my grandad he's eighty-seven, he's smoked forty a day since he went out to work at fourteen and there's not a thing wrong with him, spry as a cricket he is.'

'What's a cricket, Sean?'

'There's the game cricket, you know, test matches and whatever, there's that, but it's not that, is it? I reckon I don't know what it is, to tell you the honest truth.'

'You shouldn't use words if you don't know what they mean.'

Sean laughed. 'Sorry, Teacher.'

He wanted her to try a cigarette, so she did. It made her cough and then it made her feel sick, but Sean said it was always like that the first time and you had to persist.

They called in at the farm shop on the way to the caravan and saw Mr Vanner in the office. He was short of pickers for the Emile pears and took them both on to start next day. On the way out Liza helped herself to a James Grieve from the basket with the notice that said: *Help yourself and enjoy a great taste*. She'd taken a big bite out of it when Mrs Vanner behind the counter said in a nasty tone, 'Those apples are intended for our paying customers, if you don't mind.'

No one had ever spoken to her in that rude way

before. Sean squeezed her arm to stop her answering back, though she wouldn't have done that, she was too shocked.

'What a horrible woman,' she said the moment the door closed behind them.

'Mean old bitch,' said Sean.

Another camper had arrived at the caravan park. Whoever owned it had already put up a washing line with washing on it and tied a black terrier up to the steps. Liza glanced at the other camper, the one that was there before they came, and saw the blue glow of the screen under the raised blind.

'D'you know what we forgot, Sean? We forgot to buy the television set.'

'I can think of better things to do than watch telly,' said Sean, putting his arm on her shoulders and stroking her neck with his fingertips.

'And something to read,' she said as if he hadn't spoken. 'I'll need books to read. How can I get books?'

'I don't know.' He wasn't interested.

'I can't exist without books.'

But she went into his arms very willingly when they were inside the caravan and the door was shut. She was soon pulling off her clothes and climbing across the bed to where he waited for her. They hadn't bothered to put the bed back in the wall that morning, knowing they would be sure to need it again soon.

Mother said, 'This is Mr Tobias, Lizzie, that you've heard so much about,' and to Mr Tobias she said, 'I'd like you to meet my daughter Eliza, Jonathan.'

It was a new experience for Liza to shake hands with someone. Mr Tobias's hand was warm and dry and his handshake very firm. He got down on his haunches so that their eyes were on a level. His were

75

dark brown and his hair light brown, lighter than his skin which was very deeply tanned. Of all the men that Liza had ever seen, the milkman, the postman and the oilman, Mr Frost, Mr Tobias's man who brought the dogs, and that other one who had a beard but no name, of all of them, Mr Tobias had the nicest hands. They were thin and brown with long fingers and square nails.

And he had a lovely voice. Instead of sounding like Matt or the oilman or the man with the beard or the milkman, who all sounded different from each other, his voice was more like Mother's but deeper of course and somehow softer. It was the sort of voice you'd like to read you a story before you went to sleep.

'She's very like you, Eve,' he said. 'She is you in little. A clone, perhaps?'

'I'm afraid not,' Mother said. 'But I'm glad she looks like me.'

Liza was very surprised to see a bottle produced and two glasses, a bottle with brown liquid in it, and orange juice for her. Mr Tobias was very tall and had to bend his head to get under the doorway into their living room. He wasn't wearing jeans like most of the other men she had seen or the bottom part of a suit like Mr Frost, but trousers in pale fawn stuff like the ribbing on a jumper and a white shirt with an open neck and a brown velvet jacket. Eve told her afterwards that it was velvet. It looked, and she imagined felt, like the mole she had seen come out of an earth mountain on the Shrove lawn.

She was very shy of him. While he talked to her in his bedtime story voice, she could only stare at him with her eyes very wide open. He asked her what she did all day long and if she could read and would she draw something for him. While she was drawing a picture of Shrove with the river behind and the high hills and Heidi and Rudi running about on the grass, he said he expected she would be going to school soon. Mother said briskly that there was time enough for that and changed the subject. She wished he had let her know he was coming, she would have got some food in and given the house a special clean.

'*You* would? You're supposed to get a woman in from the village to do that.'

'I know, but they aren't reliable and they'd have to have a car. It's easier to do it myself. I prefer to do it myself, Jonathan.'

'I thought it was odd when I went through the accounts with Matt and there was no provision made for a daily.'

Mother said again, 'I prefer to do it myself.' She looked down in rather a meek way, her long eyelashes brushing her cheek. 'You pay me so generously that, really, I feel it's my duty.'

'My idea when you came here was that you would be a kind of estate manager. You had the cottage and a – well, a salary, to run the place.'

'Dear Jonathan, there's nothing to run but Mr Frost and the oilman,' said Mother and they both laughed.

Liza finished her drawing and showed it to Mr Tobias who pronounced it very good and said she must sign it. So she wrote Eliza Beck in the bottom right hand corner and wondered why Mr Tobias gave her signature such a strange long look before turning to Mother with one eyebrow up and a funny little crooked smile.

The dogs were not to sleep in the little castle this time but over at Shrove with Mr Tobias. Liza played with them until it was her suppertime and then she and Mother took them halfway up the Shrove drive and released them. She stood under the tallest Wellingtonia and called to them to run home, to run and find the master. Mr Tobias came to the front door of Shrove and down the steps and waved to them.

He had something hanging round his neck on a strap. Liza couldn't see very well from that distance but as they came closer she thought it looked rather like the thing Mother had that made music. He beckoned and put the thing up to his face, holding it in both hands. Mother went on walking towards him, telling her not to be shy, Mr Tobias was only taking a photograph of them. But Liza *was* shy, she hid behind a tree, so Mother got into the picture by herself.

By this time she had almost grown out of that baby game she used to play after she was put to bed, running from one room and one window to the other, but that night, for some reason, she felt like playing it again. Perhaps the reason was that Mother had come upstairs to check that she was asleep. Liza dived under the covers and lay with her eyes shut, breathing steadily.

She half opened an eye as Mother tip-toed out and saw that she had changed into her best skirt, the one she made herself from a piece of blue and purple and red material she bought when she went to town. Mother wore the new skirt that was very full and long, nearly to her ankles, a tight black top and a shiny black belt round her little waist. Her hair was done in the way Liza loved and which took half an hour to do, drawn back from her face and done in a fat plait that started at the crown of her head and was tucked under at the nape of her neck.

Liza thought she heard the front door close. She jumped out of bed and ran across to Mother's room and the window. Mother was letting herself out by the front gate. It was a warm evening, still daylight, but the sun low in the faded blue sky. Mother hadn't a coat or a shawl. She was going towards the gateway. Liza ran back into her own room, the turret room, stood on the chair and watched Mother passing through the open gateway and starting up the drive to Shrove.

Liza had never been left alone before, unless she was locked in and safe. Mother was walking under the trees, through the park and up to the house, she had never gone so far before. Fear sprang within her and, as it does when one is a small child, touched off immediate tears. In a moment she would have screamed and sobbed but in that moment, while her breath was held, Mr Tobias came strolling out from the back of Shrove House. He stopped and held out both hands and he and Mother looked at each other.

Somehow, Mr Tobias being there, knowing that all Mother was doing was meeting him, made everything all right. Mother took both his hands in her hands and said something and laughed. He walked round her, looking her up and down, nodded, touched the beautiful shiny plait with one finger. Then he took her hand and hooked it over his arm and they went on towards the house, walking very closely side by side. Liza no longer much minded Mother going because they were together and would only be at Shrove.

She minded a very little bit because she wasn't there with them, she felt left out. But not afraid any more. She ran back into Mother's room to see if anything was going on at the front, even if it was only rabbits feeding on the grass verges. There were always rabbits in the evening, that wasn't exciting. They couldn't get at Mother's vegetables because most things were covered in nets, the lettuces, the cabbages, the peas and the carrots, but not the beans and the strawberries because rabbits never ate them.

The sun was setting behind the woods, turning the trees black and the sky almost too dazzling a gold to look at. She watched it dip and sink until all the gold was drained away and the sky turned from yellow to pink to red. Once the sun went the bats came out. Mother had explained how they can hunt for insects in the dark, by their squeaks which humans can't hear bouncing off flying objects and echoing back at them.

A moth flew up to the window and Liza indentified it as a privet hawk, though its body was yellow and brown instead of pink and brown and its lower wings were yellowish. Perhaps it was just a common yellow underwing. Mother had brought her a moth book from the library at Shrove as well as *Frohawk's Complete British Butterflies*. She ran downstairs and fetched the book. Perhaps she would have an apple too but there were no apples at this time of the year. Instead she ate some of the strawberries she and Mother had picked before Mr Tobias came.

She couldn't find the moth, or not a picture she could be sure was of the one outside the window, and she must have fallen asleep when she got back into bed for she remembered nothing else from that night and it was the following evening or the next that she looked out of Mother's room much later, in the dusk, and saw them at the gateway of Shrove, standing close up against the wall of the little castle. Mr Tobias had his arms round Mother and he was kissing her in a way Liza had never seen anyone kiss anyone before, on the mouth.

The truth was that she had never *seen* anyone kiss anyone ever except Mother kissing her which wasn't the same thing. Mr Tobias let Mother go and Mother came into the house. Liza crept very quietly across the landing on her way back to her own room and as she passed the top of the stairs she heard Mother singing down there. Not very loudly but as if she was enjoying singing. And Liza knew the song and that it was something called Mozart, for she had often heard Mother play the record where the lady sang how she would make her lover better with the medicine she kept in her heart.

When the weekend came so did a lot of visitors to Shrove. They were all friends of Mr Tobias, Mother said, two men and three ladies and they came along the lane and past the gate-house and right in through the gates of Shrove up to the house. Liza said, could they go up there, she and Mother, and see the people, but Mother said, no, she wouldn't be going there again till Monday and Liza certainly would not.

'Why?' said Liza.

'Because I said no,' said Mother. 'Mr Tobias invited us but I said no, not this time.'

'Why?'

'I think it best, Liza.'

On the Saturday evening she saw all the people coming back from a walk. She was at Mother's window and she saw them all very clearly, passing the gate-house garden. One of the ladies had stopped to admire Mother's big stone tub that was full of geraniums and fuchsias and abutilon in full bloom.

The men were just men, nothing special, though one of them had bare skin instead of hair on top of his head, and the ladies were nice-looking but not one of them as pretty as Mother. Perhaps Mr Tobias thought so too, for he turned his head as they passed and gave the gate-house a long look. Liza didn't think he was looking at the flowers. But still there was something special about the ladies, they looked different from anyone Liza had ever seen before, smoother somehow and cleaner, their hair cut as trimly and evenly as Mr Frost cut the edge of the lawn where the flower border began. All three wore jeans like the milkman and Hugh but one had a jacket like Mother's best shoes, the suede ones with the trees in that Liza liked to stroke, and a silk scarf with a rope and shield pattern, one a wondrous sweater with flowers knitted into the pattern and her face painted like Diana Hayden's and the third a shirt like a man's but long and made of bright green silk.

Half an hour later one of their cars came down the drive from Shrove House – well, from the stable block really, where cars were kept – with Mr Tobias's Range Rover ahead of it to show the way and in the morning Mother told her they had all gone out to dinner in an hotel somewhere. By Monday they had gone away and she and Mother went up to Shrove to change the beds and clear up the mess. Or Mother did. Liza talked to Mr Tobias and he showed her his holiday pictures, he took her into the library and said she must have any book from it she wanted to read. They took the dogs down to the river and waved to the train and when they got back Mother had finished.

'I'm not at all happy about you doing this, Eve,' Mr Tobias said and he didn't *look* happy.

'Perhaps I will try to get someone,' Mother said.

Liza thought she seemed quite weary and no wonder, the house had been an awful mess. Mother had said nothing when they first arrived but Liza had stared wide-eyed at the sticky glasses, the cups and plates standing about everywhere, the powdery grey stuff mixed up with burnt paper tubes in the little glass trays and the big brown stain on the drawing room carpet.

'I should have cleared up myself,' said Mr Tobias which, for some reason, made Mother laugh. 'Come out with me tonight? We'll go somewhere for dinner.'

'I can't do that, Jonathan. I have Eliza, remember?'

'Bring her too.'

Mother just laughed again but in a way which somehow made it clear they weren't going out for dinner and that it was an absurd suggestion.

'Then you can cook my dinner. At the gate-house. It's a poky little place and I'm going to have it done up for you from top to bottom, but if we haven't a choice the gate-house it must be. Needs must when the devil drives. You're a bit of a devil, you know, Eve, and you know how to drive a man but you shall cook my dinner. If you're not too tired, that is?'

'I'm not too tired,' said Mother.

Liza didn't expect to be allowed to stay up with them. It was a nice surprise when Mother said she could, though she must go to bed straight after. Mr Tobias came at seven with a bottle of something that looked like fizzy lemonade but had its top wired on and a bottle of something the colour of Mother's homemade raspberry vinegar. The top came out of the lemonade bottle with a loud pop and a lot of foam. They had a salad and a roast chicken and strawberries and when Liza had eaten up the last strawberry she had to go to bed. Oddly enough, she went straight to sleep.

Next morning she did what she always did in the mornings, ran into Mother's room for her cuddle. Mother had always been alone in her big bed but she wasn't alone this time. Mr Tobias was in the bed with her, lying on the side nearest to the window.

Liza stood and stared.

'Go outside a moment, please, Liza,' Mother said.

A moment always meant counting to twenty. Liza counted to twenty and went back into the room. Mr Tobias had got up and done his best to get his broad shoulders and long body inside Mother's brown wool dressing gown. He muttered something, grabbed his clothes from the chair and went downstairs to the kitchen. Liza got into bed with Mother and hugged her, she hugged her so tight that Mother had to say to let go, she was hurting. The bed smelt different from usual, it didn't smell of clean sheets and Mother and her soap, but a bit like the river in a season of drought, a bit like the dead fishes washed up on the sand and like water with a lot of salt in it for cooking.

Mr Tobias came back, washed and dressed and saying it was terrible they hadn't got a bathroom, he would have a bathroom put in as a priority. And why on earth didn't Eve have a phone? Everyone had a phone. He went away after breakfast but came back in the afternoon with a present for Liza. It was a doll. Liza had very few toys and what she had had been Eve's, a rag doll, a celluloid one, a dog on wheels you pulled along with a piece of string, a box of wooden bricks.

The doll that Mr Tobias had bought her wasn't a baby but a little girl with dark hair like her own that you could wash and legs and arms and face that felt like real skin and a wardrobe of clothes for her to put on when the dress she was wearing had to be washed.

Unable to speak, Liza stared mutely.

'Say thank you to Mr Tobias, Lizzie,' said Mother but she didn't seem very pleased and she said, 'You really shouldn't, Jonathan. She will get all sorts of ideas.'

'Why not? Harmless ideas, I'm sure.'

'Well, I'm not. I don't wish her to have those ideas. But you are very kind, you are very generous.'

'What shall you call her, Liza?' said Mr Tobias in his softest sweetest voice.

'Jonathan,' said Liza.

That made them both laugh.

'Jonathan is a man's name, Lizzie, and she's a girl. Think again.'

'I don't know any girls' names. What were the ladies called who stayed with you?'

'Last weekend? They were called Annabel and Victoria and Claire.'

'I shall call her Annabel,' said Liza.

After that Mr Tobias slept in Mother's bed most nights. Liza slept with Annabel and brought her into Mother's bed in the morning, knocking on the door first as instructed to give Mr Tobias a chance to get up. He stayed at Shrove for three weeks, then four, and the dogs with him, but no more people were invited for the weekends.

Mother was very happy. She was quite different and she sang a lot. She washed her hair every day and made herself another new skirt. Every day they were either up at Shrove or Mr Tobias was with them at the gate-house and if anything was wrong it was only that when Mr Tobias wanted to take them out in the Range Rover Mother always said no. Liza very much wanted to go to the seaside and the suggestion was made, but Mother said no. All right, said Mr Tobias, come to London with me for the weekend, come to Montagu Place, but Mother said that would be worse than the seaside.

'You like it here, Jonathan, don't you? It's the most wonderful place in the world, nowhere is more beautiful.'

'I like a change sometimes.'

'Have a change then. That's probably the best thing. Have a change and then come back here to us. I can't believe the Ullswater house is more beautiful than this.'

'Come and see. We'll all go up for the weekend and you shall judge.'

'I don't want to go from here ever and Liza doesn't. I thought – ' Mother turned her face away and spoke quietly ' – I thought it might be attractive to you now because I am here.'

'It is. You know it is, Eve. But I'm young and, frankly, I'm rich. You know my father left me very well-off. I don't want to settle down in one place for the rest of my life and see nothing of the world. That doesn't mean I don't want you to see the world with me.'

Mother said she didn't want to see the world. She had seen enough of it for a lifetime, enough for ever, it was all horrible. Nor did she want the gate-house done-up and a bathroom put in. She didn't want him wasting his money on her. Luxuries of that kind meant nothing to her and Liza. If he must go away and she could tell he wanted to, he must leave the dogs with her and that way he would come back.

'I don't need a reason to come back. Matt can look after the dogs.'

'Leave them with me and then I'll know you have to come. You must always leave them with me.'

He slept in Mother's bed that last night and went back to Shrove in the morning. Later on he came to the cottage in the Range Rover and said goodbye. He hugged Mother and kissed her and kissed Liza and Liza said Annabel would miss him. They waved after the Range Rover as it went down the lane and Liza ran upstairs to watch it go over the bridge. When it was out of sight she and Mother put the dogs in the little castle and Mother said they might as well go up to Shrove to tidy up and put things to rights.

Mr Tobias had left a lot of mess, though for the past three weeks he hadn't been there much. While Mother was running the vacuum cleaner over the bedroom carpets Liza went into the morning room and looked at the door that was always locked. She tried the handle just in case it was, for once, unlocked. It wasn't. Squatting down because she was quite tall by then, she put one eye to the keyhole and closed the other. She was surprised to find she could see quite a lot, a piece of the red upholstery of a chair and the braid on its arm, the corner of a kind of table with drawers in it, the bright coloured spines, blue and green and orange, of books on a shelf. What could there be in there she wasn't allowed to see?

Liza now wished she had told Mr Tobias about the locked room on the several occasions he and she had been together in the house while Mother was cleaning upstairs or in the kitchen. But of course they had never been in the morning room, it wasn't much used and there was no reason why it should be when there were a drawing room, a dining room and a library as well. Liza was convinced that if she had asked Mr Tobias he would have fetched the key and opened the door at once.

Next time he came she would ask him. When he came back to fetch the dogs. But the weeks went by and he didn't come. He didn't write, not even a postcard, and after nearly a month Matt came in the Range Rover and took the dogs away. Mother happened to see the Range Rover coming across the bridge. It was the right colour, though she couldn't see the number, she was sure it was Mr Tobias himself coming and even more sure when she saw it in the lane. Mr Tobias had never before sent Matt in the Range Rover but he had this time and when Matt had gone and Heidi and Rudi with him, Mother went into her bedroom and cried.

Liza had never told anyone about that. Well, she had had no one to tell until now but she didn't tell Sean, she kept it locked up and secret inside her head. And when Sean said, this guy Tobias, the one that Shrove House belongs to, did he ever come, she said only, yes, he did, but he didn't stay long.

'And didn't you never go to school?'

'No, I never did. Mother taught me herself at home.'

'It's against the law, that.'

'I expect it is. But you know where Shrove is, the

back of beyond, far away from just about every-where. Who would know? Eve told lies about it. She was very open with me. She said it was important not to tell lies unless you had to, but if you had to the important thing was to know they were lies. She told some of the people that asked that I went to the village school and the other people that I went to a private school. We met Diana Hayden in the lane and Eve told her we were in a hurry because she was taking me to catch the bus for school. You have to remember there weren't many people. I mean, basically, there were just the milkman, the postman, the man who read the meter, Mr Frost and the oilman, and they weren't going to ask. None of them were there for more than five minutes except for Mr Frost and he never spoke.'

'Didn't you want to go to school? I mean, you know, kids want friends.'

'I had Eve,' Liza said simply, and then, 'I didn't want anyone else. Well, I had Annabel, my doll. She was my imaginary friend and I used to talk to her and discuss things with her. I used to ask her advice and I don't think I minded when she didn't answer. I didn't *know*, you see. I didn't know life could be different.

'When I could read, I mean really read, Eve started teaching me French. I *think* I speak quite good French. We did history and geography on Mondays and Wednesdays and arithmetic on Tuesdays. She started me on Latin when I was nine and that was on Fridays but before that we did poetry reading on Thursdays and Fridays and music appreciation.'

Sean was staring at her aghast. 'What a life!'

'I really didn't need to go to school. We talked all day long, Eve and me. We walked all over the countryside. In the evenings we played cards or did jigsaws or read.'

88

'You poor kid. Bloody awful childhood you had.'

Liza wasn't having that. She said hotly, 'I had a wonderful childhood. You mustn't think anything else. I collected things, the gate-house was full of my pressed flowers and pine cones and bowls with tadpoles in and caddises and water beetles. I never had to dress up. I never ate food that was bad for me. I never quarrelled with other children or fought or got hurt.'

He interrupted her and said perspicaciously, 'But you know about those things.'

'Yes, I know about them. I'll tell you how, but not now, not this minute. Now I just want you to know my childhood was all right, it was fine. She's not to blame for anything that happened to *me*, she was a wonderful mother to me.'

Again his face wore that incredulous expression and he shook his head faintly. She was silent and gently she took his hand. She wasn't going to tell him – or not yet – that things had changed, that the happiness was not perpetual.

Eve told her the myth of Adam and Eve, insisting as she did so that it was only that, a myth. They read the passage on the creation in Genesis and then the expulsion from the Garden in Milton, so she knew about the serpent in Paradise and later imagined it was Eve and herself who hand in hand through Eden took their solitary way.

But all she told Sean of the months before her seventh birthday was that Mr Tobias came back once, for a day and a night, a night he didn't spend at the gate-house with Eve but in his own bed at Shrove. Then he went away, if not for ever, for a very long time.

Chapter Seven

At first Sean was better at picking pears than she was. He knew how to lift each fruit from the twig on which it grew and bend it gently backwards until it came away in his hand. Liza just pulled. The pears got bruised and sometimes her fingernail went through the mottled green skin, wounding the white flesh beneath. Mr Vanner would dock her pay, Sean said, if she damaged his fruit, so she tried to be more careful. She was used to being told, it wasn't something she had learned to resent.

They picked the pears before they were ripe, before the outside turned yellow with a red blush and while the inside was still firm and waxy. Since they came to Vanner's the sun was always shining. Each morning they woke to a pale blue sky, a stillness and a white mist lying on the fields. Over the farm buildings the Russian vine spread snowy clouds of blossom and Mrs Vanner's garden was overgrown with yellow and orange nasturtiums. They began picking before it grew hot and took a couple of hours off from noon till two. At that time they had lunch, packets of crisps and a pork pie, cans of Coke and Mars bars, sticky from being kept in a hot pocket.

The pear fields were a long way from the caravan, so mostly they didn't bother to go back but ate their food sitting on the bank under the quickthorn hedge. At first they were nervous about being seen by the other pickers, but no one was interested in them, no one came their way, and on the second day they slipped into the little sheltered place where the elders made a tent of branches and made love on the warm dry grass. Both knew they would make love that evening and when they went to bed but it seemed too long to wait.

Afterwards Sean fell asleep, stretched out full-length, his head buried in his arms. Liza lay awake beside him, her cheek resting on his shoulder and her arm around his waist. She liked looking at the way his dark hair grew on the nape of his neck, in two points like the legs of an M, and she thought for the first time that it was also the way Mr Tobias's hair grew.

Mother hadn't told her the history of *her* mother and the Tobiases until she was older. She must have been about ten when she learned about her grandmother Gracie Beck and old Mr Tobias, also called Jonathan, and the will; old Mr Tobias's daughter Caroline who was Mr Tobias's (that is, Jonathan's) mother and her enormously rich husband who left her because she was so awful. When she was seven all Liza knew was that Mother and Mr Tobias had known each other since he was a big child and she a small one and that somehow or other Shrove House ought to have belonged to Mother and not been Mr Tobias's at all.

Oh, and that Mother loved Mr Tobias and he loved her. Mother told her that one evening in the winter when they were sitting by the big log fire and Liza had the doll called Annabel on her lap. Liza had noticed that Annabel often brought Mr Tobias into Mother's mind.

'The difficulty is,' Mother said, 'that Mr Tobias is a restless man and wants to see the world, while I intend to remain here for the whole of my life *and never go away*.' She said that last bit quite fiercely, looking into Liza's eyes. 'Because there is nowhere in the world like this place. This place is the nearest thing to heaven there is. If you have found heaven why should you want to see anywhere else?'

'Have you seen everywhere in the world?' Liza asked, carefully combing Annabel's hair.

'Near enough,' Mother said mysteriously. 'I have seen more than enough of people. Most people are bad. The world would be a better place if half the population were to perish in a huge earthquake. I have seen more than enough places. Most places are horrible, I can tell you. You have no idea how horrible and I'm glad you haven't. That is the way I want it to be. One day, when you have grown up the way I want you to, you can go out and have a peep at the world. I guarantee you'll come running back here, thankful to be restored to heaven.'

Liza was uninterested in any of that, she didn't know what it meant. 'Mr Tobias doesn't think other places are horrible.'

'He'll learn. It's only a matter of time, you'll see. When he has travelled about for long enough and seen enough he'll come back here. It just takes him longer than it took me.'

'Why does it?'

'Perhaps because I have seen more dreadful things than he has or just that I'm wiser.'

In the spring of that year Heather came to stay. Mother said nothing about it until the day before she arrived and then all she said was, 'You'll be sleeping in my room with me for the next week, Liza. Miss Sawyer is coming and will have your room.'

Liza knew who Miss Sawyer was from the letters Mother got. She was the same person as Heather.

'For heaven's sake don't call me that, child,' said Heather five minutes after she got there. 'My name is Heather. "Miss Sawyer" sounds like a headmistress. What's your headmistress called?'

Liza, who had understood almost nothing of what was said, simply gazed at her, her extreme thinness, her height, her small head and sleek red hair.

'Head teacher, then? I can't keep pace with all these new terms.'

Mother changed the subject. She explained to Liza that she and Heather had met while they were at college and Heather knew Mr Tobias.

'Is he still around?'

'Shrove is *his* house, Heather. Surely you remember that?'

That was when Heather first began whispering to Mother behind her hand. She gave Liza a glance, then quickly turned, put up her hand and began the whispering. 'Wishy, wishy, wishy', was how it sounded to Liza.

After she had been upstairs and seen her room, Heather said she had never before stayed in a house without a bathroom. She didn't know houses without bathrooms existed any more. But no, of course she wasn't going to allow Mother to carry hot water upstairs for her, which Mother had offered to do. She would use the bath in the kitchen like they did, only it was going to be very awkward.

Another awkwardness was what she called 'lack of TV'. Liza didn't understand that either and wasn't very interested. The weather was fine, so they went out for many long walks and Heather went for a ride in the train from Ring Valley Halt. She had to go alone. Mother said she had been too many times to want to go again, so Liza couldn't go either.

There was no car to go out in – Heather had come by taxi from some distant station – no record player, hardly any books published later than 1890, no phone, and no restaurants nearer than eight miles away. The village where Mr Frost came from had something called a pub, Mother said, but they couldn't go there because pubs didn't like children and wouldn't let them in.

'Wishy, wishy, wishy,' whispered Heather behind her hand.

'Oh, do speak out, Heather,' said Mother. 'You are creating mysteries where none need exist.'

So Heather stopped whispering and said boldly, the night before she was due to go, 'You'll go mad here, Eve.'

'No, I shall go sane,' said Mother.

'Oh, dear, how epigrammatic!'

'All right. I mean I shall become normal again. I might even be happy. I shall recapture the old-fashioned values and bring up a daughter who has been kept clear of the hideous pressures of our world.'

'It all sounds very high-flown and unnatural to me. Anyway, you won't be able to. Her contemporaries will see to that. When you get tired of being a noble savage remember I've always got a couple of spare rooms.'

Eve must have remembered those words when she was finding somewhere for Liza to seek sanctuary. Or else Heather wrote it in a letter, for she never came back and that was the only time Liza ever saw her.

Mother left Liza to her own devices while she swept the bedroom carpets at Shrove with the vacuum cleaner ('You must never say "hoovered", Lizzie') and at those times Liza explored the library. One of the books she found was of fairy stories and the tale of 'Bluebeard' was in it. After she had read it she began to associate the locked room with Bluebeard and wondered fearfully if it might contain dead brides. She thought perhaps old Mr Tobias had married several women, killed them all and left them to moulder behind that locked door.

Even when Mother showed her old Mr Tobias's portrait, a big painting that hung in the upstairs hall of a man with a proud expression and grey hair but no beard, blue or otherwise, she still wondered. She wanted to know what that thing was sticking out of his mouth, a stick with a little pot on the end of it. Mother said it was called a pipe, something you put ground-up leaves in and lit with a match, but Liza, remembering that Mother claimed to be a good liar, for the first time disbelieved her.

In a much more prideful place, where the light was bright and no eye could fail to be drawn to it, hung a portrait of the lady called Caroline. She wore the kind of dress Liza had never seen on an actual woman, ankle-length, flowing, low-cut and of silk the same red as her mouth. Her hair was chestnut-coloured, her skin like the petals of the magnolia even now blooming in the Shrove gardens, and her eyes fierce. Liza spent a long time looking at all the pictures in the house that were of real people, alive or long dead. There was no portrait of Mr Tobias and none of the rich man who had run away from Caroline.

Heather wrote Mother a thank-you letter and after that weeks went by without the postman ever coming to their door. The milkman came and said, 'The ten-thirty is late' and 'This sunshine is a real treat,' but they never saw the postman until one day he brought an envelope with a little paper book in it. Liza managed to get a fascinated look at this book, which was full of pictures of irons and hair dryers and towels and sheets and dresses and shoes, before Mother came and took it away from her. A log fire was burning in the grate and Mother got rid of the book by tearing it into pieces and putting the pieces on the fire.

After that there was no post for weeks, nothing from Mr Tobias until a postcard came, a plain one, not even a picture, with just a few lines on the back asking them to have the dogs.

'Not if it's a nuisance,' he wrote. 'Matt will willingly have them. It is only for two weeks while I go to France to see my mother.'

'Caroline,' Liza said.

Mother said nothing.

'Does she live in the house in the place called Dordogne?' Liza had spent a long time studying the large maps of France in the library atlas. 'Does she live there by herself? Is she called Mrs Tobias?' She remembered the fierce eyes and the red, mouth-coloured dress.

'She is now. She is called Caroline Tobias. When she was married she was called Lady Ellison but our Mr Tobias was always called Jonathan Tobias because that was his grandfather's wish. She lives in a house in the Dordogne her husband gave her when they were divorced.' Mother gave Liza a speculative look as if she was considering explaining something but she must have thought better of it. 'Mostly, she lives by herself. Mr Tobias goes to see her.'

'We can have the dogs, can't we?' said Liza. 'Even if Matt really wants them, we can have them, can't we?'

'Of course we shall have the dogs.'

So that Mr Tobias would be sure to come. Liza knew that only in retrospect, not at the time.

It was the day of her first French lesson ('Voici la table, les livres, la plume, le cahier.') that Matt came with the dogs. She was pursing her lips, trying to make that funny sound which is half way between an e and a u, when they heard the van coming and then the knock at the door. It was rather a cold day even for April, she remembered, and the old electric heater was switched on.

The dogs were pleased to see her, as they always

were, jumping up and licking her face and wagging the bit at the end of their backs where their tails had been chopped off. But Rudi was less violent in his affections than in the past, his breath smelt and his muzzle was going grey. Dogs had seven years to every year of ours, Matt said, and that made Rudi over seventy. Heidi, of course, was only six, or forty-two.

'Will he die?' Liza said.

Matt's hair was much longer than last time, hanging down in greasy hanks. 'Don't you worry yourself about that,' he said, 'that's a long way off.'

But Mother said, 'Yes, he'll die this year or next. Dobermans don't live much past eleven.'

Liza knew her tables. 'Or seventy-seven.'

It had the effect of making Matt ask her why she wasn't at school. Before she could reply Mother said coldly, 'It's Easter. The schools have broken up for Easter.'

Some years went by before Liza realised a vital fact about that statement, though she knew there was something odd about it at the time. Mother hadn't told a lie, it *was* the Easter holidays, but just the same the impression she had given Matt was a false one. Later on she observed other instances of Mother doing this and learned how to do it herself.

Mother asked Matt how long they were to have the dogs this time and he said two or three weeks, he couldn't be more precise. But they'd let her know.

'Still haven't got no phone, I see.'

'And never shall have.'

'It'll have to be a postcard, then.'

'I think we can leave that to Mr Tobias,' Mother said in the very cold way she sometimes had, and then, less coldly, almost as if she was asking for something she didn't want to have to ask for, 'Will he come for them himself?'

Liza didn't like the look Matt gave Mother. He wasn't smiling but it was as if he was laughing inside. 'Like you said, we'll have to leave that to him.' With one of his winks, he added, 'It'll depend on what Miss Fastley has to say.'

Liza had never heard of Miss Fastley but Mother looked as if she had, though she said nothing.

'When him and her get back from France,' Matt said.

As soon as he had gone Liza thought they would get back to the French lesson but Mother said that was enough for today and to take the dogs down to the river. They wrapped up warmly and went down through the Shrove garden. A couple of trains had very likely passed by, Liza couldn't remember details like that, but it was probable at that hour. Likely too that she had waved to the train and one or two passengers waved back. There were never more than a few to wave back.

Mother stood looking across the valley and up to the high hills where the white road ran round among the greening trees. The woods were white with cherry blossom and primroses grew under the hedges.

'It's so beautiful, it's so beautiful!' she cried, spreading out her arms. 'Isn't it beautiful, Lizzie?'

Liza nodded, she never knew what to say. There was something about the way Mother looked and the breathy edge to her voice that made her feel awkward.

'I don't mind the trains, I think in a way the trains make it better, it's something to do with all the people being able to sit inside and see how beautiful it is.'

And she told Liza a story about a man called George Borrow who sold Bibles, wrote books and lived in Norfolk, and who moved away and lived away for years because he couldn't bear it when they built a railway through the countryside he loved.

'Who's Miss Fastley?' Liza said on the way back.

Mother can't have heard her that first time because she had to say it again.

'She is one of the ladies who came to stay at Shrove for the weekend last year. She is the one called Victoria.'

'Annabel had the sweater with flowers on,' said Liza, 'and Claire had the jacket like your shoes, so Victoria must have been the one in the green silk shirt.'

'Yes, I believe she was.'

They didn't put the dogs straight into the little castle but had them in with them for the evening. Rudi lay in front of the electric heater and slept. He was tired after his walk, Mother said they had taken him too far. Liza sat on one side of the fireplace and Mother on the other side. Liza was reading *Winnie the Pooh* by A.A. Milne and Mother was reading *Eothen* by A.W. Kinglake. They sometimes read bits aloud to each other and *Winnie the Pooh* was so funny there were a lot of bits Liza would have liked to read aloud but when she looked up she saw that Mother wasn't reading but gazing sadly at the hearthrug and she had tears on her face.

Liza didn't offer to read aloud but went silently back to her book. She thought Mother was crying because Rudi was old and would soon die.

The money they earned Liza wanted to save up. Eve had set her an example of thrift. There had been the bank account and the tin in the kitchen. And, of course, the secret box in the little castle. Strict accounts had been kept of what Eve earned and what they spent and these were consulted and referred back to before a length of material was bought to

99

make a dress for Liza or a new skirt for Eve. The biggest expenditure Liza remembered was on the tape player Eve bought so that Liza could learn about music and get used to hearing the works of the great composers. She was nearly eight when that happened.

Sean appreciated her economies. He said that being sensible about money was one thing she *could* teach him. They might have Cornish pasties or pork pies and crisps for lunch with chocolate bars afterwards but it would be wiser not to go into town so much in the evenings for a meal at the Burger King or even Mr Gupta's Tandoori. One evening Sean saw a notice in the window of the new supermarket that they wanted assistants. It would only be for sticking labels on packets and putting cans on shelves but he said he was going to apply for it. The money would be at least twice what he earned at Vanner's, maybe three times as much.

'I will too, then.'

'I don't reckon you can, love. They'll want your insurance number and you haven't got none.'

'Can't I get one?'

'Not without giving your name you can't.'

They found the family planning clinic too – Liza gave Sean's name and called herself Elizabeth Holford – and a notice board at the newsagent's window on which five people were advertising for domestic help. Liza studied it thoughtfully. Housework was something she could do.

When they got back the man with the black dog put his head round the door of his camper, said hi and how about a cup of tea?

Liza could see Sean didn't want to but it was rude to say no, so they went into the man's camper, the kitchen part, where the black dog was sitting up on a counter, watching television. Instead of tea the man, who said his name was Kevin, produced a bottle of whisky and three glasses, which Liza could see made Sean feel a lot better about going in there.

The little glowing screen fascinated her, the picture was so clear and the colours so bright. But at first she was half-afraid to look in case a policeman appeared describing her own appearance or even Eve herself. There was no need to worry. This was a programme about small mammals in some distant part of the world, rat-like creatures and squirrel-like creatures, that perhaps accounted for the dog's absorption.

He was much smaller than Rudi and Heidi, less sleek and with a real tail which thumped on the counter when the squirrels jumped about, but just the same he reminded her of Mr Tobias's dogs, now long dead. She and Mother had looked after them for three weeks, not two, on that occasion and at the end of that time, without warning, Matt appeared to take them away. When Mother saw his van stop outside and saw him get out of it, his hair longer than ever and tied back now, all the colour went out of her face and she grew very white.

Liza thought she would be bound to ask him where Mr Tobias was but she didn't, she hardly spoke to him. The dogs were handed over, Liza having hugged them both and kissed the tops of their heads, and somehow she knew as she watched the van depart that they would never come again, or not both of them, or not in the way they had before. She didn't know how she knew this, for Mother said not a word about it, didn't even look out of the window but set the French book in front of Liza and told her quite sharply to begin reading.

That evening Mother said they must go over to Shrove House, which surprised Liza because they never did. They never went there after about three in

101

the afternoon. It was just after six when they walked across the parkland between the tall trees. There were cowslips in the grass and against the hedges cow parsley and yellow Alexanders. But this time Mother said nothing about how beautiful it was. They walked in silence, hand in hand.

Mother took her into the library and set her a task: to find the French books, to count them and then to see if she could find one called *Emile* by Jean-Jacques Rousseau. It took Liza no time at all. There weren't many French books, she could count only twenty-two, *Emile* among them. She took it down from the shelf, a very old book bound in blue with gilt letters, and went to look for Mother.

She was in the drawing room, talking into the telephone. Liza had never before seen anyone do that. Of course she had seen the telephone and more or less knew what it was. Mr Tobias had told her, and on that occasion she remembered, while he was explaining, Mother had frowned and shaken her head. It was Mother using it now. Liza kept very still, listening.

She heard her Mother say, 'I've said I'm sorry, Jonathan. I've never phoned you before.' Her voice went very low so that Liza could hardly hear. 'I had to phone. I had to know.'

Somehow Liza had expected to hear Mr Tobias's voice coming out of the other end of the receiver but there was silence, though she could tell Mother could hear him.

'Why do you say there's nothing to know? If there was nothing you would have come.'

Liza had never heard Mother speak like that, in a ragged, pleading, almost frightened voice, and she didn't like it. Mother was always in control of things, all-knowing, all-powerful, but that wasn't how she sounded now.

102

'Then, will you come? Will you come, Jonathan, please? If I ask you, *please* to come.'

Even Liza could tell he wasn't going to come, that he was saying, no, I can't, or, no, I won't. She saw Mother's shoulders hunch and her head dip down and heard her say in her cold voice, not unlike the one she used to Matt, 'I'm sorry to have troubled you. I do hope I haven't interrupted anything. Goodbye.'

Liza went up to her then and put out her hand. She showed her the blue book called *Emile* but Mother seemed to have forgotten what she had asked her to do and everything about it. Mother's face was as pale as a wax candle and as stiff . . .

'You lost in a dream, love?' Sean said. 'I offered you a penny for them and you never heard a word I said. Kevin wants to know if you'd like a glass of his Riesling?'

Liza said, yes, thanks, she'd love some, and when she saw the winebox and read the name she somehow managed to stop herself telling them it was pronounced Reesling, she thought their feelings might be hurt. Kevin was a small man with a nut-brown face and black hair, though not much of that was left. He might be thirty or he might be forty-five. Liza couldn't tell, she wasn't much good at guessing ages, and no wonder.

The men talked about football and then about the dog that Kevin said was a good little ratter. It had started to rain, Liza could hear it drumming on the roof of the camper. What would become of them if it rained? Mr Vanner wouldn't pay them if they couldn't pick. She suddenly thought, with a fierce hunger, not altogether unlike the desire she often had for Sean, that if she didn't soon have a book in her hands, if she couldn't soon read a book, she'd die.

103

She asked Kevin how much his TV cost and could tell at once from Sean's expression that she shouldn't have. But Kevin didn't seem to mind. He said he didn't know, he hadn't a clue, because it was one of the things he'd brought with him from their household when he and his wife split up and he reckoned it was her bought it in the first place.

'Not thinking of getting married, are you?' he said when she and Sean were going. 'Only you want to think twice. Hang on to your freedom while you can.'

'Of course we're not thinking of getting married,' said Liza, and she laughed at the very idea, but Sean didn't laugh.

She hadn't said much to Sean at all about Eve and Mr Tobias, it had all been in her head, all memories. It was he who brought the subject up next day, he must have been thinking about it, she didn't know why. They were still in bed, though it was quite late in the morning, but there was no point in trying to go out and pick with the rain pouring down.

When she first woke she had been quite disorientated, not knowing where she was but imagining she must be in the gate-house. The rain made it unnaturally dark. Half-asleep still, she had looked for the book which should have been open and face-downwards on the bedside cabinet. But there was no bedside cabinet and no book and when she turned over she rolled into the warm eager arms of Sean. Instead of reading she cajoled and kissed him into making love to her – never a hard task – which he would have said was better any day, and often she would agree.

Suddenly he said, 'This guy Tobias, he slept with your Mum? I mean, they was in the same bed?'

'They were lovers, they were like us.'

'That wasn't right,' Sean said very seriously, 'not with you in the house, not with a little kid.'

'Why not?'

She didn't know what he meant and she could tell he found it hard to explain.

'Well, it's just not. Everyone knows that. They wasn't married. Your Mum should have known better, an educated woman like her. It's one thing just the two of them but not with a little kid in the house. You got to have principles, you know, love.'

She said, no, she didn't know, but he took no notice. 'D'you reckon she thought he'd marry her?'

'She hoped he would.'

'Yeah, she must have been lonely. It wasn't right him taking advantage of her like that.'

Liza told him about the phone call and how Eve had been afterwards, quiet and preoccupied and sometimes as if she was frightened.

'Well, she was in love, wasn't she?' Romantic Sean pressed his lips into her neck. He stroked her hair. 'She loved him and she thought she'd lost him, you got to pity her.'

'I don't know about being in love,' Liza said. 'Maybe a bit. She wanted Shrove House, that was what all that was about. She wanted Shrove House for herself, to make sure she'd never be parted from it. That was the only way. If she married Mr Tobias it'd have been hers.'

He was shocked. 'That's not right.'

'I can't help it. It's the way it was. It was always like that. She wanted that place, to be there all the time and sure she could be, more than anything in the world. It was all she wanted.'

'It sounds crazy to me.' She could feel him shaking his head as it lay on the pillow beside hers. 'Whatever happened, then?'

'He married someone else,' said Liza. 'He married Victoria.'

Chapter Eight

Liza was eight years old and for as long as she could remember she had never been away from Shrove. Once a week Mother went on the bus into town to do the shopping but Liza never asked if she could come. Now, when she thought about it, she couldn't imagine why she had never said, can I come? Locked up in her bedroom or else locked up in one of the rooms at Shrove, she had been content or she had accepted.

'That was wrong.' Sean was in censorious mood. 'Suppose something had happened to you.'

'It didn't.'

'Maybe not. Just as well for her. You might have hurt yourself or the place caught fire.'

She thought but didn't say, the place burning down would have been a bigger tragedy for Eve. Shrove on fire would be worse than Liza dying in it.

'If they'd found out what was going on they could have took you away and put you in care.'

'They didn't know, whoever they are.'

'Wasn't you scared?'

'No, I don't think I was, not ever. Well, for a bit after the man with the beard, but I saw what she did about that, you see. It showed me she'd always look after me. I liked being locked up in the library at Shrove best, there or in the morning room. It was so warm.'

'What d'you mean, warm? The place was empty, wasn't it?'

'The heating was always on from October to May.'

'He must be rolling in it,' Sean said disapprovingly. 'Central heating blasting away when no one lived there and there's poor buggers sleeping rough on the streets.'

She wasn't interested, she hardly knew what he meant. 'I used to read the books. Of course there were lots I didn't begin to understand, they were years and years too old for me. Eve said to me once, "I just wonder what people would say, the ones who think you ought to have gone to school, if they could have seen you trying to read Ruskin and Matthew Arnold at seven-and-a-half".'

Sean had no comment to make on that.

'Anyway, I was never left for more than two hours. Then Eve would come for me and she'd always have something nice, some treat, coloured pencils to draw with or a new pair of socks or a painted egg. I remember once she came home with a pineapple. I'd never seen one before. Then one day she brought a picture.'

It was a painting of Shrove House. Mother had to tell her what it was or she might not have known, the painting was so strange, the colours so strong and the house not looking the way she had ever seen it. But when Mother explained that this was just one man's, the painter's, view of it, that he had chosen to paint it at sunset and after a storm, that he saw it as a symbol of wealth and power and had therefore accentuated all the yellows to express gold and the dark purples to reveal strength, then she began to understand. Mother had seen the painting in the window of a place she called a gallery and had bought it 'on an impulse'. It was cheap, she said, for what it was.

'Besides, we've got quite a lot of money,' Mother said, and proudly, 'we don't fritter money away.'

She hung the painting up on the wall in their living room where the gun had once been. When Liza climbed up on a stool to look more closely at it she saw that the words Bruno Drummond were written in red in the bottom right hand corner with the date 1982.

It was the next morning, or perhaps the morning after next, that the postman came and brought with him the letter from Mr Tobias. Mother tore open the envelope and read it. She threw the envelope into the rubbish bin, read the letter a second time and folded it up. She said a strange thing, she said it in an intense concentrated way while she stared at the folded letter in her hand.

'In ancient times they used to kill a messenger who was a bearer of bad news. It's fortunate for that postman that things have changed.'

Liza could hear his van going back up the lane. She waited for Mother to tell her what Mr Tobias had written but she didn't tell her and there was something in Mother's face that stopped her asking. There were more lessons than usual that week and sometimes they went on into the evening. That was one of the signs that something had happened to upset Mother, an increase in lessons.

On the Saturday morning, while Liza was eating her breakfast, Mother said, 'Mr Tobias is getting married today. This is his wedding day.'

'What's wedding?' said Liza.

So Mother explained about getting married. She turned it into a lesson. She talked about marriage customs in different parts of the world, how in some countries, for instance, a man could have several wives, but not here, here people could only be married one at a time. It was called monogamy. She told Liza about Islam and about the Mormons, about Christian brides in white dresses being married in churches and Jewish people under canopies stamping on glass. Then she read out something from the Book of Common Prayer about marriage being for ever until the two people were parted by death. Mr Tobias wouldn't be married like that, however, but in an office by a registrar.

'Were you ever married?' Liza asked.

'No, I never was,' said Mother.

At a quarter past twelve she said it must all be over now and they were man and wife. Liza said, wasn't he a man before, and Mother said she was quite right, it was just an expression and not a very good one. They were *husband* and wife.

'Will they come and live here?' said Liza.

Mother didn't answer and Liza was going to repeat the question but she didn't because Mother had gone a dark red colour and clenched her fists. Liza thought it best to say no more about it. She married Annabel to the rag doll in a ceremony of her own invention but she did it upstairs in the privacy of her bedroom.

And of course Mr and Mrs Tobias never did come and live at Shrove, though they stayed there from time to time, the first time being a fortnight after the wedding. Another letter came first. Mother read it, screwed it up and looked cross.

'What does he mean, get a woman in to get the place ready? He knows I'll never do that. He knows I clean it and that I'll clean it ready for his wife.' And she said those final two words again. 'His wife.'

She and Liza spent the afternoon at Shrove. Mr Tobias would no longer be sleeping in his old bedroom but in the one that had been Caroline Ellison's, in the fourposter with yellow silk curtains. With Victoria, Liza thought, though Mother hadn't said so. The fourposter was quite different from the Venetian one and made of dark brown carved wood with a carved wood roof Mother called a tester. She said that in olden times before there was glass in windows and when ceilings were very high, birds used to fly in and roost in the rafters on cold nights. You needed a roof on your bed to protect you from owl and hawk droppings.

While Mother put clean white sheets on the fourposter and mats of yellow silk and white lace out on the dressing table, Liza tried the handle of the door to the locked room on the off-chance of its not being locked for once. But it was, it always was.

Mother had said she must start writing compositions – well, stories really – and asked her to do one about getting married. Liza was already working it out in her head. She was going to have a girl called Annabel get married to a man called Bruno who brought her home to his big house in the country by a river. Annabel found the locked room while Bruno was out riding on his horse and then she found the key to the door in the pocket of his dressing gown. Next time he went out she unlocked the door and inside she found the dead bodies of three women that he'd killed before he married her because only Moslems could have more than one wife. Liza didn't know what would happen next but she'd think of something.

She expected Mr Tobias to come running to their door as he had in the past, the dogs at his heels. Mother was busy sewing, her back to the window, her feet working the treadle on the machine faster than usual and her hands guiding the cloth, but Liza sat on the step outside, waiting for him. It was October but warm and sunny, the leaves on the balsam tree still green, the blackberries and the elderberries over and the holly berries turning from green to gold. The morning had been misty but now the air was clear, the sky blue and everything very still.

They were late. Liza was almost at the point of giving up and going indoors when at last the car came, not the Range Rover but the Mercedes. Later on Liza was to learn to identify many makes of car but at that time she only knew a Range Rover, a Ford Transit van, a Mercedes and whatever kind it was the police used. The Mercedes was going quite fast, it was going to sweep straight in through the open gates, but Mr Tobias did see Liza, he stuck his arm out of the window and waved. Of course he was on the near side of the car, the side nearest to her. On the other side sat the lady who had worn the green shirt. Victoria. Mrs Tobias.

It was a pity because Liza couldn't see her very well. She wasn't wearing a green shirt this time but a fawn jumper with a neck that came right up to her chin and then folded over. Her hair was fair, a pale blonde, it was exactly the same colour as the jumper but silky instead of woolly and rough. Her face wasn't visible. Liza supposed the dogs must be in the back, though she couldn't see them. She waved and waved until they were out of sight and then she went in to give Mother all the details. That evening she expected them to come or him to come, best of all she would have liked him to come alone, and she sat in the window with Annabel, as if Annabel would draw him in some magic way.

'It must have been like turning a knife in the wound,' she said to Sean, 'the way I went on and on about him. When was he coming? Could we go up there? Poor Eve! But I didn't know any better. I was only a child.'

'I shouldn't worry. You said yourself, she only wanted him for that place of his.'

'Things aren't so simple,' said Liza. 'Anyway, they came next day, both of them.'

Mrs Tobias was tall and slim. ('Quite elegant, I

suppose,' Mother said.) Her fair hair, the colour of newly sawn wood, was cut very short like a man's but her face was painted in a way Liza had never seen before, not in the least like Diana Hayden's. The effect was more like a wonderful picture or a piece of jewellery. Her mouth reminded Liza of a fuchsia bud and her eyelids were crocus purple. She had fuchsia bud nails and on one finger were Mr Tobias's rings, gold and diamonds flashing brilliantly.

She was very nice and polite to Mother, thanking her for making the house so clean and beautiful and telling her what Mr Tobias was always saying, how she must, she just must, get a woman in to do all this cleaning. Either she found someone or she, Mrs Tobias, would absolutely have to find someone herself.

All the while Mr Tobias was looking rather strange, rubbing his hands together, walking up and down, then studying their old chromium electric heater as if he was passionately interested in things like that.

Liza said, 'Where are Rudi and Heidi?'

'I'm afraid Rudi's dead,' he said.

He looked more awkward than ever and tried to explain it away, as if it wasn't important, a dog dying. Rudi was old, he lost his appetite, he'd got a thing called a tumour growing inside him, and the kindest thing was for him to die a peaceful death.

'Did you shoot him with a gun?' Liza asked.

Mrs Tobias screamed out when she said that. 'Oh, my God, where does the child get these ideas?'

'I took him to the vet,' Mr Tobias said, 'and he was very quiet and peaceful and happy. The vet gave him an injection and he went to sleep with his head on my lap.'

'He never woke up again, he died,' said Mother, getting a very strange look from Mrs Tobias, who curled back her upper lip and showed her little white top teeth. 'What about Heidi?'

Mr Tobias said Matt had her with him in Cumbria. Heidi lived with him now, in his council house. 'Victoria's allergic to dogs.'

'It isn't something I can help,' Mrs Tobias said. 'Of course I adore them but just having one near me can bring on these horrendous attacks of asthma.'

After that they saw Mr and Mrs Tobias only in the distance. From her bedroom window, one evening, Liza saw them come walking out of the wood with their arms round each other. She heard the car go past several times and when they had been there nearly a week she heard shots.

'Mr Tobias never used to shoot things,' she said to Mother. 'Why's he doing it now?'

'I expect it's his wife's influence.'

'What is he shooting?'

Mother shrugged. 'Pheasants, partridges – rabbits, perhaps.'

Mr Tobias called on them and brought a couple of dead pheasants. A brace, he called it. He came alone. Mrs Tobias had a pain in her back and wasn't feeling well. Liza didn't think she would be able to eat things she had seen in the meadows, such beautiful birds, as beautiful as the peacocks she had seen in pictures, but when it came to it and Mother had roasted them she found that she could. When she ate the soft brown meat that seemed to melt in her mouth, she forgot about the shining blue and gold feathers and the bright beady eyes.

The Day of the Pheasant, she called it. She wrote the composition about marriage for Mother and had it given back with just a red tick on the bottom but otherwise no comment. That was the week Mother smacked her, the first and the last time this happened. Mother found her playing with the husband

and wife dolls and came upon her just as the rag doll was killing Annabel with a gun made from a twig.

It was as if she didn't stop to think but lifted up her hand and smacked Liza on the bottom. Afterwards she said she was sorry and that she shouldn't have done that.

The weather got cold very suddenly, the night frosts so heavy that in the morning it looked as if snow had fallen. The frost drove the Tobiases away. They called at the gate-house as they were leaving and Mrs Tobias, who was wearing a wonderful coat of white sheepskin, said it was shocking having no bathroom at the gate-house and one must be put in as a matter of priority. Mr Tobias had used those very words himself but done nothing about it, Liza remembered. His wife urged Mother once more to get a cleaner. After all, if she knew Mother was doing it on her own she would have to tidy up herself, her conscience would make her.

'Please, Eve,' said Mr Tobias, looking more uncomfortable than ever. 'And we'll see about that bathroom.'

The car had disappeared up the lane for no more than ten minutes before Mother and she were on their way to Shrove House to clear up the mess.

But there was no mess. Everything was clean and tidy and someone had washed the dishes and done the dusting. Liza couldn't tell how she knew this but she sensed that Mother, curiously, would have preferred a mess. While Mother was stripping the bed and putting the sheets in the washing machine, Liza made another attempt on the locked door. This time, for the first time ever, it wasn't locked. She turned the handle and the door came open.

There were no bodies, no dead brides. She found herself in a small sitting room in which was a writing desk, a pair of occasional tables, three armchairs and a sofa. On the walls, in frames of polished wood, were the kind of dull grey pictures Mother said were called etchings and a pair of vases with Chinese people on them which held bunches of dried red roses. Facing the sofa and the chairs, on a cabinet made of a rather bright golden wood with a complicated curly grain, stood a large brown box-shaped thing with a kind of mirror on the front of it. She could see herself in the mirror but not very clearly, rather in the way she could in a window with dark curtains drawn behind the glass.

'What was it?' Sean asked. 'A TV?'

'Yes, but I didn't know that then. I couldn't think what it was. The extraordinary thing was that I wasn't very interested in it. I was *disappointed*. You see I'd given that room such a terrific build-up in my mind, I thought there'd be at least some amazing wild animal in there or a box of jewels, treasure really, or even a skeleton. I'd seen a picture of a skeleton in one of the books in the library. And all there was was this box thing with a mirror that didn't even work like mirrors are supposed to.'

'But you switched it on.'

'No, I didn't. Not then, not for ages. I wouldn't have given it another thought, I'd probably never have gone back there, if Mother hadn't come in. It was her coming in and being so obviously – well, taken aback that I'd got in there and found the thing that made me so anxious to know what it was.'

'Kids are like that,' said Sean sagely.

'Are they? I don't know. I only knew me. She wasn't cross. It was more as if she was worried. It's hard to describe, I have to find an expression, sort of knocked sideways, the wind taken out of her sails. She took my hand and led me out of there and got the key and locked the door again.'

'But why?'

115

'That was the point of the whole thing, wasn't it? The whole way I was being brought up. The world had treated her so badly, it was so awful out there, that I wasn't to be allowed to go through any of that. I was to be sheltered from the world, hence no school and no visits to the town, no meeting other people, other people kept down to the minimum, a totally protected childhood and youth.'

'She taught you to express yourself all right, didn't she?' he said admiringly and he lit a cigarette as if he needed it.

Liza wished he wouldn't. The caravan quickly filled with smoke, it was so small, and it made her cough. She sighed a little before going on. 'Television would have undone a lot of her work. Once I'd seen that I'd know about the world out there, I wouldn't only want to see it, I'd start talking like the people on it and learning the sort of ways she thought were bad.'

'You said the world had treated her bad. I mean, like what? What had it done to her?'

'You won't believe this but I don't know. That is I don't know the details. She'd had me without a husband, there was that, she hadn't got Shrove when she thought she was going to, she told me a lot more about that later but she never told me what made her – well, bury herself and me down there. When she took me out of that room and locked the door again I hadn't any idea why and she didn't explain. I only knew it had something to do with the box with the glass front.'

'You said she got the key. Where did she get it from?'

That had been the most interesting thing. Mother had looked around her for the key and clicked her tongue when she saw it lying on top of the glass-fronted cabinet that was full of dolls. She locked the door and then, in Liza's presence, not bothering to hide from her what she was doing, she climbed on to a chair and from the chair on to the top of a dresser in which was kept breakfast china and cutlery. The top of the dresser was on a level with Liza's head.

On the wall above hung a large picture Liza was to learn was called a still life. This one was by Johann Baptist Drechsler and was of a bunch of roses with dew on them and fritillaries and morning glory. The painter had put a Painted Lady butterfly on a blade of grass and on the top left-hand side a moth with brown forewings and yellow underwings and a strange pattern on its back. The picture was in a thick gilt frame that stuck out six inches from the wall. Mother put the key on top of the frame, over to the right-hand side, and while she did so she explained to Liza that the moth was called the Death's Head Hawk Moth because the pattern on its back looked like a skull, or the bones inside a person's head. If this was designed to distract Liza's attention from the key and the locked room it failed to do so.

Liza knew she had about as much chance of getting up there as she had of owning a dog. But she wanted to get up there. Soon it became the thing she most wanted to do in all the world. She thought about it a lot and she thought that in that little book that had once come in the post and she had managed to study for five minutes before it was taken away and torn up, in there had been a picture of just such a box as was in the locked room at Shrove House.

When it was winter and Mother went shopping she was always locked up at Shrove because of the warmth there. Sometimes in the morning room, sometimes in the library, sometimes in one of the bedrooms. When it was the morning room she had been in the habit of spending a lot of the time just gazing at the dolls in the cabinet. The dolls were of

117

historical personages, Mother had said and had named some of them, Queen Elizabeth I, Mary Queen of Scots, a man called Beau Brummell and another called Louis Quatorze, Florence Nightingale and Lord Nelson. But now instead she stood staring at the picture of the flowers, the butterfly and the moth with the skull on its back, knowing the key was lying there on the top of the frame, though she couldn't see it even if she stood on a chair.

Her ninth birthday came and went. It was very cold and the grounds of Shrove lay under six inches of snow. A partial thaw came but the half-melted snow froze again and the house, the stables and coachhouse, the gate-house, the little castle and the owl barn were hung with icicles. Hoar frost turned all the trees into pyramids and cascades and towers of silver lace. The lane was blocked with snow drifts and Mother couldn't get out to catch the bus for town. When she did, at last, she left Liza in the library.

Reading books, playing with the terrestrial globe, looking out of one window after another at the birds in the snow, Liza came to the far end where it was always rather dark, the darkest place in that light house, and saw, resting against the wall, something long-familiar yet forgotten, the library steps.

There were eight steps, enough to get even a small person up to the topmost bookshelf. But Liza was locked in the library. Anyway, she thought the steps would be too heavy for her, they looked heavy, they were made of dull grey metal. She touched them, she put both hands to them and clasped the rails that enclosed the treads. She tried to raise them as if they would be heavy and they flew up in her hands. The steps were light, they were nearly as light as if made of cardboard, a little child could lift them, she could lift them on one hand.

118

But she was locked in. Mother came for her soon afterwards and they went back to the gate-house, through the snow. It snowed even more heavily that night and they spent next morning digging themselves out and the afternoon making cakes of dripping and bread for the bird feeders. Two weeks, three, went by before Mother could go to town again. It was soon after that, in March probably, when the snow had gone but for patches of it left in shady places, that the postman brought the letter which was to change their lives.

'Tobias again?' said Sean.

'No, we never heard from him. Well, Eve got her money all right and Mrs Tobias sent a postcard from Aspen in America where they went ski-ing but there was never a thing from him. This letter was from Bruno Drummond.

'The artist guy.'

'Yes. The Phoenix Gallery had told him about Eve buying his painting, I don't think he sold many paintings – well, I know he didn't. He said he'd wanted to phone her but he couldn't find her number in the book. Not surprising, was it, since she'd no more have a phone than she would a television. He said the painting ought to be varnished and if she'd bring it to him he'd do it. He told her where he lived and said it was easy to park her car outside!

'Of course she didn't answer. She said if the painting needed varnishing she was capable of doing that herself. And she was very annoyed with the gallery for giving him her address. She kept saying, Is nothing sacred? Is there no privacy?'

In February the Latin lessons began. *Puella, puella, puellam, puellae, puellae, puella*. And *Puella pulchra est*.

'The girl is beautiful,' said Mother, but it was herself that she looked at in the mirror.

Liza enjoyed learning Latin because it was like

doing a hard jigsaw puzzle. Mother said it would stretch her brain and she read aloud from Caesar's *Invasion of Britain* for Liza to get accustomed to the sound of it.

In March she began her collection of pressed wild flowers. Mother bought her a big album to keep them in. To the lefthand page she attached the pressed flower and on the righthand one she painted a picture of it in water colour. A snowdrop was the first one she put in and next a coltsfoot. Mother let her borrow *Wild Flowers* by Gilmour and Walters from the library at Shrove so that she could identify the flowers and find their Latin names.

The weather grew warmer and in April Mr and Mrs Tobias came down to Shrove to stay, bringing four other people with them. Claire and Annabel and a man Liza had never seen before and Mr Tobias's mother, Lady Ellison.

'Caroline,' said Liza.

'Yes,' said Mother, 'but you mustn't call her that.'

As it turned out, Liza didn't get the chance to call her anything.

Before they came Mrs (not Mr) Tobias had written to Mother and said some more about a cleaning woman.

'Can you imagine having such a person here?' Mother was calm but Liza could tell she was angry. 'She would come in a car and we should have that noise and dirt. I would have to let her in, I couldn't trust anyone with a key, and then teach her what to do and, just as important, what *not* to do. Why can't Victoria Tobias leave it alone? Why can't she just leave me to do it?'

Liza couldn't answer that. Mother thought about it all day, she *worried* about it, she kept saying she didn't want any more intruders, Mr Frost was bad enough, not to mention the postman *and* the milkman *and* the man who read the meters *and* the one who serviced the Shrove central heating, there was no end to it.

'You could do it yourself and pretend you'd got a lady to do it.'

At first Mother said, 'No, she couldn't,' and, 'How about the money?' and then she said, 'Why not? It wouldn't be dishonest to take the money so long as the work was done,' so Mother invented a woman and she and Liza thought up a name for her. They laughed until they almost cried at some of the names Liza thought up. She got them from the wild flower book, Sweet Cicely Pearlwort and Mrs Sowthistle and Fritillaria Twayblade. But Mother said it mustn't be funny, it must sound like a real name, so in the end they called her Mrs Cooper, Dorothy Cooper.

Mother wrote to Mr (not Mrs) Tobias and said she'd found a cleaning woman called Dorothy Cooper who would come once a week and if he sent the money to her she would pay her. In the week before Easter Mother gave Shrove House a tremendous spring clean while Liza sat in the library reading *Jane Eyre*. That is, for most of the time she read *Jane Eyre*. She also carried the steps out of the library and into the morning room.

At the morning room windows hung long heavy curtains of slate-grey velvet. Even when you pulled the cords that drew them across the windows they still covered about two feet of the grey and white wall on either side. Liza put the steps up against the wall on the right hand side of the right hand window. The curtains covered them, you couldn't see they were there.

It was just as well she hadn't used them to get the key down and open the door because, when she had finished upstairs, Mother came into the morning room, climbed on to a chair and then on to the

121

sideboard and reached up for the key on top of the picture frame. Liza crept out of the library and watched her from the morning room doorway. Mother unlocked the door and went into the secret room, pulling the vacuum cleaner behind her.

She was in there for half an hour. Liza kept dodging from the library to the morning room door to check on her. When she heard the howl of the vacuum cleaner from the morning room she went to the door and said she was hungry and could they go home and have lunch?

The key was in the lock of the door to the secret room. It had to be, of course it did, because Mr and Mrs Tobias and their friends were coming. Liza and Mother had their lunch in the Shrove kitchen and all the time Liza was thinking, perhaps the key will still be in that lock after they have gone away again.

It wasn't. Liza thought Mother had probably gone over there and put it back on the picture before she was even up. She had seen very little of Mr and Mrs Tobias and their friends, just the Mercedes going by once or twice with the other car following behind and once caught a glimpse of Claire and a tall old woman in a tweed skirt down on the Shrove lawn with golf clubs. Could it be Caroline? Could *that* be the Caroline of the plump white shoulders and the lipstick-coloured dress? But one evening, after she had gone to bed, she heard someone come to their front door. There was a low murmur of voices, a man's and Mother's.

She was almost but not quite sure the other voice was Mr Tobias's. They were downstairs in the living room, talking, and she crept out of bed to listen at the top of the stairs. But Mother must have heard her because she came out and called up to Liza to go back to bed at once.

The murmur went on and on, then she heard the

front door close and Mother come up to bed. If Mother had been crying it wouldn't have surprised her, she didn't know why, but instead Mother was talking out loud to herself. It was uncanny and rather frightening.

'It's all over,' Mother was saying. 'You have to get it into your head that it's all over. You have to start again. Tomorrow to fresh woods and pastures new.'

Did that mean they were going away?

'Tomorrow to fresh woods and pastures new,' Mother murmured and closed her bedroom door.

'No, of course we're not leaving,' Mother said in the morning. 'What on earth gave you that idea? Mr and Mrs Tobias are leaving and goodness knows when they'll come back again.'

Liza saw the cars come down the drive from Shrove House, the Mercedes with Mr Tobias driving and Mrs Tobias beside him and Claire in the back. A minute later along came the other car with the man driving and Caroline Ellison beside him. It stopped outside the gate-house and the man sounded his horn. Liza didn't know what he meant by it but Mother did. Mother was furious. I'm not going out there, I'm not being summoned in that way, she was fuming, it's like the Royal Family stopping outside some keeper's house, but she did go out and talked to Lady Ellison.

This enabled Liza to get a good look at Mr Tobias's mother, who had actually got out of the car. She was so tall she made Mother look child-sized. And Mother made her look like a giantess as well as uglier than ever. Liza thought her hands were like a hawk's claws that had been dipped in some poor small animal's blood.

Mother came back into the house making terrible faces of rage and disgust which the people in the cars couldn't see because her back was to them. The cars were hardly out of sight before she and Mother were up at Shrove House, where there was an awful mess to be cleared up. No doubt Mrs Tobias thought Dorothy Cooper would be clearing it up. That was when Liza found the secret room door locked and the key, so far as she knew, back on top of the picture.

It was May now but not very warm, though beautiful to look at, as Mother kept saying. The new leaves were a sharp fresh green and the cream and red flowers on the broom were out, sweet smelling and covered with bees. Last autumn Mr Frost had planted hundreds of wallflowers. Like folds of multi-coloured velvet they were, red and amber and gold and chestnut brown, spread across a whole sweep of land with not a blade of green to be seen between them. Liza picked speedwell for her wild flower collection and Mother said she could take one, but just one, cowslip.

They had lunch at home. The afternoon was for Latin, arithmetic and geography. Liza was doing long division when the doorbell rang. Because the doorbell hardly ever rang it was always a shock when it did.

'That will be Mr Frost wanting something,' Mother said, though he hardly ever did want anything.

She opened the door. A man was standing there. His car, which was the orange colour of a satsuma and looked as if made of painted cardboard, was parked outside their gate. He was quite a young man with curly brown hair long enough to reach his shoulders and very big blue eyes with long lashes like a girl's. Well, like hers or Mother's. There were little brown dots that Mother later explained were freckles sprinkled on his small straight nose. His lips were red and his small teeth very white. He wore blue jeans and a denim jacket over a check shirt and a gold ornament hanging from a chain round his neck.

Liza stared fascinated at the earrings he wore, two gold rings both in the same ear. He was carrying a bag made out of a carpet. It looked as if it was made from one of the Persian rugs at Shrove.

'Oh, hi,' he said. 'This really is the end of the world, isn't it? I'm amazed that I've found you. Let me introduce myself. My name is Bruno Drummond.'

Chapter Nine

Liza said she was like Scheherazade, telling her man stories every night. Only Sean wouldn't chop her head off in the morning, would he, if one night she was so worn out she couldn't collect her thoughts?

Sean said, 'Who was that then, that She-whatever?' – but Liza was too tired to explain.

They were both exhausted, picking Coxes. The crop was a particularly big one this year. They picked from first thing in the morning until sunset, which was as long as Mr Vanner would let them. He said he'd have to take on extra labour to cope with the crop and they wanted to stop him, they wanted to earn all the money that was going, but it was a losing battle. On the third morning a troop of women moved in to help, housewives from the village that was a mile away.

Sean wanted to hear more about Bruno but she was too tired to tell him, too tired to watch the little coloured television set she'd finally bought with the hundred pounds and some apple money, too tired for everything but making love and they only managed that because it happened in bed and they fell asleep straight afterwards.

The news was something Liza had seldom been able to watch on television even if she had wanted to. It is rarely transmitted between two and five in the afternoon. Now she learned it was for mornings and evenings, so she watched it at breakfast time and once the women had come and there was no point in working so hard, at six o'clock and nine. She was looking for something about Eve. But there never was anything.

'That's because they've had her in court,' Sean said, 'and now she's on what-d'you-call-it, remand, that's it, remand, and the papers and the telly can't have anything on about her until she comes up in court again.'

This was very much what Eve herself had told her. Liza admired Sean for knowing it. Feeling very pleased that he knew about this legal matter, she realised she had begun accepting that she knew much more than he did about almost everything but the absolutely practical things. Of course he *thought* he knew more than she but she could tell that mostly he didn't. When it was books and music and nature and art and history she knew it all and he knew nothing, so she was pleasantly surprised.

'When will that happen, Eve coming up in court?' she asked him.

'Not for weeks, maybe months.'

She was disappointed. 'Where do they do it, this remand?'

'In prison.'

Her knowledge of that had its base in her reading of fiction, *Little Dorrit* and *The Count of Monte Cristo*. She saw Victorian hell-holes, she saw dungeons with a tiny barred window up in the wall.

'What do you care?' he said. 'You ran away, you got out of that and quite right too.'

'I'm tired, Sean. I've got to go to sleep.'

She crept into his arms, her naked body close up against his. The nights were starting to get cold. He slid his mouth over hers and entered her smoothly as if it were the natural next step. They were like that, locked together, when she woke up in the deep night and moved her body gently to arouse him again. He said sleepily that he loved her and she said, 'I love you too, Sean.'

Next day wasn't the last one for picking the Coxes but Friday would be. Kevin said he was moving on before the end of the week and why didn't they follow him? They were advertising for unskilled hands at the Styrofoam Packings works on an industrial estate ten miles away. Kevin thought he'd give it a go.

But Sean wasn't interested. He knocked off early, spruced himself up, put on a clean shirt and jeans and went into town to apply for the supermarket job. Liza wasn't a bit surprised to hear he'd got it. They asked Kevin in to share a couple of bottles of wine. Kevin said his telly wasn't a patch on hers, it was wonderful really the way the colours came up so bright and the picture so sharp on a screen that size.

Liza said goodbye to the dog. She put her arms round it and its cold nose nuzzled her neck. It was a gentle mild creature. The feel of the fine skull and sleek black pelt under her lips reminded her once more of Heidi. It still made her indignant, thinking of how Mr Tobias had simply ditched Heidi when he married Victoria, handed her over to Matt as if she was a piece of furniture he didn't need any more.

She had still liked Mr Tobias but her affection for him had been shaken by his treatment of Heidi. To handle that she had blamed the changes in him on Victoria, as she guessed her mother did. It was Victoria who made him shoot things and Victoria who kept him away from Shrove.

Perhaps Victoria would die. Dogs died, so why not people? It was about this time that she began fantasising how life would be if Mr Tobias married Eve and they both went to live at Shrove House. Like children in books, she would have a father as well as a mother.

*

Sean was to start his job on Monday. They'd have to find somewhere else to put the caravan but before that he was going to take advantage of being on Vanner's land.

He often called her Teacher when Liza imparted information. This time, he said, he was going to teach her something. He'd teach her to drive.

She wouldn't be old enough to get a licence till she was seventeen, which would be in January, but she could drive on the tracks around the orchards, that was private land. They picked the last row of trees on Friday morning and collected the last pay they would get. Then Sean got her up in the driving seat of the Dolomite and taught her how to start it and use the gears. It wasn't difficult.

'Like a duck to water,' Sean said, very pleased.

She wanted to drive out on to the road and take them to wherever the new place they were going to park on would be, but Sean said no. It wasn't worth the risk. They couldn't afford to pay fines. Reluctantly, Liza agreed.

'I suppose I can't risk the police getting hold of me.'

'Anyway, it's against the law,' Sean said very seriously.

She sat in the passenger seat next to him, eating Coxes. She'd filled a cardboard box with apples she'd picked up. Vanner was so mean he didn't even like the pickers taking home windfalls.

'You mind he don't put the fuzz on you,' Sean said, but he laughed and she knew he was joking. Then he said, out of the blue, 'Your Mum, she ever try to get this Tobias away from his wife?'

'What made you suddenly ask that?'

'I reckon I was thinking about the cops and about them catching her and remembering you never said if he come back again after he had all them people there for the weekend.'

'Well, she never did, no. At least, so far as I know she didn't. She didn't get a chance, did she, with him so far away and then we weren't on the phone, we hadn't a car, we were trapped down there in a way.'

'But wasn't that what she wanted?'

'Oh, yes, it was what she wanted. She wanted to be at Shrove and be undisturbed and isolated but what she'd wanted most was to *own* Shrove. I think she gave up that idea when he got married. I mean, she gave it up for a while. It was very hard for her, she'd counted on it for so long, but she had to give it up. Of course I don't know what went on in her mind, I was only a child, but I think she regretted a lot of things, she had bitter recriminations.'

'Come again?'

'I mean she was sorry she hadn't behaved differently. You see, maybe if we'd gone to London with him when he first asked or gone travelling with him, he'd have got so close to her he'd have thought he couldn't live without her. It might only have been for a year or two and then we could have all come back to Shrove together. He and she were mad about each other then, I'm sure they were, like you and I are.'

'That's true anyway,' said Sean with a smile, looking pleased that she'd said it.

'But she wouldn't because of me. She was determined to bring me up without – well, the contamination of the world. I wasn't to be allowed to suffer as she'd suffered. If she'd gone to London with Mr Tobias she'd have had to send me to school there and I'd have met other children and seen all sorts of things, I suppose. You could say she put me first or perhaps she just put Shrove first. The irony was that she lost Mr Tobias because she put his house first. As for me, I'd have loved to live at Shrove House and have Jonathan Tobias for my father. You'll laugh, but I used to think, if I lived there and it was mine, I could get into that room.'

Sean did laugh. 'But he married someone else and that was the end of her love life.'

'Oh, no, you could say it was the beginning of it. That was when Bruno came. Now I'm grown-up I think I know what went through her mind. She thought, I've lost Jonathan, I can't waste my whole life mooning over him, so I might as well cut my losses and have a new lover. She was only a bit over thirty, Sean, she was young. She couldn't give up everything.'

'How about the bathroom? Did he have it done?'

'In the end. Not for years. He forgot about it the minute Shrove was out of sight. He meant to do it but he just forgot, he was very thoughtless. When I think about it all now I really believe that when Shrove was out of sight he forgot about Eve too. She'd come into his mind once or twice a year and then he'd send her a postcard.'

The place they found to park the caravan was a piece of waste ground at the point where a bridle path turned off a lane. No one used it much. People on horseback might notice they were there but it could be weeks before whoever owned the land did. Law-abiding Sean had tried to find out who that was but had failed. The difficulty was that there was no water supply apart from the stream which tumbled over rocks under the stone bridge a little way up the lane. That was all right to drink, Liza told the dubious Sean. Mostly they'd boil it, anyway. They could get washed in the public swimming pool next to the supermarket he'd be working at. She was full of plans. Of much of the world she might be ignorant, but she knew how to *manage*.

131

The day he started she was left alone. Winter was coming and it had started to get cold. They heated the caravan with bottled gas and an oil heater, so that was all right, but for the first time in her life she had nothing to do.

It was rainy and cold out there but she went out and walked along the public footpath down to the stream and over the bridge close by the ford. The leaves were falling now, gently and sadly dropping from boughs because there was no wind. They floated down to make another layer on the wet slippery mass underfoot. Leaves coated the surface of the sluggish stream. The sky was grey and of a uniform unbroken cloudiness. She walked for miles along woodland paths and meadow edges, keeping the church tower always in sight so that she would know how to find her way back.

Once or twice she crossed a road but she saw no one and no traffic passed her. A muntjac stag appeared under the trees, showed her his top-heavy antlers and fled through the bracken. Jays called to each other, to warn of her approach. She gathered all kinds of fungus but in spite of her knowledge feared to cook them and shed a trail of agarics and lepiotas as she walked. When it was about noon, according to her haphazard but usually accurate calculations, she made for home.

There, with no prospect of Sean coming home for four hours, she was at a loss. Never before had she been without something to read. There was no paper in the caravan and nothing to write with, no means of playing music, no collections to pore over, no needles or thread to sew with. At last she turned on the television. An old Powell and Pressburger film with Wendy Hiller in it mystified her, as such films had when the Shrove House set was available to her. Had such people ever existed, talked like that, dressed in those clothes? Or was it as much a fairy tale as Scheherazade?

When Sean came back she had fallen asleep. The television was still on and he got cross, saying she was wasting power. Next day she went with him into the town and applied for one of the jobs she had seen advertised.

Liza said she was eighteen. She had no references because she had never worked for anyone before, but she knew all about housework. She had watched Eve and later on helped her.

The house in Aspen Close was a little like the house Bruno had wanted them all to live in. But inside was different. She had never before seen anything like this large, dull, ugly room, carpeted and curtained in beige, with no pictures on the walls and no mirrors, and as far as she could see no books. Flowers which could not be real, artificial white peonies and blue delphiniums and pink chrysanthemums filled beige pottery bowls. Across the middle of a table and along the top of a cabinet lay pale-green lace runners.

Mrs Spurdell was the same colour, except that her hair was white. Her fat body was squeezed into a pale-green wool dress and underneath that, Liza thought, must be some kind of controlling rubber garment that made her shape so smooth, yet segmented and undulant. Like a plump caterpillar, shortly to become a chrysalis. The shoes she wore, shiny beige with high heels, looked as if they hurt her ankles which bulged over the sides of them.

Liza was shy at first. If Mrs Spurdell had been kind and friendly she might have found things easier but this fat old woman with the surly expression made her speak abruptly and perhaps too precisely.

'You don't sound the sort of person I was looking

for,' Mrs Spurdell was moved to say. 'Frankly, you sound more as if you'd be off to university than looking for a daily's job.'

Liza thought about that one. It gave her ideas but of course she didn't voice them. She said, 'If I can work for you I'd do it properly.'

Mrs Spurdell sighed. 'You'd better see the rest of the house. It might be too much for you.'

'No, it wouldn't.'

But Liza went upstairs with Mrs Spurdell, walking behind her. The caterpillar waist and hips and the wobbly fat legs threatened to make her giggle, so she made herself think about sad things. The saddest thing she could contemplate was Eve in prison. Her thoughts flew to Eve and she experienced a moment or two of sharp fear.

Mrs Spurdell's bedroom was all in pink. A white fluffy rabbit sat in the middle of the pink satin bed. Another bedroom was blue and a third a kind of peach colour. Liza began to hope and hope she would get the job because there were so many things here she longed to look at more closely, to study and speculate about. Then Mrs Spurdell took her into a room she said was Mr Spurdell's study and Liza saw the books. There was a whole bookcase full of them. There was a box full of white paper on the desk and pens and pencils in a jar made of some kind of green-veined stone.

She saw a few more books in the gloomy chamber Mrs Spurdell called the dining room, about twenty of them on a shelf. At once Liza began to feel differently about the house. It was no longer simply grotesque and ridiculous. It was a place with books in it and paper and pencils.

'I can keep this clean,' she said. 'It won't be too much for me.'

'I'll start you on a trial basis. You look very young.'

134

But not so young as I am, Liza thought. The amount Mrs Spurdell offered her seemed very low indeed. Even to her, ignorant as she was, it seemed low. She would have to be strong and speak up. To her surprise she heard herself say very firmly to Mrs Spurdell that two pounds fifty an hour wouldn't be enough, she wanted three pounds. Mrs Spurdell said certainly not, she wouldn't consider it, and that left Liza at a loss. There seemed nothing for it except to go but when she got up, having no idea that this was bargaining or even what bargaining was, Mrs Spurdell said to wait a minute and all right, but to remember it was on a trial basis. Two mornings a week and one afternoon and she could start next week. Tomorrow, please, said Liza.

'Goodness me,' said Mrs Spurdell in a voice that implied Liza would fail in her undertaking, 'you are keen.'

For the rest of the day she wandered about the town, doing all sorts of adventurous things, going into a pub and then a cinema. Some of these activities made her heart beat faster but she did them. They served her in the pub, though somewhat suspiciously. It seemed she could pass for eighteen. The film she saw shocked her deeply. She was also electrified by it. Were there such places? Were there huge cities of stone buildings taller than any tall tree, where the streets were gleaming loops on stilts, where a million cars went to and fro and chased each other and men made violent assaults on women? But she took it calmly when a man screamed and died, his blood spraying on to the wall behind him. After all, she had seen the real thing.

The rest of it she found hard to believe. Reluctantly, she decided it must belong in a genre of entertainment Eve had mentioned in their English literature lessons: science fiction. H.G. Wells, she thought vaguely, and John Wyndham, whose names she had heard but whose works she had never read.

If she had had access to Eve she could have asked. She asked Sean instead while they were going home in the car.

'That's Miami.'

'What do you mean, that's Miami? What's Miami?'

He was never much good at explaining. 'It's a place, isn't it? In America. You seen it on TV.'

'No.' One day she'd tell him why she hadn't. 'Have you been there?'

'Me? Come on, love, you know I never been there.'

'Then you don't know, do you? They might have made it up. They might have built it in a – in a studio. Like toys.'

'Them guys firing guns, they wasn't toys.'

'No, they were actors. They didn't really die, it wasn't real blood, it couldn't be, so how d'you know the rest wasn't made up too?'

He had no answer for that. He could only keep saying, 'Course it's real, everyone knows it's real.'

As they were going up into the caravan she said, 'If it's real I'd like to go there, I'd like to see.'

'Chance'd be a fine thing,' said Sean.

Because life is like that, you see or hear something new to you early in the day and then later the same information comes up again in quite another context, Miami was on the television that evening. Not Miami, L.A., said Sean, but it looked the same to her. Probably, then, such places existed just as, in another programme, the great castle called Caernarvon and the place called Oxford.

'Eve was there,' she said, answering the bell that rang in her head.

'What was she doing there?'

'She was at a school. It's called a university. Mrs Spurdell thought I was going to one. She said so.'

136

'Your Mum was at Oxford university?'

She was genuinely puzzled. 'Why not?'

'Come on, love, she was having you on.'

'No, I don't think so. She had to leave it, I don't know why, something to do with me being born.'

Sean didn't say any more but she had the impression he wanted to, that he was struggling to say something but didn't know how to put it. At last he said, 'I don't want to upset you.'

'You won't.'

'Well, then, d'you know who your dad was?'

Liza shook her head.

'OK, sorry I asked.'

'No, it's all right. It's just that she doesn't know, Eve doesn't know.'

She could see that she had shocked him. The spraying bullets on the screen and the spurting blood didn't affect him, nor did the violated women or the bombs that flattened a city, but that Eve was ignorant of the identity of her child's father, that shook him to the core. He was bereft of speech. She put her arm round him and held him close.

'That's what she said, anyway.' She tried to reassure him. 'I've got my own ideas, though. I think I know who it was, whatever she said.'

'Not that Bruno?'

'Oh, Sean. She didn't know Bruno till I was seven. Shall I go on telling you about him?'

'If you want.' He said it gruffly.

'Well, then. He stayed and varnished the picture. He'd brought all the stuff with him in his bag. I didn't think Eve would let him do it but she did. I didn't think she'd speak to him but I was wrong there too. She asked him how he'd ever come to paint Shrove House and he said he'd seen it from the train.

' "Not with the sun setting behind it you didn't," she said, "you must have been looking eastwards."

"Ah, but I could tell how wonderful it would be from the other side," he said, "so I came down here one summer evening and made a start. I was here a good many summer evenings." "I didn't see you," Eve said, and he said, "I didn't see *you*. If I had I'd have been back sooner." '

It was as if Sean hadn't heard a word since she said that, about not knowing who her father was. 'She must have had one bloke after another,' he said, 'one one night and another the next or even the same day. That's really disgusting. That's a terrible what-d'you-call-it to bring a child up in, especially a girl.'

'Environment,' she said. 'Why especially a girl?'

'Oh, come on, Liza, it's obvious.'

'Not to me,' she said, and then, 'Don't you want to hear about Bruno Drummond?'

Chapter Ten

The second time he came, the important time, was the day she saw the Death's Head Moth. It was June.

He was thirty-one and lived in the town, in rooms over Mullins the greengrocer's. His father was dead but his mother was still alive up in Cheshire. Once he had had a wife but she had left him and was living in somewhere called Gateshead with a dentist. Liza, who was listening to this, said, 'What's a dentist?'

Bruno Drummond gave her the sort of look that meant he thought she was teasing him and said something about expecting she'd been to one of those a few times. But Mother said, 'A kind of doctor who looks after your teeth.'

The reason for his visit, he said, was to paint the valley with the train, and perhaps he had done some painting earlier but he called at the gate-house soon after ten in the morning, stayed to lunch, and was still there in the evening. Instead of a chair he sat on the floor. He related the story of his life.

'I should never have married,' he said. 'I don't believe in marriage but I allowed myself to be persuaded. Marriage is really the first step in getting swallowed up in the killing machine.'

'What do you mean, the killing machine?' said Mother.

'Society, slavery, conformity, the poor ox that treads out the corn, walking round and round all day long, and muzzled too most likely. I'm an anarchist.

Now you'll say, what sort of an anarchist is it that marries and gets a Civil Service job to pay the mortgage? Not exactly a card-carrying one. My defence is that I got out of it after three years of hell.'

'Were you really a Civil Servant?'

'On a low rung. Of course I'd been to art school. As a matter of fact, I was at the Royal College. When I was married I worked in the DSS benefit office in Shrewsbury.'

'So how do you live now?'

'I paint, that's what I always wanted to do, but it's not lucrative. Then I paint houses too, rooms, that is. I'll tell you how I got into that. Someone, a woman, asked me what I did and I said, I paint, so she said, would you come and paint my dining room? I'd like to have spat in her face, the fool. But then I thought, well, why not? Beggars can't be choosers. And I've been doing it on a regular basis ever since – more or less, I'm opposed to regularity of any kind. I don't pay tax, I don't pay National Insurance. I suppose somewhere someone's got a record of me and keeps sending me demands to my old address. But they don't know where I am, no one does but my mother, my ex-wife doesn't. That's freedom and the price I pay is relatively small.'

'What price is that?' said Mother.

'Never having any money.'

'Yes, that's freedom,' said Mother. 'Some would call it a very high price.'

'Not me. I'm different.'

Bruno played his guitar after that and sang the Johnny Cash song about finding freedom on the open road and men refusing to do what they were told. Liza could tell Mother liked him, she was looking at him the way she had sometimes looked at Mr Tobias. Perhaps she liked his voice and the way he pronounced words, unlike the way anyone else

140

did. Liza remembered Hugh with the beard, his fuzzy cheeks and upper lips. Bruno looked as if no hair had ever or could ever grow on his smooth girlish face.

In the summer the solanum plant that climbed over the back of the gate-house showed its blue flowers at Liza's window. Mother called it the flowering potato because it and potatoes and tomatoes all belonged to the same family. When she came up to bed that evening Liza knelt on the bed up at the window and saw, a few inches from her eyes, the Death's Head Moth immobile and with its wings spread flat, on one of the solanum leaves.

The moth book had told her *Acherontia atropos* likes to feed on potato leaves. It also told her how rare a visitor to the British Isles this moth is. But she was in no doubt about it, this was no Privet Hawk. No other moth had that clear picture of a skull on its back between its fore wings, a pale yellowish death's head with black eyeholes and a domed forehead. This was the moth Drechsler had put into his painting, the one at Shrove on whose frame the key was kept.

She knew Mother would want to see it too. Mother might be quite cross, at the very least disappointed, if she didn't tell her about *Acherontia* outside the window. She went down and opened the door. Bruno was softly twanging his guitar and they each had a glass of red wine. They didn't look very busy, but Mother said she couldn't come now, Liza ought to be in bed and if it really was a Death's Head moth it would no doubt reappear next day.

But next morning it was gone, never to be seen again. Because she had found Mr Tobias in Mother's bed after just such an evening, with wine and food and enjoyment, she expected to see Bruno there in the morning. She was older now, she approached the door more tentatively and pushed it open with

141

care. Mother was alone and when Liza went to the window she saw that the little orange car was gone.

The day gone by, the first time Mother had been indifferent to the things she cared for, she called the Day of the Death's Head.

It was over a week before they saw Bruno again and that was the day Mother went into the town on the bus. She had a list with her and most of the items on it were the kind of things you bought at a fruit and vegetable shop. Liza had seen pictures in a baby's book when she was little. A greengrocer's was the correct word, Mother said.

'Can I come?'

Mother shook her head.

'All right but I don't want to be left here in my bedroom. It's boring.'

'You can go in the library or the morning room at Shrove if you prefer that. It's up to you.'

'The morning room.'

Because it was much lighter and from the windows you could see the trains go by, Mother must have thought. Or because the famous people from history were there in their glass case. Perhaps, though, she was thinking about Bruno Drummond, and not about Liza at all.

After Mother had gone and she had seen a train going south and had studied once more the wedding photograph of Mr Tobias in a sleek dark suit and Mrs Tobias in a large hat and spotted dress, she drew aside the curtain to reveal the stepladder. It was just as she had left it.

She carried it across the room and set it up close beside the picture of the flowers and the Death's Head moth. She took great care to press down the top step which would lock the ladder and make it safe. It was possible of course that the key was no longer there. Mother had been in this room many times since Liza had seen her place it on top of the picture frame and it was a wonder she had never come upon the hidden steps. Climb up and find out.

The key was there. Liza came down the ladder, unlocked the door and opened it. She stood in front of the box thing with the window on the front and studied it. There were knobs and switches underneath the window, rather like the knobs and switches on Mother's electric stove. Liza pressed or turned them one after another but nothing happened.

She understood about electricity. Their old heater wouldn't work unless it was plugged into the point and the switch pressed down. Here the plug was in but the point not switched on. She pressed the switch down. Still nothing. Try the routine of pressing or turning all those knobs and switches.

When she turned the largest knob nothing happened but when she pushed it in a buzzing sound came out of the box and, to her extreme astonishment, a point of light appeared in the window. The light expanded, shivering, and gradually a picture began to form, grey and white and dark grey, the colours of the etchings on the morning room walls, but recognisably a picture.

And not a still picture, as an etching was, but moving and happening, like life. There were people, of about her own age, not speaking but dancing to music. Liza had heard the music before, she could even have said what it was, something called Swan Lake by Tchaikovsky.

Briefly, she was afraid. The people moved, they danced, they threw their legs high in the air, they were manifestly real, yet not real. She had taken a step backwards, then another, but now she came closer. The children continued to dance. One girl

143

came to the centre of the stage and danced alone, spinning round with one leg held out high behind her. Liza looked round the back of the box. It was just a box, black with ridges and holes and more switches.

A lot of print, white on black and grey, came up on the window, then a face, then – most alarming of all – a voice. The first words Liza ever heard come out of a television set she could never remember. She was too over-awed by the very idea of a person being in there and speaking. She was very nearly stunned.

But that feeling gradually passed. She was afraid, she was shocked, she was filled with wonder, then she was pleased, gratified, she began to *enjoy* it. She sat down cross-legged on the floor and gazed, enraptured. An old man and a dog were going for a walk in a countryside very like the one she knew. Sometimes the old man stopped and talked and his face got very large so that she could see all the furrows in his face and his white whiskers. Next there was a woman teaching another woman to cook something. They mixed things up in a bowl, eggs and sugar and flour and butter, and no more than two minutes later, when the first woman opened the oven door, she lifted out the baked cake, all dark and shiny and risen high. It was magic. It was the magic Liza had read about in fairy stories.

She watched for an hour. After the cooking came a dog driving sheep about on a hillside, then a man with a lot of glass bottles and tubes and a chart on the wall, not one word of which she could understand. She went into the morning room to look at the clock. Mother couldn't get back before five and it was ten past four now. Liza sat down on the floor again and watched a lot of drawings like book illustrations moving about, a cat and a mouse and a bear in the woods. She watched a man telling people the names of the stars in the sky and another one talking to a boy who had built a train engine. If it had been possible, she could have watched all night. But if Mother came back and caught her she would never be able to watch it again, for she had intuited that the door was kept locked because Mother didn't want her to watch it at all.

At five minutes to five, most reluctantly, she turned off the set by pulling towards her the knob she had pushed in and switched off the plug at the point. She locked the door and climbed up the steps to put the key back on the top of the picture frame. It was just as well she started when she did. Carrying the steps back to hide them behind the curtains, she saw through the window Mother coming up the drive towards the house and Bruno Drummond with her.

They were early because he had brought Mother back in his car. Liza wasn't much interested in him that evening. Her head was full of what she had seen on, or through or by means of, the window on that box. She wondered what it was, how it did what it did and if there was only one like it in the world, the one at Shrove, or if there were others. For instance, did Mr and Mrs Tobias have one in London? Did Caroline have one in France and Claire have one wherever it was she lived? Did Matt and Heidi, Mr Frost and the builders? Did *everyone*?

There was nobody to ask. Why was it bad for her to see? Would it hurt her? Her eyes, her ears? They felt all right. It was strange to think of Mother knowing all about this magic and never saying, to think of Bruno Drummond knowing too, very probably having one of his own at home over the greengrocer's shop.

Why didn't they have one in the gate-house? There

was no one she could ask. She was so quiet that evening, hardly saying a word throughout the meal – which Bruno stayed for – that Mother asked her if she was feeling all right.

After she had gone to bed, she heard them go out of the front door. She got up and looked out of the window she used only to be able to reach by standing on a chair. She didn't need the chair now. They were going into the little castle. Mother unlocked the front door and they went inside. It reminded her of the dogs and when they used to live in there and she was suddenly sad. She would much rather have had Heidi and Rudi in there than Bruno Drummond. Without knowing why, she didn't like him much.

They didn't stay long in the little castle and soon she heard Bruno's car depart, but he was back next day with paints and canvas and brushes and a thing he called an easel. The easel he set up on the edge of the water meadow and began painting a picture of the bridge. Liza stood watching him while Mother did her cleaning at Shrove.

He disliked her being there, she could sense that, she could sense waves of coldness coming at her. Bruno looked sweet and gentle, he looked kind, but she guessed he wasn't really like that. People might not always be the way their faces proclaimed them to be.

Mother was watching her from the window, 'keeping an eye on you', and she smiled and waved, so Liza didn't see why she shouldn't watch *him* as he mixed up his colours from those interesting tubes of paint and then laid thick white and blue all over the canvas. She came quite close till she was nearly touching his arm. The cold waves got very strong.

Bruno stirred his brush round and round in swirls through the whitish-blue mixture and said, 'Don't you have anything to play with?'

146

'I'm too old to play,' said Liza.

'That's a matter of opinion. You can't be more than nine. Don't you have a doll?' His voice was like the voices that came out of the box in the locked room.

'If you don't want me looking at you I'll go and read my French book.'

She went into Shrove House but instead of reading her book, made her way upstairs to the Venetian Room where there was a picture she thought might look like Bruno. Or he look like it. And she had been right. It was a pious saint in the painting, kneeling in some rocky desert place, his hands clasped in prayer, a gold halo round his head. Liza sat on the gondolier's bed and stared at the picture. Bruno was just like that saint, even to his long silky brown hair, his eyelashes, and his folded lips that had a holy look. The saint's rapt eyes were fixed on something invisible in the clouds above his head.

Bruno wore two gold earrings in one ear and the saint none. That was the only difference between them as far as appearance went. Liza took her book of fairy tales on to the terrace on the garden front and sat reading it in the sunshine.

He was much nicer to her when Mother was there. She soon noticed that. They all had lunch together and he said it was amazing, seeing her reading French fairy tales. 'Like a native,' he said. 'You've got a bright one there, Mother. What do they say about her at school?'

Mother passed over that one and said nothing about Bruno calling her 'Mother'. They talked about the possibility of Bruno having his studio in the little castle and Mother explained what a studio was. Liza wasn't sure she liked the idea of Bruno being next door all day long.

'It belongs to Mr Tobias,' she said.

'I shall write to Mr Tobias,' Mother said, 'and ask if Bruno can become his tenant.'

But whether Mr Tobias said yes or no Liza never discovered, for it was into their house, the gate-house, that Bruno moved. It happened no more than a fortnight later. He moved into the gate-house and went to sleep in Mother's bedroom.

Unlike Heather, he never complained about the lack of a bathroom. Washing, he said, was bourgeois. Liza looked up the word in Dr Johnson's dictionary, which was the only dictionary in the Shrove library, but there was nothing between 'bounce' and 'to bouse', which meant to drink too much. Guesswork told her that 'bourgeois' was probably the opposite of 'anarchist'.

The little castle had a north light, which Bruno said was good for artists. Good or not, he never seemed to go in there very much, though he filled it up with his things, stacks and stacks of canvases and frames as well as brushes and jars and dirty paint rags. And he never went to town, painting people's houses.

It was at this time that Liza stopped going into Mother's bedroom in the morning. Once she had gone in, having first knocked on the door, but even so had found Bruno on top of Mother, kissing her mouth, his long brown curly hair hiding her face. Liza felt heat run up into her face and burn her cheeks, she didn't know why. She retreated in silence.

Her life had changed. She was never again to be quite as happy as she had been in those early years. A cloud had come halfway across her sun and partially eclipsed it. Until Bruno came she had sometimes been alone and enjoyed aloneness but now she knew what it was to be lonely.

Her consolation was the television set at Shrove. She found out what it was called from Bruno. Not that she told him what she watched up at the house whenever she got the chance. It was he who asked Mother why they hadn't got one.

'I can bring mine over from the flat,' he said. 'The flat' meant his rooms over the greengrocer's.

Mother said, no thank-you very much, that was something they could happily do without. He could go home and watch his own, if that was what he wanted.

'You know what I want,' he said, looking at Mother as the saint looked at the clouds.

More often alone and often lonely, Liza found it easy to go to Shrove more or less when she liked. She grew adept at climbing up for the key and hiding the steps. But – and she had no idea why – Mother had grown reluctant to lock her in anywhere since Bruno came. She had the run of the house now and carried the steps back and forth between the library and the morning room. Aged ten, she discovered to her astonishment and pleasure that she no longer needed the steps. She had grown. Like Mother, she could reach the key by mounting a chair and standing on the cabinet.

When Mother sat by Bruno while he painted, Liza watched television. On the rare occasions that Bruno took Mother out in the car, she watched television. From the television she began to learn about the world out there.

It was Bruno who put into her head the idea that it was time she saw the reality for herself.

She sat in the back of the little orange car. Mother was in the passenger seat next to Bruno and Liza could tell by the rigidity of her shoulders and the stiffness of her neck how deeply opposed to this outing she still was. She had allowed Bruno and Liza herself to win her over.

Bruno had said, 'I'm being quite selfish about this,

149

Mother. Maybe you'll think I'm being brutally honest but the fact is I want to take you out and about and to do that we have to take the kid with us.' He always called her the kid just as he always called Mother 'Mother' when Liza was being discussed. 'Taking her into town'll be a start. Get her into that and next we can all have a day out.' He whispered the next bit but Liza heard. 'I'm not saying I wouldn't rather be on our own if there's any option.'

'I can't keep going out, anyway,' Mother said. 'I haven't got time. For one thing, Liza has to have her lessons.'

'That kid ought to go to school.'

'I thought you were an anarchist,' said Mother.

'Anarchists aren't against education. They're all in favour of the right sort of education.'

'Liza is getting the right sort. If you set her beside other children of her age, she'd be so far ahead, she would be years in advance of them, it would be laughable.'

'She ought to be in school for social reasons. How's she going to learn to interact with other people?'

'My mother interacted with other people and she died a miserable disappointed woman in a rented room in her sister's house. I interacted with other people and look what happened to me. I want Liza kept pure, I want her untouched, and most of all I want her *happy*. "A violet by a mossy stone, half-hidden from the eye." '

Bruno made a face. 'I ask myself what's going to happen to that kid. How's she going to earn her living? Who's she going to have relationships with?'

'I earn my living,' said Mother. '*I* have what you call relationships, horrid word. She will be me, but without the pain and the damage. She will be me as I might have been, happy and innocent and good, if I had been allowed to stay here.'

'All that aside,' said Bruno, who liked arguments only when he was winning them, 'I still think she ought to come into town with us, Mother, for her own good.'

And eventually Mother had agreed. Just for the once. She could come for once.

Nothing happened for a while that Liza hadn't expected. There was the lane and then the bridge, the village and at last the bigger road. Cars passed them and once they overtook a car, a very slow one because Bruno's orange cardboard car couldn't go fast. Most of the things Liza saw she had seen before or else seen them on television, if not in colour. It was different in the town, mainly because there were so many people. The numbers of people staggered her so that she was afraid.

Bruno put the car in a car park where hundreds were already parked. Liza couldn't believe there were so many cars in the world. She walked along in silence between Mother and Bruno and, to her own surprise, she was scarcely aware of doing it, she took Mother's hand. The people clogged the pavement, they were everywhere: walking fast, dawdling, chatting to each other, standing still in conversation, running, dragging along small children or pushing them in chairs on wheels. You had to take care not to bump into them. Some smoked cigarettes, like on the television, and you smelt them as they passed. Quite a lot were eating things out of bags.

Liza stared. She would have liked to sit on the low wall outside that building Mother said was a church and just watch the people. Most of them in her eyes were ugly and awkward, fat or crooked, grotesque or semi-savage. They compelled her gaze but as a toad might or a frightening picture in a book, with horrified fascination.

'How beauteous mankind is!' said Mother in the

special voice she put on when she was saying something from a book. 'O, brave new world that has such people in it.' The laugh she gave was a nasty one as if she hadn't meant those words seriously.

As for a brave new world, Liza thought most of the shops nasty and boring. There were clothes in one window, magazines in another. The flowers in the flower shop weren't as nice as those at Shrove. The places which interested her most were the shop with four boxes, like the one in the locked room at Shrove, in its window, four blank screens, and the one that was full of books, but new ones with bright pictures on their covers.

She wanted to go in that shop but Mother wouldn't let her, nor was she allowed inside the one that sold newspapers, though Bruno was sent in there to buy a tape of Mozart's horn concertos. They went to the greengrocer's and bought fruit, then through a side door and upstairs to where Bruno used to live. It smelt so nasty in there, like the kitchen at Shrove after the Tobiases and their guests had gone and as if things had been left to go bad, that Liza started to cough.

Mother opened the windows. They collected some stuff of Bruno's which he packed into a case and then he picked up off the doormat the heap of letters that had come for him while he was away. For a man whose whereabouts no one knew he got a lot of letters.

Looking about her, Liza began to understand what Mother had meant when she said those things about most places being horrible. She wrinkled up her nose. Bruno's flat was very horrible, dirty and uncomfortable, with nothing in it that looked as if it had been cared for, every piece of furniture bruised or broken, the windows blue-filmed and with dead flies squashed against the panes. The only books were on the floor, in disorderly heaps.

152

She was glad to get out again, and said so, even though being out meant once more avoiding bumping into people. There seemed more of them than ever and a good many were of her own age or a bit older. They had come out of school, said Bruno with a meaning look at Mother. School stopped each day at three-thirty.

Liza had never seen children before. Well, except on the television, that is. She had never seen a real person who was less than in his or her twenties. She took back what she had thought about all mankind being ugly. These people weren't. There was a boy with a black face and a girl she thought might be Indian with deep-set dark eyes and a long black pigtail. She wondered how it would be to talk to them.

Then a boy walking along in front of her stuck out his leg and tripped up the boy beside him so that the second one staggered and nearly fell into the road in front of an oncoming car and a girl screamed and another one started shouting. Liza felt herself shrink back against Mother and hold on to her hand more tightly. She had realised what was making her feel dizzy: the noise.

Once she had turned up the sound on the television by mistake. It was like that here, a continuous meaningless roar of sound, interspersed with the squeals of brakes, music that wasn't real music strumming out of car windows, the peep-peep-peep of the pedestrian signal at a traffic light crossing, the revving up of engines. As they made their way back to the car park, a siren started up. Bruno told her it was the siren on a police car and he said the sound it made was supposed to imitate a woman screaming.

'Oh, it can't be, Bruno,' Mother said. 'Where on earth did you get that from?'

'It's a fact. You ask anyone. They invented it in the

States and we copied it. That's supposed to be the sound that most gets under people's skins, a woman screaming.'

'Well, don't talk about it to me, please,' Mother said, so loudly and sharply, that one of the ugly people turned to stare at her. 'I don't want to hear. It just expresses the worst side of men.'

'All right, all right,' said Bruno. 'Sorry I spoke. Please excuse me for living. Will madam condescend to accept a lift home, her and her charming courteous offspring?'

As soon as she was in the car Liza fell asleep. She was exhausted. The people and the noise and the newness of it all had worn her out. At home she lay on the sofa and slept, though not so deeply that she failed to hear Mother tell Bruno she had told him so, Liza hadn't liked it, it had been too much for her and no wonder. Wasn't it a horrible place, a travesty of what a country town should be and once had been, noisy, dirty and tawdry?

'She wouldn't feel that way if you hadn't sheltered her from everything the way you have.'

'I feel it and God knows I haven't been sheltered.'

'You know what you'll do, don't you, Mother? You'll turn the kid psychotic. Or maybe schizophrenic, one of those what-d'you-call-its.'

'Talk about what you understand, Bruno, why don't you?'

With half an eye open, she thought they would start quarrelling again. They were always quarrelling. But instead they did what often impeded or ended their quarrels. Their eyes met, they reached for each other and began kissing, the kind of kissing that soon got out of hand, so that they were grappling and climbing all over each other, grunting and moaning. Liza turned over and squeezed her eyes tight shut.

In the days that followed she felt unwell, what Bruno called 'under the weather', something unusual for her. She remembered the town and its people not with longing or nostalgia but with revulsion. The peace of Shrove and its land was more than usually pleasurable. She lay in the long grass and the cow parsley, watching the insect life moving among the mysterious green stems and the nodding seed heads, saw a raspberry-winged cinnabar moth climbing a ragwort stalk. There was no sound but the occasional heavy hum of a bumble bee passing overhead.

A week after their day out in the town she became ill with chicken pox.

Chapter Eleven

'Hadn't you had any of those things, measles and whatever?'

'I'd had some immunisation when I was a baby. I got chicken pox because I hadn't built up any natural immunity. I'd never been with people.'

'Did the doctor come?'

'Eve phoned him from Shrove. He said he'd come if I got worse but otherwise there was nothing to be done but let it take its course. I wasn't very bad. Eve was strict about scratching. She said if I scratched my face she'd tie my hands up, so I didn't except for one awful big spot on my forehead.'

Liza pulled back a lock of dark hair and showed him the small round hole on her left temple. 'She was afraid of me getting those all over.'

'I know you didn't,' said Sean, giving her a sidelong sexy look.

'No, nothing like that. All that happened was that I gave Bruno shingles.'

'You what?'

'The virus or whatever you call it, it makes chicken pox in children and shingles in grown-ups. It's the same thing. Eve didn't catch anything but Bruno caught shingles.'

'My grandma had that. She had it round her middle and she was dead scared because if it meets round your waist you die. That's a fact.'

Liza doubted it but she didn't say so. 'He got it on

the side of his face and down the back of his neck. He was quite ill and he looked quite ugly with all that red on his face. I thought he disliked me because I gave him shingles, that was the way I reasoned when I was nine. But if he hadn't made me go into town with them I wouldn't have caught chicken pox and couldn't have given him shingles, so it was his fault really. That was how I saw it. Of course now I know it wasn't that at all. I was in the way, I was a nuisance, I came between him and Eve.'

Now she was more or less grown-up herself and sexually involved, Liza could understand what had held Eve and Bruno together. She hadn't understood at the time. It puzzled her and made her increasingly uneasy that two people could quarrel so much, could behave as if they hated each other, but still seem to need each other's company in a hungry way.

She was aware too of something else. There was something Bruno wanted to do with her mother that he couldn't do unless Liza wasn't there. It was to do with the kissing and struggling and lying on top of Mother. Liza knew and had known for some time the facts of human and animal reproduction, Eve had taken care to educate her in these matters, but for some reason she never connected them with what Bruno wanted to do with Mother. And what, though less urgently, Mother wanted to do with Bruno. She didn't understand and she shied away from under-standing. All she knew was that Bruno wanted her out of the house as much as she could feasibly be out of it and that Mother to some lesser extent went along with this.

Without saying a word as to her destination, she went up to Shrove and watched the television in the once-locked room. It was always in late mornings and early afternoons that she watched it. Old films were what she saw and nature programmes, productions for schools and the Open University, chat shows and quiz games. Some of the programmes came from America. They taught her that Bruno was an Englishman who for some reason put on a half-American voice.

When he was well again things got worse. It was late summer and fine weather and he took Mother out in the car every day. Liza could have gone with them, Mother was always suggesting it now as enthusiastically as she had once vetoed it, but Liza wouldn't. She remembered the day in town with a kind of horror, as if the experience had been inextricably entangled with police sirens and scratching and chicken pox. So Mother and Bruno went and she stayed behind alone, often doing no more than sitting outside on the gate-house wall or lying in the grass wondering what would happen to her if Bruno prevailed and she was sent away.

More than once he had mentioned sending her to something called boarding school. Mother said she had a lot of money when she bought his picture but now she said she had none and boarding schools cost a lot. Liza clung to this. Mother had no money and Bruno had no money and no prospect of getting any. Bruno himself would never go, she was sure of that with the pessimism of a ten-year-old who believes that good things never last and bad things go on for ever. He was a bad thing that would never change, he was the hated third in their household, with as permanent a place in their lives as the balsam tree and the train.

Two things happened that autumn. Bruno's mother fell ill, very ill, and Mother heard on her radio that British Rail intended to stop running the train through the valley.

The first time Mrs Spurdell went out Liza took the

opportunity to have a bath. It was ten o'clock in the morning. The bath was a muddy beige colour and the bathroom carpet grass green and beige in little squares, but the water was hot. The soap smelt of sweet peas. When she had finished she cleaned the bathroom thoroughly, washing down and polishing all the tilework.

Mrs Spurdell had been rather reluctant to leave the house. Liza hadn't much experience of human behaviour but even she could tell Mrs Spurdell thought she would come back and find her cleaner gone and the video, microwave and silver with her. She nearly laughed out loud at Mrs Spurdell's face when her employer came in the back door to find her sitting at the kitchen table polishing that same silver. That was the first occasion on which Liza got a cup of coffee in the house in Aspen Close.

While they were together Mrs Spurdell talked most of the time. Her conversation was primarily concerned with demonstrating her superiority and that of her husband and grown-up daughters to almost everyone else but particularly to her employee. This was an ascendancy in the areas of social distinction, intellect, worldly success and money, but principally of material possessions. Mrs Spurdell's possessions were more expensive and of better quality than those of other people, more had been paid for them initially and they lasted longer. This applied to her engagement ring, a massive stack of diamonds, the allegedly Georgian silver, the Wilton carpets, the Colefax and Fowler curtains and the Parker-Knoll armchairs, among many other things. Liza had to be taught these names, shown these objects and instructed in how to examine them for evidence of their worth. She was adjured to be very careful of all of them with the exception of the engagement ring which never left Mrs Spurdell's finger. The finger was so grossly swollen above and below the ring that Liza doubted if it would come off.

The husband and the children couldn't be demonstrated but they could be talked about and photographs produced. After that first cup of coffee, reward for not decamping with the precious artefacts, a mid-morning refreshment session became the regular thing. Liza was told about Jane who was an educationalist, after having got several degrees, and about Philippa, a solicitor married to a solicitor, and erstwhile top law student of her year, now mother of twins so beautiful that she was constantly approached by companies making television commercials for the chance of using their faces in advertising, offers which she indignantly refused. Liza listened, memorising the unfamiliar expressions.

Mr Spurdell, said his wife, was a schoolmaster. Liza thought they were called teachers, that was what Bruno had called them and Sean called them, but Mrs Spurdell said her husband was a schoolmaster and a head of department, whatever that was.

'At an independent school,' she explained, 'not one of these comprehensives, I wouldn't want you to think that.'

Liza, who was incapable of thinking anything about schools, merely smiled. She never said much. She was learning.

'He could have been a headmaster many times over but he isn't one for the limelight. Of course there is family money, otherwise he might have been forced to take a higher position.'

A fresh set of photographs came out, Jane in gown and mortarboard, Philippa with the twins. The impression was subtly conveyed that their mother was prouder – and fonder – of Philippa because she had a husband and children. Liza preferred Jane who hadn't any lipstick on and wasn't simpering. She was longing for Mrs Spurdell to get up and say she was going out so that she could have another bath. It wasn't easy managing in the caravan and the swimming pool was expensive besides leaving you smelling of chlorine.

At last Mrs Spurdell put the photographs away and prepared to go out. The weather was colder today and it was a different coat she had put on, of a thick, hairy, stone-coloured cloth with lapels and cuffs of glossy brown fur. Liza was told that this coat had been bought twenty years ago – 'in the days when no one had these ridiculous ideas about not wearing fur' – and had cost the then enormous sum of sixty pounds. She had to feel the quality of the cloth and stroke the fur. 'It simply refused to wear out,' said Mrs Spurdell with a little laugh, tying her white hair up in a scarf with 'Hermes' written all over it. Liza wondered what a silk scarf had to do with the Messenger of the Gods.

She went without her bath. On her way to run it she paused at the doorway of Mr Spurdell's study. This was a room she wasn't supposed to touch beyond vacuum cleaning the floor, for his books were sacred, never to be dusted, and the papers on his desk inviolate. But Liza was alone in the house now and Mrs Spurdell would no more know she had been in there than she knew the purpose for which her hot water was often used.

Once or twice she had taken fleeting looks at the bookshelves while pushing the vacuum cleaner about but she had never examined them thoroughly. Now she did. They were of a very different kind from those in the library at Shrove. Here were no eighteenth-century works on travel and exploration, no theology, philosophy or history, no essays from the eighteen hundreds, no poetry of a century before that, no tomes of Darwin and Lyell and no Victorian literature. Mr Spurdell's fiction came in the form of paperbacks.

These shelves carried the kind of books Liza had never seen before. Accounts of people's lives, they seemed to be, and she recognised the names of some of their subjects: Oscar Wilde, Tolstoy, Elizabeth Barrett Browning. But who was Virginia Woolf and who was Orwell? Apart from these, there were books about how writers wrote what they wrote, or as far as she could gather they were about that, one called *The Common Pursuit* and another *The Unquiet Grave*. Liza sat down at Mr Spurdell's desk and leafed through his books, wondering how it was that she understood so little of what she read yet passionately wanted to understand.

Time passed quickly when she was occupied like this. It always went very fast while Mrs Spurdell was out but this time it seemed to fly by. Reluctantly, she had to stop reading because she needed at least ten minutes to look at the papers on the desk and there was no chance of Mrs Spurdell being out for more than an hour and a half. It was lucky she could do the housework in half the time allowed for it.

The papers were essays. She could tell that much. They had names written along the tops of the first pages, of their authors presumably. It took the minimum of detective work to infer that these were pupils of Mr Spurdell's. He had gone through the pages with a red pen, correcting the spelling and making acid comments. Some of these made Liza laugh. What interested her most though were the pieces of yellow paper he had stuck to the first page of each. These were small paper squares of a kind she had never seen before and which had a sticky area on them that you could nevertheless peel off.

162

She tried this carefully and then to her satisfaction re-stuck it.

Each yellow square had something different written on it in Mr Spurdell's writing. One said, 'Should get at least an A and a B', another, 'Doubtful university material' and a third 'Oxbridge?' Liza had heard of Oxford and of Cambridge but not of that place. She had to stop at this point, it would be awful to jeopardise her future chances by letting Mrs Spurdell catch her snooping. The papers replaced exactly as she had found them, she grabbed the vacuum cleaner and was removing white hairs from the master bedroom carpet when the front door opened and closed.

In a little while Mrs Spurdell came lumbering up the stairs and into the bedroom to hang up the precious coat. Liza moved along, back into the study, only to clean the carpet of course, but while she was there she wondered if she dared borrow a book. Would he know if one was missing? If one was missing for just two days? She would very much like to read the life of Elizabeth Barrett Browning. When she first met Sean she had read the 'Sonnets from the Portuguese' and memorised several of them. ('How do I love thee? Let me count the ways.') Putting herself into Mr Spurdell's shoes – a pair of them, slippers really, sat side by side under the desk – she decided that, yes, she would know if a book of hers was missing. If she had any books, if only she had.

Mrs Spurdell paid her for her morning's work. She always did this grudgingly and very slowly, choosing from the wad in her handbag the oldest and most crumpled five-pound notes, never handing over a ten. The rest of the sum she made up in small change, twenty and ten pence coins and even twos. This time she was worse than ever, giving Liza a whole seven pounds in fifty pees and tens and fives and keeping her waiting while she went off somewhere to hunt for a fiver. Eventually she came back with it, a worn and withered note that had been torn in half and stuck together with Scotch tape.

The secondhand bookshop took it. Liza had been worried they wouldn't when she handed it over in payment for three shabby paperbacks she had found among a row of others on a trestle outside. The real bookshop, the proper one in which everything sold was new, was far beyond her means.

It was nearly five-thirty and Superway would be closing. She walked along the High Street and across the marketplace. Soon it would get dark, they would soon put the clocks back and the chill of evening was already apparent. Was it cold in prison? She thought about Eve in the prison, she often did, she thought about her every day, but she never said any of this to Sean.

He was waiting for her outside the main entrance with a carrier bag full of food. Superway encouraged employees to buy the products that had reached their sell-by date and at a very reduced price. Liza and Sean walked together to the car. He told her what he'd got for their supper and then he wanted to know what was in her bag. She showed him *Middlemarch*, a *Life of Mary Wollstonecraft* and Aubrey's *Brief Lives*, and saw at once the displeasure in his face.

'We can't afford to spend money on books.'

'It's my money,' she said. 'I earned it.'

'I wonder what you'd say, Liza, if I said that when you wanted me to get your food.'

She was silent. He had spoken reproachfully and like a middle-aged person. Mr Spurdell would talk like that, she thought.

'You've got telly,' he said. 'I don't know why you need books as well.'

She got his supper and while he watched his

favourite serial, she started reading *Middlemarch*. A good many Victorian girls must have lived very much as she had, being educated at home, knowing no one but the nearest neighbours, sheltered from everything. With Dorothea Brooke she could identify, though society wouldn't have allowed Dorothea a Sean.

Now that his programme was over, she was aware that he kept glancing uneasily at her. He would have to get used to it, she thought. He would have to get used to her being more and more preoccupied with books. It came back to her, as her concentration weakened under his gaze, that Bruno had never much liked her mother reading. He had done all kinds of things to capture her attention, walking about, pacing the room, even whistling. Sometimes he had sat down beside her and taken her hand or stroked the side of her face. Liza remembered her mother jumping up on one of these occasions, shaking him off and shouting to leave her alone.

It was soon after this that Bruno had gone away to be with his sick mother. He had gone on the day the last train ran through the valley.

Liza hadn't known it would be the last train. How could she? She never saw a newspaper and she could never watch television at the times the news was on. It was a fine warm day in October, just over six years ago and a year before the hurricane. The blackberries were over and the crab-apples were ripe. Liza went down through the meadows and along the hedges looking for crab-apples to make into jelly. You boiled the apples, then strained them through a cloth tied to the four legs of an upturned stool before adding the sugar. She had seen Mother do it many times and thought it was time she tried.

Before she had picked a single apple, before she had even found a tree, she saw the people lined up along the railway line. She thought she was dreaming, she closed her eyes and opened them again. Never in her life had she seen so many people all at once except on television and that didn't count. There must have been hundreds. They stood along the railway embankment, on both sides of the line, between the boundary of the Shrove land and the little station that was called Ring Valley Halt, and each one of them was holding a big placard.

From where she was Liza couldn't read what was on the placards. She forgot about crab-apples and jelly, stuffed the big plastic bag she was carrying into her pocket, and ran down the field path towards the river.

Some of the placards said, 'Save our Railway' and others, 'For BR read USSR' and 'Last Train to Chaos'. On the far side a group of people were holding a long banner with 'Will BR care when we miss the train?' on it. Liza sensed something was going to happen, though she couldn't tell what. Besides, the sight of so many people fascinated her, there were more than on that day in town, there were more than in the film she'd seen about Ancient Rome.

Reserved by conditioning if not by nature, she considered concealing herself in the bushes to watch. She didn't want to talk to anyone, talking to strangers was something she was beginning to find hard, she met so few. It had been a dry autumn and the river was low, at this point just a broad sheet of shallow water trickling and splashing over boulders. While on this side she couldn't talk to anyone, but even as she thought that she had her shoes and socks off and was wading across.

It was too late to hide. They all seemed to be looking at her. Before she could pretend to be merely taking a walk, a woman had grabbed her by the arm and evidently mistaking her for some other child, asked where on earth she had been and to take hold of this banner at once.

It was a replica of the one on the other side and it took four people to hold it up. Liza did as she was told and held on to the bit above the letters BR. A man was to the left of her and a boy to the right. Both of them said hi and the boy said, did she live round here? Up in one of the cottages, Liza said, you couldn't quite see from here, but only half a mile away.

'On your own doorstep then,' the man said. 'Your family use the train a lot, do they? Or should I say, did they?'

'Every day,' Liza said.

It wasn't the first lie she had ever told. She'd been telling lies regularly to Mother about where she'd been when she'd really been watching television.

'They take it for granted everyone's got a car,' the man said. 'Has your dad got a car?'

The woman on the other side of him said, 'Sexist. Why not ask if her mum's got one? Women are allowed to drive here, you know. We're not talking about Saudi Arabia.'

Liza was just saying they hadn't got a car – she didn't count Bruno's – and thinking of saying she hadn't got a dad, when the train whistle sounded on the far side of the tunnel. It always whistled going into the tunnel and coming out of it, it was a single-line track and maybe there was a remote possibility of another train meeting it in the dark and going headlong into it. There wouldn't be any more such possibilities, however.

'The last train ever,' the man said. 'The last poor bloody train.'

When it came out of the tunnel and whistled again some of the people cheered. Liza could hardly believe her eyes when the four people holding the banner on the other side and three others with placards all began climbing down the embankment towards the line. The seven, four men and three women, took up their positions right across the line, in the path of the oncoming train, holding their banner and their placards aloft. The train could now be seen in the distance, heading this way.

What if it didn't stop? What if it came right on, ploughing the people down, as Liza had seen in a television film about the Wild West? She held on tight to the banner, clenching her fists round the cloth, making white knuckles.

'Look at them,' shouted the woman who had seized her arm, 'The Magnificent Seven!'

As the train came on the crowd began to sing. They sang, 'We Shall Overcome'. Liza had never heard it before but the tune was easy, she soon caught on and began singing it too. 'We shall overcome one da-a-a-a-ay. – Deep in my heart/ I do believe/ That we shall overcome one day!'

The engine driver saw them in plenty of time. You could hear him applying the brakes, a long low howl like a dog baying. The train came slowly on and ground to a halt a good hundred yards from where the Magnificent Seven held their banner and the placards aloft. The crowd started singing 'Jerusalem'. The engine driver and another man in the same kind of uniform got down from the train and came marching up the track to argue with the protestors. All the train doors and windows opened and passengers stuck their heads out. Then they too began getting out and pouring along the line.

It was more than ever like a Western film when the Indians came or the mob of robbers from Dodge City. Liza and her fellow-banner carriers moved closer to the line to get involved in the arguments, there was a lot of shouting and threatening and one man had to

168

be restrained from punching the engine driver. It wasn't his fault, anyway. Liza thought it most unfair. But she enjoyed every minute of it, she hadn't enjoyed anything so much since before Bruno came. In fact, thinking about it afterwards, she understood she hadn't enjoyed anything since the coming of Bruno.

She stayed with the protestors right over lunch and well into the afternoon. They gave her sandwiches and biscuits from their lunches, all of them believing her parents were down by the station and she had somehow got detached from them. The train people went on arguing. The Magnificent Seven stood firm. After a while some British Rail officials arrived, there was talk of the police, the protestors on the embankments sat on the grass and a couple of people fell asleep. Liza listened to a discussion about nuclear power, destruction of the environment and the betrayal of democracy. She noted all the words, stored them in her memory without understanding anything that was said, until at last growing bored, she wandered away.

She was still barefoot, her shoes tied to her belt with the socks stuffed inside them. From the position of the sun and the feel of the air she calculated it must be at least three-thirty. She sat down on the grass to put her socks on. As she was tying her shoelaces, she heard the train start and turned round to watch it.

The protestors must have been persuaded, cajoled or threatened into leaving the line. Gradually the train gathered speed, passed between the rows of the defeated demonstrators, and came to the station. Liza saw it leave again and finally disappear into the curve that the hills swallowed, the last train for ever.

She went home by way of the Shrove garden, across the smooth lawn cut by Mr Frost that morning. Mother was sitting on the wall in front of the

169

cottage, eating an apple. The orange car wasn't there.

'Where have you been? I was worried when you didn't come home for lunch.'

Lies were easier and safer. 'I took my lunch with me. I made sandwiches.'

Mother wouldn't have known. She'd been in bed with Bruno. Where was he, anyway?

Before she could ask, Mother said, 'Bruno's gone up to Cheshire to be with his mother. His mother's very ill.'

Nothing could have been better, more calculated to make her happy, nothing except to hear he wasn't coming back.

'He may be gone a long time,' said Mother.

She took Liza into the house and when they were inside and the door was closed she put her arms round her and said, 'I'm sorry, Liza. I've been neglecting you, I haven't been a good mother to you lately. I can't explain but you'll understand one day. I promise things will be like they used to be now we're alone again. Will you forgive me?'

Mother had never apologised to her before. She hadn't had to until Bruno came. Liza would have forgiven her anything now Bruno was gone.

It had been the Day of the Last Train.

Sean said gruffly, 'Did he ever do anything to you, this Bruno guy?'

'Hit me, d'you mean?'

Sean said, no, not that, and explained what he did mean.

'I never heard of that,' Liza said. 'Do men really do that?'

'Some do.'

'Well, he didn't. I told you, he hated me. He wanted to be alone with Eve and I got in his way. It

170

wasn't always like that, he quite liked me at first, he painted that portrait of me, the one I told you about. He was always painting pictures of Eve and then he said he'd do one of me. I sat on a chair inside the little castle and he painted me. He was very kind then. I had to sit still for a long time and he bought cranberry juice for me, I'd never had that before, and biscuits with icing on that Eve wouldn't let me have. He used to buy lots of things for me when they went shopping. When I look back, I think he was just trying to ingratiate himself with Eve.'

'Do what?'

'Ingratiate himself. Make her like him more. But then he must have realised he didn't have to do that, she liked him enough. And he changed. When he was ill and he realised he couldn't persuade Eve even to send me to a day school, that was when he changed. I can't tell you how relieved I was when I knew he'd gone, I was so happy.'

Sean turned off the television. It was a concession, Liza realised that and closed her book. He put his arm round her.

'Who was that woman you were talking about, the one who told her husband stories?'

He'd remembered, Liza thought, pleased. 'Scheherazade. She was an Eastern woman, an Arab, I suppose. Her husband was a king who used to marry women and have them executed the morning after their wedding nights. He'd have their heads chopped off.'

'Why did he?'

'I don't know, I don't remember. Scheherazade was determined not to have hers chopped off. On their wedding night she started telling him a story, a very long one that she couldn't finish but he longed to know the end so much that he said he'd keep her alive until the morning after the next night so that he

171

could hear the end. But it didn't end or she started another and so it went until he got sort of addicted to her stories and couldn't have her killed and in the end he fell in love with her and they lived happily ever after.'

'What about all the other poor women he'd killed?'

'Too bad for them,' said Liza. 'I don't suppose that bothered her. Why did you ask about Scheherazade?'

'I don't know. I wanted you to tell me a bit more about what happened. You've stopped telling me.'

'Lucky to be alive then, am I?' She laughed but he didn't. 'What happened next, after Bruno'd gone that is, is that Mr and Mrs Tobias came down. It was the first time for about a year. Mr Tobias said he wanted to meet Bruno and Eve had to tell him where Bruno had gone. Seeing his paintings was the next best thing, Mr Tobias said, so Eve took him and Mrs Tobias into the little castle and the first thing they saw was the portrait of me.

'Of course they saw other pictures too and Mrs Tobias, Victoria, said she'd like to buy one. She wanted one he'd done of Shrove by moonlight. "Oh, I adore it," she said and she clapped her hands and when Eve said four hundred pounds she didn't even flinch. Mr Tobias – Jonathan, why do I keep on calling him that, like a child? – he wrote a cheque for it there and then and gave it to Eve.'

'Didn't she wait to ask Bruno?'

'I suppose she knew he wanted to sell them. Anyway, she didn't wait. She was very pleased about getting money for him. Next day Jonathan started shooting and Victoria did too. There was a pair of partridges used to strut about, I'd got fond of them, red legs they were and a beautiful pattern on their backs. She shot them both. I wish I'd had a gun, I'd have shot *her*. When they'd shot all the birds they

172

wanted they went back to London and as soon as they'd gone Eve sat down with me and told me the whole story of old Mr Tobias and Caroline and *her* mother and why she never got Shrove for herself.'

Chapter Twelve

Eve's parents had gone to work for old Mr Tobias and his wife when Eve was five and Jonathan was nine. Jonathan didn't live at Shrove at that time but he came down for the holidays with his mother and father, Caroline who was Lady Ellison and her husband, Sir Nicholas Ellison. Then Sir Nicholas left Caroline and Caroline went back home to her parents.

Eve's father was a German called Rainer Beck, he'd been a prisoner of war in this country and after the war was over he didn't go back to Germany but stayed on and married Gracie, the daughter of the farmer he worked for. They were married for ages without having any children and Gracie had given up hope, she couldn't believe it when she was pregnant after ten years. The baby was a girl and they called her Eva after Rainer's mother in Hildesheim.

Agricultural labourers were nearly the worst paid of all workers and in any case, as farms became mechanised and you could run hundreds of acres with only a couple of men, they weren't much needed. Gracie saw the housekeeper and handyman's jobs advertised in *The Lady* magazine while she was at the dentist's, so they applied for it and got it. One of the inducements was that a house went with the job.

Old Mr and Mrs Tobias interviewed Gracie and offered her the job at once. Rainer was too hard for them to pronounce, so they called him Ray.

The Tobiases liked making people change their names. Jonathan had been christened Jonathan Tobias Ellison but at his grandfather's suggestion he dropped the Ellison and became Jonathan Tobias. He went away to his public school but he was at Shrove in the holidays and he and Eve grew up together. That was the way she put it, grew up together. They were inseparable, they were best friends.

Old Mrs Tobias was ill, she died when Gracie and Rainer had been there a year, and soon after that Caroline went off with a man she'd met on holiday in Barbados. Jonathan remained at Shrove. Sometimes he went to stay with his father but mostly he was at Shrove telling Eve he was going to marry her when he grew up. He and she would marry and live together at Shrove for ever until death parted them.

Ray wasn't a gardener or a butler but a handyman. Mr Frost, who was quite young then, came up from the village on his bicycle – the same bicycle, Eve said – to do the garden. There wasn't enough work for Ray to do full-time. By a great stroke of luck he got a job in the village working for a builder as a bricklayer, the job he'd been trained for all those years ago in Germany. Ray put in a few hours every week at Shrove, cleaning the windows and the cars. It was Gracie who was the important one. But for Gracie the place would have fallen apart. With Mr Frost's daughter to help her three times a week, she kept Shrove clean and did all the cooking. She did the washing and ironing, ordered the groceries, made jam and pickles, acted as secretary to Mr Tobias and, increasingly, as his nurse. She was indispensable.

Eve went first to the village school, then to the school in town where you had to pay fees. Mr Tobias paid her fees. She was very bright, brighter than Jonathan, Mr Tobias said, and he adored Jonathan. Gracie thought he was going soft in the head, maybe

175

it was the onset of Alzheimer's, when he said Eve would very likely get to Oxford. Gracie's sister had had nine months at a secretarial college and she looked on that as the summit of academic ambition.

Mr Tobias didn't have Alzheimer's but a very slow growing cancer. He was eighty and malignant growths proceed slowly in people of that age. He could get up and walk about, go out in the car with Ray to drive him and lead quite a normal life. But sometimes he had to go into hospital for radiotherapy and then, when he came home, he was very ill for a while. There was plenty of money and he could easily have afforded private nursing but he didn't want anyone near him but Gracie.

The doctors at the hospital – they were called oncologists, Eve explained – called him their longest surviving cancer patient. The primary cancer had been detected nine years before and still he lived on. It wasn't Mr Tobias who died but Rainer Beck. The planning authority had given permission for some 'in-filling' in the village and Ray's employer was putting up a house on the site between the row of cottages and the village hall. While Ray was laying bricks for the front wall he keeled over and died of a heart attack with his trowel still in his hand.

'He was clutching on to it and the cement got hard,' said Liza. 'The cement stuck it on to his dead hand and they had to prise it open. They had to break his fingers. It was either that or burying him with that trowel in his hand.'

Sean turned his mouth down. 'Yuck. Do you mind?'

'I'm only telling you how it was.'

'You don't have to go into details.'

When Ray was dead Gracie began worrying about her future. One week she had a husband's income to depend on and the next week she hadn't. She never

176

would have again. She had no home of her own, a sixteen-year-old daughter dependent on her and an employer who might die and leave her jobless at any moment. Caroline occasionally reappeared at Shrove, beautifully dressed, arriving in a big new car, still not divorced, still married to Sir Nicholas and supported by him, but often with a man friend in tow. She had never liked Gracie, disapproved of the friendship between her son and 'the housekeeper's girl' and made it plain Gracie wouldn't last there a week after her father was dead.

Gracie laid her troubles before Mr Tobias. She was young enough to get a job if she left now. Her sister was a travel agent with a small business in Coventry, from which her partner had just pulled out. If Gracie would join her, learn the business and take the partner's place, she'd help her with a mortgage on a flat. But it would have to be now, not next year or in five years' time when Gracie would be well over fifty.

It happened that she said all this just at the time the doctors had discovered another lump on Mr Tobias's spine. Once it was removed, he'd have more radio-therapy and be convalescent for weeks. He begged Gracie not to leave him. Caroline had gone off again. Not that she ever did a hand's turn in the house and she was too squeamish, she said, to be a nurse. Jonathan was up at Oxford. If Gracie left he would have to resort to private nurses and that would kill him.

Gracie told her sister she would need a while longer to make up her mind. Meanwhile Mr Tobias went into hospital and the growth on his back was surgically removed. He became extremely ill.

'I expect she hoped he'd die,' said Liza.

'Come on, Liza, the poor old fellow. He was all on his own with no one giving a bugger what happened to him. It's only natural he didn't want her to go.'

177

'She had to think of her future. Rich people like him just use people like my grandmother, Eve said. It wasn't as if he couldn't afford to pay nurses.'

'Money never brings happiness,' said Sean with a sigh.

'How do you know? Have you ever known any rich people? I have. Jonathan was ever so rich all the time I knew him and he was happy for years and years.'

Mr Tobias came home and Gracie nursed him. She moved herself and Eve out of the gate-house and up to Shrove. For a whole two weeks before he could get up she had to give him bed pans and dress the wound on his back which started suppurating. The doctor came every day and said she was wonderful. Meanwhile Eve sat for her O-Levels and passed in eleven subjects. Mr Tobias called her into his bed-room to congratulate her and gave her fifty pounds 'to buy some dresses'.

'What about me,' said Gracie when he was up and about again, 'what's going to become of me? My sister's starting to get impatient.'

Mr Tobias had been thinking about it and he told her the decision he'd come to. If she would guarantee to stay with him until he died, having sole care of him and nursing him – she could have any help in the house she wanted – if she'd do all that, he would leave her Shrove House in his will. He knew she loved it, he knew how she appreciated this beautiful place.

'It's my daughter that loves it,' said Gracie, so shocked by what he'd said that she couldn't think of any other answer to make. It was Eve who couldn't bear the thought of leaving. This had held her back from agreeing to her sister's proposition nearly as much as Mr Tobias's dependency on her. Eve worked so hard and did so well at school, was such a

happy girl, because she loved Shrove and its sur-
roundings and the whole lovely valley. And being
with Jonathan whenever he's at home, thought
Gracie, though not saying this aloud. She hadn't
dared tell Eve there was a chance they might leave
and go up to Coventry.

'So what do you think of my idea?' Mr Tobias had
perhaps expected more enthusiasm. It came. Gracie
was stunned, Gracie couldn't believe what he'd said.
Did he really mean it? What about Caroline? Wasn't it
Caroline's by right?

'Caroline hates the place,' said Mr Tobias, confirming what Gracie had long known. 'She couldn't wait
to get away. Besides, she may not have lived with
Nicholas for the past ten years but he's still mad
about her and he'll leave her everything he's got,
you'll see. He's not a well man, poor Nicholas, he'll
not last as long as I will and when he goes Caroline
will be a rich woman.'

It took Gracie five minutes to say yes. Yes, she'd
stay. 'Then you can phone my solicitor and ask him
to pop in sometime next week,' said Mr Tobias.

The new will was made and Mr Frost and Mr
Tobias's doctor witnessed it. In the presence of the
testator and of each other, Eve explained. That was
the law.

Mr Tobias made a quick recovery after that.
Making sure that Gracie stayed spurred him on to get
better. He was up and actually walking about the
garden by the time Jonathan came home for the long
vacation. Gracie's sister took a friend of hers into the
travel agent's business, a woman who had been
secretary to the managing director of a domestic
airline.

Having no secrets from her daughter, Gracie told
Eve about the will. It made Eve feel as if Shrove was
already hers. She had always felt about Mr Tobias as

if he were her grandfather and now she saw herself inheriting the place as his natural heir. It was true what her mother said that she loved it. All she wanted, aged seventeen, was to live there for ever. With Jonathan, of course. Jonathan could come and live there with her.

Eve got three A-Levels to A and went to Oxford. Jonathan was still there, though he had his degree, and they saw a lot of each other.

'What does that mean?' said Sean. 'D'you mean they was lovers?'

'I suppose. Yes, I'm sure they were. Eve didn't actually say. Well, she wouldn't then. Not to me. I was only ten.'

'Old enough to see her in bed with one man after another.'

Liza shrugged. There was no answer to that. Eve and Jonathan must have been lovers. What was there to stop them? Besides, Liza had her own very personal reasons for knowing they were. Back at Shrove, Mr Tobias lived on. He often had setbacks and once he had a bad fall trying to get down the steps from the terrace, his arm was broken, and while they X-rayed it they found cancer in the bone. Gracie nursed him through it all.

At the end of her first year at Oxford Eve came home for July and August and September and Jonathan with her. They spent all their time together. But when Eve went back Jonathan didn't go with her. He stayed behind to be with his grandfather that everyone said was really dying now. There were no audio books in those days and Jonathan spent hours every day reading aloud to Mr Tobias.

Jonathan was going to be 'something in the City'. That was what Eve had said. Liza didn't know what it meant and Sean had only a hazy idea.

'In a bank maybe,' he said, 'or a stockbroker.'

'What's that?'

'Don't know really. It's like doing stuff with shares.'

'Anyway, he didn't. He didn't have to because his father died and left him everything, all his money which was millions – well, a million or two – and the house in London and the place in the Lake District. He got to be something called a 'Name' at Lloyd's, whatever that is, but it wasn't work. Caroline got the house in France and something called a life interest in a lot more money. Only no one knew.'

'What d'you mean, no one knew?'

No one at Shrove knew. Gracie and Mr Tobias knew Sir Nicholas Ellison was dead, of course they did, Gracie sent a wreath from Mr Tobias to the funeral, but they thought all the property had gone to Caroline. Eve knew. Jonathan had written to her at Oxford and told her, but it didn't occur to her to tell her mother, it didn't interest her much who got the money, Jonathan or Caroline, one of them was bound to have done.

Mr Tobias must have assumed it was all Caroline's. After all, he had forecast it would be. 'There was so much money, you see, Liza,' Eve said. 'These people, they don't know how much money they have got. People like us, we always know, down to the last pound, maybe the last fifty pee, but the Tobiases and the Ellisons of this world, they could have two million or three or something in between, they don't exactly know. It's all in different places, making more, accumulating, and they lose count of how much there is.'

There was money slurping around, lots of it, more and more, some coming from here and some from there. Maybe Mr Tobias didn't even care, didn't worry about it, didn't *think* about it. He was very old and very ill and very rich and the last thing he was

181

going to get precisely sorted out in his mind was who had what when it came to money.

Something unexpected happened next. Eve had been two years at Oxford, Jonathan divided his time between visiting her and visiting his grandfather. Mr Tobias at eighty-four was very feeble and needing constant attention but was not in danger. It was autumn. Gracie, who had been fit all her life, suddenly had alarming symptoms. They did tests and told her she had cancer of the womb. She was rushed to hospital for a hysterectomy.

There was nothing for it but nurses, a nurse for the day and a nurse for the night. Jonathan couldn't manage the bedpans and the blanket baths. The nurses were there all the time, a rota of nurses coming and going. Jonathan sat with his grandfather, wrote letters to Eve, shot pheasants. What else happened while Gracie was in hospital became clear after Mr Tobias was dead.

He bitterly resented her leaving him. It was impossible to make him understand that she had had no choice. It was her life that was threatened. Perhaps she should have explained to him more carefully what was happening to her. But she was afraid. For once, she was thinking of no one but herself.

As for him, it was as if he refused to admit that anyone but himself could have a life-endangering disease. He spoke to her in the tone of a disappointed father whose daughter has let him down by behaving immorally or in some criminal way. He constantly alluded to 'the time you left me on my own'.

Gracie took over the care of him once more. The nurses left. Jonathan left for France and his mother. Gracie had been told not to lift heavy weights for six months and Mr Tobias, though so old and thin, was very heavy. When she couldn't lift him up in bed properly and prop him on pillows, he grumbled and reproached her.

Eve came home at Christmas, returned to Oxford in January. She was expected to get a first.

'What's that?' said Sean.

'The best kind of degree. Like getting a first prize.'

By the time the spring came Mr Tobias couldn't be at home any more, he was too ill. He was taken to a nursing home where he went into a coma, lingered for a few weeks and died in May. Gracie was sad in a way but he had been so unkind to her these past months that she had lost most of her affection for him. She knew Shrove was hers now. When she woke up on the morning after Mr Tobias's death she had gone outside and laid her hands on the brickwork of the wall, saying, 'You're mine, you're mine.' But she thought she should phone the solicitor to ask when she could legally take possession.

He told her his client had left everything to Jonathan Tobias Ellison, known as Jonathan Tobias. Well, not quite everything. There was a legacy for her of a thousand pounds.

'He made a new will while she was in hospital,' said Liza.

'He got Jonathan to send for the solicitor and the nurses were witnesses. In the presence of the testator and of each other.'

'You mean Jonathan fixed it.'

'Eve says not. She says he told his grandfather he didn't need Shrove, he had what his father left him. But Mr Tobias didn't understand or didn't want to. He told him he wouldn't leave it to "that woman who's deserted me".'

'What did your grandma do?'

'What could she do? Eve didn't mind too much, not then. It would be all the same to her in the end

183

because she and Jonathan were going to get married.'

Jonathan asked Gracie to stay on at the gate-house. He might live at Shrove one day but not yet. All she would have to do would be a kind of caretaker. No nursing, no cooking, it would be almost the same as if it were actually hers. Gracie wouldn't, she was too humiliated. As for Eve, it made her furious. Where was she supposed to go in the holidays until she and Jonathan were married? Gracie was adamant. She went off to Coventry and rented her sister's spare bedroom.

That was nearly the end. Eve didn't come into the story for a while and when she reappeared she had no degree, first or otherwise, but she did have a baby.

'Me,' said Liza.

'Is that all you know?'

'She said she'd tell me when I was older.'

Eve knew Jonathan was going to South America. He had already started going to places, 'just to see what it was like'. 'Come too,' he said, but of course she couldn't go to Brazil or Peru or wherever it was at the start of the university term. They quarrelled a bit about that and didn't see each other for a fortnight but the day he went to catch his plane for Rio Eve went to Heathrow with him to see him off.

He was expected back after three months, after six months, but he didn't come back, he stayed and stayed. Eve had to leave Oxford because she was going to have a baby. In a Coventry hospital Gracie was dying. She hadn't had the hysterectomy soon enough.

After she was dead Eve and Liza stayed with Eve's aunt. She made it plain she didn't want a niece and a great-niece in her little house, she didn't like babies, but she meant to do her duty. Eve had a hard time making ends meet. For one thing, she was in a bad psychological state, she'd never got over what happened before Liza was born, though she never wished she'd had an abortion. She'd never considered it, she wanted Liza to know that.

'Fine thing to tell a kid of ten,' said Sean.

'OK, I know what you think of her. You don't have to go on and on.'

Heather got in touch with her and said, come and live with me. Eve was so unhappy with her aunt that she accepted, though Heather's flat in Birmingham was tiny with only one bedroom. They all three lived there as best they could. Heather found Eve a job teaching in a private school where they would take on staff who weren't qualified. She put Liza with a baby-minder but that wasn't very satisfactory. When she went to pick her up in the afternoon she found the babies, all six of them, strapped into push-chairs that were stuck in front of the television.

'So I had seen television before, when I was one, but I couldn't remember.'

It made Eve determined never to let her child watch it. And that started a train of other ideas about bringing up her child. If only she had somewhere to live, but there was only one place in the world she really wanted that to be.

Jonathan didn't know where she was. She'd changed her job twice and the baby-minder three times before he found her. Liza was three and Eve had had a job handing out freebee magazines in the street, another trying to be a secretary and learning to type at the same time, and Liza had fallen over at the baby-minder's and cut her head. Jonathan had found a letter at Shrove with the aunt's address on it and thinking it worth a try, came to find her. One evening he rang the bell at Heather's flat.

When he said he'd a proposal to put before her she

thought for one mad moment he was going to ask her to marry him, even now, even after all that had happened. He was friendly but cool. Would she like to live in the gate-house at Shrove in exchange for keeping an eye on the house? That was the expression he used, 'keeping an eye on'. He would pay her a salary, a handsome one, as it turned out.

She accepted. She really had no choice.

'It got her back there, you see. It got her to the one place in the world she wanted to be, even though in the gate-house she was like the Peri outside the gates of Paradise.'

'The *what*?'

'Peris were superhuman beings in Persian mythology, sometimes called Pairikas. They were bad spirits, though they hid their badness under a charming appearance, but of course they couldn't get into Paradise.'

'Of course not,' Sean said sarcastically.

'And that was it, you see. That was how we came to live there and it all began.'

Chapter Thirteen

Bruno was gone and life went back to what it had once been. Lessons resumed. It was just as well Liza liked learning because she seldom had a chance in his absence to get up to Shrove and watch television. Mother taught her relentlessly. Sometimes the way she instructed and lectured was almost ferocious in its intensity.

Winter came and with it the sunless days and long nights. Every morning the two of them went walking but they were only gone for an hour and the rest of the day was spent with Liza's books. Occasionally Mother would insist that they spoke only French, so breakfast, lunch and supper were eaten in French and their discussions of other subjects were in French. She set Liza an examination in English, history and Latin. Liza learned whole pages of poetry by heart and in the evenings she and Mother read plays aloud, Mother taking all the male parts and she the female. They read *Peter Pan* and *Where the Rainbow Ends* and *The Blue Bird*.

Bruno was never mentioned. If letters came from him Mother never said so. Now that Liza was older she didn't get up so early, Mother was always up before her, so Liza wouldn't have known if letters had come. She knew Heather sometimes wrote, her letters were left about. The Tobiases sent a Christmas card, as did Heather and the aunt. Did we send them cards? Liza wanted to know. Mother said no, certainly not. It was absurd celebrating Christmas if you didn't believe in the Christian God, or indeed any god at all, but she gave Liza a lesson on the Christian religion just as she taught her about Judaism and Islam and Buddhism.

One day, shortly before Liza's eleventh birthday, she was looking through Mother's desk for a pad of lined paper Mother said was in the middle section, when she came upon a letter in Bruno's writing. She recognised the writing at once. Without ever having been told, she somehow knew that reading other people's private correspondence was wrong. It must have come from all the highly moral Victorian books she read from the Shrove library, the works among others of Charlotte M. Yonge and Frances Hodgson Burnett. She read it just the same.

Mother had gone upstairs. She could hear her moving about overhead. Liza read the address, which was somewhere called Cheadle, and the date, which was the previous week, and the first page of the letter. It started 'My darling lovely Eve'. Liza wrinkled up her nose but she read on. 'I miss you a lot. I wish I could call you, it's crazy us not being able to call each other in this day and age. *Please* ring me. You can call me collect if you're afraid of J.T. getting his knickers in a twist. Now my ma is dead I'm not poor any more, do you realise that? It won't be much longer now, I've just got all this stuff to see to, inevitable really, and I must grin and bear it. Just to hear your voice would . . .'

She had to stop there because she heard Mother's footsteps on the stairs. She didn't dare turn the page over. Much of what she had read about 'calling' and 'collect' was incomprehensible but not 'it won't be much longer now'. He was coming back. For a moment she wondered why his mother's dying stopped him being poor but then she remembered the tale of Shrove and old Mr Tobias and understood.

It was a hard winter. A little snow fell before Christmas but the first heavy fall came in early January. It lay in deep drifts, masking the demarcations between the road surface and the grass verge, then piling up to hide the ditch and spread a thick concealing cloak over the hedgerow. And when it melted a little it froze again, more fiercely than ever, so that the thawed snow, falling in drops and trickles, turned into icicles, pointed as needles and sharp as knives.

Icicles hung round the eaves of the gate-house like fringe on a canopy. A crust of ice lay on top of the thick snow. It had been two days since a car had been able to get down the lane. The council, Mother said, hadn't bothered to snow-plough it because they were the only ones living there and they hadn't a car.

The postman stopped coming, which pleased Liza because it meant no more letters from Bruno. While the lane was blocked like this Bruno couldn't come. The little orange car would never get through where the post van failed. And still the snow fell, day after day, adding more and more layers to the deep quilt of crisp whiteness that covered everything.

They fed the birds. They had a bird table for breadcrumbs, two bird feeders made of wire mesh to fill with nuts and they hung up pieces of fat on string. One morning Liza saw a woodpecker at one of the wire feeders and a tree creeper, hanging on its tail, both pecking at the nuts. Remembering Jonathan taking photographs, she said she wished they had a camera but Mother said, no, your own mind is the best recording instrument, let your memory photograph it.

And then she said the bird was like *Trochilus*, a kind of humming bird. So Liza looked *Trochilus* up in the encyclopedia and she thought she saw what Mother meant, for its other name was the Crocodile

189

Bird, so-called because it is the only creature that can enter with impunity the mouth of a crocodile and pick its teeth. It also cries out to warn the crocodile of an impending foe.

Liza loved the snow. She was too old to make snowmen but she made them. She made herself an igloo. When it was finished she sat inside her igloo, eating a picnic of Marmite sandwiches and Nice biscuits and rejoicing in the snow that would keep Bruno away, wishing as hard as she could that more and more snow would fall, that it would lie heavy and impenetrable in the lane until March, until April. Mother had told her about a very bad winter when she was a little girl, even before she and Gracie and Ray came to Shrove, when the snow started in January and lasted for seven weeks and all the water pipes froze. It was a bad winter but to herself Liza called it a 'good' winter.

Mother had a cold that she must have caught in the town the last time she went there before the snow came. Coughing kept her awake at night so she lay down to rest in the afternoons and when she did Liza made her way up to Shrove for an hour or two of television. She had missed the old films and schools programmes and quiz shows. She was beginning to understand too, in a vague puzzled way, that the small square screen was her window on to a world of which she otherwise knew very little.

The second time she went up there she saw the snow plough as she came out of the cottage gate. It was clearing the lane. The big shovel on the front of it was heaving up piles of snow, spotted like currant pudding by the gravel lodged in it, and casting it up on the verges. Liza felt sure this would somehow open the way for Bruno. It was as if he had been waiting on the other side of the bridge in his orange car for the snow plough to come and make a smooth clean road for him.

190

But when she returned there was no car and no Bruno. She should have asked Mother, she knew that, she should have said to Mother, 'Is Bruno coming back?' but she couldn't bring herself to do this. She was afraid of being told yes and of being given a definite time. Doubt was better than knowing for sure.

The snow thawed and he hadn't come. All that was left of the snow were small piles of it lying in the coldest shady places, map-shaped patches of snow on the green grass. Mother's cold went when the snow did, so there was no more television but plenty of lessons. In February, on a freak warm day, Liza went up into the wood to see if the aconites were out and when she got back a car was parked outside the cottage, a dark brown car of a shape and make she had never seen before. Instead of a letter of the alphabet at the start of the registration number there was one at the end. She had never seen that before either. The car was called a Lancia.

The Tobiases, she thought, having long dropped the respectful Mr and Mrs. They were always getting new cars. She went warily into the house, preparing to say a cool hallo before going upstairs. The memory of the partridges remained with her and now the story of Gracie and the grandfather too.

She saw Bruno before he saw her, she moved so quietly. He was sitting on the sofa beside Mother, holding both her hands in his and looking into her eyes. Liza stood quite still. He was unchanged, except that his long soft wavy hair was longer and his freckles had faded. He still wore denim jeans and a leather jacket and the two gold earrings in the lobe of one ear.

Perhaps there was some truth in the theory she had read that you can sense when someone is staring very intently at you, for although she hadn't moved or made a sound Bruno suddenly raised his head and met her eyes. For a moment, a very brief instant of time, there came into his face a look of such deep hatred and loathing that she felt a shiver run straight down her back. She had never seen such a look before but she knew it at once for what it was. Bruno hated her.

Almost immediately the terrible expression had passed and a look of bland resignation replaced it. Mother also looked round, dropping Bruno's hands. Mother said, 'Goodness, Lizzie, you're as quiet as a little mouse.'

Bruno said, 'Hi, Liza, how've you been?'

That was the way he talked. Not like an English person and not like an American person – she had heard plenty of them on television – but as if he lived midway between the two countries, which was impossible because it would have been the Atlantic Ocean. She noticed a red blush on Mother's face. Mother hadn't told her he was coming. She must have known. Why hadn't she told her?

'What d'you reckon to my new jalopy, then?'

'He means his car,' said Mother.

'It's OK,' Liza said, a television expression that made Mother frown. 'I liked the orange one.'

'The orange one, as you call it, has gone to where all bad old cars go when they die, the breakers' yard.'

'Where do the good ones go, Bruno?' said Mother.

'They go to people like me, my sweet. The one outside's what I mean by a good one. It was my ma's, still is, as a matter of fact, I've never transferred it. She had it for ten years and only did seven thousand miles in it.'

Mother was laughing. Liza thought, she didn't tell me because she knows I hate him. I wonder if she knows he hates me? In that moment she lost some of her respect for Mother, though not her love. That was the evening when, as soon as she could get Mother alone, she asked if she could start calling her Eve.

'Why do you want to?'

'Everyone else does.'

If Mother thought 'everyone' a bit thin on the ground she didn't say so. 'You can if you like,' she said, though not in a happy voice.

Liza had been wrong when she thought Bruno hadn't changed. She would have understood that he had even if Eve hadn't pointed it out, if Eve hadn't said while they were having their dinner, 'You used not to care about money, you used to be indifferent to it.'

He had been talking about all the things 'they' could do now he had his mother's house to sell.

'You'd better wait till you've sold it,' said Eve in the dry voice she sometimes used.

'I've practically done that small thing,' Bruno said in his twangy tone. 'I've got a buyer who's even keener to buy it than I am to sell.'

That was in the boom time of five and a half years ago. Eve said she understood you could sell anything these days, a remark which went down less than well with Bruno, who started insisting on how lovely his mother's house was, how he *and* she would have been delighted to live in it if only it hadn't been in the north.

'You can leave me out of it,' said Eve. 'I live here and I'm going to live here for the rest of my life.'

He wasn't an anarchist any more. He had forgotten about money and property being unimportant. Having a big house to sell and a proper car and some thousands of pounds in the bank had gone to his head.

'I didn't even have a bank last time I was here, Eve.'

'Aren't we going to talk about anything but money?' said Eve.

She was so rough with him, 'scathing' was the word, that Liza really expected him to go off somewhere for the night. But the guitar music went on playing softly and persistently downstairs, sometimes Bruno sang in his Johnny Cash or his Merle Haggard voices and she wasn't really surprised when, hours later, their footfalls on the stairs woke her and she heard them go into Eve's bedroom together.

The only good that came of Bruno's return was free afternoons for watching television. Lessons didn't stop but once more they became few and far between. Bruno was almost always there and when he was he sneered at Eve's teaching methods, picked on her for not being a qualified teacher and went on and on about how 'the kid' ought to be at school.

'Why ought she?' Mother said at last.

'Come on, Mother, she's not getting a proper education.'

'Don't call me Mother, you're only two years younger than I am. How many children of eleven have you come across that can read, write and talk French, can do a Latin unseen, recite Lycidas and give you a thoroughly good précis of at least four Shakespeare plays?'

'She doesn't know any science and she doesn't know any maths.'

'Of course she doesn't. She's only eleven.'

'That's the age they're supposed to start these things, remember?'

'You teach her, then. You were good at maths, you're always saying.'

'I'm not a teacher,' Bruno said. 'I'm not like you, I know my limitations. She needs real teachers. I bet that kid couldn't do a simple sum. I'm not talking about calculus and logarithms and all that, I'm talking about, say, long division. Come on, Liza, you've got a bit of paper there. Divide eight hundred and twenty-four by forty-two.'

Eve snatched the paper away. 'Nobody needs to divide eight hundred and twenty-four by forty-two on paper any more. Even I know that, out of the world as I am. You have calculators to do that for you.'

'Calculators can't do algebra,' said Bruno.

And so it went on. Liza knew very well – though Eve didn't seem to – that Bruno only wanted her to go to school to be rid of her, get her out of the way. He didn't care whether she learnt algebra or got to know about biology, he just didn't want her there when he was there. She understood now, because Bruno had told her, that Eve was breaking the law in not sending her to school. Bruno made a lot of that, he was always saying how Eve broke the law, though he was breaking it himself not buying a new Road Fund licence for his car.

But for all the fault he found with her, Bruno wanted to be with Eve, he wanted her to be with him. When his mother's house was sold he wanted to buy a new one for him and Eve to live in. It could be near Shrove, only in the town, for instance, or in one of the villages on the other side of the valley. He liked it round here, he was happy enough to stay round here, knowing how Eve loved it.

'I thought you wanted to be free,' Eve said. 'That's what you always used to say, how you loved freedom, how you didn't want to be tied down.'

'I've changed. Becoming a property owner changes you. You start to understand the meaning of responsibility.'

'Oh, really, Bruno, you'll be asking me to marry you next.'

'I can't. I'm already married, you know that. But I do want to live with you for the rest of my life.'

'Really?' said Eve. 'I don't know what I want to do for the rest of my life except stay here.'

'But that's what I'm saying. We'll stay here. You *can* stay here. You'll only be four or five miles away.'

'I mean here. *Here*. On this spot. You may as well make up your mind to it, Bruno. You can buy a house if you want, I'll even drop in sometimes if you ask me, but I'm staying here.'

Bruno never said anything about Liza living in the house he was proposing to buy. She wanted to ask Eve what was really going to happen. Did she mean it when she said she wouldn't leave here in any circumstances? Was she definite about not living in Bruno's house? And what about Liza? Would Eve give in to Bruno and send her away to school? Liza longed to ask Eve for the truth, she desperately wanted to know, but she was never alone with Eve, Bruno was always there.

In March, when the weather got a bit warmer, he and Eve started going for a lot of drives in the brown car with the out-of-date Road Fund licence that had been Bruno's mother's. Eve tried to get Liza to come with them but Liza wouldn't. She went up to Shrove instead and watched television. Bruno had said, and Eve hadn't denied it, that they went on trips looking at houses that were for sale.

'If I did come with you,' Eve said one evening when they were all sitting round the fire in the cottage, 'if I did, which I wouldn't dream of, but if I did, what would we live on? Have you thought of that? Your mother's bit of money won't last for ever. It won't last for *long*. While you're here you live off me, in case you need reminding, but if I left here my money would stop. I get paid for being here, have you forgotten that?'

'I'm a painter. If I don't make much it's because I refuse to compromise, you know that. But things are looking up. You know what they say, nothing succeeds like success. Those Tobiases bought my painting, didn't they? Or we could start up in business, you and me, we could be interior decorators, for instance.' Something she had said seemed to strike him for the first time. 'What d'you mean, you wouldn't dream of it? Why've you been coming to look at all these houses with me if you wouldn't dream of it?'

'I've told you,' she said, 'I've told you a hundred times. You buy a house, go on, if you want to, I'll go with you and look at it but I'm not living in it. I'm living here in this house, at Shrove. Is that clear?'

They had this conversation every evening, or one very like it, until Liza didn't listen any more. She sat reading her book or went up to bed while they argued. But one evening things took a different turn. It had been a bad day, a day on which a nasty frightening thing happened, something quite unforeseen.

The weather was perfect, the kind of April day that might have been June, but clearer and fresher than June would be. Bruno was out painting somewhere. This meant that Liza could have her Latin lesson without fear of interruption, which might be sarcastic comment or derive simply from his presence, silent, looming, his eyes sometimes cast upwards.

If Liza had been able to express it in words she would have said Bruno was taking them over, controlling them, setting the pace or calling the tune. But she knew none of these expressions, only that where Eve had ruled he was fast becoming the ruler. Eve was sharp with him or scathing but she resisted him less and less. She was gradually ceasing to give Liza lessons because of his disapproval.

197

They could have this one because he wasn't there. As if it were something wrong or against the law they had to do it in secret. The French lesson had to be outside in the garden. This, Liza suspected, was because if he came back sooner than he had said, he would think they had gone out somewhere, he wouldn't look for them down there under the cherry tree.

The cherry blossom was out everywhere and the woods were white, not sprinkled with white as when the blackthorn flowered in March, but a pure clean white like a fallen cloud. When the lesson was over Liza and Eve went out walking to look at all the cherry trees because Eve said, quoting a poet, that you could only see it once a year which meant that at her age she probably only had forty more chances. They went to the woods down by the bridge and to their own wood and after that Eve went home in case Bruno was already there.

Liza wandered off on her own. She crossed the bridge and began walking along the old railway line, for six months now disused, but the rails and sleepers still there. If you followed the line, just walking along it and through the quarter mile of tunnel, out the other side into another valley, eventually you'd come to the town and then another town and at last to the big city. Not yet but perhaps one day she would do that.

It was six o'clock in the evening but not yet sunset. The warmth had lasted and there was no wind. She walked along the line the other way, towards the station at Ring Valley Halt. Would they have taken the station name away? And what had become of the building, red brick with a canopy and a gingerbread trim, with windowboxes and tubs of flowers, which had also been the signalman's house?

She didn't see Bruno until she was no more than a

few feet from him, until she couldn't avoid him or hide. The station house looked just the same from a distance but as she came closer she saw that the curtains upstairs were gone and the door marked 'private' stood open. Instead of flowers in the windowboxes and the beds that ran along the backs of both platforms, weeds had sprung up. Where last year there had been daffodils and grape hyacinths grew dandelions. Liza climbed up on to the platform and made her way through the door marked 'exit' into the room where people had bought tickets, through that room and, suspecting nothing, out of the main door on to the sandy lane that had been the station approach.

Bruno was sitting there, not on his camp stool but on the low wall with his easel in front of him. He was holding up a brush loaded with gamboge and he was staring straight at her.

Of course, what he had really been staring at was the station entrance from which she had come. She went closer, she went right up to him, because retreat was impossible. The picture he was painting was of what could be seen through those open doors, the empty line, the deserted platform, paint peeling off the gingerbread fringe on the canopy, the sunflower faces of the dandelions.

When Eve wasn't there he didn't bother with any of that 'hi, and how are you?' He cast up his eyes, the way he often did when he saw her. She was at a loss, suddenly frightened with no real reason to feel fear. Could she just pass on? Was it possible to ignore him and go on up the sandy path until she was out of his sight?

The brush approached the canvas, touched it, painted in the dandelion petals. His box of paints, the heap of paint-stained rags, the jar of sticky brushes, were on the wall beside him. He drew the brush away and began wiping it on a strip of cloth which she saw had been torn from an old skirt of Eve's, a skirt she remembered her wearing years before, when first they came to Shrove.

He spoke in a tone that was at first mild and conversational. 'You're old enough to realise what's being done to you. She's denying you your birthright – well, what's the birthright of kids living in civilised countries. We're not talking about the Third World. This is the United Kingdom in the nineteen eighties, in case she hasn't noticed.'

Liza said nothing.

'She's crippling you. She might as well have chopped off one of your legs or arms. In another way she's buried you. You're not dead but she's buried you just the same. In one of the remotest parts of England. She's cut you off. You're not much better than one of those poor devils that get lost as babies and bears or wolves raise them.'

'Romulus and Remus,' said Liza.

'There you are, you see. That's just it. You know all that stuff, that god-awful useless crap, but I bet you can't tell me who the President of the United States is.'

Liza shrugged, the way Eve did.

'You're so like your goddamn mother you might be her clone, not her daughter. Maybe you are, eh? Only you don't know what a clone is, any more than you know what H_2O is or pi or anything that's not Shakespeare or fucking Virgil.'

The word was new to her. Strange, then, that she sensed he shouldn't have used it, it shouldn't be uttered in her presence. A blush climbed up her neck and made her face hot.

'I'm gonna say just one more thing to you and then you can go home to her and tell tales out of school. That's a laugh, isn't it? Out of school is right. I'm gonna say one more thing and it's this. If you don't get yourself sent to school right now, in the next six months at the very outside, if you don't you won't have a chance of life, you'll be lost for ever. All that learning'll be wasted. It's all very well her saying education doesn't have a purpose, it's not *for* anything, it's all very well her quoting fucking Aristotle or Plato or whoever and saying it's for turning the soul's eye towards the light or some shit like that, but you try telling that tale when you want to go to college, when you want a job, when you haven't got any qualifications, not even O-Levels. Who's going to give a shit about your French and your Romulus and Remus then?'

'I hate you,' Liza said softly.

'Big deal. I'm not surprised. I've been telling you this in your best interests and maybe you'll realise it one day. When it's too late. The best thing you can do is go home and tell her you want to go to school. The term starts next week. You go and tell her that.'

Liza did go then. She walked until she was sure he could no longer see her and then she ran. She was shaking inside and something she called her heart felt as if it had swelled up until it was too big for her chest, until it must burst.

If she had met Eve at that moment, as she was running along the footpath by the maple hedge, if Eve had come out to look for her and they had met, she would have thrown herself into her mother's arms and told her everything he had said. But she didn't, Eve was at home making the dinner. And by the time Liza reached the gate-house she had slowed her pace to catch her breath, she had collected her thoughts.

The awful knowledge had come to her that whatever she told Eve of the things Bruno had said, it would make no difference. Eve was somehow

201

conquered by him, in ways beyond Liza's understanding. It was as if she didn't really like Bruno any more than Liza did herself but still she wanted him there and she wanted him to like her. Rude to him she might be but she wanted him to look at her in that way he had, as if she were an angel in the clouds.

She even dressed in a different way to please him, with her hair loose down her back, the jade beads round her neck and sashes and scarves and chains decorating her, things he'd bought her on their outings. The two of them clattered around in beads and chains, their hair shaggy, barefoot or wearing boots. He talked his mid-Atlantic language and sometimes Eve, precise pedantic Eve, echoed his expressions. Why then did Liza have this rooted idea that though Eve would never tell him to go, she would be just as happy as Liza if he were gone?

Calling out to Eve in the kitchen that she was back, she went upstairs and looked hard at her own face in the mirror. She had never noticed it before but now she could see that what he had said was true in at least one respect, she did look like Eve, she was exactly a younger version of Eve, same features, same golden-brown flushed skin, clear water-brown eyes and golden-gleaming dark brown hair, exactly as curly and exactly as long.

That day, when she remembered the weeds' sunshaped faces and the yellow paint on the brush tip, she thought of as the Day of the Dandelions but she was growing out of giving names to special days and she only ever named one more.

After a little while she heard Bruno come in. His arrival was followed by utter silence. She hoped for something, though she hardly knew what. Perhaps she hoped that Eve, without being told, would somehow guess her unhappiness and the reason for it. She would guess and make things right again, as she used to do when Liza was miserable. Bruno being reprimanded over her, really reprimanded, was something she longed to see. She could bear Bruno if Bruno were changed, were made nicer.

As silent as they were themselves, she tip-toed down the stairs.

The two of them were on the sofa, embraced, wound round each other, devouring each other, so closely locked it looked as if it must hurt. At that sight Liza's sense of isolation, even of rejection, was so great as to amount to panic. A sound escaped her, she couldn't help herself, a whimper of pain. They were too preoccupied with each other to hear her.

Or Mother was. Bruno's blue angelic eye appeared above Mother's curved cheek. It stared at Liza coldly, unblinking. The worst thing was that it went on staring while Bruno's mouth kept sucking Mother's mouth and Bruno's hands clutched and pummelled her back.

Liza turned and ran. She remembered the Andrew Lang fairy stories from long ago and thought he had put Mother under an evil spell.

Chapter Fourteen

'Magic spells,' Sean said indulgently, 'they don't happen in this day and age.'

'This one did.'

'What did you do, make a wax what-d'you-call-it and stick pins in him?'

She didn't understand. 'I didn't have to do anything. He did it himself. I could have told him there were things meant more to her than he did. Well, two things.'

'Shrove and you.'

'Shrove, anyway. I mattered but not as much.' She hesitated. 'I can't help wondering now how much I matter, Sean. I know she's in prison but it's as she said, it's not a dungeon, it's not the Tower of London. They'd let her try to get in touch, wouldn't they? She doesn't know where I am, she thinks I'm with Heather, but she can't have checked or she'd know I'm not. And then wouldn't they have the police look for me?'

'You can't have it both ways, love. You can't not want them to look for you and want them to.'

'No, you're right. But still I think it's that she loved me when I was a child and she could sort of re-make me, shape me the way she wanted, but when I grew up she lost interest. I could *feel* her losing interest.'

'You've got me now.'

'I know. I'll go on about Bruno and breaking the spell, shall I? He must have been very stupid to

204

threaten her and not see it wouldn't work. I see that now but I didn't then, I was too young. I thought she'd send me away and leave the place and if that happened I thought I'd die.'

Bruno kept on and on at Eve to come and live with him in this house he wanted to buy. He'd found somewhere he liked but he wouldn't make the vendor an offer until he got a promise out of Eve. His mother's house was sold by then and he'd got far more for it than it was worth, as often happened in the late 'eighties. The place he'd found was a big house built fifty years before on the edge of the village where Eve went to catch the bus for town.

Even Liza had been to see it. They took her with them in the car. She thought it very ugly with the dark wooden strips on the yellow plaster, done to look like houses she'd seen in pictures of when Elizabeth I was on the throne of England, the red roof and the windows made of hundreds of tiny diamond-shaped panes.

The garden was very big, which Bruno kept saying Eve would like, and surrounded on three sides by enormously tall hedges of the cypress Liza knew was called *leylandii*. The ugliest tree in the world, Eve had once said. They drove through the village and Eve pointed out the place where Rainer Beck had fallen down dead while building the wall of bricks. Someone else must have finished building the house between the row of cottages and the village hall, for there it stood, looking quite old, as if it had been there for a hundred years.

Almost into town, on the outskirts, they called at a supermarket that looked a bit like Bruno's new house, but fifteen times as big and only on one floor. It was another first time for Liza, going in there, and she enjoyed it tremendously. She walked slowly past the shelves, counting how many kinds of fruit juice there were, how many sorts of canned vegetables. The different varieties of biscuits numbered over a hundred. There were dozens of types of food she didn't recognise, that she wouldn't have known were food at all. The soaps and sprays and cleansers fascinated her. She could happily have spent the rest of the day there but Eve got fidgety and made her leave as soon as they had bought their fruit and cornflakes. Liza was being exposed to just the kind of thing Eve most dreaded.

It was that evening, when they were quarrelling again about the house, when Liza was curled up in an armchair reading *Kim* in the crimson and gold Shrove library edition, that Bruno suddenly said, 'Does Mr Jonathan Tobias, your liege lord and master, by any chance know that kid doesn't go to school? That she's never been to school?'

The question distracted Liza from Kim Rishti Ke and the Eye of Beauty and she looked up. The truth was that Jonathan Tobias didn't know. Even she knew that, or guessed it. Of course she was always at home when the Tobiases came to Shrove but they didn't come often and always came in the school holidays or at half term. If Jonathan Tobias had ever asked Eve how she was getting on at school she no doubt lied to him. Liza hadn't actually heard her do so but she wouldn't have been surprised.

'He doesn't know, does he?'

'It's no business of his,' Eve said.

'It's everyone's business in the community. If he knew I doubt if he'd let you stay here. It's not just the not going to school, it's all the rest of it. Keeping her isolated here, not employing a woman to clean because you don't want any more prying eyes, keeping the money yourself you're supposed to pay to this non-existent woman, not to mention letting her run wild at Shrove, taking what she wants out of the library. Look at her now. That's probably a first edition she's got there. A first edition in the hands of an eleven-year-old who's never even been to school!'

'I didn't keep her isolated enough,' Eve said quietly. 'I didn't keep myself isolated the way I promised myself I would. I've been weak, I've been a fool. The biggest mistake I made was letting you in.'

He said to Liza, 'Go to bed. It's nearly nine o'clock at night and you've no business down here.'

'Don't you dare speak to her like that!' Eve stood up, facing him. 'This is Liza's home, she can do as she likes. Do you really think threatening me is likely to make me come and live with you in that mock-Tudor monstrosity? Don't you know anything about human beings?'

He flinched from the flash of her eyes. 'I thought you liked the house,' he said sulkily. 'I thought you did. You didn't say anything about it being a monstrosity.'

'And you who called property-owners bourgeois! Truly money is the root of all evil if it changes people the way it's changed you.'

Liza got up, took her book and said she was going to bed. She got half way up the stairs and stopped, listening. They were off again. Did she want to hear what was said or didn't she? She couldn't be sure. If he made Eve believe he'd tell the Tobiases, wouldn't she have to give in? Wouldn't she have to send Liza to school and go and live with him, whatever she said about not being forced by threats? Would school be like the school in *Jane Eyre*?

She crept down again and listened.

'I don't have to tell Tobias,' Bruno had stopped calling Eve 'mother'. 'I only have to contact the County Education Authority. No, it's not spite, Eve, it's not revenge, it's my duty. It would be anyone's duty.'

207

Eve said in a wheedling voice, the kind of tone Liza had never heard her use, 'And if I agree, that is if I go and live in that house with you, you'll keep silent about this?'

'More or less. Hopefully, I'd persuade you that what you're doing is wrong but I wouldn't take any direct action. Not for a while, anyway.'

'I think you're right when you say they would take her into care. I also think it probable I should lose this house and my job. Without this place I really don't know what would become of us.'

Liza came closer to the door.

'There's no point in being so goddamned sarcastic.'

'I'm not being sarcastic. I mean it. I'm simply being frank about the facts. Without this place I don't know what would become of us. There's nowhere I could go and keep Liza.'

'There is a place you can go. A real home. A far better home than this antiquated little dump. A hovel without a bathroom!'

Liza heard Eve's little laugh. 'And you called yourself an anarchist. You were a free spirit.'

'All right. I can be frank too. Have you ever heard of an anarchist with money or a free spirit with a hefty bank balance? Can't you see it's for the best, Eve? Can't you face up to it and go the whole hog, come and live with me and give up this whole crazy project? Let the kid go to school and lead a normal life like other kids. I could afford fees for boarding school, you know, a good *co-ed* private school. She could come home at weekends.'

There was silence. Liza held her breath. The door was suddenly flung open and Liza saw the wild face Bruno wasn't allowed to see, the dilated eyes and curled lip, the nostrils narrowed like a cat's.

'Go to bed at once! How dare you listen at doors!

208

Perhaps you *should* go away to school, perhaps I've been wrong all these years. I haven't just sheltered you, I've spoilt you. Go to bed now.'

Liza seldom cried but she did that night. She wept until she slept, woke again at the sound of Eve and Bruno coming up to bed together, whispering tenderly, no longer angry, reconciled, content with each other.

Years later, three or four years, she went back to look at the house Bruno had wanted to buy.

It was on the other side of the valley, about two miles away by road or one as the crow flies and as she walked, wading through the river where the water was low and crossing the disused railway line. By this time the rails and sleepers had been taken away and the line was a grassy track between embankments overgrown with gorse and wild flowers. Climbing the slope, she looked back at the station house where on the frightening occasion she had encountered Bruno painting. The painting he had done Eve had liked and hung it up in the cottage living room. Every time Liza looked at the dandelion faces in the foreground she remembered the gamboge yellow on his raised brush as he spat out those harsh words to her.

She climbed the hillside, took the footpath, then went across the fields that were private land yet where no one ever came but the sheep that grazed there. It was scarcely a village, just a church, a meeting hall and a green with a few old houses and the four newer ones built round a half-moon shaped road. The people who had bought the house she called Bruno's, though it never had been his, though he had never even made that offer for it, had cut down all the Leyland cypresses and painted the walls pink. A child's climbing frame stood in the middle of the lawn. Lying down asleep inside a wire enclosure was a big yellow dog with a feathery tail and long ears.

She might have lived there herself. But perhaps not, perhaps there had never really been a chance of that. She sat on the green for a while, then lay face-downwards in the sun, the prickly, scented grass pressing into her skin. When she got up she could feel with her fingertips the ridges the grass had made on her cheek, like wrinkles.

This time, for a change, she went back through the woods, though it was a longer way round. There were still great spaces in here where giant trees had fallen and no new ones yet been planted. Rocky outcrop appeared all over this hillside, among the trees as well as on the open heathland. It was very pale grey rock which sometimes looked white, like bones lying among the brown beech leaves and the gnarled dark tree roots. You might fancy you saw a skull but when you approached more closely you could see it was only a bowl-shaped lump of rock, just as the bone-white strips among the brambles were limestone, not a weathered femur or humerus.

'Did she give in to him, then?' said Sean.

'I don't know. I don't exactly know what happened. I never saw him again.'

Sean put up his eyebrows. 'What, you mean you never saw him after that night?'

'I told you, I didn't get up very early. I came downstairs at about nine and Eve said he'd gone out painting. It was midsummer, you see, and sometimes the light was best for painting very early in the morning. He often went out early. Now he didn't need to earn his living he painted all the time. We had our lessons. We'd got into the way of having them while he was out of the house. I can't remember

210

but I think it was French that morning and maybe history. Yes, it was history because I remember Eve wanted me to read Carlyle's *French Revolution* and I couldn't, it was too hard for me, too many difficult words.'

'Surprise, surprise,' said Sean.

'She was cross. She grumbled at me and called me a coward for not trying harder. I mean, you have to understand she was hardly ever cross with me and never about things like that. But she was irritable and jumpy that morning. When it got to midday she said she'd made a picnic lunch for me, it was too nice a day to stay in, I should be out in the fresh air. That was unusual too, if there was to be a picnic she always came with me, but not this time. You may wonder how I remember all this, all the details, but the fact is I've thought about that day a lot ever since, I've turned it over and over in my mind.'

Bruno's car was parked outside the cottage, where he always left it. That signified one thing to Liza, that he couldn't be far off. If he went to paint more than a mile away he always went in the car. Carrying her picnic, she made her way cautiously towards Shrove House. This time she wasn't going to let herself come upon him by chance as she had when she went marching confidently through the station. He was nowhere to be seen, he must have gone northwards through their wood or down the lane towards the river bridge.

The sun was too hot to walk or sit out in and in the shade under the trees flies swarmed. She let herself into Shrove, into its silent rooms that were as cool in summer as they were warm in winter, replaced *Kim* on the library shelves and took down *Stalky and Co*. For the next four hours she sat watching television.

On those days when she had been out for a long time she always had to brace herself before going home and confronting him again. It had got worse as she knew him more thoroughly, not better, and on the way home she reflected how terrible the future was, filled with days of meeting and being with Bruno, or else – and she hardly knew if this would be worse – going away to the school of his choosing. And still she would see him, for her weekends and holidays would be spent in the 'monstrosity', exiled from Shrove.

His car was gone. Her heart leapt up, then dipped again. Of course it most likely only meant he and Eve had driven off somewhere and would return in time for supper. She went despondently into the house. Eve was at home and alone, preparing a chicken to roast, mixing the stuffing and setting the giblets on to boil.

'Where's he gone?' She no longer used his name when speaking of him.

Eve's face showed nothing, neither happiness nor sadness, it was blank, her large brown eyes empty. 'He's gone. Gone for good. He's left us.'

At once Liza was enormously happy, bubbling over with delight, with joy. Some precocious sense of what was fitting restrained her from crowing or cheering. She said nothing, she just looked at Eve. Her mother set down the spoon she was holding, rinsed her hands under the tap, dried them and put her arms round Liza, hugging her tight.

That evening they read Shakespeare together. Liza took Macbeth's part and Eve Lady Macbeth. As Eve predicted, there was a lot of the scene where the wife urges the husband to murder the old king that Liza couldn't understand but she didn't get cross when Liza spoke sentences wrongly or put incorrect stresses on certain words. Afterwards, they played a tape of Mozart's *Sinfonia Concertante* and then had a French conversation, all things they hadn't been able to do when Bruno was there.

Liza was so happy that she should have slept soundly that night but she didn't. She fancied she heard all sorts of sounds, creaking boards and thumps and something heavy being dragged down the stairs. It could all have been in dreams, it was impossible to know. For instance, she had no reason to believe Eve didn't come to bed until four or five in the morning, only a feeling or intuition that she hadn't. It wasn't as if she had been into the other bedroom to look. The car she thought she heard at one point was probably farther away than she believed, not passing the gate-house door but a hundred yards away in the lane.

She said nothing about it in the morning, for she and Eve had never been in the habit of telling each other their dreams. Nothing could be more boring, Eve sometimes said, than other people's dreams. But later, while her mother was up at Shrove, cleaning the house in her role as Mrs Cooper, Liza went into the little castle that Bruno had used as a studio.

His easel was there and his two boxes of paints as well as innumerable extra tubes of colour, the names of which fascinated her, though she had never cared to show her interest in front of him. Rose madder tint, light veridian, Chinese white, burnt umber. How strange of him to have gone without his painting things. Even stranger that he hadn't cleaned the brushes he always complained were so expensive, but left them dipped in an inch of turpentine in a jam jar. Pictures, finished, half-finished, blank canvases, rested against the wall. Her own portrait was there.

It was not for a long time that she connected the paint rags in the little castle with Bruno's departure. Then, during that morning visit, they were just rags, a rather larger than usual pile of them filling up nearly half the floor-space. A much larger than usual pile, in fact. Old skirts of Eve's torn into strips, a sheet that went on her own bed until she put her toe through a hole in it, a ragged towel.

Another odd thing about the paint rags, which didn't particularly register at the time but remained in her memory, was the colour of the paint on them. One had a streak of sap green on the edge of it and another looked as if it had mopped up a spill of prussian blue, but for the most part they were stained reddish-brown – and not just stained, coated in that colour.

Liza tried to decide what colour it might be. Not crimson or scarlet lake or vermilion, it wasn't bright enough for that. Too dark for rose madder tint and not dark or dull enough for vandyke brown. Light sienna? Burnt sienna? Either was possible but that didn't explain why Bruno had used so much of it.

Did the mess in here and the stack of canvases mean he was coming back? She looked for his clothes in Eve's wardrobe, the leather jacket, the check shirts, the sweatshirt with 'University of California, Berkeley', mysteriously printed on it. Everything was gone. Sometimes he used to leave his gold earrings on Eve's dressing table but these too had gone with him. The awful possibility that, having gone, he might still tell tales of Eve to the Tobiases or to education authorities, brought her down from euphoria into the depths again.

She had to ask.

'He won't be telling anyone anything,' Eve said. 'Believe me. I promise.'

A letter came addressed to him and Eve opened it. He had asked her to do that, she said. Inside the envelope was a note from an estate agent who wrote that he would have phoned but it appeared that Mr Drummond and Mrs Beck were ex-directory. Was Mr Drummond still interested in making an offer for

'The Conifers'? The name, for some reason, made Eve laugh a lot.

She wrote a letter to the estate agent but Liza didn't see what she had said. They went out together to post it, up the lane to the main road where there was a little old post box with VR on it for Victoria Regina, which meant it had been there for a hundred years.

The month was July and Liza was eleven and a half. The good weather lasted for only a short time, it rained and grew cold and Eve and Liza stayed in, doing more lessons than they had for months. Liza could write French composition now and recite from memory Keats's 'Ode to a Grecian Urn'.

Because it was so wet the Tobiases didn't come down as they had said they would and in August Jonathan Tobias came alone. Liza noticed he had some grey in his hair. Perhaps because Victoria wasn't with him he spent more time at their house than he had done for years. Liza couldn't help overhearing some of the things that were said, for Jonathan seemed to think that when a person was reading they were deaf to everything.

Victoria, he said, was in Greece with friends. To Liza, Greece was a place full of grey stone temples with colonnades and marble statues and where gods lived in the rivers and trees. It hardly accorded with her ideas to hear that Victoria and her friends found beaches there to sunbathe on and big hotels to stay in, the kind of thing, Jonathan said, that they preferred over Shrove or Ullswater.

Sometimes, aware that she had looked up from her book, he would lean closer to Eve and speak in a whisper, wishy-wishy-wishy, the way she remembered Heather murmuring. And Eve nodded and looked sympathetic and whispered something back. It troubled Liza that Jonathan seemed to think Bruno was only temporarily away, for this made his departure seem less than permanent.

'I can't help being envious, Eve,' he said one sunny afternoon.

The summer had come back and they were all having tea in the garden, under the cherry tree. The bird cherries were ripening to yellow and red and there was scarlet blossom on Eve's runner beans. The courgette plants had flowers shaped like yellow lilies and the gooseberries were dark red beads, but beads which grew hair on their crimson skins.

'Of *me*?' said Eve. 'Envious of me?'

'You've got someone you can be happy with. You're in a good relationship.'

Liza waited for Eve to deny it or even tell him not to say 'relationship'. She didn't. She gave Jonathan a mysterious sidelong glance, her eyes half-closed.

'I don't want you to envy me,' she said. 'I'd rather you were jealous.'

There was silence. At last Jonathan said, 'Of him?'

'Why not? How do you think I have felt about Victoria?'

Eve got up then and carried the tea things into the house. Instead of following her, Jonathan sat there on the grass, looking glum. He pulled a daisy out of the lawn and picked the petals off. Liza thought he was getting to look old. The freshness had gone out of his face and there were lines across his forehead. His eyes had once been of the most piercing clear blue but the colour was muddied like a blue china bowl with dirty water in it.

She expected him to stay to supper and perhaps for the night. Where Bruno had been, beside Eve in bed, he would be found in the morning. But he didn't even stay to eat with them and was gone by seven. Next day Liza thought Eve seemed particularly pleased and happy and she connected this with the appearance of Jonathan at their door at nine in the morning, calling in to say goodbye on his way back to London.

Sean said, 'This is five years ago you're talking about, right?'

She nodded. They were in bed now, snuggled close together for warmth under the two quilts. Sean had bought a second one he'd seen in a closing down sale. The caravan got bitterly cold at night but if they kept a heater burning the condensation was streaming down the walls by morning and their pillows felt damp. Liza, her head on his shoulder, his arms tightly round her, thought of those warm dry weeks, her bedroom with the windows wide open at night, lessons, lessons, lessons, every day in the garden, and Eve saying, 'You see, if you went to a so-called proper school you'd be on holiday now, you wouldn't be learning anything but just running wild.'

'Wasn't that round about the time of the big storm? What they called the hurricane? I remember because it was when I'd just got to be sixteen, I'd got my first job and I had to get up at five. I was in our kitchen at home, making myself a cup of tea, and the oak tree next door blew over and came through the roof. It was only a lean-to, our kitchen, and the roof broke like an eggshell. Lucky I was quick off the mark, I got out just in time. It must have been like September.'

'It was October. October the fifteenth.'

'What a memory! I reckon you had a lot of trees come down at Shrove. Is that how you remember?'

The Day of the Hurricane, the last day she ever gave a name to.

'You're not to hurry me, Sean. I'll get to that soon. We got the hurricane very badly at Shrove, we were

217

one of the worst hit places, and you'll see why I remember it, the precise date and everything. But there was something else happened first.'

The outbuildings at Shrove House were seldom used. They had been stables once and there was a coach-house. The stables were built in the same architectural style as the house, of small red bricks with white facings, a pediment over the central building and above it a clock tower on which the clock face was blue and the clock hands gold. The weather-vane on the tower was a running fox with brush extended.

Mr Frost kept his lawn mowers, the big one he rode on and the small one with which he did round the flower-beds, in the section of stable to the left of the coach-house. Other garden tools were kept in there as well as a ladder and an industrial vacuum cleaner. As far as Liza knew, no one had ever kept cars in the stables. Perhaps they might have done when old Mr Tobias was alive but Jonathan always left his car standing out in the courtyard in front of the stables and visitors left their cars there too. The stables were really useless, no one went into them, and they remained standing, Liza had heard Jonathan say, only because they were pretty and also a listed building. That meant they were of historic value and must never be pulled down.

She had never been inside them, though she had once seen Mr Frost come riding out of the section by the coach-house on the little tractor that pulled the mower. She came to search them as a last resort.

It was years since she had needed the library steps to climb up to the picture frame for the key to the television room. At nearly twelve she was almost as tall as Eve, would be much taller by the time she was grown-up. Eve, in any case, had long ceased to bother to hide the key or even take it out of the lock. She must have decided Liza was too old now to be seduced by the charms of television, too mature to be intrigued by locked rooms, or thoroughly conditioned in the discipline of a sequestered life. These days she even pushed the vacuum cleaner about in that room in Liza's presence and seemed to take it as quite natural her daughter never asked what the box with the screen on it was.

When she needed the steps but couldn't find them it was for quite another purpose, their primary purpose. *The Confessions of an English Opium-Eater* were on the top shelf, far out of reach. The book would have been out of Jonathan's reach and he was six feet three. Although she knew that it was all of two years since she had put the steps back in the library, that she had several times used them in the library since then, she still went to look behind the long curtains in the morning room.

Returning to the library she saw why they had been replaced. The new ones were up in the dark corner, farthest from the windows, wooden ones this time, perhaps of dark oak, and almost invisible against the dark oak floor where the carpet ended. They were not really steps at all but more like a piece of a staircase consisting of three stairs. Jonathan must have brought them with him when he came in August. Liza could see without attempting to move them that even when she stood on the top stair she wasn't going to be high enough to reach that shelf.

She started to search the house for the missing steps. Eve said she wasn't old enough yet for de Quincey, she wouldn't understand the *Confessions*, there would be plenty of time for her to read it when she was older. And Liza hadn't even wanted it that much when she first came into the library. The title had drawn her to it, for it seemed to have something to do with those drugs she heard about on television. But she wanted it now. She wanted it because she couldn't have it, she couldn't reach it, it was up there in its faded blue binding with the faded gilt flowers on its spine, smugly sitting where it had sat undisturbed for years, for perhaps a hundred years.

The steps wouldn't be in any of the bedrooms but she searched the bedrooms. She found clothes that must be Victoria's in the wardrobe of what she had always thought the nicest bedroom, a big light room that looked across the water meadows to the river. A skirt hung there and a pair of jeans and the green silk shirt she had been wearing the first time Liza ever saw her. There were also an embroidered white cotton nightdress and a matching dressing gown. It looked as if Victoria had been sleeping in that room while Jonathan slept in the big room at the front. The steps weren't in there either, nor in any of the cupboards, nor downstairs in any of the rooms that gathered round the kitchen, the boot room and the pantry, the washing room, the larder and the store room.

Liza went outside to the stables. She could hear the drone of Mr Frost's mower from the bit of lawn behind the shrubberies. The stables were never locked. There were no locks on the doors, though the coach-house had a padlock fastening together the handles on each of its double doors. For some reason, she left looking in the section where the mower had been till last, which was strange because it was the obvious place. Except for the one where the tools were kept, the stables were all quite empty. She couldn't open the coach-house doors, only peer through the cracks in them. They were old doors with quite a big split between two of the boards. She could just make out a car inside.

The steps were propped up against the wall

between where the tractor had been and where the small mower stood. Liza took them into the house, carried them into the library and climbed up to get *The Confessions of an English Opium-Eater*. It was while she was coming down with the book in her hand that the significance of a car in the coach-house where no car had been before fully struck her.

Mr Frost was now in sight, wheeling round the big lawn on his tractor, wearing gloves and ear muffs. He didn't see her. She replaced the steps, then thought better of it, carried them out again and propped them up in front of the locked doors. High up under the pediment were two small windows.

Liza climbed the steps to the top. That brought her just high enough to see over one of the windowsills. The car stood in the middle of the coach-house floor with plenty of space around it. Even so, she couldn't see the name of the make but she could see the registration plates with the letter at the end of the number instead of the beginning. It wasn't too dark to make out the colour, a deep brown, the burnt sienna of Bruno's paintbox. Bruno was gone, but this was Bruno's car, the Lancia car Bruno's mother had had for ten years and only driven seven thousand miles.

The sound of the mower approaching made her look round. Mr Frost got off his tractor to open the stable. He never talked much, he wasn't the kind of grown-up to ask what she was doing.

'Mind you don't fall,' he said.

Going home, carrying the book, she had thought of that night after Bruno had left, how she had slept so uneasily and dreamed so much she couldn't tell in the morning what had been dream and what real. The car she had heard – that had been Bruno's car. She had heard Eve driving Bruno's car up here to hide it in the coach-house.

221

Sean was asleep.

Liza wondered how long he had been asleep, at what point in her narrative he had ceased to listen. Scheherazade. Did the king or sultan or whatever he was fall asleep while she told her stories? Was that in fact the reason she never reached the end of each tale? Because her husband fell asleep first?

Sean was snoring lightly. She pushed him over on to his side so that his back was towards her. Another thing she wondered about was if the sultan and Scheherazade made love before she started on the story or in the middle or what? They must have done that, that was the point of his marrying all these women, wasn't it? There was nothing about it in the book she had read. There wouldn't be, she thought, people cut things out of versions meant for children. Even for children who'd seen what she had seen.

Invisible in the dark, she smiled to herself at Sean's squeamishness. She hadn't told him about the smell of those stained rags, nor, to spare him, about the red paint finger-prints on the stone floor of the little castle. Up in the vaulted ceiling among the beams a spider had caught the Death's Head Moth in its dusty web. Sean wouldn't have wanted to hear about that either, the rare moth long dead among the dusty threads, but the skull pattern on its back still palely gleaming.

Chapter Fifteen

A disused airfield near the place where the caravan was parked provided them with somewhere for Liza to have her driving lessons. With Sean in the suicide seat – his words – she drove up and down the old runways and learnt how to do a three-point turn on the flat area outside a dilapidated hangar.

'You'll pass your test first go,' Sean said.

As November began, Liza began to think more and more about Eve and about her trial which was surely due. She regretted now that when she had the chance she hadn't learned more about crimes and justice and courts. Eve would have known, Eve could have told her.

For instance, would they have it here in the city which had once been the place the train started from? Or would it be far away in London at what she thought might be called Newgate? I must go to London sometime, she thought to herself, it's absurd never having been to London, even Sean's been to London. She ought to start buying newspapers but she didn't know which one would be best. Already she had seen enough of them to know that the little ones with the tall headlines would only print the most sensational or sexy parts of a trial while the big ones with pictures of politicians might not print it at all. Television might only have it on once and that on the evening Sean was watching his football.

Life wasn't easy in the caravan. If you wanted to be

warm you also got wet. Sean got hold of a tarpaulin from a farmer who had used it to protect a haystack from heavy rain and they spread it right over the caravan. That helped but it also made it dark. All their water had to be fetched from the stream and boiled. It was impossible to wash clothes and bed-linen which had to be taken to the one launderette still remaining within a ten-mile radius. They used two inches of water in a bowl and tried to wash themselves all over in that.

Liza had got very good at sneaking baths at Mrs Spurdell's, taking a towel to work and quite often managing to have a bath while Mrs Spurdell was actually in the house, waiting till she was on the phone – she spent hours on the phone talking to her daughter or her friends – and taking two minutes in the tub before giving the bathroom a clean. Even so, Mrs Spurdell had once or twice remarked on the quantity of water she had heard gurgling down the plughole.

At the school half-term, when Mr Spurdell had also been in the house, bathing was impossible, the risk was too great. His study was upstairs next door to the bathroom and he was usually in the study, or liable to go in there. On that late October day, a Monday, she arrived at Aspen Close determined on having a bath. Mrs Spurdell would be out for an hour, having her hair done. Liza had overheard her making the appointment. She was therefore dis-mayed to find Mr Spurdell at home, apparently recovering from the 'flu which had struck him down on the previous Friday afternoon while he was reading, according to his wife, Spenser's *Faerie Queene* with the A-Levels English form.

He wasn't up but she had no reason to believe he was asleep. Mrs Spurdell said he would probably get up later and come down in his dressing gown. Then, if she was still at the hairdresser's, Liza could make him a cup of tea. Mrs Spurdell put on her new Burberry. She tied a plastic rain-hood round her head, not because it was raining, it wasn't, but to make sure she had it with her to protect her set on the way home.

Liza thought she would have to do what she had advised Sean to do. Knowing nothing of hotels, she just the same understood that they must have a great many bathrooms. The Duke's Head, which she passed on her way to Aspen Close, must have more bathrooms than in any private house. If Sean didn't want to pay for the swimming pool or the showers, why didn't he just walk into the Duke's Head, march upstairs as if he was a guest there, find a bathroom and have a bath? Who would know? He'd have to make sure to take a towel with him, of course, he could put a folded towel inside his jacket and take a plastic bag to put it in after it got damp.

It was stealing hot water, Sean said, it was dishonest. He was quite shocked. Stay dirty then, said Liza. She wouldn't think twice about doing it, in fact she'd probably do it on her way to meet him after work. Realising that she couldn't because she had forgotten her towel made her feel cross and she thumped her way into the study, dragging the vacuum cleaner behind her.

Mr Spurdell had acquired two new books since she was last in there. Liza cared very little about Mrs Spurdell having a new Burberry or her hair done or unlimited hot water or Mr Spurdell driving a six-months-old BMW, but she did envy them the books. She resented them for the books, it made her hate Mr Spurdell especially, though in many ways he seemed nicer than his wife. She sometimes saw him on Friday afternoons, he returning home just before she was due to leave. The new books he had got were a *Life of Dickens* and the *Collected Short Stories* of Saki.

What wouldn't she give to read that *Life of Dickens*! She could never afford it, she wouldn't even be able to afford it when it came out in paperback. Quickly she forgot all about Mr Spurdell. She ceased to listen for him. The *Dickens* in its brown and gold jacket was in her hands, she was sitting at the desk reading the introduction, when he came quietly into the room. It was only because of the little dry cough he gave that she knew he was there. She jumped up, clutching the book.

He was a small man, as thin as Mrs Spurdell was fat. Liza had sometimes thought they were like Jack Sprat and his wife, he able to eat no fat and she no lean. He looked old, an old man who should have retired by now, his jowls melting into a withered neck, his head bald but for a white fringe round the back. Over striped pyjamas he wore a brown tweed dressing gown with a cord round the waist tied in a neat bow.

His genial smile brought her immense relief. She wouldn't have to go back to Sean now and tell him she'd got the sack. Relief became indignation when he said, still smiling, apologising as if to an ignorant child, that it was a pity there were so few pictures in that book.

'I don't want pictures,' Liza said and she knew her tone was surly.

Up went his white tufts of eyebrows. 'How old are you?' he said.

After she had spoken the truth she remembered too late the lie she had told his wife. 'I'm nearly seventeen.'

'Yes, I would have guessed about that. Some of my pupils are your age, only they prefer to be called students.' He held out his hand for the book and she gave it to him. 'Thank you. I haven't read it yet.' Without knowing in the least how she could tell, she

226

fancied this was the way teachers behaved. Bossy. Commanding. Imparting information. As she thought this, he imparted some. 'Dickens was a great English writer, some would say the greatest. Have you read any of his books at school?'

'I don't go to school,' she said, and added, 'any more. I don't go any more.' What did he think, that she took days off school to come and work for his wife? 'But I've read Dickens. I've read *Bleak House* and *David Copperfield* and *Oliver Twist* and *Nicholas Nickleby* and *A Tale of Two Cities*.'

His evident astonishment gave her a lot of pleasure. She thought he'd ask her why she left school so young, she was prepared for almost anything, but not for him to point to the several volumes of Dickens he had in paperback and ask her if she had read *Our Mutual Friend*.

'I told you the ones I've read,' she said but not this time in the surly voice.

'Well, you're a surprising young lady. Not quite what you seem, is that right?'

Liza thought this was truer than he knew. She changed the subject, asked him if he would like her to make him tea, and when he said he would, preceded him downstairs.

Mrs Spurdell was back before the kettle had boiled, recounting to her husband some long tale of how the hairdresser had read their daughter's name in a magazine, as the author of a letter to the editor about family law. The hairdresser – 'who was really quite an intelligent girl, considering' – had cut out the letter but forgotten to bring it. She would bring it next time. Philippa was so modest she hadn't said a word about it. She hadn't mentioned it to her father, had she?

While this was going on Liza went back upstairs. She finished the study, she made the bed Mr

Spurdell had just vacated and ran the vacuum cleaner across the carpet. By then it was time to leave. Mrs Spurdell was paying her, fishing about in a jar on the windowsill for a five-pound note and claiming to have mistaken a ten-pee piece for a fifty-pee, when her husband came back into the kitchen and handed Liza *Our Mutual Friend* and *The Old Curiosity Shop*.

'I should like them back some time but there's no hurry.'

'You'd better write your name on the fly-leaf, dear,' said Mrs Spurdell. She laughed reminiscently. 'Do you remember how Jane used to write inside *her* books, *This book was stolen from Jane Spurdell*?'

It was extremely rude but Liza didn't care. Having something new to read was wonderful. She'd been spinning out the *Life of Mary Wollstonecraft*, making it last, which was an irritating way to have to read something. Mr Spurdell giving her *Our Mutual Friend* was rather interesting, a sort of coincidence, because that was the book she'd tried to read when she gave up on *The Confessions of an English Opium-Eater*. Eve had been right about that, she wasn't old enough for it, and she hadn't been old enough for *Our Mutual Friend* either but she would be now.

She'd started to read it that same evening, when she got back from finding Bruno's car in the Shrove coach-house. It was a strange thing but she'd never really considered telling Eve what she'd found or asking her why the car was there. She thought she knew why and then she wasn't sure if she did or not. It might only mean that Bruno was coming back, that for some reason he had gone without his car and Eve was storing it for him, he hadn't gone for good. Eve had said he had but Liza no longer entirely trusted Eve to tell the truth.

After concentrating on it for all of an hour, she had

abandoned the de Quincey and attempted *Our Mutual Friend*. Perhaps she was tired because she hadn't been able to cope with more than the first page. She still lay awake a long time, wondering about the car and what might have happened to Bruno. Nobody had ever known where Bruno was except his mother and now his mother was dead. His wife hadn't known and nor had his wife's friend the dentist. The estate agent had but Eve had written to him.

That was the night she dreamed Bruno was with them still but about to leave. His silky brown hair was tied back with a piece of ribbon so that you could clearly see the two gold rings in his ear. And his face had even more than usual that angelic look, like a saint in a painting, that so belied the rough speech which sometimes came from that cherubic mouth. She didn't see him leave in the dream, Eve told her he had gone, and later she heard a gun being fired. She was walking in the wood and she heard shots behind her. But this was all in the dream, not in life. On the actual night after Eve said Bruno had gone she had heard no shots, she had heard nothing but a heavy object dragged downstairs and a car being driven away.

Where had the car been all day? Bruno couldn't have gone away in it or it wouldn't have been there for Eve to drive up to Shrove in the night-time. But it wasn't there, it hadn't been outside when Liza came home. So had Eve hidden it somewhere? Liza realised she could have hidden it almost anywhere, behind the birch tree copse or under the overhanging branches of a hedge, she could have hidden it a few yards from the gate-house and Liza wouldn't have seen.

Watching a football match that was coming from

somewhere in Germany, Sean didn't for a while try to stop her reading. He no more expected her to watch football than she expected him to read Dickens. They had a bottle of wine the supermarket had on sale, the week's special offer.

Rain lashed the tarpaulin that covered the caravan. A howling gale blew the rain in savage spurts against the uncovered parts of the windows so hard it sounded as if they must break. The caravan rocked and shivered.

Liza and Sean sat close together with one of their quilts wrapped round their legs. While Liza read about Eugene Wrayburn Sean watched the German team soundly beat the English one. He switched off with a sigh and, having first put his arm round her, began to comb her hair. It was a cunning move on his part, he knew the sensuous pleasure she took in it, stretching like a cat and extending her neck as the comb passed slowly through the curtain of smooth dark hair.

He said softly, 'What had happened to him, Bruno, I mean?'

Liza closed her book. 'I don't know. I mean, I didn't know then. I found out later.' She considered. 'You'll have to wait till I come to the hurricane.'

'OK, then what about those Tobiases? They split up, didn't they?'

'Not till the following year. But I never saw Victoria again. Jonathan wrote to Eve and told her he was living at Ullswater and Victoria was living in the London house and soon after that Victoria left altogether. I think she went off with someone.'

'So your Mum started hoping again?'

'Yes. But that was a way off. I don't know what she felt about the divorce – they got divorced two years later – she never showed me her feelings about that. Somehow I think she understood she'd played it all wrong before.'

'She should have made herself harder to get,' said Sean.

'Or easier. If she'd gone with him to all those places he wanted her to go to, even to London sometimes, if she'd done that I don't think he'd have ever taken up with Victoria. Eve was prettier than Victoria and cleverer and he'd known her since forever, she had all the advantages. Except that she'd never go away from Shrove, not even for a weekend.' She looked up at him. 'Should I have made myself harder to get, Sean? I was easy, wasn't I? I just jumped into your arms.'

'Oh, you.' He laughed and putting the comb down, hugged her in his arms. 'You was a real little innocent, you didn't know no better.'

'Was I? Shall I tell you about the hurricane?'

'Wait a minute, I'll fill up your glass. There's one thing I want to know first. Didn't no one come looking for Bruno?'

'Who was there to look? If his mother had still been alive it might have been different. If he'd said he wanted to buy that house. If he'd been to a lawyer or whatever it is you have to do when you buy a house. If the sale of his mother's house hadn't gone through and he'd still been waiting for the money. If he'd still been living in those rooms over the greengrocer. But as it was, nobody knew where he lived and no one needed to get in touch with him.'

'It gives you the creeps when you come to think of it.'

'I went back into the little castle and everything of his was gone, the paintings, the canvases, the paints and that pile of rags. It was all gone and the place had been scrubbed out. Even the ceiling, she'd cleaned the ceiling and got rid of the spider's web with the moth in it.'

'Those rags, what was it you thought was on

231

them?' Sean spoke in a low voice, tentatively. 'You never thought that was paint, did you?'

'I did then. Now I think it was blood.'

Sean was silent, his face grim. After a moment or two he said, 'Tell about the hurricane, then.'

'There's one other thing first. That picture Bruno painted of me, it turned up on our living room wall. One morning I came downstairs and there it was. Eve had taken away the Shrove at sunset picture and put the one of me there instead.'

'What did she do that for?'

'I don't know. It didn't look like me but I suppose she liked it. I'll come to the hurricane now.'

As if to encourage her the wind slapped another burst of rain against the window behind them. The caravan rattled. It hadn't rained that night, the Night of the Storm, the Hurricane, the Great Gale. The storm had been dry, an arid tempest that came up out of the Atlantic bearing salt on its back. Salt lay in drifts on the windows of Shrove next day, white as frost, dry crystals the wind had sucked off the sea.

'All the leaves were still on the trees,' she said, 'that was the worst of it. If the branches had been bare the gale wouldn't have been able to pull the trees over but they were still in full leaf, leaves don't really fall till November, and they made the treetops like great sails.'

'Was you at the gate-house, you and your Mum?'

'When weren't we there? We never went anywhere.'

She would have slept through it, enormous though the noise of it was. A heavy sleeper, at the age of eleven she would have slept through bombs falling. Eve woke her up. Eve, who was frightened of nothing, was frightened of this. She woke her up for companionship, for someone to be with, not to be alone while the world was torn to pieces around her.

It was just after four in the morning, pitch dark and the wind roaring up the valley like an invisible train, a ghost train. The real train that had once run along the valley had never sounded as loud as this. They still had electricity when she came downstairs, rubbing her eyes, peering about her, but the lights went out as she entered the living room. Somewhere out there the wind had brought the power lines down.

'What is it? What's happening?'

Eve said she didn't know, she'd never heard wind like this. Not in this country. We didn't have hurricanes.

'Perhaps it's not a hurricane,' Liza said. 'Perhaps it's the end of the world. The Apocalypse. Or a nuclear bomb. Someone's dropped a nuclear bomb.'

Eve, putting candles into jam-jars, said how did she know about things like that? How did she know about the Apocalypse? Who had told her about nuclear bombs? The television, thought Liza. She didn't answer.

'Of course it's not a bomb,' said Eve.

The candle flames guttered as the windows rattled. Something of the wind penetrated even in here. The curtains bellied out and flattened again against the glass. Eve tried the radio before she remembered that electricity worked that too. For the same reason she couldn't make tea. The nearest gas was five miles away. Liza thought how isolated they were, the nearest house in that village where Bruno had nearly bought a house two miles distant. It was like being marooned on an island in the midst of a rough sea.

She looked out of the window, the glass shuddering against her face. It was still too dark to see much beyond the tendrils of creeper which cloaked the gate-house till the leaves fell. These streamed out in

233

the wind like blown hair, pulling a black curtain across the window. An enormous crash from somewhere not too far distant drove her back into the middle of the room.

'Come away,' said Eve.

Roof tiles clattered off one by one, three of them, each making a sharp crack as it fell and smashed on the stones. The wind was both constant and sporadic. All the time it blew at a steady rate but it came in gusts too, each one thunderous, tearing through trees and leafy branches, between tree trunks, among bushes, each gust blowing itself out on a howl and a final crash. The earth shook and the ground heaved.

'The trees,' said Eve, and then, 'the trees.'

Her face was white. She put her hands over her ears, then brought them down and clasped them, wringing them. Dismayed, Liza watched her pace the room. This was Shrove where it was happening, Shrove which meant more to her than anything in this world or out of it. These were Shrove trees and at each nearby or distant crash Eve winced. Once she put her hand over her mouth as if to stop herself crying out.

At about six it started to get light. Dawn had been a yellow bar across the eastern horizon. Liza crept out into the kitchen to look at it, for Eve wouldn't let her go upstairs. The wind abated not at all with the pale spreading of light but seemed to take new life from it, roaring and tossing and circling with a shrill whistling sound. A single leafy branch spun in the air and crashed to the ground. The walls of the gate-house shuddered. The windows rattled. Liza watched the darkness recede from the sky, the livid streak fade, the grey colour whiten and a mass of high, clotted, scurrying cloud reveal itself.

The cherry tree lay across the garden, its branches

and dense foliage spread over the lawn, the flower-beds, Eve's kitchen garden, its roots pointing dark brown thready fingers into the air. As she watched, the whistling wind, the invisible engine, struck the ash that marked the edge of the lane and the giant tree shuddered. It seemed to hold itself suspended before a quivering convulsed it and it toppled over out of Liza's sight, leaving a sudden white space where all her life had stood this strong, stout, leaf-crowned barrier. She gasped, putting her hand up to her lips.

'Come away,' said Eve. 'Don't look.'

It wasn't until the afternoon that the gale blew itself out. Eve had tried to go outside before that but the wind had beaten her back. Broken branches and twigs, dying leaves, covered the front garden and the lane. One of the Shrove gates had come loose from its fastenings and slammed shut, tendrils of solanum trapped between its iron curlicues.

Liza had never seen her mother in such a tragic mood. She was unhappier than she had been when she heard of Jonathan Tobias's marriage. She was worse than unhappy, she was distraught. The sight of the fallen cherry tree made her weep and she kept crying out that it wasn't real, it couldn't be true.

'I can't believe it, I can't believe it. What's happening? What's happened to our climate? This is madness.'

From the gate-house they couldn't see much. The balsam still stood, though stripped of one of its limbs, but fallen trees blocked their view on all sides. It was as if the gate-house had been surrounded by a barricade of broken tree trunks and branches, as if the wind, invested with purposefulness and malice, had built it up to hem them in. They were in the midst of a fortification of wind-hewn timber. Liza could see that they would have to climb over logs and

235

scramble through leafy boughs to get out of the front gate. Eventually they emerged together at three in the afternoon, clambering over the balsam's huge bough which blocked their way.

Liza felt very small and alone but she would have considered herself too old to take Eve's hand if Eve hadn't taken hers first. Hand in hand, they stumbled towards the gateway of Shrove. Inside the park devastation lay on both sides of them, ruined trees and shrubs in heaps where they had fallen, havoc as if man-made, Eve whispered, like pictures she had seen of countryside after battles. Tree stumps stood with shredded trunks pointing skywards. A bird's nest, a huge structure of thick twigs and woven reeds, had been torn from some once high treetop and lay in their path.

'Paradise destroyed,' Eve said.

Two of the great cedars had gone. The limes were down, most of the ancient trees, only the slender supple birches and the little pyramidal hornbeams remaining. Laying waste the park, the wind had spared the house which stood staring calmly at them, its glazed eyes all intact, its roof unscathed. All that was changed was that a stone vase had tumbled off a pillar at the foot of the steps.

A pale sun, weak and watery, though no rain had fallen, gleamed like a puddle of silver among the soft drifting clouds. Beyond the gardens, beyond the water meadows, a waste of felled willows and splintered poplars, beyond the shining ribbon of the river, the high hills showed hollow places in their woods, holes in the fabric of tree cover as if scissors had ripped rents in cloth.

The air was scented with sap from the ripped leaves and salt from the distant sea. All was silent, the birds silent, but for a plover making its unearthly cry as it wheeled above them.

'Eve was in an awful state,' Liza said to Sean. 'She was like someone bereaved. Well, like I imagine someone bereaved would be. You know you read in books about people tearing out their hair. She almost did that. I found her sitting in our living room clutching handfuls of her hair. She moaned and cried and threw herself about as if she was in pain. I didn't know what to do, I'd never seen her like that.

'I wonder if she'd have been half as bad if it wasn't trees that had been destroyed but me. That was when I began to get the feeling Shrove was more important to her than I was. It frightened me and I didn't know what to do.

'There wasn't anyone I could turn to, you see. There wasn't anyone. Well, the milkman came and he was useless. Now the trains didn't run any more he could only talk about the weather and I'd had enough of weather for a lifetime. Mr Frost came to see if there was anything he could do. I said, you could get her a doctor and I think he thought I was crazy. What's she got wrong with her, then, he said, and I couldn't answer him, I knew he'd think Eve was mad or I was. No one's phone was working, he said, and it might be a week before we got our electricity back. I was left alone with her and I felt helpless. I was only eleven.

'She calmed down a bit next day. She lay on the sofa. We couldn't cook anything but we'd got bread and cheese and fruit. I went up to Shrove and found a packet of a dozen candles. I found a Calor gas burner we could boil a kettle and an egg on, though it took hours. She fell asleep in the afternoon and I went up into the wood, the bit we called our wood.

'I don't know why I went really. It didn't upset me the way it had her but I'd seen enough fallen trees and destruction to last me for ever. But I still went up there. Maybe I thought that if somehow the wind hadn't done much damage there, if for some reason it had escaped, that would be something to tell her and cheer her up.

'Afterwards I wished I hadn't gone. I wished I'd stayed at home with her. It caused me such a lot of worry.'

'What d'you mean?' Sean asked.

'You'll see. It was what I found there,' she said. 'Of course it didn't matter in the end.'

As soon as she came close to the wood, to what had been the wood, she knew her hope had been forlorn. From a distance you couldn't see what lay beyond the outer circle of trees, she and Eve hadn't been able to see when they walked up the lane on the previous day, for the oaks and chestnuts on the perimeter remained standing. Like a whirlwind the gale had bored its way in through the outer ring and once inside behaved like a maddened animal, spinning in circles and destroying every vulnerable thing in its orbit.

Not quite everything, she saw as she came carefully between the standing oaks. A few young trees still stood. Here and there a giant had resisted the onslaught while one or two mature trees leant at an angle, their final collapse delayed. But between them lay devastation.

The leaves on the tumbled limbs and branches were still fresh. They were still as if growing from twigs that proceeded from branches that grew from a living rooted trunk. A sea of leaves lay before her. There was no wind now, only a little breeze, a joke of nature playing with destruction, that fluttered all the leaves, scalloped oak and pointed cherry, five-fingered chestnut and oval beech. The leaf sea was a dark quivering green from which protruded here and there an upturned root like a fin or a broken trunk

238

like the funnel of a wrecked ship. It reminded her of the sea after a storm in a picture in the library at Shrove, for the real sea she had never seen.

For a while she stood there, just looking. Then she waded into the sea of green. Once she began, the image ceased to hold, the comparison was wrong. This was not a matter of striding through water but of clambering across a rough terrain. Where once had been paths and clearings were broken wood and torn brambles, concealed stumps to trip her up and shattered logs to block her way.

Yesterday she would have been incredulous if anyone had told her she might not find her way through the wood. But so it was. Everything was different. The wind had laid it waste and made a nearly impenetrable wilderness where yesterday morning had stood the ranks of trees and between them, in the depths, had stretched aisles of mysterious green shade. All was havoc now and all was curiously the same. Was it here, for instance, that the great isolated beech had stood, spreading its branches in an arc so huge as to form a circle of deep shade with a radius of fifty yards in which no grass or plant could grow? Or was it here that the larches had been, conifers leafless in the winter but green with new needles in the spring? She couldn't tell, but when she found the beech, felled and prone, its vast trunk grey as a wet seal, its wrenched-out roots clotted with earth and stones, when she saw that she could have cried like Eve.

Struggling onwards, climbing over fallen trunks and pushing aside sheaves of thick foliage, she made her way aimlessly, hardly knowing what she was seeking. Somewhere it hadn't happened? A region of the wood miraculously untouched?

There was just one place. But this only because no trees had stood in the clearing she came to. She had

239

an idea where she was now, in the very heart of the ruined wood, its centre, where once a ring of cherry trees and field maples had encircled a grassy space. On the tree stump in the middle of that grass she had sometimes picnicked.

She moved towards it now and sat down on the broad flat smooth stump. She looked about her, aware for the first time of the silence. No birds sang. There had always been birds in the wood but at the hurricane's assault they had departed.

The maples and cherries had mostly fallen but some still stood, the biggest and oldest leaning at a steep angle. She wondered if it would be possible to save those half-fallen trees, if there was some way of hauling them up and holding them. Who would do it? Who was there to care? She got up and made her way to the half-toppled cherry, put her hands on its trunk. It felt firm, as steady as an upright, growing tree.

There was nothing to do now but go back, to try to find her way back through the welter of broken branches. She ducked under an overhanging limb of maple, looked down and recoiled, jumping backwards and hitting her head. She scarcely felt the pain. Her breath indrawn sharply, she put her hand up over her mouth, though she had no inclination to cry out.

Almost at her feet, *at* her feet until she had retreated that step or two, lay a long bundle of sacking. She could see it was a sack, of the kind Eve said they used to put potatoes in and of which there was a pile in the stable at Shrove, though it was stiff with earth and gravel. And it wasn't just a sack, it was a bundle with something inside it. A length of string, now quite black, had been tied around the top and another length around the bottom.

No, not the top and the bottom, Liza found herself

saying, but the head and the feet. She came a little closer, not frightened but awed. It had made her flinch and jump back at first; now she was curious. Whatever this was, the storm had unearthed it, tearing up a tree root and heaving it out of its burying place.

Its burying place . . . She was conscious of the smell now. It was a smell she had never smelt before. Strange, then, that she knew it was of something rotten, something that decayed, reminding her – yes, she knew what it was – of long ago, when Heidi and Rudi used to come. One of them had buried a meaty bone and later, perhaps weeks later, Eve while gardening had dug it up, stinking, maggoty, as green as jade, a beautiful colour really . . .

She knelt down. She held her breath, somehow knowing she must hold her breath. There was a tear in the sacking at the top of the bundle just above the string. She picked at it, making the hole bigger. It split open quite suddenly and a flood of soft brown silky hair spilt out. It split into her hands, thick and slippery. The hair came off in her hands and she was holding it. She stumbled away and was sick among the broken branches.

Chapter Sixteen

'It was Bruno?' Sean said.

She nodded.

'You poor kid. A kid might never get over something like that.'

She wished he wouldn't say 'somefink' but there was nothing to be done about it.

'Well, I did. I got over it. I didn't even dream about it. It's a funny thing, you know, but you can't help being sick. It's not what your mind does, it's your body. I was curious, I really wanted to know, I suppose you could say I was *interested*. I knew it was Bruno's hair, I knew it was Bruno dead in there, and I hadn't liked Bruno, I'd hated him, I was glad he was dead, but I threw up just the same. Weird, isn't it?'

He didn't understand. 'You must have been shattered to bits. You didn't know what you was doing.'

Useless to persist. She gave up trying. 'I didn't know what to do next. There wasn't anything I could do but go back home and leave that thing lying there for anyone to find.'

'Let's get this straight,' said Sean. 'She'd killed him, right? She's real bad news, your Mum, isn't she? She'd killed him like she killed the man the dogs went for?'

'Oh, yes, she'd killed him. I don't know how. I never said anything about it to her. I was only eleven but I knew she'd killed him and – well, there didn't seem anything to say, if you know what I mean.'

He didn't know. She could tell that. 'She was in a state, anyway. She was depressed, in a real black depression, for quite a long time. I wasn't going to tell her a thing like that, not something that would worry her as well.'

'There must ha e been someone you could tell. Tobias, like, or the old chap – Frost was his name? No one'd have expected you to get the police, not at your age, but hopefully they'd have done that for you. Didn't you never think of that?'

It was dark in the caravan. She looked at him in the dark and made out his puzzled expression. 'She's my *Mother*,' she said quietly. He didn't respond, and when she said how it had worked out for the best, how the body was concealed once more, he hardly reacted. 'She killed him because he threatened everything,' Liza said. 'He was going to part her and me and make us leave Shrove.'

'OK. No need to get excited.' Sean hesitated. 'How did she do it?'

'I don't know. I didn't hear any shots that day he disappeared but I wouldn't have so far away. You remember that blood on the rags in the little castle? I think she may have used a knife.'

He had gone a little pale. 'Wasn't you scared of being with her? I mean, she could have turned on you.'

'Oh, no.' Liza laughed. 'I was like the bird that lived inside the crocodile's mouth, I was safe who-ever else wasn't.'

'I wish you hadn't told me, not that about the sack and the hair. I shan't get no sleep.'

'I shall,' said Liza, and she was asleep very quickly, her arm round his waist and her forehead pressed between his shoulder blades. If he lay awake, haunted by what she'd told him, she was oblivious of it.

Cautiousness made her rather quiet next morning. She boiled the water for their tea and performed her perfunctory face-washing in silence. It was perhaps unwise to go into too many details with him. She had told him rather too much on the previous night but now she would be more careful. She hadn't liked that remark of his about the police. Eve had been arrested, had no doubt appeared in one court, was somewhere in a prison, but still there must be many things they didn't know and need not know.

It wasn't one of her days at Mrs Spurdell's but still, 'I'll come into town with you,' she said. It was almost the first thing she'd said that morning. She took the spare set of car keys with her.

For the first time she went all the way into the Superway car park with him, noting where he put the car. He went off into the store and, having bought a pair of bath towels at Marks and Spencer, she wandered casually into the Duke's Head where she encountered no one in the front hall or on the stairs.

There was no soap in the bathroom. She should have thought of that but how was she to know? She took a bath just the same, enjoying a prolonged soak in the hot water, free from any anxiety about Mrs Spurdell returning unexpectedly, and dried herself on both of the thick fleecy towels. On her way out a man in a suit and tie asked her if she needed help. Liza said she was looking for Mrs Cooper. She didn't know many names, having come across so few people, and had to fall back on those from fiction or, as in this case, the name of Eve's invented cleaner.

'Is she staying in the hotel?'

Liza said she was expected today or tomorrow. The man looked in his book and said she'd made a mistake but cast no suspicious glances at the Marks and Spencer's carrier full of wet towels. He didn't seem at all cross, or anxious for her to go and as he talked about the fictitious Mrs Cooper, speculating about where this woman might be staying or how a member of his staff could have made an error, Liza was aware that the way he looked at her and the way he spoke were full of admiration. As Sean would put it, he fancied her.

From Sean alone had she experienced this, had accepted it without thinking others might share his feelings. Now she was beginning to understand desiring her wasn't some idiosyncrasy of his but might even be common. She felt her power.

'Don't hesitate to come back if we can help you at all,' the man said as she left.

At the rear of Superway she got into the car and started the engine. She drove round the town, teaching herself things Sean hadn't been able to teach her on the airfield. How to start on a hill, for instance, and how to stop in a hurry. He would have been cross because she hadn't got a licence or insurance, but that didn't matter because she wasn't going to tell him.

She had to wait nearly an hour for the bus to get her back and then there was a mile-long walk from the bus stop in the rain.

The days that followed her discovery of Bruno's body remained very fresh in her mind. They were dark days, there was no electricity and they lit log fires to keep themselves warm. Because Eve did almost nothing, sat staring at the wall or hid herself in bed, Liza did her best to clear up the front garden, moving all but the biggest and heaviest branches. She went up to Shrove every day on her own, fetching back useful things from the kitchens, firelighters and nightlights, stone hot-water bottles, tinned food, coffee and sugar. It was stealing, she now supposed, though she hadn't thought of that at the time.

One afternoon she went up to watch television. She hadn't associated the television with the electricity supply but she did when she switched it on and nothing happened. It occurred to her to try the phone, though she had never used a phone, but that too seemed dead and stayed silent no matter how many of the buttons she pressed.

She and Eve had no idea of what might be happening in the outside world. That, she now understood, was what Eve had always wanted, to be isolated, to be cut off from all that lay beyond Shrove. But she had hardly wanted it to this extent. Liza suddenly thought of the radio in Bruno's car. That didn't work off mains electricity, somehow it worked off the car itself, perhaps by some means from the engine.

Bruno's radio would tell them what the hurricane had done, if the whole world was devastated, if the electricity had gone for good, if all the phones had been destroyed. But it was no good thinking of that. She wouldn't know how to start the engine or turn the radio on and even if she could find out, the car was locked away in the coach-house and the key hidden somewhere.

Next day it no longer mattered, for the electricity men came to mend the lines. Their van went past the gate-house, bumping over broken twigs and dead leaves. Later, when she went out, she came upon them up on the high poles, restringing cables, and one of them, thinking perhaps that she came from Shrove itself, called out to her that her TV aerial was broken. The storm had torn it from the roof and it was hanging over one of the chimneys.

Liza didn't know what he meant. She had never heard of a TV aerial. To her the complicated grid

246

thing that looked like one of the shelves from their oven was just something you saw on roofs, probably a kind of weather vane. After the men had gone and the lights and heating came on again, she went up to Shrove to watch television.

This time it came on but not properly. The picture ran about all over the place, it rolled over as if someone were turning a handle inside it, lines formed or the screen looked like a piece of coarsely woven grey material. You couldn't see the people's faces clearly and their voices sounded as if they all had colds.

It was a long time before Liza made the connection between the failure of the television and the broken oven shelf on the roof. She thought it had simply gone wrong. It was old and it had gone wrong. She felt helpless, knowing there was nothing she could do without telling Eve. Her viewing afternoons were over. Jonathan never watched television, this set had been his grandfather's, and he certainly wouldn't get a new one or have the aerial mended.

She walked sadly back to the gate-house. Watching Eve, who hardly spoke, who went through the motions of getting their supper while her thoughts were far away, Liza decided that her mother had no more cause for grief than she had, who had lost just as much, who had lost her only friend.

She had grown up a lot in the weeks that followed the hurricane. It was as if she aged three or four years. She began to know all sorts of things, she was sure, that people don't usually know at eleven. For instance, how to be alone with a woman nearly mad with misery and grief, while feeling – yes, she'd felt it even then – that somehow it was wrong to care so much about a *thing*, a place, a piece of land, a house. If she cared in the same way about the television set she was only a child while Eve was grown-up. It only

247

made her pity her mother the more. She had to look after her, be kind, not trouble her, encourage her in the only thing that distracted her: giving lessons, imparting knowledge. Liza sometimes worked at her textbooks from early morning until late in the evening just to keep Eve's mind off the destruction and the mess out there.

The other thing that helped this fast growing-up was her anxiety over Bruno's body. Eve had buried it in the first place because she wanted it hidden, because if it was found she might be in serious trouble. Liza had some inkling of the kind of trouble from reading the Victorian novelists. *Oliver Twist* was her handbook and so was *The Woman in White*. Did they still hang murderers? She couldn't ask Eve. And what did hanging actually mean? What bit of you was hung up? She knew a lot more about beheading. From reading about the French Revolution and Mary Queen of Scots and the wives of Henry VIII she knew quite a lot about chopping off heads.

Would they hang Eve? She was really frightened when she thought of that, she was a child again, more like five than eleven, afraid of bad men coming and taking her Mummy away. Like Eve and the spoilt woods she wanted to hide herself and pretend it wasn't real. Besides, if she asked Eve about hanging it might make her think she had something more to worry about. Liza didn't ask. She and Eve worked at English literature and history and Latin from morning till night.

Until the day came when Eve didn't get up at all. She lay in bed with her face turned to the wall. Liza went out for the first time for days. It was the last day of October, the 31st, Hallowe'en, a dry, grey, breezy morning.

The ruined wood looked different because all the leaves had died. They hadn't turned brown like the

248

leaves on the remaining living trees, but still green, had dried up and curled and shrivelled. As she pushed her way through the wreckage the dead leaves crackled. From the depths a pheasant gave its rattling cry and above her in the single standing trees she heard doves cooing. The birds had come back.

Her heart was in her mouth (as she had read) or perhaps she was only starting to feel sick again as she came to the clearing where the flat smooth stump stood. But there was no fear of being sick this time or of smelling the smell of maggoty bone, for the bundle had gone.

She had a moment of absolute panic, of wanting to run and not knowing where to run to. Someone had come and found Bruno and taken him away. Then she saw what had happened. The body in the sack was still there, was somewhere down there, *inside* there. The leaning cherry tree had fallen and hidden it. The cherry tree she had clasped in her hands to test how stable it was had not been stable at all, had fallen next time the wind blew, and its broad solid trunk dropped on top of the bundle, driving it back into its grave.

Liza examined the place carefully. There wasn't a sign of that bundle unless you knew what to look for, unless you detected the corner of a sack protruding from where the lowest branch grew out of the cherry trunk. She tried pushing it under but it wouldn't go, so she dragged across branches and fetched armfuls of twigs, piling them up to conceal what remained of Bruno.

No one could find it now until men came to clear the wood. She hadn't thought of that at the time, she had simply been relieved, had believed it hidden for ever, but no more than a few days after this a lot of workmen came in a lorry with chainsaws and axes. Jonathan came too. The men began by clearing the gate-house garden and then they started work on the fallen and damaged trees in Shrove Park.

That worried Liza a lot. She was sure they would move into the wood and begin shifting the logs and broken trees. For a whole day she worried about it until Jonathan – who sat for hours in the cottage with Eve, the two of them sighing and shaking their heads over what the hurricane had done – remarked in passing that the 'little' wood was to be the last place to be cleared. It might be two years before they began to clear the 'little' wood.

Eve got up for Jonathan and pulled herself together. She washed her hair and braided it on the back of her head, she put on her tight black top and her blue and purple skirt and smiled and made herself beautiful for Jonathan.

He came and he did what Liza hadn't seen him do for years, put his arms round Eve and kissed her. When Eve sent her away and said to write her history essay upstairs – she called it her 'homework' as if all her lessons weren't done at home – Liza listened outside the door. She heard Eve tell Jonathan it was half-term. Perhaps it was. In that case what she said wasn't really untrue. Of course, that depended on what you meant by a lie. It was a lie if by lying you meant intending to deceive. Eve certainly intended to deceive Jonathan in thinking Liza went to school.

They talked for a long time about the hurricane damage. Both knew a lot of statistics about this being the first hurricane in England for so many hundred years and about so many million trees being destroyed. They talked about the Great Storm of 1703. It was all rather boring. After she'd heard the bit about delaying till last the clearing of the wood where Bruno's body lay, Liza decided to go upstairs and start writing about the rise of Napoleon Bonaparte. At that moment Jonathan changed the

250

subject and told Eve quite abruptly that Victoria had left him for a lover and the two of them were living in Caracas. There was no hope of a reconciliation, this was what the court called 'irretrievable breakdown'.

Just as Eve began to say something Liza thought might be interesting there came a great thudding at the front door.

Eve said in a theatrical way, 'What fresh hell is this?' and then explained with a laugh that someone called Dorothy Parker had said it first.

The person at the door was only one of the workmen looking for Jonathan to ask about some tree or other, whether to chop it down or leave it as it was, a torn-in-half tree. Liza went upstairs and, not being sure whether Caracas was the capital of Venezuela or Ecuador, looked it up in her atlas.

Jonathan stayed for less than a week. Liza was almost sure he'd spent one night in Eve's bedroom. It was a feeling she had, no more, for she hadn't heard them go to bed, had slept soundly all night, and when she came down in the morning there was no sign of him. But she was older, she was beginning to be very aware of things like that.

In January she was twelve.

Next time Liza went to Mrs Spurdell's it was for one of the afternoon stints, so there was time to put up her hair the way Eve had for special occasions, in a thick braid on the back of her head. It made her look several years older, she decided. She took with her the books she had borrowed.

Mr Spurdell seldom got home before she left but he did that day and he had been in no more than ten minutes when a woman arrived in a red car. Cleaning the bedroom windows, Liza saw her come up the path towards the front door. She was tall and good-looking in a masculine way, with dark hair tied back at the nape of her neck. Her trouser suit was dark grey with a pinstripe and her shirt was red silk. But the most attractive thing about her was her warm and intelligent expression which made her look incapable of saying an unpleasant or stupid thing.

Liza waited for the doorbell to ring. Instead she heard the front door open. She must have a key of her own, she thought, and guessed who this was. Jane, she who wrote in her books that they had been stolen from her. But she had been much younger then, of course. Jane, the daughter who was something to do with education. Now she could see a resemblance to the photograph.

How could a poor shrivelled-up little man like Mr Spurdell and a fat white-haired creature like his wife have a daughter as nice to look at as this? It was a great mystery. She finished her windows and went downstairs. No one bothered to introduce her, she wasn't surprised about that. Mr and Mrs Spurdell just went on talking as if she wasn't there, as if she were a robot cleverly programmed to sweep floors and dust furniture.

Liza said to Mrs Spurdell that she had finished. Was there anything more she wanted her to do? Mrs Spurdell said no, there wasn't, and gave her a look as from a feudal lady to a serf, so Liza went into the kitchen and sat at the table, waiting to get her money.

After a moment or two Mr Spurdell appeared. He saw the books she had brought back on the kitchen table and began to interrogate her about their contents. Who was Miss Gradgrind? What did Dickens mean by Mrs Sparsit's Coriolanian nose? What did Mr Boffin collect? Who was Silas Wegg? Liza was surprised but not disconcerted. She had had plenty of this from Eve and was answering his questions with the enthusiasm of the scholar who thoroughly knows her subject, when the good-looking education woman came into the kitchen.

She raised her eyebrows and gave Liza a wink. 'Come off it, Dad, what d'you think you're doing, putting her through an examination? You're lucky she's too polite to tell you where you can put your questions.' She held out her hand to Liza and said, 'Jane Spurdell. You must excuse my father. He never really leaves school.'

'That's all right,' she said and thinking quickly, gave Sean's name. The elder Spurdells had never asked her surname. 'Liza Holford.'

Mr Spurdell wasn't at all put out. 'This young lady is a dark horse, Jane. I caught her reading my Dickens. I suspect she is on sabbatical or else she is in our house cleaning for purposes of research. What can they be, I ask myself. Shall we set out to discover her secret?'

'Speak for yourself, Dad,' Jane Spurdell said, 'and leave me out of it. Her secret, if she has one, is her own atfair.' She smiled at Liza in a very friendly way. 'I say I do like the way you've done your hair. Is it very difficult?'

Liza was explaining that while it wasn't very difficult to do it took a long time, you had to allow yourself half an hour, when Mrs Spurdell arrived with her purse in her left hand and a handful of loose change in the other. Liza could tell she didn't at all like finding her conversing on equal terms with her daughter.

'Perhaps you should have been a hairdresser,' she said unpleasantly. 'When you've finished the demonstration, I'd like to get through the business of your pay.'

Jane Spurdell looked ashamed of her mother, as well she might, Liza thought, and even more embarrassed when she asked for a loan of two pound coins

253

to bring the total up to twelve. Mr Spurdell had gone upstairs but as she was going he appeared in the hall with paperbacks of *Little Dorrit* and *Vanity Fair*. Liza said nothing about having already read *Vanity Fair*. She was watching, with barely suppressed laughter, Mrs Spurdell's face as Jane said goodbye and it had been nice to meet her.

In the car, going home, she thought of telling Sean about Jane, how nice-looking she was and how friendly. But she didn't tell him. Without quite knowing why, she sensed he wouldn't like it. He had hated school, alternatively called the teachers power-mad and a bunch of snobs. He would think being an educationalist a job for a woman only if she couldn't get a man.

Instead, because he was curious to know, she spoke about the year at Shrove that followed the hurricane. It was strange how much he loved stories. How would he manage if he ever got a girlfriend who couldn't tell him stories? But, of course, he never would get another girlfriend, for they were to be together for ever and ever.

'My TV was broken in the storm – well, I thought of it as mine – and I knew I'd never get another. I did lessons all the time instead and gradually Eve got better. It was a lovely summer that year, that was the start of all the lovely summers, the best we'd ever had.'

'The greenhouse effect,' said Sean.

She was surprised he knew and then angry with herself for being surprised. 'Well, maybe,' she said. 'I wouldn't know. Eve said they had summers like that at the beginning of the century, before the First World War.'

'How did she know? She wasn't old enough to know.'

Liza shrugged, the way Eve did. 'The milkman

254

said, hot enough for you? He said it every day, he must have picked it up somewhere. The heat didn't stop the men. They worked hard at Shrove, clearing up all the mess, and it didn't look so bad. They'd even planted some new trees in the park and down by the river. The trees did very well because it was like wetlands down there. Even Eve said things weren't as bad as she'd feared and Mr Frost said every cloud has a silver lining and now with them big old trees gone you could see views you'd never seen before. I think that was the longest sentence I ever heard him speak.

'Jonathan came down to Shrove a lot that year. It was funny really, he never seemed to notice that I was home all the time. I mean, through May and June and July, when everyone else of my age was at school. And in the same sort of way he didn't seem to notice that Mrs Cooper never came to clean while he was staying at Shrove, though once he was there for nearly two weeks. I suppose he'd had people waiting on him all his life, he took it for granted things got done, cleaning and meals got ready and his clothes washed. He ate his meals with us or Eve took them up to him at Shrove. She collected his washing too and washed and ironed it and took it back to him.

'I never heard him say thank you or even mention it, though perhaps he did when I wasn't there. There were nights I think she spent at Shrove with him, then and at lots of times in the future. If she did she left the gate-house after I was asleep and came back very early in the morning. Things were back where they had been before he married Victoria, or she thought they were. She hoped they were.

'They talked for hours about his marriage. They· forgot I was there, I didn't have to listen outside the door. She was always asking him about Victoria and the divorce but I never heard him say a word about

Bruno. And all the time Bruno's car was up in his stables and Bruno's dead body was lying in his wood. Rotting in his wood and the worms eating him.'

'Liza,' said Sean warningly. 'Do you mind?'

'Sorry. You *are* squeamish. I don't think Jonathan was interested, I don't think he cared. He was only interested in Jonathan Tobias and people were important to him only as being useful to Jonathan Tobias. Maybe we're all like that. Are we?'

'I'd put you first, I know that.'

'Would you? That's nice. I kept remembering the story she'd told me about old Mr Tobias and my grandmother and how Eve'd thought then that she and Jonathan were going to get married. It didn't matter about her mother not getting Shrove because she and Jonathan were going to be married. She'd thought like that when I was little and he came down for those three weeks and it was all happening again.

'She thought he'd marry her when he got his divorce. She'd been trying to get him for seventeen years.'

Chapter Seventeen

When you're telling someone a serial story you don't say that now you've come to a bit where nothing much happened. It makes your listener not care about the outcome. Somehow Liza knew this and stopped herself saying it to Sean. Yet, in her twelfth and thirteenth years nothing much had happened. Eve had made her work ferociously hard at English and history and languages. She had taught her to sew and to knit and had unravelled old sweaters for Liza to knit up again. They had listened to music together, but there had been no drawing or painting, as this perhaps was a reminder of Bruno. Liza missed the television and felt sad on the day the council rubbish collectors came and she saw the old set thrown into the back of the truck.

But nothing of great moment happened. No one came to clear the wood. The British Rail workmen did take up the rails and sleepers where the line had been but they didn't fill in or block up the tunnel and the tunnel mouth now yawned like the opening of a cave.

Bruno's car remained locked up in the coach-house. Once every five or six weeks Liza went to check that it was still there. Occasionally, she checked Eve's jewel case to see if the gold ring was still there. It was, it always was. And when Eve wasn't wearing earrings there were three pairs in the case.

Jonathan came and went. If he talked about Victoria it was only to complain about the amount of money she would expect from him when the divorce went through. Money and property. She would want the Ullswater house and no doubt would get it. He sent a postcard from Zimbabwe and that autumn brought two people with him to Shrove that she had never seen before, a man called David Cosby and his wife Frances. They came down for the shooting.

'David is Jonathan's cousin,' said Eve.

Liza knew about cousins, she had read about them in Victorian novels.

'He can't be his cousin,' she objected. 'Not if Caroline didn't have brothers or sisters and his father didn't.'

'David is his second cousin. He is old Mr Tobias's nephew's son. He loves Shrove, he loves it nearly as much as I do, I know he wishes it was his.'

'If he loves it so much why hasn't he been before?'

'He's been living in Africa for twelve years but now he's come home for good.'

David Cosby's face was as dark and shiny a brown as the panelling in the library at Shrove while his wife's was wrinkled and yellow. The result of the suns of Africa, thought Liza, who had just read *King Solomon's Mines*. They stayed two weeks. This time Eve seemed to be in a rather different position. Liza noticed it without quite being able to say how it was different. Perhaps it was that the three of them at Shrove, unlike Victoria and her friends, didn't treat Eve in any way like a servant. She went up there for dinner three times – Jonathan had caterers to come in and cook the partridges they shot – and left the washing up for Mrs Cooper to do in the morning.

The funny thing was, of course, that there was no Mrs Cooper, so Eve had to run up there while they were all out with the guns or in their car and play her pretending-to-be-the-cleaner game. It was a strange thing to do and it made Liza uneasy.

Eve became altogether rather strange in those two uneventful years. Or perhaps she had always been strange and when she was a child Liza hadn't noticed. She had just been Mother. Now, although Liza still knew very few people, she knew more than she ever had before. She could make comparisons. She could begin to question their way of life at the gate-house, particularly her own. Why did Eve never want to know anyone or go anywhere? Did other people have such a passionate attachment to a place as she had to Shrove? What was the purpose of doing such a lot of lessons, doing them all the time, on Saturdays and Sundays as well, Eve teaching and she learning for hours on end day in and day out? Why?

Eve had stopped going into town. She had found a grocer who would deliver once a week, and what he didn't bring the milkman would. When she did go, a rare once every two or three months, it was to buy books for Liza to learn from, and for another, stranger, reason: to take money out of the bank. Now Jonathan's cheques were sent to the bank by post and the money later drawn out to be hidden at home.

One day, after Eve had come back from town, having paid her only visit there of the entire winter, Liza saw her go into the little castle, carrying a small brown paper parcel. Eve, as far as she knew, had never possessed a handbag. Liza only knew hand-bags existed because she had seen Victoria and Claire and Frances Cosby carrying them. She saw Eve go into the little castle with the package and come out after a minute or two without it.

Later on, choosing a time when Eve was up at Shrove being Mrs Cooper, Liza investigated the little castle. It appeared quite empty. There was nothing now to show it had ever been occupied, either by dog or man. She didn't take long to find the loose brick and thence the iron box and the money.

Dozens of notes filled the box, five-, ten-, twenty- and even fifty-pound notes. She didn't try to count them, she could see there were hundreds of pounds. Besides, she had very little idea of what money was worth. She could have said what five pounds would buy in the time of Anthony Trollope but not what it would buy today, though she suspected a lot less. Eve had never hinted at the amount of money Jonathan gave her. All that Liza knew was that it came in cheques. She sent these cheques to the bank, brought back the money and hid it here in the wall.

Wasn't that the purpose of a bank, to look after your money? Liza didn't really know. Perhaps everyone behaved like this. Perhaps no one really trusted banks.

But Liza found herself often watching her mother after that, watching her behaviour, anxious to see what she would do next. She watched her as once she had listened at doors. There was no listening any more because Eve never talked to anyone but Liza and occasionally Jonathan on his rare appearances. Sometimes she tried to catch Eve unawares, watch her when she didn't know she was being watched. She would go to bed early, then creep downstairs to watch Eve unobserved from the stairs. But she never saw her do anything except ordinary expected things, reading and listening to music or marking one of Liza's essays or test papers.

She was fourteen before she began asking herself, what will become of me when I grow up? Shall I live here with Eve for ever? When she has taught me all the English there is to learn and all the history and French and Latin, what will we do then? What shall I do with all of it?

'Be me,' Eve had said, 'me as I might have been if I had stayed here, happy and innocent and good.'

Did she want to be Eve? Did she want to be those things?

That spring, while Jonathan was staying at Shrove on his own, the woodsmen came back to clear the 'little' wood.

'Bruno had been dead for nearly three years. I wanted to know how long it took before a body turned into a skeleton but I didn't know how to find out. There weren't any medical books at Shrove or any on forensics. You see, I thought that if he was bones by now they might not notice so much if they dug him up. I was hoping the sack would have rotted and Bruno just be – well, scattered bones.'

'It beats me,' said Sean, 'the way you can talk about it. A lovely young girl like you, it's weird. You're always the same, like talking about death and stuff that makes other people throw up, you talk about them like they're normal.'

She smiled at him. 'I suppose it is normal for me. Dead bodies don't upset me. I know I was sick when Bruno's hair came off in my hand but that wasn't *me*, it was a sort of reflex. I expect even doctors do that when they first start.'

'You could have been a doctor, d'you know that?'

'I still could,' said Liza. 'But that's not the point. Maybe other people are taught as children to flinch from death and blood and all that, I mean they're conditioned, but I never was. You've got to remember Eve taught me everything she knew about academic things but there must be thousands of things children know who lead an ordinary life and go to school that I never heard of. There can't,' she said rather proudly, 'be many people who've read the whole of Virgil's *Aeneid* in the original and seen two people murdered by the time they're sixteen.'

He recoiled a little. The look on his face made her

261

smile again. 'Don't worry about it, Sean. It can't be changed, that's the way it is. I'm different from other girls and in some ways I expect I always will be.'

'You've got me now,' he said. It was something he liked saying and when he said it he always took hold of her hand.

'Yes, I've got you now. Anyway, as I was telling you, the men went up to start working in the wood and I was very anxious. I don't know if Eve was. She was always out and about with Jonathan when she wasn't teaching me. But as it turned out they never found anything. Jonathan had given them instructions to leave some of the logs lying and some dead trees to provide habitats for the wildlife. The cherry log was one they left. It was just chance or luck, whatever you like to call it.'

'Luck?' said Sean.

'Luck for Eve, wasn't it? I think she'd been waiting to see what happened. As soon as she knew all was well up there, she got Jonathan to recharge the battery on Bruno's car.'

'She did what?'

There hadn't been any real risk. Jonathan hadn't suspected Bruno was dead. In his eyes, Bruno was just a young healthy man who had been living with Eve, who got tired of her or of whom she got tired, and who moved away. True, he had left his car behind but Eve had furnished Jonathan with all sorts of reasons for that: it had been his mother's, it was old, where he would be living he had nowhere to park a car. Jonathan was no doubt pleased to be told the car was going at last, Bruno was coming for it, the Shrove stable would be vacated. Recharging the battery on jump leads from his own car engine was a small price to pay for that. Liza didn't know if this was how it was, she told Sean, but it seemed a fair guess.

262

Eve didn't say a word to Liza about Bruno. It was Liza who overheard her telling Jonathan Bruno would come for the car tomorrow, the day incidentally that Jonathan himself was going back to London.

'I wondered what she'd do, how she was going to handle it. I even pretended to go out for a long walk in the afternoon to give her a chance to move the car. She did move it and she went off in it but only to town. She came back an hour later with the boot full of groceries and left the car parked outside the cottage.'

'What did she say when you asked when Bruno was coming?'

'I never did ask,' said Liza. 'She expected me to ask but I didn't. I knew where Bruno was, I knew he couldn't be coming. I knew his body was up in the wood under the leaves I'd piled round it. We were absolutely silent with each other about it. There was Bruno's car and she was using it – *we* were using it, she drove me to the village once and into town – I had a rash and had to see the doctor – but she never mentioned Bruno and neither did I. Then one day the car wasn't there any more.'

'What d'you mean?'

'She got rid of it. I don't know how or where. But she must have done. She must have driven it somewhere in the night. I've no idea what happened to it, I don't know about things like that, I don't know how you'd get rid of a car.'

'Just leaving it parked somewhere, I reckon. Hopefully someone'd nick it.' Sean considered. 'If the police got it in the end they'd try to find the owner and they could, that'd be easy, they'd do it in seconds on the computer.'

Liza said thoughtfully. 'The owner was dead. I don't mean Bruno, I mean his mother. It was still in her name, he said so.'

263

'I don't reckon they'd go to the trouble of tracing who the car'd been passed on to and if they tried they wouldn't find him, would they? And they wouldn't search either, not for a man of his age. They'd reason he'd gone off abroad somewhere. Your mum was clever.'

'Oh, yes, she was. If they searched for him they never came near us. We never saw a policeman since that one came about Hugh with the beard. When Mr Frost died it was an ambulance that came, not the police.'

Mrs Spurdell greeted Liza with the news that her daughter Jane had just been appointed Senior Adviser for Secondary Education to the County Council. She was bursting with pride. Since Liza had very little idea what this appointment signified she could only smile and nod. Mrs Spurdell said it was a team leadership role and payment was on the Soulbury Scale, information that served only to confuse Liza further.

Though she had said nothing about an errand of mercy two days before – and Mrs Spurdell spoke constantly of her advance plans – she announced that she was on her way out to visit a friend in hospital. Liza guessed the visit was taking place only because there was exciting news to impart and wondered just how ill the friend was when she saw her employer take some weary-looking grapes from the refrigerator as a gift and transfer them to a clean plastic bag.

As soon as Mrs Spurdell had gone Liza had a bath. Then she went into Mr Spurdell's study to see if he had any new books and spent a happy half-hour reading a short story by John Mortimer. It was about courts and barristers and judges and opened to her a whole unknown new world. It also made her think

about Eve and wonder when there would be anything in the papers about her. How long must it be
before she came to trial?

To save buying one, she always went quickly
through Mr Spurdell's newspaper. As usual, there
was nothing. Time to get down to the cleaning, but
before she started she looked up Jane Spurdell in the
telephone directory. It was the first time she had ever
looked up anyone in a phone book but it wasn't hard
to do. She was listed twice, not as 'Miss' but as Dr J.
A. Spurdell. Liza would never forget the address. By
a curious coincidence that might be a good omen of
something, the number was the year of her birth and
the street name startlingly familiar: 76, Shrove Road.

She'd never forget it but why should she want it?
Perhaps it was only that she'd liked her, she liked her
better than any woman she'd ever known except
Eve. Of course that wasn't difficult, seeing that the
other women she'd known were Heather and
Victoria and Frances Cosby and Mrs Spurdell. When
you liked people, Liza decided, you wanted to know
everything you could about them.

Mrs Spurdell kept her waiting while she rum-
maged about in one handbag after another for fifty
pee. This made her late and Sean was already there,
out on the pavement, when she got to Superway. He
had news for her, he was quite excited, but insisted
on saving it up until they were in the car on the way
home.

'They want me to go on a training course.'

'Who's they?'

'Superway. It's a management training course.
They're pleased with me, the way I do my work and
the way I always get in on time and all that. It's in
Scotland, it's a six-month course, and hopefully at
the end of it if I'm any good I'd go on to what they call
Phase Two.'

Liza didn't know what to say. She didn't really understand, so she listened.

'I've never said any of this to you, love. I've never talked about myself much. But I've always reckoned to not being much, if you know what I mean – well, rubbish, to be perfectly honest with you. I was useless at school and I left the day after I was sixteen. I'd been skiving off for months before that. No one ever suggested CSEs to me, I mean it'd have been a laugh. I never even saw myself doing nothing but unskilled labouring work, and that's what I did do. Then Mum got her new fella and they didn't want me, so I moved out. Well, I reckon I've told you all that. I got the car and the van and I took to the road and if I thought about it at all I reckoned I'd be living from one odd job to another until the time come to draw my pension. And now this has come up. It's sort of shook me. It's given me something to think about, I can tell you.'

She was moved by him because she hadn't known he could be so articulate. He was so beautiful. It would mean something to her if he could speak and think as handsomely as he looked.

'What will you be?' she said slowly.

'I don't know about "will". I said it's given me something to think about. As for what I'd *be* – well, hopefully I'd *be* a manager one day. I'd sort of have my own store, maybe one of them big new ones on an estate.'

'We went to one of those, Eve and Bruno and me.'

He made a movement as if to brush this aside impatiently. 'Yes, you said. I'd have a lot to learn. I'd be an assistant manager first. It'd take a while. But I'm young, love, and I'm keen.'

She wouldn't mind going to Scotland. Now she had begun, she liked travelling about and imagined moving from place to place during the next few years. 'Are you going to, then?'

'I told them I'd like to think about it. I said to give me a couple of days.'

The caravan was cold and damp. It usually was these evenings when they got home. Liza lit the burners on the oven, the oven itself, opening the door, and started the oil heater. Very soon the condensation began, the water running down the windows and lying in pools. She didn't much mind, as she said to Sean, you didn't have to look at it. So long as she had fish and chips or takeaway, books to read and a warm bed with Sean to make love with, she didn't care much. Now she had it and knew she could have it whenever she wanted, she seldom watched television. There was something to be said for being brought up without luxury, without many material possessions. Unlike Eve, she had never wanted Shrove or thought it might be hers.

One gloomy evening rather like this one and Jonathan in gloomy mood, she heard him tell her mother he had made his will and left Shrove to David Cosby.

'It should remain in our family,' he said like a character in a Victorian novel.

'He's ten years older than you,' said Eve.

'His son can have it then. They're all fond of the place. There's one thing, Victoria won't want it, she won't ask for this place in settlement, she hates it.'

Aged fourteen, taller than Eve, looking like a young woman, Liza was developing a woman's understanding. She had begun to ask herself how it could be that Jonathan who had known Eve since he was a boy, who had been close to her, her lover off and on (and now very probably on again), could have so little comprehension of how she felt about Shrove. He could talk with casual indifference about it to Eve who loved it better than any person, better perhaps Liza sometimes thought than her own child, he could talk about it to her as if it were just a piece of property, a parcel of land, even a nuisance. And he could talk about leaving it to a cousin whom, until this year, he hadn't seen for twelve years, without it apparently crossing his mind that he might leave it to Eve, as his grandfather had promised to leave it to Eve's mother.

Liza suspected that he too didn't like Shrove much. It was October now and this was only the second time he'd been down this year. His real life was elsewhere, doing things she and Eve knew nothing about. And he knew nothing about what they did. He never asked. It was as if Shrove was something to be packed up in a box when he was away from it and she and Eve puppets to be packed up with it.

Next day he was back again at the gate-house telling Eve his divorce decree had at last been made absolute and Victoria had 'taken him to the cleaners'. He was free now. Liza heard him ask Eve if she ever heard from Bruno these days. She said she hadn't and she never would, that was all over and she was free as air. She was as free as he was.

Liza was listening outside the door and Eve and Jonathan were sitting in there in the dusk, the lamps unlit. She heard her mother say that about being free and then she heard the silence. Next morning Jonathan went off to London and thence to France where his mother was dying.

A postcard with a picture of a French cathedral on it came after about a week to say that Caroline Ellison was dead. Smiling rather unpleasantly, Eve said she supposed he thought a churchy card was suitable for announcing a death while one with mountains or trees on it wouldn't be. Jonathan didn't sound grief-stricken, though it was hard to tell from a postcard. Eve was sure he would come back now but he didn't and six months later they got a card from him in Penang.

Before that, before the winter started, Liza found Mr Frost lying dead on the grass beside his tractor.

No one knew how old he was. Eve said very old because his daughter had only been a few years younger than her own mother who would be seventy if she had lived. For the past few years he had done nothing beyond sitting on the tractor and driving it round the lawns. It was Eve who pulled out the weeds and put the mowings on the compost heap.

It was in early November, an exceptionally dry sunny November, when Liza found him. He had been giving the grass its last cut before the winter. She was walking up from the river, taking the short cut across the Shrove garden. The sound of the mower had stopped ten minutes before and she thought he must have finished for the day. But the tractor was still there, in the middle of the sunny lawn, yellow leaves of lime and chestnut falling on to the grass, on to the tractor's black leather seat and scarlet bodywork, and on to the body of the old man lying beside it.

At first she didn't know he was dead. She was immensely curious. Her hand on his forehead encountered the coldness of marble. She could see that his veiny blue eyes were dead, they were quite lightless, and there was no breath from his slack mouth or movement of his chest. He no longer looked like a person but rather like one of the statues on the terrace, a prone figure in pale cold stone.

The strange thought came to her that Eve would bury him. At once, immediately, she knew this was nonsense but she had thought it. She ran to the cottage and Eve came back with her and they went into Shrove House and phoned for an ambulance.

269

They couldn't think what else to do even though they knew he was dead.

Mr Frost had died of old age. His heart had broken – it had literally broken – with age. And who, now, was to do the Shrove garden?

No one in the depths of winter. There was nothing to do when the snow came and the frost set hard. On the day Liza became fifteen the snow fell so thickly and for so long they had to dig their way out of the front door.

But snow seldom lasts for long in England. In February, where it had lain were clumps of snowdrops, and by March the grass was starting to grow, there were catkins on the hazels and the blackthorn was in bloom. Liza had her lessons in the morning and after lunch Eve went out on the tractor to cut the Shrove grass. The wide stretches of lawn were easy to mow, it wasn't much more than a matter of sitting on the seat and steering, but the edges had to be cut as well and the awkward bits between the new trees. Eve was on her knees pulling out the weeds after sunset, almost until dark.

Liza had never asked her why. She stopped asking questions of her mother after Bruno disappeared. It wasn't a conscious decision on her part not to ask but as if a voice inside her bade her be silent. Asking was dangerous, asking would only do damage, provoke lying, cause embarrassment. Don't ask. So she had never asked, why go on pretending to Jonathan that Mrs Cooper exists? What harm can it do to you or me if a woman comes here to clean? She had never asked, what did you do with Bruno's car? And now she didn't ask, why are you doing this work in the garden? Why don't you find a successor to Mr Frost?

Not only was she silent about these things, she also supported Eve in her subterfuges, it seemed natural to do so, it seemed right. For a long time now, when the rare people she saw asked her about school, how she was getting on, if she was on holiday, she had been saying, all right, and yes, she was. Jonathan had once asked her, as he was leaving, if Mrs Cooper was expected next day and Liza had said yes, knowing it would be Eve herself who would clear up at Shrove. She even told Eve he'd asked her. Wasn't she the crocodile bird who warned its host of impending danger?

It was now Eve who performed the tasks that had once been Mr Frost's. Liza wondered if Jonathan even knew Mr Frost was dead. Perhaps Eve herself simply kept the cheques for his pay Jonathan sent her. She now had the entire care of Shrove House, its gardens and its grounds in her hands, with Liza helping. Liza hated gardening but she couldn't be there and watch Eve do it all on her own, so she trimmed the edges with the long shears and pushed the little hand mower about, so bored she could have screamed.

Then, around midsummer, Eve found a man to do it. It was a very hot summer, the hottest of Liza's life except the one when she was a six-month-old baby. The grass stopped growing and the sun burnt it brown, so there was watering to do instead of mowing. Sometimes Eve was so tired with carrying watering cans and pulling the hosepipe about that she fell asleep on their sofa and Liza had to get the supper. The weeds still grew too. Nothing stopped the nettles growing and the burdock.

Eve said, 'I have to keep it going. I have to look after the young trees. It's so beautiful, I can't let it get in a mess. There's not a lovelier place in England. I can't bear to think of it all going to ruin.'

Her hands were stained and cracked, the fingers ingrained with dirt, the nails broken. The sun had burnt her face dark brown but her nose was peeling.

271

Liza saw threads of grey in her dark hair, which had nothing to do with the sun but perhaps something to do with her hard life. Now that Liza was older she was beginning to see that Eve had made her life hard of her own volition, had made all kinds of difficulties for herself where there might have been ease and pleasantness. But she never asked why.

She did ask, why him, when the old man appeared at the gate saying he'd heard in the village they might be wanting someone to help out at Shrove. From whom had he heard? The postman perhaps, the milkman. Eve was to tell Jonathan he'd heard from Mrs Cooper. He wasn't quite as old as Mr Frost, his hair wasn't even grey, but his face was very lined and withered. A hump grew out of his back which made Liza shrink a little when she saw it. She had always been accustomed to physical beauty or at least conformity. The old man's back was curved as if his spine had been bent into a bow the way you could bend a willow twig. He had strong arms and very large hands.

Eve said, yes, he could come twice a week. She sounded reluctant, grudging, and Liza understood that she had wanted to keep Shrove all to herself. It wasn't just a matter of not having people who might gossip or tell tales about the place, or it wasn't that *any more*. She wanted exclusive possession of Shrove. If she was going to take Gib on – that was the only name they knew him by – it was because she was worn out, she had hurt her back and had to rest, she could no longer cope alone.

'But why him?' said Liza.

'He lives alone, he's not very bright, he won't try to take over. He can't talk much, didn't you notice?'

Gib had an impediment in his speech that made him hard to understand. He liked riding the mower, he worked hard, and if he couldn't tell a cultivated plant from a weed, he did his best, trimming the edges and sometimes proudly leaving in the midst of smoothly hoed earth a fine specimen of dandelion Eve said he had lovingly nourished up. She went round after he had gone, pulling up the weeds he had nurtured.

Jonathan came in August, while Gib was still with them, and talked a lot about the holiday he was about to take in British Columbia and the Rocky Mountains. He had no wife now and since his divorce he had brought no other woman to Shrove except his cousin's wife Frances Cosby. But he didn't ask Eve to go with him to Canada. Once or twice Liza thought he came very near to doing this but he didn't ask her. Perhaps he remembered the rebuff he had received all those years ago when Liza was little or else he thought she wouldn't be able to leave Liza and they couldn't take Liza because she, of course, was at school.

Would Eve have gone if he'd asked her? Would they somehow have managed about Liza, said she could take time off school? Seeing her mother's sad, almost grim expression, after Jonathan had gone, she thought that this time she would have said yes.

He didn't ask her but he did, at last, have the bathroom done. It was ten years since he had first promised to do it but when Liza pointed this out Eve only shrugged and said they must be thankful for small mercies.

Jonathan had gone to the bathroom to wash his hands, only there was no bathroom, there was just the kitchen sink. Perhaps it wasn't pretence when he said he thought a bathroom had been put in years ago, he was sure of it, he thought Victoria had arranged it. Perhaps he really believed that. Eve only smiled and claimed she had forgotten his promises. But the builders came before he had left Shrove, built an annexe on to the back of the gate-house and turned it into a bathroom.

One of the builders was Matt. They had always wondered what he did, Eve and Liza, and now they knew. He was a bricklayer, like Rainer Beck. The other one was some relation of his, a young man with yellow hair dyed pink at the front. The weather was so hot that Liza lay out in the back garden in the sun after bathing in the river. She had a black swimming costume that had been Eve's. The noise Matt made when he saw her was a whistle on two notes, the meaning of which was lost on Liza who took no notice of it. She took almost no notice of either of them for neither was handsome and she already knew that she preferred good-looking people.

The whistle was repeated and Eve came out and told her to cover herself up or come indoors. She explained that Matt and his cousin found Liza attractive, now she was growing up, and that was their low and vulgar way of showing it.

Liza digested this and pondered it for a long time. She wondered why there wasn't anything low and vulgar about the way Jonathan had made a similar sound when he saw Eve all prepared for him and dressed up in a black and scarlet skirt and black jumper from the good-as-new shop in town. But perhaps his laughing afterwards and kissing Eve made it all right.

Gib was taken ill. The postman who brought Eve the message said he was often ill. He wasn't strong and the jobs he took on never lasted, though he tried, he did his best. By this time it was autumn and the grass at least no longer needed attention. And the rain came at last, day after day of it, until the river rose above its banks and flooded the wetlands, so that the trees stood in water to half way up their trunks.

274

They were quite alone, Eve and Liza, in those last months of her sixteenth year. Gib didn't come back and there wasn't, anyway, much to be done in the garden. The oilman came and filled the tank while Eve and Liza were out walking, so they didn't see him, and the postman took to delivering their few letters before either of them was up. As for the milkman, he disappeared and was replaced by a man with red hair who whistled all the time. He told Eve *their* milkman had gone into a home because the dairy had found out about his mental age and said he could no longer work for them.

Jonathan was on the other side of the world, in Hawaii, as they knew from a not-at-all churchy card with a picture of a girl surfing on white waves. A card came from Heather on holiday in Cornwall and another one at Christmas with a note in it saying she'd moved to London and this was her new address.

Once the spring had come, Eve began to fret about the garden. She seldom went to town any more but she had to make the occasional visit. She had to go to buy Liza's jeans, her first pair, that Liza had been nagging her about for ages. When she came out of the jeans shop she saw an advertisement in the newsagent's window next door.

It said: 'Strong man will do indoor and outdoor decorating, clearing sites, general labouring, gardening and odd jobs.' There was a box number which Eve said meant he came into the shop and collected the replies he'd had. Liza didn't think much more about it because Eve hadn't been able to put a phone number on her reply and had said it would come to nothing, no one wrote letters any more.

But he must have written and his letter come while Liza was still in bed in the morning because Eve announced one day that she thought she'd found a gardener and not, she hoped, a septuagenarian this time. She probably didn't guess how young he was either.

'His name is Sean Holford,' she said, 'and he's coming for an interview on Tuesday.'

Chapter Eighteen

Seeing her mother's picture in the paper was a shock, worse than seeing what the dogs did, much worse than finding Bruno. She was sitting in Mrs Spurdell's kitchen waiting for her money and enjoying her own clean scented-soap smell. She had managed a bath and was screwing up her courage to ask Mr Spurdell if she could borrow his *Morte D'Arthur*, which wasn't a paperback, when he came into the room carrying a newspaper.

He didn't say anything, he looked at her, and when his wife appeared, rummaging for change in two handbags, made her look at the paper too. They both stared at Liza. Then Mr Spurdell said, 'Isn't that an almost uncanny resemblance?'

Mrs Spurdell said nothing. She was looking rather cross, the way she always did if Liza appeared to be briefly the focus of attention. Shaking his head as if in incredulity, Mr Spurdell handed Liza the paper, pointing with one finger at a photograph.

Liza's heart began to beat very fast. The picture was of Eve. She stared at it. It showed a much younger Eve and had apparently been taken some years before and, as she looked, she remembered. Jonathan had taken it. Eve and she had taken the dogs back to Shrove one summer evening and Jonathan had come down the steps and taken a photograph. She should have been in it but she'd been shy and had hidden behind a tree.

The day that picture was taken was the Day of the Nightingale. How it came to be in a newspaper she had no idea.

'You're the spitting image of her, my dear,' said Mr Spurdell. 'It struck me as soon as I saw it. Quite amusing, eh? I thought to myself, I'll run downstairs and show this to Liza before she goes. Not that I imagine she'll be overjoyed to find she looks like a murderess, eh?'

They didn't know then, they hadn't guessed. Liza forced herself to smile as she looked up and met his eyes.

'I don't see the likeness myself,' Mrs Spurdell was saying. 'That creature, the one in the paper, is quite spectacularly good-looking, criminal or not. If you didn't know you'd take her for a film star.'

Liza wanted to scream with laughter, though she knew it was hysterical, it hadn't much to do with amusement. She tried to read what the paper said, but the print swam and bobbed about. The headline she could make out: Alleged Killer buried Man's Body. She *must* get hold of this paper.

Mr Spurdell was already holding out his hand for it. 'I suppose, strictly speaking, we shouldn't call her a murderess or a criminal. She is still on trial, she hasn't been found guilty yet. Can I have my paper, please, my dear?'

Even if he thought it odd, she must have that paper. Knowing her voice must sound hoarse, she said, 'Could I – do you think I could keep it?'

He gave his indulgent humouring laugh, a laugh she sometimes thought, seeking words for it, heavy with patronage and patriarchy. 'And how am I to do my crossword puzzle?'

The problem was solved by Mrs Spurdell's snatching the paper out of her hand and thrusting into it – for once in the form of one note and two coins – the

278

twelve pounds for her four hours' work. Liza got up and left without another word, without even a goodbye. She had forgotten all about *Le Morte D'Arthur*.

The nearest newsagent had no morning papers left. The next one was closed. On some previous occasion in Aspen Close she had heard Mr Spurdell talking about the evening paper that used to be on sale but which had ceased to exist some months before. By the time she met Sean she was nearly distraught, pouring it all out to him in an incoherent stream.

Sean was always good in a crisis. He liked comforting her, keeping calm, showing his manly strength. He liked her weak and vulnerable. Tomorrow they would buy the newspapers, they would buy all the newspapers. Hadn't Mr Spurdell said the trial wasn't over? It would have been going on again today. They would watch the television, every news there was.

When they got home he made tea for her. He hugged her and said not to worry, she had him, he would do all the worrying for her, leave it to him, and he began kissing her and stroking her. That led of course to making love and they were in bed for an hour, consequently missing the six o'clock news.

At nine there was nothing about Eve and nothing at ten. Sean, who had seen hundreds of television programmes and videos about murders and police investigations, said this might be because it wasn't a sensational enough case. It wasn't a child or a young girl who had been murdered or something that had attracted a lot of public attention when it happened.

'I just wish I knew more about it,' said Liza, who was a lot calmer by now. 'I wish I knew about the law.'

'You can't know about everything.'

'I'd like to be a lawyer. One day I'll *be* a lawyer.'

279

Sean laughed. 'Dream on, love. The other day you was going to be a doctor.'

She was in a fever of anticipation when they drove into town next morning. It wasn't one of her days in Aspen Close and she would either have to pass a solitary day wandering about the market place and spend hard-earned cash on the cinema or else go home on the bus. But she couldn't wait till Sean came home before seeing the papers.

They bought three, all so-called quality newspapers, but the story was almost identical in each of them. This time there was no picture of Eve. In the first one, which Liza read feverishly, still sitting in the car, the headline was: Gate-house Murder Premeditated, says QC.

The account was very long, filling nearly half a page. Try as she would, Liza couldn't take in more than the first two paragraphs.

'I don't understand it, Sean. I don't know what it means. It says she's been charged with the murder of Trevor Hughes. Who's Trevor Hughes? I've never heard of him.'

'You better read it all. Read all three of them. Look, love, I've got to go or I'll be late. I wouldn't want to be late, not at this juncture. You can stay here in the car, no one'll see you.'

She sat in the car in the Superway's underground car park and read the accounts in all the papers. None of them had a word about the murders Liza knew Eve had committed. All the accounts were about this Trevor Hughes, a sales representative aged 31, who had been missing from home for twelve years. It appeared that he had quarrelled with his wife and instead of leaving for a holiday with her as they had planned, had gone off on his own.

Mrs Eileen Hughes said she had identified her husband from his watch and his wedding ring, which had his name and hers inside it. A dentist had identified him by his teeth. How did they do that? Liza wondered. If she enquired of Sean he would ask if she wanted to be a dentist as well and tell her to dream on.

They had found shotgun pellets buried with the man. Buried in the wood? But surely only Bruno was up there. Now they were talking about this man being buried as well. It didn't seem as if Eve had said anything in the court or anyone had said anything on her behalf. But it was going on again today. At the end of the article it said, the trial continues.

Liza felt bewildered. She wanted desperately to know, she wished there was someone she could ask, but the only person she could think of was Mr Spurdell. Reading the newspaper accounts, she had been afraid of coming on her own name but she hadn't, her name wasn't mentioned. Would it be mentioned tomorrow?

She passed a tedious yet anxious day mooning about the town. The admiring manager was off today so it wasn't even interesting taking a clandestine bath in the Duke's Head. She bought three paperback books, spending two-thirds of the twenty-four pounds she had earned that week. Sean would be cross. She sensed already that Sean was going to expect her to be pleased if her mother got sent to prison for years and years. How long would it be anyway? At least they'd stopped hanging people.

In the afternoon, after having a hamburger and a sundae in McDonalds, she went to the cinema and saw *Howards End*. Why had she never read any E.M. Forster? Because he was born too late to be in the Shrove library, she thought rather bitterly. Next week she'd buy *A Passage to India*, that was by him she was sure, and anything else he'd written. It took considerable strength of will to make herself leave the cinema and not sit there and watch the programme all the way through again.

Sean was waiting. Sean was sure the trial would be on TV tonight. They switched on at six and again at nine and ten but it wasn't on.

Liza said, 'I've been thinking. I know who Trevor Hughes was. He was the man with the beard. It says here he went missing twelve years ago and that was twelve years ago. I was four. I thought the policeman who came called him Hugh. D'you remember I said Hugh? But it wasn't, it was Trevor Hughes.'

'The man the dogs went for,' said Sean. 'The one she shot.'

'They must have searched the gate-house and found the ring with the initials and the date inside. But why him?'

'It's a mystery,' said Sean. 'Like you say, why pick him? Why not the others?'

'I don't know. I don't know anything. I feel so ignorant.' Liza thrust her hands through her hair and looked at him mutinously. 'We can't go to the police, there's no one we can ask. It's beyond me, it's driving me mad.'

When he saw the new books Sean didn't say a word. She realised that she couldn't always predict how he would react. He was kind, he was good to her. She thought of the men in the books she'd read and the book she was reading now, she remembered Trevor Hughes and Bruno and Jonathan and thought she was lucky to have Sean. Once or twice she repeated it to convince herself, she was lucky to have Sean.

Quite a long time had passed after Eve told Jonathan the new gardener's name before Liza met him. She first saw him on the day he started, but didn't let him see her. It was mid-March and cold, she had been out for a long aimless walk and was

282

coming back, her boots sinking into the marshy ground above the river. That winter she had been taking more and more of these walks, she had been growing increasingly frustrated with solitude, with sameness, with never seeing another face but Eve's. Lessons had become repetitive and she sensed that Eve had taught her almost all she knew. All that was left now was to write more essays about Shakespeare, examine more pieces of eighteenth-century prose, translate more de Maupassant and do more Latin unseens. She had read all the books in the Shrove library she would ever want to read. Television was almost forgotten, what it had been like, why she had enjoyed it.

Was the whole of life going to be like this? Sean had asked her later on why she hadn't run away. He hadn't understood the extent of her learning and the depths of her ignorance. At the thought of running away, before she met him, she had felt almost faint with fear. She had never been on a bus or in a train, never bought anything in a shop herself, scarcely been in one, never made a phone call and, most important of all, never had any sort of relationship with a contemporary.

So she went for long walks, sometimes to the isolated villages, there to gaze at a village shop or the notice board inside a church porch, to read a bus timetable or stand outside a school and watch the children come out. She was teaching herself about the world Eve had kept from her. Once, anticipating Sean's question, she had even said, I could run away. But the very words, unspoken except in her mind, had terrified her. She saw herself standing in an empty street at night with no idea where to go, how to find food or a place to sleep. She imagined herself not running away but running *home*, throwing herself pathetically into Eve's arms.

But what was going to become of her? She often imagined the future and in the blackest way. She saw herself old, thirty or more, and Eve a really old woman, the two of them going on just the same, everything the same except that the new trees had grown tall with thick trunks and spreading crowns. Would she become the Shrove gardener when Eve was too old to do the work? Or the successor to Mrs Cooper? She would be sent to town with the shopping baskets and the list, to cross the bridge and wait for the bus.

She saw herself crossing the marketplace, avoiding with fear the jostling teenagers, let out like effervescent water from an opened bottle. Stepping into the road to avoid them, keeping her eyes downcast like a nun she had seen in a picture. Afraid to speak to anyone but shopkeepers and then only to ask in a whisper for what she wanted.

Thinking this way, she came dispiritedly up among those trees that were still saplings and saw someone in the Shrove garden. He was a long way off and for a moment she thought he must be Jonathan. But Jonathan wouldn't be clipping the yew hedge. Jonathan never did anything, he never pulled out a weed or plucked a dead head from a rose.

The man was working on the hedge with a pair of hand clippers. It must be the new gardener. She was still too far away from him to see much but even from a hundred yards off she could tell he was young. Not young as Jonathan or Bruno were but really young, the same sort of age as herself. She had never thought of hiding from Mr Frost or Gib but she was suddenly urgently sure that this man mustn't see her. He mustn't be allowed to see her casually approaching him.

It was easy to avoid his eye, a matter of keeping to the trees and, when the garden was reached, making her way towards the house. Why she was behaving so covertly she didn't ask herself, for she couldn't have replied.

She approached stealthily, careful not to step on a twig or, when she reached the path, let her feet make a sound on the gravel. Now he was no farther away from her than the length of their sitting room in the gate-house. She looked at him between the branches and the dull pointed leaves of evergreens. He had finished the hedge and was lifting armfuls of clippings into a wheelbarrow, a tall, straight young man, a boy, with broad shoulders and narrow hips. His hair was raven black. She thought of it like that because that was the way the poets wrote. His face was turned away from her. She thought she might shriek with disappointment if she didn't see his face. But at the same time she knew she'd make no sound whatever he did, wherever he went.

Had she made a sound? She wasn't aware of it, unless her breathing itself had become noisy. There must have been something to make him turn from the barrow he was about to wheel away and look in her direction.

He couldn't see her. She could tell that. She stared. He was absolutely beautiful. His face was a pale olive colour but with a flush on the cheeks and his eyes were a dark bright blue. She saw a perfect nose and perfect lips and thought of the stars in those old films she had seen and of engravings of statues in ancient books and portraits by Titian.

His hands were long and brown. Once she had admired Jonathan's hands but no longer. This man had stars in his eyes and his gaze showed that he dreamed of wonderful things. The gods she read about lived in groves like this, half-concealed by leaves.

Because he couldn't see her and could now hear

nothing, he shrugged a little and began wheeling the barrow away. He should have had a spear and a winged chariot but all he had was shears and a wheelbarrow. Liza didn't mind. She didn't even mind him going and she didn't want him to come back. In a strange way she had had as much as she could take for the present. An unexpected energy filled her and she ran all the way home, arriving breathless and throwing herself down on the sofa.

In a voice as casual as she could make it, she said to Eve, 'Which days does the new gardener come?'

'Mondays, Wednesdays and Fridays. Why?'

'Nothing. I just wondered.'

The following afternoon she went to Shrove and searched for a picture he might resemble. She had done that when Bruno came but this was different. That had been for the satisfaction of curiosity, this was an act of worship. Upstairs, next to the painting of Sodom and Gomorrah, was a portrait of a young man in black silk and silver lace. Eve called it 'indifferent eighteenth-century two-a-penny stuff' but Liza had always liked it and now she gazed in wonder. Their new gardener in elegant fancy dress made her shiver, but pleasurably.

Next day was Friday and she watched for his car from Eve's bedroom window. It was a big old car, dark blue with patches of rust on the bodywork, but if she hadn't known a car had to have a driver she'd have thought it was moving along by its own volition. Rain fell all day on Monday, so he couldn't come, and it was Wednesday before she had a glimpse of him. His car was parked on the gravel by the coach-house. She let herself into the house, went upstairs and into the bedroom with the fine views, the one Victoria had used and where she had left her clothes in the wardrobe. It made her jump to see him just outside the window, almost directly below her.

Clematis climbed across the garden front of Shrove House. He was on the steps, the old ones that used to be in the library, tying the clematis vines to the trellis. If he had turned his head to the right and lifted it a little he would have seen her. Any noise she might make wouldn't attract his attention today. He was wearing a headset and had a Walkman attached to the belt of his jeans.

In the week that had gone by she had sometimes wondered if she was remembering him as more beautiful than he actually was. Now she saw that he was even more beautiful than she remembered. Why did she care so much? She was dreadfully bewildered by it all. Was it just because he was the first person of her own age she had ever known? But she didn't know him.

He looked round suddenly and saw her. She was seized with shyness, with shame almost, and felt the blood rush into her face and burn her cheeks. He put up one hand in a salute and grinned. This made her retreat at once and run out of the bedroom. There was a mirror in a gilt frame hanging on the wall halfway down the stairs. Although she had never done this before, she stopped on the staircase and looked at herself in this mirror.

She thought she was – well, very pretty. Better than that perhaps. Nice eyes, big and dark, a full mouth, good skin, Eve always said, and lots of long dark hair. But – did all girls look like this? She need not be quite so naïve. In the town she had seen others, but how could she judge? The old television images had grown vague and misty now. Why, anyway, did it matter? She continued to stare at herself, as if contemplating a great mystery.

For a moment or two, for five minutes perhaps, she had forgotten the boy on the steps. Narcissistically, she communed with herself, studying her smooth face and soft pink lips, the slim body and full breasts. How would she look in a dress like Caroline's? Red silk, low-cut. That almost made her laugh. She was wearing blue jeans, a black jumper with a polo neck, and Eve's old brown parka.

Because she knew he was in the back garden, she let herself out of the front door without a thought. She didn't peer from a window first but came straight out. And there he was, standing on the paving, studying the climbing hydrangea that clustered all across the front of Shrove House.

She stood quite still, staring at him, not knowing what to do, without a word to say.

He smiled. 'Hi, there.'

Something tied her tongue.

'D'you live here?'

She must speak. This time she wasn't blushing. She fancied she had gone pale.

'I saw you at the window, so I thought maybe you lived here. But the lady said no one did. At any rate you're not a ghost.'

That should have made her laugh but she couldn't laugh. She found her tongue but not her poise. 'That was my mother said that. We live at the Lodge.'

'Out in the sticks, isn't it? It could give you the creeps.'

Eve would hate him for 'the creeps'. 'The sticks' she failed altogether to understand. 'I have to go,' she said. 'I'm late.'

'See you then.'

She didn't dare run. Guessing he was watching her, she walked down the drive, through the park, certain his eyes were on her. But when she looked back he was gone. His car passed her almost before she was aware of it and there he was waving to her. She was too confused to wave back.

At the gate-house she read *Romeo and Juliet*: 'Would

that I were a glove upon that hand/That I might touch that cheek.' Her future, the loneliness and the sameness, the oddities of Eve, all were forgotten. His was a face 'to lose youth for/To occupy age with the dream of . . .' She turned to poetry for she had no other comparisons and no other standards.

Talking to Eve, she longed to speak his name but was afraid to. Once she had uttered it she wanted to talk about him all the time, yet she knew nothing about him.

'Where does Sean live?'

'In a caravan somewhere. What possible interest can it have for you?'

'I wanted to know where Gib lived.' It was true. Let Eve believe that, knowing so few people, she was more interested in those she did know than others who had led different lives might be.

'Where does Sean keep his caravan?' This time she need not have used his name but she did use it.

'How should I know? Oh, yes, he said down by the old station. Have you been talking to him?'

Liza looked her between the eyes and said, 'No.'

This was the place where she had been so frightened. She had come through the station, carefree, enjoying the day, happy in the sunlight, and had seen Bruno sitting there with his painting things, in his lifted hand a brush loaded with gamboge. He had frightened her with his naked hatred.

'You've never told me why you came that day,' Sean said. 'D'you know, it was seven months ago. We've known each other seven months. What made you come?'

'I wanted to see where you lived. The way I felt, you want to know everything about a person, where they live, what they eat and drink, what they like doing, the way they are when they're alone. You

289

want to see them against different backgrounds.' She thought about it. 'Against every possible background. You want to see how they'll be in the rain and what they do when the sun shines on them. How they comb their hair and fill a kettle and wash their hands and drink a glass of water. You want to see how they go about doing all the ordinary things.'

Sean was nodding earnestly. 'That's right, that's it. You're a clever girl, love, you sort of know it all.'

That made her impatient. She waved him away. 'I didn't mean to see you. I certainly didn't mean you to see me. I just meant to see where you lived and – well, creep away.'

'But I saw you and I come out.'

She said reflectively, as if talking of other people, another couple. 'It was love at first sight.'

'Right on. That's what it was.'

'I wasn't hard to get. I didn't keep you guessing. I went into the caravan with you and when you asked if I'd got anyone I didn't know what you meant. I said I'd got my mother. You tried again, you said, was I seeing anyone? It was hopeless. You had to ask me if I'd got a boyfriend. Then you said, would I come for a walk with you, and I knew it was all right because that's what people said in all those Victorian novels I'd read.'

'And the rest,' said Sean, 'like they say, is history.'

'You must get the newspapers today. I won't be going in till the afternoon. I'm going to ask Mr Spurdell to explain it to me. I mean, explain why Trevor Hughes.'

'And what you going to do if he twigs?'

'If he guesses, d'you mean? He won't.'

When she had finished her work, and she made sure she finished in good time, she went along the passage and tapped on Mr Spurdell's study door. He had come in about half an hour before and gone straight up there.

He was wearing his half-glasses, gold-rimmed, and they made him look older and more scholarly than ever.

'If you haven't done my room you'd better leave it,' he said.

It angered her rather that he hadn't even noticed. She had taken particular care over the study, dusting his books and putting them back meticulously in the correct order.

'May I ask you something?'

'That rather depends on what it is. *What* is it?'

She plunged straight into the middle of things. 'If someone murdered three people, A, B and C, and the police knew about C, why would she – I mean he or she – be accused in court of murdering A only?'

'Is this some crime thriller you're reading?'

Easier to say it was, though she was doubtful as to what he meant. 'Yes.'

He loved explaining, he loved answering questions. She knew he did and that was why she had been so sure he wouldn't suspect anything. Anyway, he was far more interested in instructing than in her.

'It seems probable that though the police know about C they cannot prove he or she murdered him. The same may apply to B. He or she is indicted for the murder of A because they are certain that is something they can prove in such a way as to make a case stand up in court. There, does that help you find whodunnit?'

'Why not accuse – indict – the person with killing A *and* C?'

'Ah, well, they don't do that. You see, if your putative murderer were to be found not guilty by a jury and acquitted the police could come back with C – or for that matter B – and bring him into court all over again on this different charge. If they charged him with both and he was acquitted they would have lost all hope of punishing him.'

It was always 'he' and 'him', as if nothing ever happened to women and they did nothing. 'I see,' she said, and then, 'Where would he – she – be while they were waiting to come into court?'

He began talking about something called the Criminal Justices Act 1991, a legal measure to do with sentencing and keeping people in prison, but when he got to the point of the Act just being implemented 'now, while I speak, Liza,' his phone began to ring. She turned to go but he motioned to her to stay while he picked up the phone.

'Hallo, Jane, my dear,' she heard him say, 'and what can I do for you?'

The conversation wasn't a long one. She felt that she would have liked to send some message to Jane Spurdell, something like her good wishes, but of course she couldn't do that. Replacing the receiver, Mr Spurdell said, 'I thought you might like to borrow another book.' He added rather severely, 'Something worthwhile.'

This was perhaps a reference to what he believed she was reading at the moment. She took her opportunity.

'How long do they send a murderer to prison for?' Since her introduction to newspapers, she had read, she thought, of quite short sentences for killing people. 'I mean, does it vary according to how they've done it or why?'

'If someone is convicted of murder in this country the mandatory sentence is imprisonment for life.'

She grew cold. 'Always?' she said, and he thought she didn't know what 'mandatory' meant.

'The word signifies something of the nature of a command. Something mandatory is something which must be. We don't have degrees of murder here, though they do in the United States. If it were manslaughter now, the sentence might be quite short.'

The term meant nothing to her. It would look suspicious if she kept on questioning him. He had picked two Hardy novels in paperback off his shelves. She hadn't read them, she thanked him and went downstairs to get her money.

Chapter Nineteen

That day Eve had been in the witness box.

Liza was astonished to read that she admitted killing Trevor Hughes. Yet she had pleaded not guilty. Perhaps you could explain that when you understood her counsel was trying to get the charge changed from murder to that word Mr Spurdell had used: manslaughter. Sean seemed to know all about it.

Today there was a photograph of Trevor Hughes, a faceless man, his features buried in that thick fair beard. Eve said she had killed him because he tried to rape her. She was quite alone in the house, there was no one living nearer than a mile away. She got away from him, ran into the house to get her gun and shot him in self-defence.

Prosecuting counsel questioned her very closely. You could imagine there was a lot more than appeared in the paper. He asked her why she had a loaded shotgun in the house? Why did she not lock herself in the house and phone for help? She said she had no phone and he made much of a woman being nervous enough to have a loaded gun at hand but no phone. When she knew he was dead why had she not phoned for help from Shrove House where there was a phone? Why had she concealed the death by burying the man's body?

Before she had given her evidence someone called Matthew Edwards gave his. They didn't put things in order in the newspaper but arranged them in the most sensational way. It took Liza a moment to realise this was Matt and reading what he had said took her back to that early morning long ago when she'd looked out of the window and seen him releasing the dogs from the little castle.

He told the court of the freshly dug earth he had seen and the dogs running about sniffing it and how Eve hadn't been able to answer when he asked if they'd been burying bones. Liza remembered it all. Eve hadn't answered, she'd just asked him if he knew what time it was and told him the time in an icy voice, six-thirty in the morning.

The trial would end next day. That meant this day, today. It would be over by now. Counsel for the Defence made a speech in which he spoke of Eva Beck's hard life. She had more cause than most women to fear rape, for she had already suffered it.

Liza stopped reading for a moment. She could feel the thudding of her own heartbeats. Unconsciously, she had covered the paper with her hand as if there was no one behind her, as if Sean wasn't there, reading it over her shoulder.

'You'll have to read it, love,' Sean said gently.

'I know.'

'Want me to read it to you? Shall I read it first and then read it to you?'

She shook her head and forced herself to take her hand away. The uncompromising words seemed blacker than the rest of the account, the paper whiter.

At the age of 21, returning to Oxford from Heathrow where she had been seeing a friend off on a flight to Rio, Eve Beck had hitched a lift from a truck driver. Two other men had been in the truck. It was driven to a lay-by where all three men raped her. As a result she had been very ill and had undergone prolonged psychiatric treatment. The rape had made her into a recluse who wanted nothing more from life than to be left alone and do her job as caretaker of the Shrove estate.

The society of other people she had eschewed and was virtually unknown in the nearby village. She had been living with a grown-up daughter who had since left home.

Liza sat very still and silent when she had finished reading. All her questions were answered. She could feel Sean's eyes on her. Presently he laid his hand on her shoulder and when she didn't reject him, put his arm round her.

After a moment or two she said quietly, 'Ever since I was about twelve, which was as soon as I could have ideas about it really, I've believed I was Jonathan Tobias's child. I didn't like it much, I'd stopped liking him much, but at least it meant I had a father.'

'He still could have been.'

'No. She never told me all that stuff, that in the paper, but she did say she hadn't seen Jonathan for two weeks before she went to see him off for America. One of those men in the truck was my father. There are three men about somewhere, they might be in the town here, or driving a lorry that we've passed on the road, and one of them's my father.' She looked at him and away from him. 'I expect I'll get used to it.'

She could see Sean didn't know what to say. She made an effort. 'It's mostly not true, what they said. She killed people because they threatened her living at Shrove. She killed them because they tried to stop her having what she wanted. No one's said anything about the way she loves Shrove. And as for me, I'm just the grown-up daughter who's left home.'

He put his arms round her.

*

296

Grown-up. Sean had asked her about that. Not the first time they met at the caravan nor the second, but soon. She had gone for a walk with him, as promised, telling Eve she was spending the evening in Shrove library, there were books there she wanted that were too heavy to carry home. After the walk they sat in the caravan. He had a beer and she had a Coke.

That was when she started telling him how she'd lived, isolated, almost without society, in the little world of Shrove. 'How old are you?' he'd asked, admitting she looked a year or two older than she was but still afraid she might say she was only fifteen.

That first time he didn't even kiss her. Two evenings later it was too hot to walk far, a close humid throbbing dusk, and they had flung themselves down in the long seed-headed grass by the maple hedge. She had looked at his face, six inches from her own, through the pale reedy stems. There was a scent of hay and of dryness. The feathery seedheads scattered brown dusty pollen on his hair. He parted the thin strands of grass and put his mouth on hers and kissed her.

She couldn't help herself, she had no control. Her arms were round his neck, she was clutching his hair in her hands, kissing him back with passion, putting everything she had read about love and desire into those kisses. It was he who restrained them, who jumped up and pulled her to her feet and began asking her if she was sure, did she know what she was doing, if they were going 'all the way' she must be sure.

It wasn't possible for her to think about it. When she tried to think, all that happened was that she saw images of Sean and felt his kisses, growing hot and weak, growing wet in an unanticipated way that no instruction or reading had led her to expect. She tried to think calmly and reason it out but her mind became a screen of Sean pictures, Sean and herself together pictures, her body shuddered with longing, and she got no further about being sure or knowing what she was doing than she had in the meadow. It came down to this: when next she saw him she would do everything and anything he wanted and everything she wanted, but if she never saw him again she would die.

She read *Romeo and Juliet* again but it no longer seemed to be about what she was feeling. On Monday evening it was raining, so they met in the caravan and made love as soon as they met, falling upon each other in a breathless joyful ecstasy.

It seemed a long time ago now.

Sean switched on the television and they watched the news. For the first time, so far as they knew, it contained something about Eve. They had to wait until almost the last item. The last was about attempts to put an end to bull-fighting in Spain but before that the newscaster announced laconically that Eva Beck, the killer in the Gate-house Murder case had been found guilty and sent to prison for life.

Sean held her, he kept his arm round her all night, hugging her tightly when she awoke whimpering. But still he didn't understand how she felt. She no longer had any identity. With Eve's denial – for whatever good purpose – she had ceased to be anyone, and with the revelations of Eve's history, been made worse than fatherless.

No words could be found to express what she felt. She had nothing to say to Sean, so she spoke about the everyday mundane things, what they would eat for supper, what food items he should bring back from the store. It was clear that he was relieved not to talk about Eve or the trial or Liza's own new vulnerability, and it pained her, it angered her. Once or twice, during their disturbed night, he had told her she must put 'all that' behind her.

Just as he was leaving she surprised him by saying she was coming too.

'It's not your day for Mrs S., is it?'

She shook her head. He must think she was coming into town because she didn't want to pass this day alone in the caravan. She sat beside him, saying how nice the weather was, a wonderful sunny day for the start of December. In just over a month's time she would be seventeen but he didn't know when her birthday was, though he might have guessed. When they were first together they hadn't talked much. It had been all love-making and the aftermath of love-making and its renewal.

Anxious as ever not to be one minute late, he hurried into the store. The car keys were in his pocket but she had brought the spare set. A map he never used, his sense of direction was so good, was tucked into the back of the glove compartment. She studied it, left it lying unfolded on the passenger seat.

They couldn't do much to her if they caught her driving without a licence or insurance. The way she was feeling today she didn't much care what anyone did to her. It no longer mattered if they caught her and found out who she was because she was no one, she had no identity. She was just the grown-up daughter who had since left home.

She drove past where the caravan was and out on to the big road. The world seemed entirely different here and had seemed so for the past three months but for all that it was only about twenty miles from where she was going. Passing a garage, she glanced at the petrol gauge. It was all right. The tank was nearly full. She began to wonder how she would feel when she came to the bridge and saw the river with the water meadows beyond and the house floating, as it seemed, above the white mists that lay low on the flat land, when she saw the domain which was the only place she had ever known until a mere ninety days ago.

But when the time came she experienced no startling reaction. It was a brisk breezy day without mist. The sun shone with a sharp winter brightness. Shrove House had never appeared so brilliantly unveiled. From halfway across the bridge, half a mile distant, she could pick out the dark spindly etching the clematis made on the rear walls and the features on the faces of the stone women in the alcoves.

The sun flashed sharply off the window from which she had watched Sean the second time she had seen him. She drove up the lane. Someone had been hedging along here, had mercilessly ripped back the high hawthorns. The gate-house appeared suddenly as it always did when the bend was passed. It looked the same as ever and the gateway to Shrove was the same except that the gates, for the first time that she could remember, were shut. The gates, which except on the day after the storm had always stood folded back like permanently open shutters at a window, were so firmly closed that the park could only be seen through their elaborate iron scrollwork and the curlicued letters: Shrove House.

She walked up the garden path to the gate-house. Her key she had always kept. She pushed it into the lock and opened the front door. Inside it was icy cold and smelling of damp. The smell was the stench of hollows in the roots of trees where fungus rotted.

The kitchen was dim and dark because the blind was pulled down. Raising it a little, she looked out, and then she let the string go and the blind spring up to its roller with a crack, she was so shocked by what she saw. The back garden, which had been neat with Eve's vegetable beds and flower borders, with the new tree planted to replace the fallen cherry, the small lawn, all of it was a wilderness of thin straggly weeds. These had not sprung up among the untended cultivated plants but were weeds growing on dug earth. The whole garden had been turned over with spades.

For a moment she couldn't imagine what had happened. Had someone else lived here temporarily, dug the garden and then departed? Had some new and zealous gardener taken over and left again?

Then she remembered what the paper had said about Eve burying the body of Trevor Hughes. Somewhere out there it must be that she had buried him, where Matt said the dogs had sniffed the earth. The police had excavated here, looking for more perhaps, looking for a graveyard. Their spades had made this wilderness. She thought of the numberless times they had sat out in the garden under the cherry tree, the work Eve had done, hoeing, planting, harvesting, but it affected her very little. It troubled her no more than walking in a cemetery.

She pulled the blind down once more and turned her attention to the interior of the gate-house. Having been away from it for so long, she saw these rooms with new eyes, eyes educated enough by variety to find them strange: the vaulted ceilings, the pointed Gothic windows, the dark woodwork. It seemed remarkable now that she had lived here all her life or as long as she could remember.

This room, the living room, was not as it had been when she left it. Of course, she couldn't tell how soon Eve had gone after her own departure. But she wouldn't have left it like this, the pictures crooked, the ornaments on the mantelpiece in the wrong order, the hearthrug out of alignment. It struck Liza that she had no idea who owned this furniture. Was it Eve's or did it belong in the Lodge? Had it been there when Eve and she first came? The sofa had never stood quite like that, pushed flat against the wall. Someone had searched this room. The police had searched it. She had seen this sort of thing in a detective serial on television.

There was something missing from the room. A picture. A pale rectangle on the wall showed where it had once hung, her own portrait, the picture Bruno had painted of her.

It had never, in her opinion, looked much like her. The colours were too strong and her features too big. But Eve had liked it. Perhaps Eve had been allowed to take it with her, had it with her now, would keep it through those long years. The idea was comforting.

Had the police also searched the little castle?

The green studded door was still unlocked. If they had searched surely they would have locked it after them? Liza loosened the brick at the foot of the wall between the lancet windows, pulled it out and found the iron box. The money was still there. She took the box with its contents.

Back in the gate-house she went upstairs. She looked into Eve's bedroom, neat as a pin, desolate. The jewel case was there in the drawer but it was empty. No gold wedding ring of course, she had expected that, but no earrings either or jade necklace or brooches. She wondered what had become of them.

From the cupboard in her own bedroom she took her warm quilted coat, the two skirts Eve had made her, the red and blue sweater Eve had knitted.

The curtains were drawn in here, for no good reason that she could see. She drew them back and looked across the ruined gate-house garden to the grounds of Shrove. It gave her a little shock to see David Cosby walking across the grass between the young trees. He had a dog with him, a red and white spaniel. Once she was sure he wasn't looking in this direction, she drew the curtains again.

His walk was taking him nowhere near the little wood. Liza put the metal box and the clothes into the boot of the car and locked it. She wondered if she dared leave it there for the ten minutes it would take her to do what she had to do and decided she must.

The sun still shone with unseasonable brightness. It was so late in the year that the shadows were long, even at noon. The ground was dry for early December, under her feet softly crackling strata, layer upon layer of them, of fallen leaves. She made her way into the little wood, not wanting to go but aware that she had to. This was as important a mission as the quest for the iron box of money.

Much of the clearing operations she had witnessed but not this replanting. It was unexpected, an unforeseen act. New trees with the deer and rabbit guards on their thin trunks stood everywhere in carefully planned groups. She took heart from the sight of the two dead larches left to stand as a feeding place for woodpeckers and the broken poplar that had put out new branches.

The cherry log lay where it had lain from the time of its fall, or she thought it lay like that. How could she be sure? It was deep now in dead leaves, awash with them almost, with a tide of brown beech leaves that hid two-thirds of the log. But all those leaves had fallen since October . . .

She squatted down and began burrowing into the leaves with her hands. The relief at the feel of sacking against her fingers was so great she almost laughed aloud. Wedged beneath the log, the bundle was still in place, winter after winter were burying it deeper.

Leaves would turn to leaf-mould and leaf-mould to earth. One day the log itself would be buried as the level of the ground gradually and very slowly rose, while Bruno slept on, undisturbed.

There were no policemen standing by the car taking notes, no David Cosby with his young inquisitive dog. She got into the driving seat and drove down the lane, over the bridge, and took the road to the village where Bruno had wanted to take Eve to live. There, in the village shop, she bought a pack of ham sandwiches, a can of Coke and a Bounty bar for her lunch. It amused her a little that she had found buying these things in this shop so easy, she who had never dared go in there in former days.

But before that she investigated the contents of the iron box.

The previous time she had looked into the box, and helped herself from it, she had had very little idea of the value of money, what was a lot and what wasn't much. It was different now. She had lived a lifetime of experience in three months, had earned money and knew what things cost. Sitting in the driving seat in a secluded spot by the churchyard wall, she opened the box and counted the notes.

They amounted to something over a thousand pounds: to be precise, a thousand and seventy-five. Liza could hardly believe it. She must have made a mistake. But she counted again and again she reached the figure of a thousand and seventy-five. The money lay heavily on her, not on her hands, but like a burden on her back. She shook herself and tried to see it differently, as a blessing. No longer daring to leave it in the car, she carried the thousand pounds stuffed in her pockets as she went over to the shop. Because there was so much of it she felt she could afford a ham sandwich instead of cheese.

*

The car restored to the Superway car park, she wandered about the town, afraid to steal a bath at the Duke's Head in case she got caught and they found all that money on her. There wasn't time to go to the cinema. Instead she went to the bookshop, acquiring undreamt-of marvels, among them *The Divine Comedy* in translation, Ovid's *Metamorphoses* in the original *and* translation, before telling herself she must be careful with the money, she must be prudent. They needed that money, she and Sean.

All the same, she postponed telling him about it. Later would do, another day would do. Nor did she show him the new books. She had been to Shrove, she said, she had fetched her clothes. All he was concerned about was her driving the car uninsured and without a licence, he was rather angry about that. She hadn't dreamt, when first she knew him, that he would turn out so law-abiding.

The first hint of it she'd had was when the man who owned the land beside the old station discovered that the caravan was parked there and told him to move on. Liza, remembering that day when she had stood with the demonstrators and the last train had come down the line, said he need not move more than a dozen yards. If he parked it by the platform he would be on British Rail land and they never came near the place, they wouldn't find out. Sean wouldn't do it. He said he knew he was wrong being on that man's land without permission, he wasn't sticking his neck out again. He'd move over the bridge and up through the fields and woods to Ring Common where anyone could be.

It was four or five miles away. Of course he went on coming to Shrove to do the garden. Liza never spoke to him while he was on the mower or doing the edges or weeding, it amused her to walk past him with a casual 'hi' or even a shy 'hallo' if Eve was with her, remembering their love-making of the previous evening. How had she known that her association with Sean wouldn't be acceptable to Eve? That Eve and she were Capulets and Sean a Montague? Instinctively, she had known it, and had kept their love an absolute secret.

At the same time it brought her enormous pleasure to watch him about the grounds of Shrove when he had no idea she was watching him. Observing his handsomeness and his grace, she liked to remember and to anticipate. She even enjoyed the pleasure-pain of needing to go up to him and touch him, kiss him and have him touch her, needing it passionately but still making herself resist.

One day she saw a man talking to him. It was a shock to realise that the man was Matt. The past couple of times Jonathan had been at Shrove he had brought Matt with him. It was a long time since they had seen Jonathan, she and Eve, though weeks rather than months. The years when he had scarcely come at all were gone by. He had been at Shrove in April and now it was June. Matt was talking to Sean about something or other, pointing at this and that in what seemed to Liza a hectoring way before going back to the house.

'What was he saying to you that day?' she asked Sean five months later. 'Matt? When you had to stop the tractor and take off your visor?'

'I don't know. What does it matter? I reckon it was only to boss me about. Maybe it was to cut the tops off the lilacs, prune the lilacs. I never knew you was supposed to do that.'

'We didn't know Jonathan was coming. He didn't warn us, but he often didn't. I told Eve I'd seen him, I knew she'd want me to do that so that she could get dressed up and wash her hair before he came. That was the evening he first started talking about the money he'd lost. He didn't mind me being there, he talked about it in front of me. He was what they call a Name at Lloyd's. D'you know what that means?'

'Sort of. I saw about it in the papers. They were a sort of insurance company, only very big and sort of important, and something happened so they had to fork out more than they'd got.'

'It was to do with that Alaskan oil spill, that was the start of it. And they had more claims than they could – I think "meet" is the word. Instead of making money, all the people who were Names found they had to pay money. Jonathan was one. He said he didn't know how much it would be yet but he thought a lot and, luckily he had the house in France to sell that had been Caroline's. He looked very miserable. But, you know, we didn't take it very seriously, Eve and I. Or Eve didn't. I wasn't interested. She was interested, she was interested in everything that concerned him, but even she didn't believe he was having a job finding money. She was so used to the Tobiases and the Ellisons having so much of it. They were the kind of people, she said to me, who'd say they were poor when they were down to their last million.'

Sean shrugged. He put his arm round Liza. 'Feeling a bit better, are you, love? About you-know-what?'

She knew what. The revelation in the paper. Eve's past life. 'I'm all right. Only I'd like to go and see her.'

'Your mum?'

'Not yet. Maybe after Christmas. I'll find out where she is, where they've put her, and then I'll go and see her.'

'You're amazing, you really are. After what she done? After she murdered three blokes? After the way she brought you up? She's bad news, love.'

'She never did me a bit of harm,' said Liza. 'She's

307

my mother. You can understand why she killed those men, I can understand it. There was one place in the world she had a sanctuary, there was one kind of life she could live and stay – well, not mad, and they all wanted to take it away from her, one after the other.'

'Not Trevor Hughes.'

'Yes, he did. In a way. Jonathan had said she was there to see how she got on, but she knew he meant how it suited *him*. She was on *trial*. It wouldn't have suited him if his dogs had had to be destroyed because she'd set them on someone.

'And Bruno was going to make her leave unless she sent *me* away. You can understand why she killed them, she didn't have a choice. They'd got her in a corner and she acted like an animal would. And now I've read what happened to her before I was born I know she was getting her revenge too, she was taking vengeance on three men for what three men had done to her.'

'Not the same men,' Sean objected.

'Oh, of *course* not. Don't you understand anything?' Immediately, she was remorseful. 'I'm sorry. I'll tell you about the last one, shall I?'

He shrugged, then said a rather sullen, 'Yes.'

'I'll tell you about how she shot him.'

Chapter Twenty

This would be the last of Scheherazade's stories, she said. Not a thousand and one nights but nearer a hundred. Three and a half months of nights to tell a life in.

'When did I run away, Sean?'

'It was August. No, it wasn't, it was September the first.'

She began counting on her fingers. 'That was something I never learnt. I never learnt much arithmetic. I make it a hundred and one nights tomorrow.'

'Is that right?'

They were coming home from work on the following day, the hundredth day. Liza had carried the money with her to Aspen Close, she dared not leave it in the caravan. Stopping work at lunchtime, she had walked round the town until she found a shop to sell her a money belt. In the public lavatory in the marketplace she packed all the notes into the belt and put it on over her jeans. She was so slim the belt looked smart, not cumbersome.

She still hadn't said anything about the money to Sean and he believed that all she had fetched from the lodge were her clothes. Glad of the quilted coat, she rubbed her cold hands together. The heater in the car worked only fitfully.

'I'd got to June, hadn't I?' she said. 'It was when Jonathan first started going on about money. He'd brought Matt with him.'

'He was always coming out in the garden telling me how to do my job,' Sean grumbled.

'Did he? I didn't know that. Matt was a builder up in Cumbria but his business had failed. If it wasn't for him Eve wouldn't be in prison. He hated us. I think it was because he'd once thought Eve beautiful but he disgusted *her*.'

Sean nodded. 'That'd be it. She treated him like dirt.'

'If it wasn't for him the police wouldn't have suspected anything and Eve would still be at the gate-house and so would I.'

'I ought to thank him then, didn't I?'

She smiled. 'Jonathan sort of took him under his wing. He was getting married or he wanted to get married and Jonathan had some idea of getting him a place to live near Shrove and having him manage the grounds. While he was there he went out every night shooting rabbits by the car headlights. There was all this banging of guns night after night and the lights blazing over the fields. I hated it, I never liked Matt.'

'Them little devils have to be kept down, love. I never seen so many rabbits as there was last summer. And pigeons, they tear the crops to bits.'

'When he stayed at Shrove he slept in a room over the coach-house. There are seventeen bedrooms at Shrove but he had to sleep out there. He had to use the outside lavatory behind the stables and wash under the tap that was there for watering the horses.'

Sean said seriously, 'Tobias couldn't have him in the house, not a servant. Matt wouldn't have expected it.'

Liza gave him a look. She shook her head a little at him but he had his eye on the road. 'Jonathan told Eve you were just a temporary measure. Those were his words. He was going to give you the sack at the end of the summer, at Michaelmas – whenever that is

– and have Matt and his wife live over the coach-house. He said he'd have things done to it to make it possible to live there. Put in one of his famous bathrooms, I expect.'

'He did give me the sack. Well, he got that Matt to do it.'

'I was in a panic when he first said it. I thought he'd get rid of you and you'd have to go and I'd never see you again.'

They had reached the place where the caravan was. Sean put his arms round Liza and hugged her.

'You didn't trust me.'

'I don't think I trusted anyone by then, not even Eve.'

Inside the caravan they lit the gas and the oil heater. The warmth came quickly, though it was a damp smelly heat. Sean lit a cigarette to make the atmosphere worse and opened the bottle of wine he had brought from Superway and began unwrapping the samosas and onion bhajis for their supper. Pulling off her coat, Liza hugged herself inside the comfort of the sweater Eve had made. She talked, drinking her wine.

Eve hadn't liked that idea of Matt and his wife living at Shrove. Jonathan said it meant she could get rid of Mrs Cooper, she wouldn't have to handle the wages and the organisation, she'd have nothing to do but *be* there and, of course, she'd be in authority over them, they'd have to do as she said.

'Why can't we go on managing as we are?' she wanted to know.

It would be easier for her this way, Jonathan said, and besides he had to find something for Matt, he had a duty to Matt.

Liza knew what her mother was really feeling. By this time she understood most of Eve's deeply emotional attitude towards Shrove. Eve didn't want anyone, anyone at all, coming between her and that house and that land, that domain. She even resented Sean being there. Mr Frost had been there before she came, was there when her own mother was, she accepted him like she did the train and the inevitable weekend guests, but Sean was new. Of course she said none of this to Jonathan and that night Jonathan stayed at the gate-house. Liza felt very strange about that because she was deep in a sexual relationship of her own and she understood what when on beyond the wall dividing their bedrooms.

Next day she found Eve standing in front of the mirror, peering closely at her face, plucking out a grey hair. She came up behind Eve, not meaning to do this, not meaning to make the contrast. It all happened by chance that her face was reflected behind Eve's, a yard or so and twenty-two years between.

Eve turned round and said, '*Mater pulchra, filia pulchrior.*'

Liza didn't know what to say. She could hardly reply that it was true the mother was beautiful but the daughter more so, nor pretend not to understand. A lame, 'I think you look lovely,' was all she could manage. But she wondered what the hectic light in Eve's eye portended and her wild behaviour that day and her sudden bursts of too loud laughter.

As it happened, she overheard what Eve said to Jonathan. She'd got in the habit of listening at doors. It was a way of trying to save her life. Sometimes, these days, she felt her whole life was in jeopardy. If Matt came would Eve stay? If she and Eve went where could they go? If Sean went, what would she do? She would die. As soon as she sensed Eve or Jonathan or both of them wanted her out of the way she knew they were going to talk secrets she should have been privy to, because it was she most of all that they threatened.

312

That evening she had been at the caravan with Sean. Well, more than the evening. She had been with him from the time he stopped work at four until nine when he drove her back to Shrove. Home again at the gate-house, she thought at first that they had gone out somewhere or to Shrove House.

Jonathan's jacket was hanging over the back of a chair but that meant nothing. She went to her bedroom and looked out of the open window towards the house, expecting to see them walking in the pale red light of the sunset afterglow. But they were much nearer at hand. They were sitting on a rug spread out on the grass in the garden just below her window. Or Eve was sitting, her knees drawn up and her arms wrapped round them, while Jonathan lay on his back, looking up at the thin moon which had appeared in the still light sky.

They weren't speaking but Liza knew that once they did speak she would be able to hear every word. She crouched on the bed with her chin on the windowsill, thinking about Sean, how he had said to her that evening to come and live with him in the caravan. He had asked her, he had said he missed her too much when she wasn't with him, and what was there to keep her here? She couldn't answer that, she couldn't say, 'I'm frightened to go.'

In a way she wanted to terribly and in another way she didn't want to at all. Yet it was only a couple of years before that she'd been always asking herself what would become of her and how would she ever get away? The silence down there was oppressive. When she was beginning to think she might as well go down there and join them, Eve spoke.

'Jonathan, will you marry me?'

It was a worse silence this time. Anything would have been better than this silence. He was no longer looking at the moon but at Eve. She said with great

313

bravery – how Liza admired her courage! – 'I asked you to marry me. Women can do that, can't they? We were going to be married once, when we were very young. It all went wrong, we both know why, but is it too late to make it right?'

He sounded ashamed, Liza thought. 'I'm afraid it is too late, Evie.'

Eve made a little sound. She whispered, 'Why is it?'

'The time for that's gone by, Evie. I'm sorry but it's just too late.'

'But why is it? We're always happy when we're together. Don't I make you happy? Hasn't it always been – good with me?'

'I shan't marry again. I'm better alone and maybe you are too. I'll be frank, I don't want to be married. I've tried it and it didn't work. Victoria and I were all right until we got married. It was then that things started to fall apart. It would be the same with you and me.'

'Then I have humiliated myself for nothing,' Eve said in a hard voice, but almost at once she had turned back to him and suddenly cast herself upon him, clutching him in her arms and crying, 'Jonathan, Jonathan, you know I love you, why won't you stay with me? Why have you kept me like this for all these years? I've waited for you for so long, I've waited for ever and still I can't have you. Jonathan, please, please . . .'

Liza couldn't bear any more of it. She jumped off the bed and ran away into Eve's room, the way she had done when she was a child.

'She should have known better than that,' said Sean.

'It was ironical, wasn't it? There was I being begged to go and live with you and not daring to and there was she begging Jonathan to marry her and being rejected.'

His reply disturbed her, though it was complimentary to herself. 'No, well, you're sixteen, aren't you, love? And she's a bit past her sell-by date.'

'Jonathan was older than she.'

'He's a man. It's different. I bet he didn't stay that night.'

She digested the first part of these remarks. This was a point of view she hadn't previously come across and she found it deeply unsatisfactory. 'He went back to Shrove about half an hour later and he and Matt went off next day. I thought he'd never come back but he did.'

'Too right he did and that Matt with him. It was the end of August. Matt come up to me all smiles like he was going to give me a raise. It was ten minutes before I was due to leave and I was using that bit of time to thin out the plums. There was so many plums on that damn tree the branches were breaking. He said like he was my boss, "Holford, we shan't need your services after the weekend, thanks very much." It was a Wednesday and he said he wouldn't need my services after the weekend. I said, "Is that what you call giving a person notice?" He went on smiling. "Take it or leave it," he says to me, "you get paid up to Friday afternoon," and he just walked off.'

Liza hadn't seen Sean on that Wednesday evening so the news of his dismissal reached her at second-hand. She was nearly frantic when she heard. They weren't in the Lodge but at the house. It was such a rare thing for her and Eve to be asked up to the house when Jonathan was there that she had sensed something awful was going to happen.

Jonathan came to the gate-house at about four in the afternoon. She and Eve were indoors, it was rather a chilly day for late August, and Jonathan talked to them from the window. He didn't come in.

315

He just said, 'Come up to the house for a drink about six, I've got something to tell you.'

Eve was sore. She seemed truculent and sulky. No one but Liza would have guessed what she was suffering from was simple unhappiness. 'Tell us what?' she said.

He didn't answer. 'I'll take you both out for a meal afterwards, if you like,' he said.

Probably Eve was imagining all kinds of dreadful things – though nothing so dreadful as the truth. Jonathan received them in the drawing room, very grand. They sat in one of the groups of crimson and gold chairs and sofas that were arranged in each corner of the room round a marble or ormolu table. A good deal of the glory was lost when Matt came shambling in with bottles and glasses on a tray and peanuts in a packet. Matt's hair was down on his shoulders now but it had gone grey and he had grown a big belly, so that Liza couldn't imagine what sort of a woman would think of marrying him. She had never seen a drunk person nor heard the word Jonathan used and would have thought Matt ill if Eve hadn't explained later.

'How dare you come in here pissed? Put the bloody nuts in a dish and then get out.'

Jonathan had been drinking too, she could smell it on his breath when he leant towards her and asked her if she was allowed a glass of wine.

'I've just had Matt give that young man of yours the push,' he said to Eve.

'What young man of mine?'

'The gardener.'

'You've sacked him? Why?'

Liza could hear the relief in Eve's voice. She was aghast but Eve was relieved because she was expecting something worse. So that was all Jonathan had got them up there for, Eve was no doubt thinking, to

316

tell me he's got rid of Sean Holford to make room for Matt and Mrs Matt, and now he'll be wanting me to get rid of Mrs Cooper.

And what am I going to do? Liza thought feverishly. Suppose he's gone, suppose he never comes back, suppose I never see him again?

'I told you I'd got something to tell you, Eve. It's not that I've fired the gardener. It's not that Matt will be taking over. No one will be taking over. The fact is I'm going to have to sell the house. Shrove House will have to be sold.'

Trembling for her mother, Liza turned slowly to look at her. Eve was stone-still. She had gone white and suddenly she looked tremendously old, not thirty-eight but sixty-eight, an old woman with a lined forehead and mouth that has fallen in.

'Don't look like that, Evie,' Jonathan said. 'D'you think I want to do it? I've no choice. I told you about my financial difficulties. I've got to put more into Lloyd's than I dreamed was possible, it's been a frightful shock to me. But you must know what's happened to the Names, it's been all over the papers day after day – no, I forgot, you don't read the papers. The fact is I've got to find getting on for a million and I can't do it without selling Shrove. If I get fifty thousand for Mama's house in France I'll be doing well, it's more than I can hope for, thirty's more likely. I've been trying to sell it for two years. Again I was going to say you know what's happened to the property market but, no, I don't suppose you do know. I have to sell Shrove. When I do it will just cover me, I shall just keep my head above water.'

Eve was staring at him. This was the first time Liza had ever drunk wine and she was making the

317

most of it. It helped. She held out her glass for more and Jonathan filled it absently.

'For God's sake, Eve, say something.' He tried, incredibly, facetiousness. 'Say something if it's only goodbye.'

Liza saw her make an effort. She saw her suck in her lips and raise her shoulders as if in pain. The voice, when it came, was breathless and thin.

'You can sell Ullswater.'

'The Ullswater house belongs to Victoria now – remember?'

'Why were you ever such a fool as to marry her?'

'D'you think I haven't asked myself that over and over?'

'Jonathan,' said Eve, holding her hands tightly clenched together, 'Jonathan, you can't sell Shrove, it's unthinkable, there has to be an alternative.' She thought of one. 'You can sell the London house.'

'And where am I supposed to live?'

Eve, who hadn't taken her eyes off him, seemed to stare even more intently. Not liking the look in her mother's face, the glazed, hardly sane look, Liza shifted uncomfortably in her chair. Eve said, 'You can live here.'

'No, I can't.' Jonathan was growing irritable. 'I don't want to live here. Things are bad enough without my having to live in a place I dislike.' He sounded like a petulant child. 'All right, I know I've never told you I don't like this place, but the fact is I don't, I never have. It's isolated, it's miles from anywhere, and you mayn't have noticed this, but it's damp. Of course it is, stuck in a bloody river valley. Victoria got fibrositis through staying here.'

'God damn Victoria to hell,' said Eve in a voice to make Liza jump out of her skin.

Jonathan wasn't put out. 'All right. Willingly. I wish she was in hell. I'm sure I've suffered from her

318

more than you have, more than you dream of. Never mind her, anyway. I do have to sell this house, I have to have the million it'll fetch.'

'You won't be able to sell it. Even I know that. I may live out of the world but I've got a radio, I know what goes on. The house market's the worst it's been in my lifetime. You won't find a buyer. Not at the price you're asking you won't.'

Jonathan refilled Eve's glass from the dry sherry bottle. She lifted the glass, watching him. For a moment Liza thought she was going to throw the contents of the glass at him but she didn't. Nor did she drink from it.

Jonathan said calmly, 'I have. I have found a buyer.'

Eve made a little pained sound.

'A hotel chain. They're embarking on a project called Country Heritage Hotels. Shrove will be their flagship, as they call it.'

'I don't believe you.'

'Come off it, Evie, of course you believe me. Why would I say it if it wasn't true?'

'The deal,' said Eve, 'the contract, whatever, I don't know about these things – is it settled?'

'Not yet. They've made an approach and I've told my solicitor to tell them a tentative yes. That's as far as we've got. You're the first person I've told.'

'I should think so,' Eve said scornfully.

'Of course I'd tell you first, Evie.'

'What will become of me, of us? Have you thought of that?'

Jonathan began saying he would find her a house. Matt and his wife would stay at Shrove until it was bought by Country Heritage and then they would have to have a home found for them. His idea was perhaps to find a pair of semi-detached cottages. On the other side of the valley possibly, and he named

319

the village where Bruno had nearly bought a house. Property was for sale all over the place and much of it going for a song.

There was no question of abandoning Eve. He hoped he knew his responsibility towards her. Unfortunately for her, the hotel chain wanted the gate-house for use as their reception. They had specifically stated this in their offer.

Eve said flatly, 'I will never leave here.'

'That's all very well. I'm afraid you must. Do you think it's pleasant for me having to tell you this? Come to that, d'you think I like selling half my property? My grandfather would turn in his grave, I know that.'

'He wouldn't,' said Eve. 'Not where he is, rotting in hell.'

'I don't see the use of talking like that. It doesn't help.'

'I will never leave here. They will have to take me away by force if they want me to leave here.'

It was a prophecy soon to be fulfilled.

The next day, after a sleepless night, a night when she didn't go to bed at all, Eve went up to Shrove to plead with Jonathan. By that time Liza was already telling the news to Sean and Sean was urging her to come to him, to leave her mother and Shrove and come and live with him, she was old enough, the law couldn't stop her.

Coming back, she encountered Matt in the stable yard with a fat middle-aged woman in an apron. The presence of his wife didn't stop him eyeing Liza up and down in a lecherous way – just as he had eyed Eve all those years ago – and telling her she'd grown up into a lovely girl who'd soon have all the boys after her.

Jonathan came back with Eve and they spent the

day arguing, Eve alternately pleading and shouting, occasionally weeping. As far as Liza knew, they spent the day like this. At four she went out to meet Sean and didn't get home till nearly ten. Eve didn't say anything, she uttered no word of reproach. Liza could hardly believe her eyes when Jonathan put his arm round Eve, lifted her off the sofa and led her upstairs to her bedroom where he closed the door on the pair of them for the rest of the night.

Outside the usual banging started and the flaring lights as Matt went rabbit-hunting. Liza drew her curtains. She sat on the bed thinking about Sean. He would never come back to Shrove to work. Apple-picking had already begun in the Discovery orchards to the north of here. In less than a week he'd be moving on to earn as much as he could picking apples from dawn till dusk through September. How did two people communicate when neither had a phone? Sean didn't even have a postal address.

He said he'd drive over on Monday and they'd meet in the little wood. Why the little wood? she'd asked and he'd said because it was romantic. He'd also said she'd got to tell him if she was coming. Didn't she love him enough to come?

Secure in her love and companionship now, Sean said, interrupting the story, 'I still don't know why you had to keep me on the hook so long.'

'I've told you often enough. I was scared. I'd never been away. As far as I could remember, I'd never even slept in any bed but mine at the gate-house.'

He patted the bed they were sitting on. 'We never slept much, did we, love?'

'Jonathan was practically living at the gate-house that weekend,' said Liza. 'They were all over each other, more than I'd ever seen them. Eve'd never been demonstrative in public. Perhaps I wasn't public, perhaps she didn't care, I don't know. They were hugging and kissing in my presence but for all that, Jonathan could never be got to say he wouldn't sell Shrove. She'd plead and cajole and kiss him and at the end of it he'd just say, "I've got to sell".'

Then Eve gave up. On Sunday evening Liza heard her say, 'If it must be, it must be.'

She reached for Jonathan's hand and held it. Jonathan gave her a look which to Liza, who now knew about such things, seemed full of love.

'We'll find a nice house for you and Liza, you'll still have the countryside, the place itself . . .'

Jonathan stayed the night but left early in the morning before Liza was up. She came downstairs to find Eve seated at the breakfast table, glittery-eyed and galvanic with barely suppressed energy, her hands clasping and unclasping.

'He's going to sell Shrove, he's absolutely determined.'

'I know,' Liza said.

The tone of Eve's voice changed, and became dreamy, reminiscing. 'He's asked me to marry him.'

'He hasn't!'

'The irony of it, Lizzie, the irony! Of course I said no. "No, thanks," I said, "you're too late." What's the good of him to me without Shrove?'

It was for Shrove she had wanted him. If he had married her a year ago he could have put Shrove in her name and kept it safe from his creditors. She laughed a little, not hysterically but madder than that, a manic laugh. Still, Liza couldn't believe she had been as abrupt with Jonathan as she implied, for he was back at the Lodge in the late morning.

When she heard Eve say she'd go pigeon-shooting with him later, Liza thought the world was turning upside-down faster than she could cope with. Eve never killed birds or animals. Now she was saying the pigeons destroyed the vegetables she grew and would have to be kept down. Jonathan sounded quite happy to teach her to shoot with the four-ten, the gun, Liza thought, she had used to shoot the man with the beard. Only Jonathan, of course, had no idea of that.

Neither of them seemed deflected from their purpose by the fact that in a month or two Shrove would be sold, Eve would have left the gate-house and it would hardly matter to her whether the vegetables survived or not.

In the afternoon Liza went up into the little wood to meet Sean. In arranging where to meet she had been careful to arrange this trysting place a good distance from where Bruno's body lay. They made love on a bed of soft dry grass, walled-in by hawthorn bushes. But afterwards, holding her in his arms, Sean grew grave. He had to work for his living, he wasn't going on benefit if he could help it. For the next two days he could take a job clearing a house of furniture for a dealer in town but after that he'd have to move on to where the apples were. He wanted her. Would she come?

He couldn't wait for ever, he couldn't really wait beyond Thursday. And after that how would they get in touch with each other?

She hadn't liked that, the fact that he wouldn't wait. In the romantic plays and books she had read, the true lover had been prepared to wait indefinitely, not make conditions and threats. She got him to say that he'd come back here next Saturday, same time, same place. By then she promised she'd have made up her mind. She would have separated herself from her mother and come to him or else she'd be staying. Was it her imagination that he had seemed reluctant? Instead of ardour her request to him had been met with doubts about whether he

323

could make it, much depended on where he was, he would do his best.

When he had gone and she had watched him go, heading for the place where he had parked the car, far up the lane, when she had seen the last of him as the trees absorbed him, the tears came into her eyes and she started to cry. They were tears of frustration, of impotence and self-pity at her own indecisiveness. Wiping her eyes on the backs of her hands, then rubbing them with her fists like a child, she walked slowly back the way she had come.

It was nearly six, she calculated, the sun still high in the sky but some of its heat departed. Sean and she had been together for three hours but it had seemed no more than three minutes. She was thinking about her dilemma once more, wondering if some middle way could be found, some compromise, whereby she could continue to be here with Eve and keep Sean nearby, when she heard the first shot.

Liza's instinct, whenever there was shooting in the grounds, was to take herself as far away from the neighbourhood of those reports as possible, even to cover her ears. Her dread was of actually seeing a bird fall to the ground, bloody and with feathers flying, or a rabbit brought down as it fled for cover. But this time she was not exactly sure where the shot had come from, it was often hard to tell. At any rate, it wasn't in this wood and wouldn't be in their back garden.

She saw Matt first. Although she knew of Jonathan's intention to shoot pigeons, when she caught sight of Matt in the far distance, almost up by Shrove House, she thought it was he who was after the birds. Then she saw Jonathan and Eve standing together between the largest remaining cedar, the blue *Atlantica glauca*, and the group of new young trees. They weren't very far from her, no more than a hundred yards, quite near enough for her to see that they had only one gun between them.

Jonathan had been demonstrating something and now he put the shotgun into Eve's hands. Holding it gingerly, she raised the barrel in a clumsy way, with what seemed an effort. He gave her a kindly glance, then adjusted her hands, moving them farther apart. Their shadows had lengthened as the sun sank and now streamed out thin and dark across the leaf-patterned grass. When Jonathan clapped his hands to make the pigeons fly Liza stopped looking, opened the gate and let herself into the gate-house garden.

She had forgotten to cover her ears. The gun went off, once, twice, three times. There came a cry no bird could have made, a high-pitched scream quite clearly audible from where she was. She stood still. For a moment a little child again, she saw in her mind's eye the bearded man as he died on the grass in the dusk.

Almost without realising it, she had put up her hands over her ears. But there was to be no more firing. She took away her hands, she turned round and saw Matt running across the grass, waving his arms.

Between the trees, on the open green that the sun and shadows dappled, Jonathan lay sprawled on his back. Eve had dropped the gun and stood looking down at him, her hands clasped under her chin. Liza ran into the house.

Chapter Twenty-One

'She'd shot him,' Liza said. 'I knew at once it was on purpose. If he was dead he couldn't sell Shrove and it would go to his cousin David Cosby who loved the place and wouldn't dream of selling it. It was the only way to make sure she got it. Marrying him wouldn't have worked, he'd still have sold it.

'The way she looked at me, I read it all in her face. The trouble was Matt. Who knows what she'd have done if Matt hadn't been there? Pretended to find Jonathan dead that evening or next day and made people believe he'd been out shooting alone? But Matt had seen. I don't mean he'd seen her do it, but he'd seen them together firing at the pigeons.

'Eve said to me to tell the police you saw nothing, tell them you don't even live here, you're just visiting, and then she said, why tell them anything? You don't have to be here. Matt didn't see you. So I went and sat in the little castle and they didn't know I'd been there. I think I knew then that she wanted to handle it all on her own.

'The police suspected her of killing Jonathan but they could never prove it, no one saw it happen, you see. I've been thinking a lot about it since the trial and that's the conclusion I've come to, that once they suspected her of killing Jonathan they remembered Bruno going missing and then they started thinking about the man called Trevor Hughes. They'd actually questioned her about him and she'd denied ever seeing him but they'd got a record of it, they never forgot. I expect that's what happened.

'When they searched the gate-house they didn't find Bruno's earrings because she was wearing them. She was wearing them the night before I left so I'm sure she still had them on next morning. They did find Trevor Hughes's wedding ring with his initials inside and his wife's.

'They must have asked Matt if he knew anything about Trevor Hughes. Or else Matt went to them of his own accord and told them what he remembered that morning when the dogs behaved in that strange way. If she'd killed him they wondered what she'd done with his body and eventually they started digging.

'I'm sure they'd have liked to indict her for shooting Jonathan but they were afraid she'd be acquitted. And they got nowhere trying to trace Bruno. But when they found Trevor Hughes's bones they found shot among them that came from that four-ten shotgun, that same one Jonathan was using to teach her to shoot pigeons. And they must have found his watch too for his wife to identify. I expect it went on for weeks after they first arrested her. I'd really like to know how they managed that – I mean, did they charge her with murdering Jonathan and then give that up and charge her with manslaughter instead just to hold her? And when did they think they'd got enough evidence to be sure of getting a conviction on a Hughes murder charge?'

Sean was staring at her incredulously. Liza smiled at him. 'I told you, I'd like to be a lawyer. I'm interested in the law.'

'You're a bright girl. You shouldn't be cleaning for that old woman.'

Liza shrugged. It didn't seem important, it was only temporary. She began clearing their takeaway containers off the table. 'D'you want a cup of tea?'

327

'In a minute,' he said. 'I've got something to tell you first. Now it's my turn. *I've* got something to tell *you*.'

She filled the kettle, lit the gas and, catching sight of his expression, turned it low. 'What, then?'

'I've been accepted for the management course.'

As soon as the less than enthusiastic words were out, she regretted them, knew she should have congratulated him. But she had said, 'Well, you knew you would be.'

A flush darkened his face. 'It's not been as straightforward as that. As a matter of fact, it was touch and go. They only took five out of two hundred applicants.'

'And you're one of the five? That's nice.'

She must have sounded kind but indifferent, maternally indulgent perhaps. He said, 'Listen to me, Liza. Come and sit down.'

Her sigh was audible but she sat down next to him.

'The course starts in the New Year but they want me up there next week. It's in Scotland, a place near Glasgow. They wanted to put me in a flat with the other four, that's the way they fix it, but I'll have you with me, so I said I'd see to my own accommodation. I never said caravan, I wasn't telling them all my private affairs.'

'Glasgow?' she said. 'That'll be a long way from wherever Eve is. But I don't suppose it'd be for long, would it? Didn't you say six months?'

'Liza, hopefully this is only the start. You've not been following me. This is a new way of life. It's great the things they'll do for you once you've shown you're up to the course. For one thing, the idea is to manage one of their stores and they're building new branches all the time. There's one they're putting up now on the M3. Hopefully I could be assistant manager of one of them by this time next year. They'll help you with a mortgage on a flat.'

328

He must have seen she didn't know what he meant. While he explained what a mortgage was, she fidgeted about, suddenly wanting a cup of tea more than anything in the world but not quite liking to get up and make it. He took hold of her hand, imprisoning it.

'It's a great chance for me. It's sort of made me see myself differently, like I'm not the person I reckoned I was, I'm better, I could be my own man, a responsible person with a real career.'

Yes, she thought, you even talk better. It's made you articulate, you can suddenly express yourself. Then he shocked her.

'There's something else I want to tell you, love. I want you to marry me, I want us to get married.'

It was as much as she could do to speak. *'Married?'*

'I knew it'd be a surprise.' He leant towards her and gave her a quick kiss on the cheek. Fondly he said, 'You silly nana, you've gone all red. If it's on account of your Mum, I don't mind that. It'll be just the same to me as if you was any other girl with a normal family.'

'Sean . . .,' she began but it was as if she hadn't interrupted him.

'I'll get paid when I'm training, that's another great thing. Hopefully you won't have to work no more. I wouldn't want my wife going out cleaning anyway. And when the kids start coming you'll want to be at home . . .'

This time she shouted to break the flow. 'I'm not yet seventeen years old!'

'That's OK. You have to be over sixteen to get married, not over seventeen. It's seventeen for a driving licence.'

She burst out laughing. It was too much. Unlike him though this would be, he had to be making some elaborate joke. It was a moment or two before she understood, before she saw from his hurt face that he was deadly serious. 'Oh, Sean, don't look like that, don't be so *silly*.'

'Silly!'

'Well, of course it's silly talking about marrying and having children and one of those things, a what-d'you-call-it, a mortgage. We've got our lives to live first. I'm not even grown-up really. In the law I can't sign a contract or make a will or anything.'

'Shut up about the fucking law, will you?'

She flinched a little, got up and went to the stove. 'I want my tea if you don't,' she said in a chilly voice, Eve's voice. He was sullen as she had never seen him. Suddenly she realised that she had never crossed him, everything had gone pleasantly for him until this evening, but now the sultan was looking at her head and sharpening his sword.

'I don't mind coming to Scotland for a bit,' she said in a conciliatory voice. 'I'd quite like somewhere else for a change. We could try it. You might not like the course.'

He took his tea without a thank-you. 'You'd better listen to me, Liza. Have you thought where you'd be without me? You'd be lost, you'd be nothing. Thanks to the way that bitch brought you up, you wouldn't last five minutes on your own. You don't even know what a mortgage is! You never knew what the pill was! The best you can do to earn your living is cleaning or picking apples. You don't know nothing except for rubbish out of books. She's crippled you for life, and you're going to need me to get you through it.'

It was an echo of Bruno, Bruno's words outside the old station. She brought the teacup to her lips but the tea seemed tasteless.

'I'll be your husband, I'll look after you. There's

some as'd say it was a pretty big thing I was doing, considering who and what your mother is. You don't reckon I'd rather live in this clapped-out old van than in a decent flat, do you? It'd be OK sharing with those guys but I've a responsibility to you, I know that, and I'll be taking the car and the van up to Glasgow on Friday. I won't say I'll be taking them anyway, whether you come or not because you'll have to come, you don't have no choice.'

'Of course I have a choice.'

'No, you don't. It's like this, you have to come with me just because you can't be left here with no place to live, no family, no friends and – you have to face it, love – no skills. The truth is you're more like six than sixteen. It's not your fault but that's the way it is.'

She said nothing. Taking her silence for acquiescence, he turned on the television. She thought he looked pleased with himself. The look on his face was Bruno's when he thought he had persuaded Eve to move into that house with him. After a little while he opened a can of beer and began to drink from the can. He must have been aware of her eyes on him, for he turned round, grinned and made the thumbs-up sign, intended no doubt to reassure. She picked up the book Mr Spurdell had lent her, *First Steps in English Law* and found the place she had reached in it the day before.

That was the first broken night she had had since she shared a bed with Sean and almost the first that they hadn't made love. She lay awake, thinking how much she had loved him and wondering how that could have changed. How could you feel so passionately for a person and then, suddenly, not care any more at all? A few words, a gross gesture, an insensitive assumption, and it was all gone. Had it been like that for Eve and Bruno?

She was out all day on Saturday, roaming the fields

331

by herself, but on Sunday it rained and she lay in bed, reading. When she refused to get up and tidy the place, shake out the mats, help him fetch water, he accused her of sulking. They both went to work in the morning and met as usual at five. It was dark, pitch dark, when they reached the caravan, and there was no water. They had forgotten to fetch the water before they left. Liza took the bucket and a torch.

It struck her as somehow silly that it was pouring with rain yet they had no water. She held the bucket under the pipe that protruded from the hillside, filled it and made her way back, once nearly falling on the slippery mud.

Once in the caravan she opened a can of Coke. She was washing her hands at the sink before she saw what he had done to the books. She glanced into the living area as she reached for the towel. A piece of book jacket, a torn-off triangle, red lettering on a black background, lay on the table. It brought a constriction to her throat. They had no waste basket, only a plastic sack under the sink. The sight of its contents made her feel rather dizzy. Sean wasn't looking at her, he was watching television, a can of beer beside him, a lighted cigarette in his left hand. She had the feeling he was consciously not looking at her, forcing his eyes to fix on the screen.

Easier than rummaging in that sack was to see what he had done by examining the books which remained. *Mary Wollstonecraft* was gone and *The Divine Comedy* and the *Metamorphoses*. *Middlemarch* was gone. With bile rising into her mouth, she saw that he had spared *First Steps in English Law* and the two Hardy novels. Those belonged to Mr Spurdell and he knew it. Sean was always law-abiding. He wouldn't destroy 'other people's' property. She didn't count as other people, she was his.

She walked across and switched off the television. He jumped up and for a moment she thought he would hit her. But she had misjudged him there. Sean wouldn't hit a woman.

'Why?' she said, the single word.

'Come on, love, you know why. You've got to put all that behind you, that life. You've left the place, she's gone, you're out in the real world now. Them books, they was just a way of hiding yourself from real life. Hopefully you're not going to need them in the future. We've got our whole future before us. Isn't that what you said yourself?'

Had she? Not in that context, she was sure. He was triumphant, he was in charge. She felt as angry as she now guessed Eve must sometimes have felt.

'They were *my* books.'

'They was *ours*, love. We've been through that before. OK, so you bought them with the money you earned. How would you like it if I said that Coke you're drinking was mine because it was my money paid for it? It's the same thing.'

It was illogical and Eve had taught her to be logical, to be reasonable. Eve must have felt like this when Bruno pretended to have a social conscience to cloak his need to possess her utterly. She must have felt like this when, after seventeen years of striving and repudiation, of hope and humiliation and desertion, Jonathan had at last asked her to marry him.

Liza was impotent, she had nothing to say, she could only imagine how he would twist what she said. She set their food out, she made tea, she put the television on again and was rewarded by his seizing her hand and squeezing it in his own. Together they watched an episode in a Hollywood mini-series. Or Sean watched it while she fixed her eyes on the screen and took her mind elsewhere.

She could clean a house and fetch water from a

spring and read books but it was true what he said, in other ways she was more like six than sixteen. She couldn't manage on her own. Even if she worked eight hours a day for Mrs Spurdell or someone like Mrs Spurdell she would still only earn £120 a week, and she doubted if she *could* do eight hours house-work a day. Where would she live? How would she afford anything?

Was there anyone in the world who would pay her to translate Latin into English for them? She knew nothing about it but that she doubted that they would. Besides, she knew from investigating in Mr Spurdell's study that you had to have certificates and things, diplomas, degrees, before people would employ you to do things which weren't housework or putting packets on a shelf in a supermarket.

She had nowhere to live. Jonathan Tobias might have helped her about that, but he was dead. She had no father, only one of three men who knew nothing of her existence. Eve didn't seem to care for her. Eve didn't know where she was or what had happened to her but perhaps, in Eve's position, she wouldn't care either. Or Eve might care very much, might be in an agony of anxiety, when she found out as she must have, that Liza had never got to Heather's. But no one had come looking for her, no one had put pieces in the paper about her or on the television. Liza knew there was no one to look after her but Sean. There was only Sean.

He held her hand. Soon he had his arm round her. She was full of cold dislike for him which she somehow knew would have warmed into simple irritation after a night's sleep. If he would leave her alone. If he would leave her to come to terms with it in her own way. She had to, after all. She had to make the best of it because without him she was useless and helpless.

334

Only he wouldn't leave her alone. He must have been able to tell how hostile she was to him, he must have sensed her reluctance to be touched by him and understood something by the way she took his hand off her leg when he began running it up and down her thigh. They would have to share a bed, she was resigned to that, but when she realised he intended making love she spoke a firm, 'No!' And then, 'No, please, I don't want to.'

But making love wasn't at all what happened. She had asked him once if he would ever force her and he had treated the question as ludicrous. But he took no notice when she told him she didn't want him, she didn't want to do it. He silenced her by clamping his mouth over hers. He held her hands down, tried to force her thighs apart with his knee, and when that didn't work, with his foot. To justify himself, he pretended she was playing coy and laughed into her mouth as he thrust like a dog in the street, as he shoved his penis hard inside her, held her arms stretched out the width of the bed, pinioning her.

She was powerless. It hurt, as it had never hurt even the first time. When it was over and he was whispering to her that he knew she had really enjoyed it, he could always tell if a girl liked it, she thought of Eve and Trevor Hughes. Eve had had a pair of dogs to call but she had nothing.

He fell asleep immediately. She cried in silence. It was weak and foolish, she was a baby to do it, but she couldn't stop.

Eve would never have tolerated such treatment. Eve never permitted persecution. Not since what had happened on the way back from the airport. Her own suffering was nothing like as terrible but bad enough, a foretaste of a possible future. Eve had revenged herself on three men for what three men had done to her. That was why she had done those

335

things, for vengeance more than for fear or safety or gain. More for vengeance than for Shrove.

Was this then what her own life would be? Making love when she wanted to and also making love when she didn't want to. Or doing *that* when she didn't want to. After what had happened, she thought she would never want to again. She remembered the day of Jonathan Tobias's wedding and how Eve had used the occasion as an opportunity for a lesson, as she so often did. She had taught Liza about marriage and marriage customs but had said nothing of having to do what a man wanted when you didn't want to, of men getting their way because they were stronger, of working for them and waiting on them and submitting to their right to tell you what to do.

Perhaps she hadn't because Liza had been only a child then. It was a lifetime ago and she was a child no longer. But once more she was in a position where she couldn't run away. And it was worse than last time when all she needed was courage. Now she had nowhere to run to.

One other thing Eve had done for her, though, apart from teaching her so many of the things Sean said were useless, and that was to teach her to rough it. Life had never been soft. They made their own pleasures with the minimum of aid, without toys, television, videos, CD players, external amusements. Eventually, after years, they had got their bathroom. The gate-house had an old fridge and an even older oven, but there was no heating upstairs, no down quilts or electric blankets of the kind she'd seen at the Spurdells', no new clothes – those jeans and the padded coat were the only things she possessed not made by Eve or from the Oxfam shop – they'd had none of that takeaway or processed food she'd got used to with Sean but never really trusted. They'd made their own bread at the gate-house, grown their own vegetables, made their own jam and even cream cheese. Everywhere they went they'd had to walk once Bruno was gone.

Her mother had given her a kind of endurance, a sort of toughness, but what use was that in the world of Spurdell and Superway? You didn't need to be tough, you needed certificates and diplomas, families and relations, a roof over your head and means of transport, you needed skills and money. Well, she had a thousand pounds.

She could see the money belt on the table where he had thrown it when he stripped her. If he knew about the money he would want it. Once he wanted it, he would take it. He would say that what was hers was theirs and therefore his. She got up, washed all traces of him off her body, pulled on leggings and the blue and red sweater for warmth and, curling the money belt up as tightly as she could, thrust it inside one of her boots. Keeping as far from him as she could, on the far edge of the bed, she went to sleep.

Chapter Twenty-Two

Proudly showing Liza her box of decorations which had all come from Harrods, Mrs Spurdell said it was too early to dress the tree yet. But there was no point in deferring the purchase of it until later when the best would be gone. Philippa and her children were coming for Christmas. Jane was coming. Having once told Liza Philippa's Christian name, Mrs Spurdell had since then always referred to her as Mrs Page while Jane was 'my younger daughter'.

It was the first Christmas tree Liza had ever seen. Indeed, it was the first she had ever heard of and the rationale for uprooting a fir tree, winding tinsel strings round it and hanging glass balls on the branches was beyond her understanding. As for Christian customs, Eve had taught her no more about Christianity than she had about Buddhism, Judaism and Islam.

She could hear Mr Spurdell moving about in his study upstairs. His school had broken up for Christmas. With the two of them in the house she had no chance of a bath. She scrubbed out the tub and put caustic down the lavatory pan. While she was cleaning the basin it occurred to her to look in the medicine cabinet. There, among the denture cleaning tablets, the vapour rub and the corn solvent, she found a cylindrical container labelled: Mrs M. Spurdell, sodium amytal, one to be taken at night. Of its properties she knew nothing except that it evidently made you sleep. She put the container in her pocket.

If she didn't have her money in her hand before she gave notice, she thought it quite likely Mrs Spurdell would refuse to pay her. While she pushed the vacuum cleaner up and down the passage, she worked out various strategies. Determined to be honest and not to prevaricate, she knocked on the study door.

'Do you want to come in here, Liza?' Mr Spurdell put his head out. 'I won't be a minute.'

'I'll do the study last if you like,' she said. 'I've brought all your books back.'

'That's a good girl. You're welcome to more. I've no objection to lending my dear old friends to a sensible person who knows how to take care of them. A good book, you know, Liza, "is the precious lifeblood of a master spirit".'

'Yes,' said Liza, 'but I don't want to borrow any more. Can I ask you something?'

No doubt, he expected her to ask who said that about a good book but she already knew it was Milton and knew too, which was very likely more than he did, that it came from *Areopagitica*. He was all smiling invitation to having his brains picked.

'How can you find out where someone's in prison?'

'I beg your pardon?' The smile was swiftly gone.

Now for the honesty. 'My mother has gone to prison and I want to know where she is.'

'Your mother? Good heavens. This isn't a game, is it, Liza? You're being serious?'

She was weary with him. 'I only want to know whom to write to or whom to phone and find out where they've put her. I want to write to her, I want to go and see her.'

'Good heavens. You've really given me quite a

339

shock.' He took a step forward, glanced over the banisters and spoke in a lowered voice, 'Don't give Mrs Spurdell a hint of this.'

'Why would I tell *her*?' Liza made an impatient gesture with her hands. 'Is there a place I could phone? An office, I mean, a police headquarters of some kind?' She was vaguely remembering American police serials.

'Oh, dear, I suppose it would be the Home Office.'

'What's the Home Office?'

Questions that were requests for information always pleased him. Prefacing his explanation with a 'You don't know what the Home Office is?' he proceeded to a little lecture on the police, prisons, immigration and ministries of the interior. Liza took in what she needed.

She drew breath and braced herself. Sean's words came back to her, about being more like six than sixteen, about being helpless. 'Please may I use your phone? And may I look in the phone directory first?'

He was no longer the benevolent pedagogue, twinkling as he imparted knowledge. A frown appeared and a petulant tightening of the mouth. 'No, I'm afraid you may not. No to both. I can't have that sort of thing going on here. Besides, this is the most expensive time. Have you any idea what it would cost to phone to London at eleven o'clock in the morning?'

'I'll pay.'

'No, I'm sorry. It's not only the money. This isn't the kind of thing Mrs Spurdell and I should wish to be involved in. I'm sorry but no, certainly not.'

She gave a little bob of her head and immediately switched on the vacuum cleaner once more. When the bedrooms were done, she came back to the study and found him gone. Quickly she looked for Home Office in the phone book. Several numbers were listed. She wrote down three of them, knowing she didn't want Immigration or Nationality or Tele-communications.

The house was clean and tidy, her time up. It seemed harder than it had ever been to extract twelve pounds from Mrs Spurdell, the last pound coming in the shape of fifteen separate coins. Liza thanked her and said she was leaving, she wouldn't be coming any more. Mrs Spurdell affected not to believe her ears. When she was convinced she asked rhetorically how she was supposed to manage over Christmas. Liza said nothing but pocketed the money and put on her coat.

'I think you're very ungrateful,' said Mrs Spurdell, 'and very foolish, considering how hard jobs are to come by.'

She began shouting for her husband, presumably to come and stop Liza leaving. Liza walked out of the front door and shut it behind her. All the way down Aspen Close she expected to have to run because one of them was pursuing her but nothing like that happened. If the manager who admired her had been on duty in the Duke's Head she would have asked him if she might use his phone, but there was a woman in reception. While she was occupied at the computer Liza walked upstairs and had a bath.

Not waiting for Sean but going home on the bus, it occurred to her as she climbed to the front seat at the top, that for a six-year-old – like the milkman with a child's mental age? – she hadn't done badly. Surely she had been resourceful? She had acquired a soporific drug, discovered how to find her mother, had even found the phone number, had given in her notice, had a bath and lacking a towel, dried herself on the hotel bathroom curtains.

Would she have done better if she'd grown up in a London street and been to boarding school?

Sean had finished at Superway. He had unpacked his last carton of cornflakes and last can of tomatoes. A little wary of her still but no longer sullen, he described how the manager had shaken hands with him and wished him well.

'Does anyone know about me?' Liza asked him. 'I mean, the people at your work? Do they know you've got a girlfriend that lives with you and who I am and all that?'

'No, they don't. I keep my private affairs to myself. So far as they know, I'm all on my own.'

'Will you drive to Scotland?'

'Course I'll drive. What you got in mind? First-class train tickets and a stopover in a luxury hotel. You've got a lot to learn about money, love.'

He began fretting about a new law that had come in, excluding caravans from all land except where the owner's express permission was given. The sooner they were gone the better. Would the law in Scotland be different? He'd heard it sometimes was. Liza knew more about it than he did, she had read it up in Mr Spurdell's newspaper. For instance, she knew that if your caravan was turned off a piece of land and you weren't allowed to park it anywhere else, the local authority was bound to house you. It might not be a real house or a flat, it might be only a room, even a hotel room, but it would be *somewhere*. She wasn't going to say any of this to Sean and risk a sneer about her cleverness and her aspirations.

All the time they had been there she had kept the caravan very clean. Cleanliness was ingrained in her, Eve had seen to that, and she could no more have left her home dirty than she could have failed to wash herself. For all that, it was a poor place, everything about it shabby, worn, scraped, scuffed, chipped, broken, cracked and makeshift-mended. But the gate-house had been shabby too. Would she want anything like the 'monstrosity' Bruno had picked or the Spurdells' house, she who had been spoiled for choice by Shrove?

The caravan and the car, a home and a means of transport. With those life would be possible, some kind of future would be possible. She watched Sean speculatively. Spartan living wasn't all that Eve had taught her.

No one had known where Bruno was and no one had cared but an easily fobbed-off estate agent. Trevor Hughes had had an estranged wife, glad to see the back of him. No one knew Sean wasn't alone. Her existence, her presence in his life, all this he had kept secret. He had left Superway and at this branch they would think no more about him, no doubt he was already forgotten.

At the Glasgow end they would expect him to turn up for the course on Monday. If he didn't come they wouldn't set in train a police alert but conclude that he had changed his mind. She knew little about life but the experiences she had had were of a peculiar nature. Few could look back on a similar history. She knew from experience, from the disappearance of Trevor Hughes and Bruno Drummond, that the police do little about searching for missing men in their particular circumstances. In this case it was unlikely an absent man would even be reported missing.

Sean's mother had long since lost interest in him. His brothers and sisters were scattered in distant places, long out of touch. The chain-smoking grand-father was too ancient to care. The people he called friends were pub acquaintances and caravan-site neighbours like Kevin.

While Sean watched television, she looked at

343

herself long in the glass, the cracked piece of mirror ten inches by six which was all she and Sean had to see their faces in. It had seemed to her that Eve had never changed. The woman she had run away from a hundred days and nights ago was in her eyes the same woman, looking just the same, as the Mother who had brought her to Shrove when she was four, not older nor heavier nor less fresh. Yet now as she looked at her own face it was a youthful Eve that she saw, different from the Eve of the present, an Eve she had forgotten but who came back to her as herself. As Jonathan had once said, as Bruno had said, she was a clone of that Eve, fatherless, her mother's double, her mother all over again.

With her mother's methods, with her mother's instincts. What would Eve have done? Not put up with it. Never yielded. Eve would have argued, remonstrated, reasoned – as she had – and when all that was to no avail, when they wouldn't agree or see her point of view, appeared to give in and behaved in a conciliatory way.

Retreating to the kitchen where he couldn't see her, she re-read the instructions on the label of the sodium amytal carton. One would evidently send him to sleep. Two, surely, would put him into a deep sleep. And while he slept? He had often reproached her for not being squeamish enough, for an ability to confront violence and blood and death.

She had never been taught a horror of these things. Unlike children who go to school, children with siblings and friends and mentors, she had never been conditioned. If she was horrified by any of violent death's aspects it was at her own weakness in vomiting when she had found Bruno's body. But if Eve had never taught her to shrink from the sight of blood, she had instilled into her the need to be a perfectionist, to be good at everything she did. She

344

would do this well, cleanly, efficiently and without remorse.

'What time do we start in the morning?' she asked him.

'First thing. Hopefully we can be on our way by eight.'

'At least it's stopped raining.'

'The weather forecast says an area of high pressure's coming. It's going to get cold, cold and bright.'

'Shouldn't you put the towing bar on tonight?'

'Christ,' he said. 'I forgot.'

She doubted if she could do it herself. In the past, when he had done it, she hadn't bothered to watch him. This evening, of course, she watched him all the time, studying what he did, assessing him in every possible situation, as she had done in those early days when she was in love with him.

Perhaps, at sixteen, you were never in love with the same person for long. It was violent, it was intense, but of short duration. Did teachers like Mr Spurdell, or people like Eve, ever ask if Juliet would have gone on being in love with Romeo?

Sean worked by the light of a Tilley lamp and a rechargeable battery torch. Wrapped in the thick wadded coat, she sat on the caravan steps in the quiet and the darkness, appreciating for the first time how silent it was here and how remote. Like Shrove. This place had the advantages of Shrove. Not a single light was visible, not an isolated pinpoint, in any direction across miles of hills and meadowland. The black land rolled away to meet the nearly black sky. If she strained her ears the gentle chatter of the stream was just audible.

Above her now the stars were coming out, Charles's Wain pale and spread out and Orion bright and strong. The white planet, still and clear, was

Venus. The air had that glittery feel to it, as of unseen frost in the atmosphere. Metal clinking against metal occasionally broke the silence as Sean worked, that and the soft ghostly cries of owls in the invisible trees.

She hooked her thumbs inside the money belt, feeling its thickness. How was it she knew that if she let Sean live and went up north with him he would sooner or later find out about that money and demand it himself? She did know. She could even create the scene in her mind with her telling him it was hers, hers by right of her Mother, and Sean saying she wasn't fit to have charge of money, he'd look after it and put it towards the home they'd buy.

He finished coupling the car to the caravan. They went back inside and he washed his hands. It was late, past eleven, and as he kept saying, they had to get up early.

'Don't you worry, I'll wake you,' he said. 'You know what you are, sleep like the dead. I don't reckon you'd ever wake up without me to give you a shake.'

She didn't argue. Her dissenting role was past and now she was all acquiescence. Eve had given in to Bruno over the house and to Jonathan over the sale of Shrove. Perhaps she had murmured, 'Yes, all right,' to Trevor Hughes before she bit his hand. You gave in, you smiled and said a sweet, 'You win'. You lulled them into believing theirs was the victory.

'Wake me up at seven and I'll make you tea.'

It wasn't unusual for her to say that, she often said and did it. He never had a hot drink at night, always had one in the morning. She put the pill container behind the sugar basin, opened the drawer where they kept cutlery, their blunt knives and forks with bent tines, and checked that the one sharp knife was there, the carver. It was good to be the kind of person

346

who didn't flinch from weapons or the consequences of using them.

He was already in bed. Her throat felt dry and her stomach muscles tightened as they had on the previous night and the night before. On neither of those nights had he touched her. Last evening he hadn't even kissed her. But she was afraid just the same, of his strength and her own weakness, knowing now something she'd never realised and would once have refused to believe: that a woman, however young and vigorous, is powerless against a determined man.

When she came to bed and switched off the light she fancied she could feel his eyes on her in the darkness. Gradually, as always happened, she became accustomed to the absence of light and the darkness ceased to be absolute, became grey rather than black. The moon had risen out there, or half a moon to give so pale a light. It trickled thinly round the window blinds.

His eyes were on her and his lips tentatively touched her cheek. He must have felt her immediate tension for he sighed softly. An enormous relief relaxed her body as he rolled over on his side away from her. She withdrew to the side of the bed, to put as many inches as she could between herself and him.

She would sleep now and in the morning she would kill him.

Chapter Twenty-Three

Dreaming, she was herself and not herself. She was Eve too. She looked down at her hands and they were Eve's hands, smaller than hers, the nails longer. A shrinking had reduced her to Eve's height.

Yet she was in the caravan where Eve had never been. She knew she was dreaming and that somehow, by taking thought, by a process of concentration, she could be herself again. It was dark. She could just make out the shape of Sean lying in bed and a hump in the bedclothes beside him as if another body lay there, *her* body. She had come out of her body the way the Ancient Egyptians believed the Ka did. But it felt solid, her hand tingled when she drew a nail across the palm. It was no longer Eve, for Eve had come in and was standing at the foot of the bed.

They looked at each other in silence. Eve's hands were chained, she had come out of prison, and Liza knew – though not how she knew – that she must go back there. In spite of the chains, painfully, with a great effort, Eve reached up and took the gun down from the caravan wall. There was no gun there but she reached up and took it down. A little moonlight gleamed on the metal. Long ago, years and years ago, Liza had known that her mother took the gun down from the wall but she had never seen her do it.

Eve came up to her, holding the gun in her manacled hands. She did not speak yet her message communicated itself to Liza. It would be easy. The first time only was hard. Sleep would still be possible and peace of mind and contentment. Long days of forgetfulness would pass. Eve smiled. She began to whisper confidingly how she had wrapped herself in a sheet, taken a kitchen knife and crept upstairs to the sleeping Bruno.

Liza cried out then. She reached for Sean, for the bed, for the body of herself and entered it again, her body growing round her, waking as she woke. And then she was up, huddled and crouching in a far corner. The moon still shone and its greenish light still infiltrated the caravan, seeping between window frames and blinds. It was icy cold.

Gradually full wakefulness returned. The cold brought it back. Strangely, the dream had been quite warm. She fumbled around in the half-dark, first for Mrs Spurdell's pill container, then for the sweater Eve had knitted. As she pulled it over her head, the dreadful feeling came to her that once her eyes were uncovered again she would see Eve standing there, chained, smiling, advising.

She opened her eyes. They were alone, she and Sean. It struck her as very strange, almost unbelievable that she had meant to kill him.

More cold would come in but still she opened the caravan door. The steps glittered with frost. She prised the top off the pill carton and threw the pills into the long wet grass in the ditch. The frost burned her bare feet and when she was back inside again sharp pains shot through them.

Despair seemed to have been waiting for her in the caravan. It was there in the cold darkness and the smell of bodies and stale food. The world hadn't fallen apart when Eve told her to go. It was falling apart now, one staunch rock after another tumbling and landsliding, Eve, Sean, herself. Soon the ground beneath her feet would founder and split and swallow her up. She gave a little cry and in an agony of grief and loneliness, flung herself face-downwards on the bed, breaking into sobs.

Sean woke up and put the light on. He didn't ask what was the matter but lifted her up in his arms, held his arms tightly round her and pulled her close to him, burrowing them both under the covers. Murmuring that her hands were frozen, he squeezed them between their bodies, against his warm body.

'Don't cry, sweetheart.'

'I can't help it, I can't stop.'

'Yes, you can. You will in a minute. I know why you're crying.'

'You don't, you can't.' Because I can't kill you, because I'll never kill anyone, because I'm not Eve.

'I do know, Liza. It's because of what I done the other night, isn't it? It seemed funny at the time, like a joke, and then I got to remembering what you'd said to me when we first done it, back in the summer, like I'd never make you if you didn't want to, and I'd said I never would. I've been ashamed of myself, I've hated myself.'

'Have you?' she whispered. 'Have you really?'

'I didn't know how to say it. I was like embarrassed. In the light, in the daytime, I don't know, I couldn't say it. I'm not like you, I can't express myself like you. I've felt that too, maybe you never knew it but I have, you being like superior to me in everything.'

'I'm not, I'm really not.'

'It's so bloody cold in here I'm going to light the gas. I don't reckon we'll sleep no more. It's nearly six.'

Wiping her wet face on the sheet, she watched him get up, wrap himself in the clothes that lay about, and then put a match to the open oven. Her eyes hurt with crying and she felt a little sick.

What he said next suprised her so much she sat bolt upright in bed.

'You don't want to come with me, do you?'

'*What*?'

He got back into bed and pulled her down under the bedclothes. He hugged her and held her head in the hollow of his shoulder. His hands were always warm. That hadn't really registered with her before or she had taken it for granted. She remembered the sunny summer days and how she had watched him, that first time, from among the trees at Shrove and his puzzled look as he stared unseeing at her, aware as people mysteriously are of being observed.

He said it again, 'You don't want to come with me,' but not this time in the form of a question.

Shaking her head under the bedclothes, she realised that the movement indicated nothing to him and she whispered a small, 'No.'

'Is it because I – I forced myself on you?'

'No.'

'I'd never do it again. I've learned my lesson.'

'It's not because of that.'

'No, I know.' He sighed. She felt his chest move with the sigh and was aware of his heart beating under her cheek. 'It's because we're not like the same kind of people,' he said. 'I'm an ordinary – well, I'm working class and you're – you may have been brought up in that cracked way but you're – you're light years above me.'

'No, no, Sean. No.'

'You only got to listen to the way we talk. I know I get words wrong and I get grammar wrong. Hopefully that'll change when I get into management. I might say you could teach me but that wouldn't work. In a funny sort of way, I knew it wouldn't work when it first started last summer, only I wouldn't admit it even to myself. I suppose I was in love – well, I know I was. I'd never been in love before.'

'Nor I.'

351

'No, I reckon you never had the chance. I had but I never was. Not till you. Only, love, how'll you make out on your own?'

'I'll manage.'

'I do love you, Liza. It wasn't just for sex. I loved you from the first moment I saw you.'

She put up her face to him and felt for his mouth with her mouth. The touch of his lips and the feel of his tongue on hers quickened her thawing body. She felt the quick familiar ripple of desire. He sighed with pleasure and relief. They made love half-clothed, buried under the piled covers, his hands warm and hers still icy, while the blue gas flared and the water from condensation flowed down the windows.

It was eight when they woke up, much later than he had intended. She was making tea, wearing her padded coat, when he said, 'I'll tell you what I'll do, I'll leave you the van.'

She turned round. 'The caravan?'

He thought she was correcting him again. 'OK, Teacher, the *cara*van. Always got to be right, haven't you? Always know best. That's what you'd better be, not a doctor or a lawyer, but a teacher.'

'Did you really mean you'd leave me the caravan?'

'Sure I did. Look at it this way, I was going to take the van on account of you but if you're not coming it'd be better for me to share with those guys, it'd be easier.'

'You could sell it.'

'What, this old wreck. Who'd buy it?'

Her hesitation lasted only a moment. 'I've got some money,' she said. 'I found it when I went to Shrove. It was Eve's but she'd have wanted me to have it.'

'You never said. Why didn't you tell me?'

'Because I'm horrible – or I thought you were. Don't be cross *now*. It's a lot, it's more than a thousand pounds.'

352

She was ashamed because she'd thought he'd grab the money as soon as he got the chance and here he was shaking his head.

'I always said I'd not live off my girlfriend and I won't. Even – ' he smiled a bit ruefully ' – if you're not my girlfriend no more. You'll need it, love, whatever you do. I'd get in touch with that Heather if I was you. Hopefully, she's been wondering what you've been up to. It'll be a relief to her. And then maybe you and her can go together to see your mum.'

Liza gave him his tea. 'I'll tell you what I'm going to do, Sean, I'm going to cook us a big breakfast of eggs and bacon and fried potatoes and fried bread and if it stinks out the caravan, who cares?'

'We'll meet again one day, won't we?' he said as he started on his first egg. 'You never know, we might both be different.'

'Of course we'll meet again.'

She knew they never would. Whatever became of him, she would be different beyond recognition.

'You'll need someone to look after you.' He fretted a bit as he packed his bags. They were Superway plastic carriers, the only luggage he had. Guilt over her made him fret. 'You'll get hold of Heather, won't you? That money you've got, it's not all that much. I'll tell you what, I'll drive you into town, it's on my way. You can phone her from there.'

'All right.'

'I'll feel easier, love.'

Instead of hating the new situation, he was relieved. Just a bit. She could tell that, she could see it in his eyes. Tomorrow it would be more than a bit, it would be overwhelming. He wouldn't be able to believe his luck. As it was, now, he was forcing himself to put up a big pretence of being sad.

'I'll worry about you.'

'Write down where you'll be,' she said, 'and I'll write to you and tell you what's happened to me. I promise.'

He gave her a sidelong look. 'Don't put in too many long words.'

The two phone boxes in the marketplace were both empty. Sean parked in front of them. He felt in his jacket pocket and gave her all the change he had: coins to phone Heather and coins to phone the Home Office. There were enough of them to last even if people at the other end kept her waiting while they went off to find someone. First, he said, she must get on to directory enquiries for Heather's number. She'd got the address still, hadn't she?'

'But maybe you'd better come with me, after all, love. Just for a week or two, until we've found some place for you to go, until you're sure of this Heather.'

She shook her head. 'You've left the van behind, remember? You've left me the van.'

That he was grateful for her use of his term she could see in his eyes. They seemed full of love, as they had been in those early days, at apple-picking time, in the warm sunny fields. She put up her face and kissed him, a long soft passionless kiss. It troubled her, and always would, that she had thought of killing him. Even if she hadn't really been serious, even if it was a fantasy created out of stress and memory, it would always be there. More than anything else, it would be responsible for making any further love or companionship or even contiguity between them impossible.

'Drive off,' she said. 'Don't wave. I'll be OK. Good luck.'

But she watched the car go, she couldn't help herself. And he did wave. He did a funny thing, he blew her a kiss. She was left in the cold marketplace, on the pavement, with shoppers all around her.

354

The phone boxes weren't empty any more. A woman had gone into one of them and a boy into the other. She sat down on the low brick wall built round a flowerbed, an empty flowerbed, the earth thinly sprinkled with frost. It didn't matter to her how many people went into those phone boxes, if a queue of fifty formed, if someone went in and vandalised them like they'd done to the one outside Superway, pulled the phones off the wall, it wouldn't matter to her because she didn't mean to phone anyone. What she had to do now was think how to find out where a certain street was.

She thought about it. If she didn't fix her mind on something practical it would fill up with fear, with the realisation of her utter aloneness. Sooner or later she was going to have to confront that but not now. A picture of herself as a silly little ignorant girl sitting on a brick wall weeping, rose before her eyes and she resolved not to let it become real. She would go into a shop and ask.

They didn't know. The shop was full of small objects Liza thought were called souvenirs, brooches and key rings and little boxes, fluffy animals and plastic dolls and china mugs, that she couldn't believe anyone would want to possess. The people who worked there all came from outside the town. 'You could get a street plan,' one of them said. 'How do I?' she asked and if they looked at her strangely, they nevertheless said, 'A paper shop, yes, that's the best place, there's one three doors along.'

And there was. And they had a street plan. They didn't seem to think it was a funny thing to ask for. It was a long way away, her destination, two miles she calculated from the rough scale.

On the way she passed street people who had been out all night on the pavement or in doorways if they were lucky. It brought back to her what Sean had said about 'poor buggers sleeping rough'. Would she be one of them? It was a possibility. A thousand pounds wasn't the fortune she had thought it when she first took the iron box. It didn't seem much when you could pay a twentieth part of it for that pair of shoes she saw in a shop window she passed.

The shops stopped soon after that and there came a place with a red fire engine half out of its door. Seeing one like it on television made identification possible. Next-door was a big imposing building with a blue lamp over the door and a notice board on either side of the entrance. The blue lamp, like the one on the car, told her what it was before she read the County Police sign.

She stopped and stared at the poster on the notice board. The strange thing was that she recognised the painting in it as Bruno's before she knew it for her own portrait. The big features, the strong colours, that had never been her features and colours. No one passing would know it for her. If anyone came by they would never connect the brown and yellow daub on the poster with the girl who stood looking at it.

No doubt it was the best the police could do. It was all they had. Probably they had never before come upon a missing person who had never had her photograph taken. The poster said: *Have you seen this girl?* It said she was missing, gave her name and age, her height and weight and the colour of her hair, and said that anyone knowing her whereabouts should be in touch with them.

Liza turned away. She felt enormously more cheerful, she felt full of hope. Eve hadn't forgotten her, Eve did need her. If no one had found her it was because the only likeness of her that existed was Bruno's strange daub. She began to walk fast along this street of small red houses, all linked together in a long row of roofs and chimneys and tiny gardens, each with its car at the pavement. Warmth began to spread through her and she felt the blood come into her cheeks.

The house she was going to wouldn't look like these, she had decided, but either like Mr and Mrs Spurdell's or else like the one Bruno had nearly bought, or a mixture of the two. That sort was beginning to appear now, prim, neat houses each hugging to itself its small walled piece of land.

The name of the place where she had grown up and the year of her own birth. Shrove Road was on the edge of the town where the country started. Number 76 wasn't at all what she had expected but a house that looked as if it were left over from some distant past time when there were no other buildings but the church and the manor and the farms. This one had been a small farmhouse, she thought, which even now stood in a big piece of land with trees on it.

She was suddenly afraid. Of no one being at home, of her assumptions and assessments being all wrong, of walking back again to the bus stop past the street people. The bell by the front door didn't chime like the one in Aspen Close or toll like the bell on the door at Shrove. It buzzed. She took her finger away as if the insect that made the buzzing had stung it, then, more confidently, pressed again.

Jane Spurdell didn't recognise her. Liza could tell that and, inspired, she grasped a handful of her hair and pulled it to the back of her head.

'I know. It's Liza. Wait a minute, Liza Holford.'

'Yes.'

'Come in. You must be cold.' A glance outside had told her Liza had come on foot. From where? 'I'm miles from anywhere.'

'I'm used to being miles from anywhere,' Liza said, and that was the start of telling her. Not all, not a

357

hundred nights of life story, just the essentials and an outline of her present state.

Jane Spurdell made coffee. They sat in her living room which was a mess but a nice mess with books on shelves and piled on tables and even on the floor.

'I want to study the law but I've a long way to go, I know that. I've got to get – ' she couldn't remember the names of the examinations – 'oh, GC Levels or something. And I want to find my Mother and go and see her. I've got a thousand pounds and a caravan to live in.'

'The law sounds a good idea. Why not?' Jane Spurdell said. 'You can use my phone if you want to phone your mother.' She looked a little wary. 'I'm not sure about the caravan, I mean if you came to ask me if you could park it here, I'd have to think about that one.'

'No, I've got it on a place where they'll make me move and when I can't they'll move me and find me somewhere to live. They have to.' Liza finished her coffee. She was warm now and feeling strong. 'I came to ask you one thing I know you can do for me.'

'Yes?'

Liza didn't want to face it that for a moment Jane had sounded like her Mr Spurdell. She said in a rush, 'Please can you arrange for me to go to school?'

It was relief that Jane felt. Liza could tell that. Whatever she had expected it hadn't been that. She had anticipated begging, requests for money, time, attention – even, perhaps, affection.

'Yes, of course I can,' she said, relief beaming in her smile. 'Nothing easier. It's not difficult. You can start somewhere in January. I only wish more people were like you. Is that all?'

Liza gave a great sigh. She was going to be all right and she wasn't going to burst into tears of relief or make confessions. A good time was beginning and she was going to think of that and be a Stoic.

'That's all I want. To go to school.' She held out her cup, 'And please may I have another cup of coffee?'

SIMISOLA

To Marie

Chapter One

There were four people besides himself in the waiting room and none of them looked ill. The olive-skinned blonde in the designer tracksuit bloomed with health, her body all muscles, her hands all golden tendons, apart from the geranium nails and the nicotine stains on the right forefinger. She had changed her seat when a child of two arrived with its mother and homed to the chair next to hers. Now the blonde woman in the tracksuit was as far away as she could get, two seats from himself and three from the very old man who sat with his knees together, his hands clutching his checked cap in his lap and his eyes on the board where the doctors' names were printed.

Each of the GPs had a light above his or her name and a hook underneath it on which coloured rings hung: a red light and rings for Dr Moss, green for Dr Akande, blue for Dr Wolf. The old man had been given a red ring, Wexford noticed, the child's mother a blue one, which was exactly what he would have expected, the preference for the senior man in one case, the woman in the other. The woman in the tracksuit hadn't got a ring at all. She either didn't know you were supposed to announce yourself at reception or couldn't be bothered. Wexford wondered why she wasn't a private patient with an appointment later in the morning and therefore not obliged to wait here fidgeting and impatient.

The child, tired of marching back and forth on the seats of the row of chairs, had turned her attention to the magazines on the table and begun tearing off their covers. Who was ill, this little girl or her overweight pallid mother? Nobody said a word to hinder the tearing, though the old man glared and the woman in the tracksuit did the unforgivable, the outrageous, thing. She thrust a hand into her crocodile-skin handbag, took out a flat gold case, the function of which would have been a mystery to most people under thirty, removed a cigarette and lit it with a gold lighter.

Wexford, who had been successfully distracted from his own anxiety, now became positively fascinated. No fewer than three notices on the walls, among the exhortations to use a condom, have children immunized and watch your weight, forbade smoking. What would happen? Was there some system whereby smoke in the waiting room could be detected in reception or the dispensary?

The child's mother reacted, not with a word to the woman in the tracksuit but by sniffing, giving the little girl a vicious yank with one hand and administering a slap with the other. Screams ensued. The old man began a sorrowful head-shaking. To Wexford's surprise the smoker turned to him and said, without preamble, 'I called the doctor but he refused to come. Isn't that amazing? I was forced to come here myself.'

Wexford said something about GPs no longer making house calls except in cases of serious illness.

'How would he know it wasn't serious if he didn't come?' She must have correctly interpreted Wexford's disbelieving look. 'Oh, it's not *me*,' she said and, incredibly, 'it's one of the servants.'

He longed to know more but the chance was lost. Two things happened simultaneously. The blue light for Dr Wolf came on and the door opened to admit the practice nurse. She said crisply, 'Please put that cigarette out. Didn't you see the notice?'

The woman in the tracksuit had compounded her offence by dropping ash on the floor. No doubt she would have ground her fag end out there too but for the nurse taking it from her with a little convulsive grunt and carrying it off into hitherto unpolluted regions. She was unembarrassed by what had happened, lifting her shoulders a little, giving Wexford a radiant smile. Mother and child left the waiting room in quest of Dr Wolf just as two more patients came in and Dr Akande's light came on. This is it, thought Wexford, his fear returning, now I shall know. He hung up the green ring and went out without a backward glance. Instantly it was as if those people had never been, as if none of those things had happened.

Suppose he fell over as he walked the short corridor to Dr Akande's room? Already twice that morning he had fallen. I'd be in the best place, he told himself, the doctors' surgery – no, he corrected himself, must move with the times, the medical centre. The best place to be taken ill. If it's something in my brain, a growth, a bloodclot. . . . He knocked on the door, though most people didn't.

Raymond Akande called, 'Come in.'

This was only the second time Wexford had been to him since Akande joined the practice on Dr Crocker's retirement, and the first visit had been for an anti-tetanus injection when he cut himself in the garden. He liked to believe there had been some sort of rapport between them, that they had taken to each other. And then he castigated himself for thinking this way, for caring, because he knew damned well he wouldn't have involved himself with likings or dislikings if Akande had been other than he was.

This morning, though, these reflections were nowhere. He was concerned only with himself, the fear, the horrid symptoms. Keeping calm, trying to be detached, he described them, the way he fell over when he got out of bed in the morning, the loss of balance, the floor coming up to meet him.

'Any headache?' said Dr Akande. 'Any nausea?'

No, there was none of that, Wexford said, hope creeping in at the door Akande was opening. And, yes, he had had a bit of a cold. But, you see, a few years ago he'd had this thrombosis in the eye and ever since then he'd. . . . Well, he'd been on the alert for something like it, a stroke maybe, God forbid.

'I thought maybe Ménière's syndrome,' he said unwisely.

'I'm no believer in banning books,' said the doctor, 'but I'd personally burn all medical dictionaries.'

'OK, I did look at one,' Wexford admitted. 'And I didn't seem to have the right symptoms, apart from the falling bit.'

'Why don't you stick to the judges' rules and leave diagnosis to me?'

He was quite willing. Akande examined his head and his chest and a few reflexes. 'Did you drive yourself here?'

His heart in his mouth, Wexford nodded.

'Well, don't drive. Not for a few days. Of course you can drive home. Half the population of Kingsmarkham's got this virus. I've had it myself.'

'Virus?'

'That's what I said. It's a funny one, it seems to affect the semi-circular canals in the ears and they control the balance.'

'It's really just that, a virus? A virus can make you fall down like that, out of the blue? I measured my length in the front garden yesterday.'

'It's quite a length to measure,' said Akande.

'Didn't have any illuminating visions, I suppose? No one to tell you to stop kicking against the pricks?'

'You mean visions are another symptom? Oh, no, I see. Like on the road to Damascus. You're not going to tell me that was all Paul had, a virus?'

Akande laughed. 'The received view is that he was an epileptic. No, don't look like that. This is a virus, I promise you, not a case of spontaneous epilepsy. I'm not going to give you anything for it. It'll get right in a day or two on its own. In fact, I'll be surprised if it doesn't get right immediately now you know you haven't got a brain tumour.'

'How did you. . . ? Oh, well, I suppose you're used to patients with irrational fears.'

'It's understandable. If it's not medical books, it's the newspapers never letting them forget about their health for five minutes.'

Akande got up and held out his hand. Wexford thought it a pleasant custom, that of shaking hands with patients, the way doctors must have done years ago when they made house calls and sent bills.

'Funny creatures, people,' the doctor said. 'For instance, I'm expecting someone this morning who's coming on behalf of her *cook*. Send the cook, I said, but that apparently wouldn't do. I've a feeling – without foundation, I must tell you, mere intuition – that she's not going to be too overjoyed when she finds I'm what my father-in-law's boss used to call "a man of colour".'

For once, Wexford was speechless.

'Have I embarrassed you? I'm sorry. These things are always just under the surface and sometimes they bubble up.'

'You haven't embarrassed me,' Wexford said. 'It was only that I couldn't think of anything to say that would be . . . well, a refutation or a consolation. I just agreed and I didn't care to say that.'

5

Akande gave him a pat on the shoulder, or one that was aimed at the shoulder but landed on his upper arm. 'Take a couple of days off. You should be fine by Thursday.'

Halfway down the corridor Wexford met the blonde woman heading towards Akande's room. 'I know I'm going to lose my cook, I can just see it coming,' she said as she passed him. A miasma that was a mix of Paloma Picasso and Rothman Kingsize hung in her wake. Surely she hadn't meant the cook was going to *die*?

He went jauntily out, pushing open both of the double doors. Only one of the cars in the car park could possibly be hers, the Lotus Elan with the personalized number, AK 3. She must have paid a lot for that, it was one of the earliest. Annabel King, he speculated. Anne Knight? Alison Kendall? Not all that number of English surnames begin with K, but then she certainly wasn't of English origin. Anna Karenina, he thought, being silly.

Akande had said he could drive home. In fact, Wexford would have enjoyed walking home, he loved the idea of walking now he had stopped falling over or being afraid of falling over. The mind was a funny thing, what it could make the body do. If he left the car here he'd only have to come back for it later.

The young woman waddled and the child skipped down the medical centre's shallow steps. Full of good cheer, Wexford wound down his window and asked them if they'd like a lift. Somewhere, anywhere, he was in the mood to drive miles out of his way if need be.

'We don't take lifts from strangers.' To the child she said very loudly, 'Do we, Kelly?'

Snubbed, Wexford withdrew his head. She was quite right. She had behaved wisely and he had not.

He might be a combined rapist and child molester cunningly disguising his nefarious motives by a visit to the doctor. Leaving, he passed a car he recognized coming in, an old Ford Escort that had been re-sprayed bright pink. You hardly ever saw a pink car. But whose was it? He often had a brilliant eidetic memory, faces and townscapes recorded in full colour, but the names got lost.

He drove out into South Queen Street. It was going to be nice telling the news to Dora and he indulged himself by thinking what might have been, the horror, the communicated dread, the putting of two brave faces on it, if he'd had to tell her he'd an appointment at the hospital for a brain scan. None of that was going to happen. Would he have been brave if it had? Would he have *lied* to her?

In that case he'd have had to lie to three people. Turning into his own garage drive, he saw Neil's car already there, thoughtfully parked on the far left to allow his own passage. Neil *and* Sylvia's car, he had better learn to say, for they had just the one between them now, since hers had been given up when her job went. They might not even be able to afford this one, the way things were now.

I ought to be gratified, he thought, I ought to be flattered. Not everybody's children come flying to the bosom of Mum and Dad when misfortune strikes. His always did. He ought not to have this reaction, this immediate response to the sight of the Fairfax car which was to ask: what now?

Adversity is good for some marriages. The warring couple put aside their strife and stand united against the world. Sometimes. And the marriage has to be in a pretty bad way before this happens. Wexford's elder daughter's marriage had been bad for a long time and it was different from other people's bad

7

marriages chiefly in that she and Neil stayed doggedly together, ever seeking new remedies, for the sake of their two sons.

Once Neil had said to his father-in-law, 'I do love her. I really love her,' but that was a long time ago. A lot of tears had fallen since then and a lot of cruel things been said. Many times Sylvia had brought the boys home to Dora and just as often Neil had taken himself to a motel room on the Eastbourne road. Her educating herself and working for the social services had solved no problems, and nor had their lavish foreign holidays or moves to bigger and better houses. At least, money or the lack of it had never been an issue. There was enough, more than enough.

Until now. Until Neil's father's firm of architects (two partners, father and son) felt the recession, then its bite, then was punched and undermined by it into collapse. Neil had been without work for five weeks now, Sylvia for nearly six months.

Wexford let himself into his house and stood for a moment, listening to their voices: Dora's measured and calm, Neil's indignant, still incredulous, Sylvia's hectoring. He was in no doubt they were waiting for him, had come expecting to find him there, ready to be diverted from his brain tumour or embolism by their catalogue of troubles: joblessness, no prospects, increasing mortgage debt.

He opened the living room door and Sylvia fell upon him, throwing her arms round his neck. She was a big tall woman, well able to embrace him without finding herself clutching his middle. For a moment he thought her affection occasioned by anxiety for his health, his very life.

'Dad,' she said, she wailed, 'Dad, what d'you think we've come to? I mean, *us*. It's unbelievable but it's happening. You won't believe it. Neil's *going on the dole*.'

8

'It won't exactly be dole, darling,' said Neil, using an endearment Wexford hadn't heard on his lips for many a year. 'Not the dole. Benefit.'

'Well, it amounts to the same thing. Welfare, social security, unemployment pay, it comes to the same. It's all unbelievably ghastly, happening to *us*.'

It was interesting how Dora's quite soft voice could penetrate this stridency. It cut through it like a fine wire splitting a chunk of extra strong cheddar. 'What did Dr Akande say, Reg?'

'A virus. Apparently, there's a lot of it about. I'm to take a couple of days off, that's all.'

'What a relief,' Dora said lightly. 'A virus.'

Sylvia made a snorting sound. 'I could have told you that. I had it myself last week, I could hardly keep on my feet.'

'Then it's a pity you didn't tell me, Sylvia.'

'I've got more things to think about, haven't I? I'd be laughing if feeling a bit giddy was all I had to contend with. Now you're back, Dad, perhaps you can stop Neil doing this. I can't, he never takes any notice of what I say. Anybody's got more influence with him than his own wife.'

'Stop him doing what?' said Wexford.

'I've *told* you. Going to the – what's it called? – the ESJ. I don't know what that stands for but I know what it is, the combined dole place and labour exchange – no, they don't call it that any more, do they?'

'They haven't called it that for years,' said Neil. 'The Job Centre.'

'Why should I stop him?' Wexford said.

'Because it's hateful, it's degrading, it isn't the kind of place people like us go to.'

'And what do people like us do?' Wexford asked in the voice that should have warned her.

'Find something in the appointments section of *The Times*.'

9

Neil began to laugh and Wexford, his anger swiftly changed to pity, smiled sadly. Neil had been studying the situations vacant daily for weeks now, had written, he had told his father-in-law, over three hundred letters of application, all in vain.

'*The Times* don't give you any money,' said Neil, and Wexford could hear the bitterness in his voice, if Sylvia couldn't. 'Besides, I have to know where I stand on our mortgage. Maybe they can do something to stop the building society repossessing the house. *I* can't. Perhaps they can advise me what to do about the kids' schools, if it's only to tell us to send them to Kingsmarkham Comprehensive. Anyway, I'll get money – don't they call it a giro that they send you? One thing, I shall soon know. And I'd better, Reg, I'd better. We've got just two hundred and seventy pounds left in our joint account and that's the only account we've got. Just as well, I expect, since they ask you what savings you've got before they pay out.'

Wexford said quietly, 'Do you want a loan? We could let you have a bit.' He thought, swallowed. 'Say a thousand?'

'Thanks, Reg, thanks very much, but it had better be no. It'll only postpone the evil day. I'm very grateful for the offer. A loan ought to be paid back and I can't see how I'd ever repay you, not for years.' Neil looked at his watch. 'I must go,' he said. 'My appointment with the new claims adviser is for ten-thirty.'

Dora must have spoken without thinking, 'Oh, do they give you an appointment?'

It was odd to see how a smile could sadden a face. Neil hadn't quite winced. 'You see how being unemployed demotes you? I no longer belong among those who can expect social grace. I'm one of the queuers now, the waiters-in-line who are lucky to be seen at all, who get sent home with nothing and told to come back tomorrow. I've probably lost my style and my surname too. Someone'll come out and call, "Neil, Mr Stanton will see you now". At ten to one, though I'm due there at ten-thirty.'

'I'm sorry, Neil, I didn't mean . . .'

'No, of course you didn't. It's unconscious. Or, rather, it's a shift the consciousness makes, an adjustment in the way you think about a prosperous architect with more commissions than he can handle and someone who's out of work. I have to go now.'

He didn't take their car. Sylvia needed it. He would walk the half mile to the ESJ, and later on . . .

'Get the bus, I suppose,' said Sylvia. 'Why not? Half the time I have to. If there are only four a day that's too bad. We have to watch our petrol consumption. I expect he can walk five miles. You used to tell us your grandfather walked five miles to school and five miles back when he was only ten.'

There was a settled despair in her voice Wexford didn't like to hear, much as he deplored her self-pity and her petulance. He heard Dora offering to have the boys for the weekend so that Sylvia and Neil could get away, if only to London where Neil's sister lived, and he seconded that rather too heartily.

'When I think,' said Sylvia, who was given to doleful reminiscence, 'how I slaved to get to be a social worker.' She nodded to her husband as he left, resumed while he was still in earshot, 'Neil didn't exactly adapt his lifestyle to help. I had to arrange to get the boys looked after. I'd still be working at midnight sometimes. And what has it all come to?'

'Things must get better eventually, dear,' said Dora.

'I'll never get another job with the social services, I *feel* it. Do you remember those children in Stowerton, Dad? The "home alone" kids?'

Wexford thought. Two of his officers had met the parents at Gatwick coming off a plane from Tenerife. He said, 'Epson, weren't they called? He was black and she was white . . .'

'What's that got to do with it? Why bring racism into it? That was my last job as a child care officer before the cuts. Little did I dream I'd be a housewife again before those kids went back to their parents. Will you really have the boys for the weekend, Mother?'

That was the woman he had seen driving the pink car. Fiona Epson. Not that it was important. Wexford debated whether to go upstairs and lie down or defy the doctor and return to work. Work won. As he left the house he could hear Sylvia lecturing her mother on what she called acceptable forms of political correctness.

Chapter Two

When the Akande family had moved to Kingsmarkham a year or so before, the owner-occupiers on
either side of number twenty-seven Ollerton Avenue
put their houses up for sale. Insulting as this was to
Raymond and Laurette Akande and their children,
from a practical point of view it was to their
advantage. The recession was at its height and the
houses took a long time to sell, their asking prices
regularly falling, but when the newcomers arrived
they turned out to be nice people, as friendly and as
liberal-minded as the rest of the Ollerton Avenue
neighbours.

'Note my choice of words,' said Wexford. 'I said
"friendly", I said "liberal", I didn't say "non-racist".
We're all racist in this country.'

'Oh, come on,' said Detective Inspector Michael
Burden. 'I'm not. You're not.'

They were in Wexford's dining room, having
coffee, while the Fairfax boys, Robin and Ben, and
Burden's son Mark watched Wimbledon on tele-
vision in the room next door with Dora. It was
Wexford who had begun this topic of conversation,
he hardly knew why. Perhaps it had arisen out of
Sylvia's accusation when they discussed the Epsons.
He had certainly been thinking about it.

'My wife's not and nor is yours,' Burden said, 'nor
our children.'

'We're all racists,' said Wexford as if he hadn't

spoken. 'Without exception. People over forty are worse and that's about all you can say. You were brought up and I was brought up to think ourselves superior to black people. Oh, it may not have been explicit but it was there all right. We were conditioned that way and it's in us still, it's ineradicable. My wife had a black doll called a gollywog and a white one called Pamela. Black people were known as negroes. When did you ever hear anyone but a sociologist like my daughter Sylvia refer to white people as Caucasians?'

'As a matter of fact, my mother referred to black people as "darkies" and she thought she was being polite. "Nigger" was rude but "darky" was OK. But that was a long time ago. Things have changed.'

'No, they haven't. Not much. There are just more black people about. My son-in-law said to me the other day that he no longer noticed the difference between a black person and a white one. I said, you don't notice the difference between fair and dark, then? You don't notice if one person's fat and another's thin? What possible help to overcoming racism is that? We'll be getting somewhere when one person says to another of someone black, "Which one is he?" and the other one says, "That chap in the red tie."'

Burden smiled. The boys came in, banging the door behind them, to announce that Martina had won her first set and Steffi hers. Surnames scarcely existed as far as they and their contemporaries were concerned.

'Can we have the chocolate biscuits?'

'Ask your grandmother.'

'She's gone to sleep,' said Ben. 'But she said we could have them after lunch and it's after lunch now. It's the ones that are chocolate *with* chocolate chips and we know where they are.'

14

'Anything for a quiet life,' said Wexford, and he added gravely, with a hint of scolding in his voice, 'but if you start on them you must finish the whole packet. Is that understood?'

'*Kein Problem*,' said Robin.

After the Burdens and Mark had gone Wexford picked up the booklet his son-in-law had left him to look at, the ES 461. Or rather, the Xerox of the booklet. The original had gone back with Neil to his interview with the Employment Service. Neil, whose method of handling his misfortunes was to wallow in them, with the maximum self-created humiliation, had gone to the trouble of photocopying all nineteen pages of what the Employment Service chose to call a 'form'. He had taken the collection of turquoise blue, green, yellow and orange papers to Kingsmarkham Instant Print where they had a colour copier so that Wexford could see an ES 461 in all its glory (his words) and read the demands a beneficent government made of its unemployed citizens.

A new word had been coined for the first page: 'jobsearch'. There were three pages of notes to be read before completing the 'form' and then forty-five questions, many of them multiple enquiries, which made Wexford's head spin to read. Some were innocuous, some desperately sad, some sinister: Does your health limit the work you can do? asked number thirty, following twenty-nine's, What is the lowest wage you are willing to work for? Sights were set humbly for the enquiry, Do you have any academic qualifications (for example, O Levels, GCSEs, City and Guilds)? Do you have your own transport? asked number nine. Four wanted to know: If you have not worked for the last twelve months, how have you spent your time?

This last made his anger rise. What business was that of these Client Advisers, these small-time civil servants, this *government* department? He asked himself what answers they expected apart from 'looking for work'. Having a fortnight on Grand Bahama? Dining at Les Quat' Saisons? Collecting Chinese porcelain? He pushed the coloured pages aside and went into the living room where Navratilova was still battling it out on Centre Court.

'Move up,' he said to Robin on the sofa.

'*Pas de problème.*'

Doctors used to tell you to come back and see them next week or 'when the symptoms have cleared up'. These days they are mostly too busy to do that. They don't want to see patients without symptoms, not if they can help it. There are too many of the other kind, the ones that really ought to be in bed and visited at home, but who are obliged to stagger down to the medical centre and spread their viruses round the waiting room.

Wexford's virus had apparently flown away at the moment Dr Akande spoke his magic words. He had no intention of going back for a mere check-up and even disobeyed the doctor in taking no days off. From time to time he thought about that question, the one that asked how the victim of 'jobsearch' had spent his or her time, and he wondered how he would answer. When he wasn't at work, for instance, when he was on leave but hadn't gone away. Reading, talking to grandchildren, thinking, drying the dishes, having a quick one in the Olive with a friend, reading. Would that satisfy them? Or was it something quite other they wanted to hear?

But when Dr Akande phoned him a week later, he was first guilty, then apprehensive. Dora took the call. It was getting on for nine in the evening, a Wednesday in early July, and the sun not yet set. The french windows were open and Wexford was sitting

16

just inside them, reading Camus' *The Outsider*, thirty years after he had first read it, and swiping at mosquitos with the *Kingsmarkham Courier*.

'What does he want?'

'He didn't say, Reg.'

It was just remotely possible that Akande was so thorough and painstaking a general practitioner that he troubled to check up on patients who had been no more than marginally unwell. Or else – and Wexford's heart gave a little hop and a thud – that 'falling sickness' he had had wasn't the minor matter Akande had diagnosed, wasn't the result of a generalized but petty plague, was in fact much more serious, its symptoms the forerunner of . . .

'I'm coming.'

He took the receiver. From Akande's first words he knew he wasn't to be *told* anything but *asked* something; the doctor wasn't dispensing wisdom but coming cap in hand; this time it was he, the policeman, who must make the diagnosis.

'I'm sorry to trouble you with this, Mr Wexford, but I hoped you might help me.'

Wexford waited.

'It's probably nothing.'

Those words, no matter how often he heard them, always caused a small shiver. In his experience, it was nearly always something and, if brought to his attention, something bad.

'If I was really worried I'd get in touch with the police station but it isn't on that scale. My wife and I don't know many people in Kingsmarkham – of course, we're relatively new here. You being my patient . . .'

'What has happened, doctor?'

A small deprecating laugh, a hesitation, and Akande said, using a curious phrase, 'I'm trying in vain to locate my daughter.' He paused. He made another attempt. 'I suppose what I mean is, I don't know how to find out where she is. Of course, she's twenty-two years old. She's a grown woman. If she wasn't living at home with us, if she was somewhere on her own, I wouldn't even know she hadn't come home, I wouldn't . . .'

Wexford cut in, 'Do you mean your daughter is missing?'

'No, no, that's putting it too strongly. She hasn't come home and she wasn't where we expected her to be last night, that's all. But as I say, she's grown up. If she changed her mind and went somewhere else . . . well, she has that right.'

'But you would have expected her to let you know?'

'I suppose so. She's not very reliable about that kind of thing, young people aren't, as you may know, but we've never known her to . . . well, it looks as if she's deceiving us. Telling us one thing and doing another. That's the way I personally see it. My wife, on the other hand, is worried. That's an understatement, she's very anxious.'

It was always their wives, Wexford thought. They projected their emotions on to their wives. My wife is rather anxious about it. It's bothering my wife. I'm taking this step because, frankly, the whole thing is affecting my wife's health. As strong men themselves, *macho* men, they would like you to believe they were prey to no fears, no anxieties, and to no desires either, no longings, no passions, no needs.

'What's her name?' he asked.

'Melanie.'

'When did you last see Melanie, Dr Akande?'

'Yesterday afternoon. She had an appointment in Kingsmarkham and then she was going over to Myringham on the bus to her friend's house. The friend was having a twenty-first birthday party last evening and Melanie was going to it and afterwards to stay the night. They have their majority at eighteen, so what they do is have two parties, one for eighteen and one for twenty-one.'

Wexford had noticed. He was more interested in the suppressed terror he could detect in Akande's voice, a terror the doctor overlaid with a pathetic optimism. 'We didn't expect her home till this afternoon. If they don't have to they don't get up before noon. My wife was working and so was I. We expected to find her at home when we got in.'

'Could she have been in and gone out again?'

'I suppose she could. Of course she has her own key. But she was never at Laurel's – that's the friend. My wife phoned them. Melanie hadn't turned up. And yet I can't see that that's too much to worry about. She and Laurel had had a row . . . well, a disagreement. I heard Melanie say on the phone to her, I can remember her very words: "I'm going to ring off now and don't count on seeing me on Wednesday." '

'Has Melanie a boyfriend, doctor?'

'Not any longer. They broke up about two months ago.'

'But there might have been a . . . a reconciliation?'

'I suppose there might.' He sounded grudging. When he said it again he sounded hopeful. 'I suppose there might. You mean, she met him yesterday and they've gone off somewhere together? My wife wouldn't like that. She has rather strict ideas on these matters.'

Presumably, she'd prefer fornication to rape or murder, thought Wexford rather sourly but he didn't, of course, say this aloud. 'Dr Akande, you're probably right when you say this is nothing. Melanie is somewhere where she has no access to a phone. Will you give me a ring in the morning, please? As

19

early as you like.' He hesitated. 'Well, after six. Whatever happens, whether she appears or phones or doesn't appear or phone?'

'I've got a feeling she's trying to get through to us now.'

'In that case let's not occupy the line any longer.'

His phone rang at five past six.

He wasn't asleep. He had just woken up. Perhaps he awoke because he was subconsciously troubled about the Akande girl. As he picked up the receiver, before Akande spoke, he was thinking, I shouldn't have waited, I should have done something last night.

'She hasn't come back and she hasn't phoned. My wife is very anxious.'

I expect you are too, Wexford thought. I would be. 'I'll come and see you. In half an hour.'

Sylvia had married almost as soon as she left school. There had been no time to worry about where she was or what was happening to her. But his younger daughter Sheila had caused him sleepless nights, nights of terror. Home in the holidays from drama school, she had made a speciality of disappearing with boyfriends, not phoning, giving no clue to her whereabouts until, three or four days later, she'd phone from Glasgow or Bristol or Amsterdam. And he had never got used to it. He would tell reassuring stories of his own experiences to the Akandes, he thought, as he showered and put his clothes on, but he would also report Melanie as a missing person. She was female, she was young, therefore they would mount a search for her.

Some days he walked to work, for his health's sake, but it was usually two hours later than this that he started off. This morning was hazy, everything was still, the sun a brighter whiteness in a white sky.

20

Dew lay on the roadside turf high summer had burnt straw colour. He didn't see a soul in the first two streets, then as he turned out of Mansfield Road, he met an old woman walking a minuscule Yorkshire terrier. No one else. Two cars passed him. A cat carrying a mouse in its mouth crossed the road from thirty-two Ollerton Avenue to twenty-five and dived through a flap in the front door.

Wexford didn't have to knock at twenty-seven. Dr Akande was already waiting for him on the step.

'It's very good of you.'

Resisting the temptation to say 'no problem' in one of Robin's polyglot versions, Wexford stepped ahead of him into the house. A nice, dull, ordinary sort of place to live in. He couldn't recall having been into any of the detached four-bedroomed houses of Ollerton Avenue before. The street itself was tree-lined, heavily tree-*shaded* at this time of the year. It would rob the interior of the Akande house of light until the sun came round and for a moment, until he was inside the room, he failed to see the woman who stood at the window, looking out.

The classic stance, the time-honoured position, of the parent or spouse or lover who waits and waits. *Sister Anne, sister Anne, do you see anyone coming? I see only the green grass and the yellow sand. . . .* She turned round and came towards him, a tall slender woman of about forty-five dressed in the uniform of a ward sister at Stowerton Royal Infirmary – short-sleeved navy blue dress, navy belt with a rather ornate silver buckle, two or three badges pinned at the left breast. Wexford hadn't expected someone so handsome, so striking to look at, such an elegant figure. *Why* hadn't he?

'Laurette Akande.'

She held out her hand. It was a long slender hand, the palm corn-coloured, the back deep coffee. She managed to smile. He thought, they always have these wonderful teeth, and then the blood rushed up into his face the way it hadn't done since he was a teenager. He *was* a racist. Why, from the instant he'd walked into this room he'd been thinking, how odd, it's just the same in here as in anyone else's house, same sort of furniture, same sweet peas in the same sort of vase. . . . He cleared his throat, spoke firmly.

'You're worried about your daughter, Mrs Akande?

'We both are. I think we've cause for worry, don't you? It's two days now.'

He noted she didn't say it was nothing, she wasn't saying it was just the way young people behaved.

'Sit down, please.'

Her manner was peremptory, a little offhand. She lacked her husband's *Englishness*, perhaps his bed-side manner. This was no time, he thought, for tales of the adolescent Sheila's truancy. Laurette Akande spoke briskly, 'It's time we did this officially, I think. I mean, we have to report her missing. Aren't you too high up to take care of it?'

'I'll do for now,' Wexford said. 'Perhaps you'll give me some details. We'll start with the name and address of these people she was supposed to spend the night with. I'll have the boyfriend's name too. Oh, and what was this appointment she had in Kingsmarkham before she was due to leave for Myringham?'

'It was at the Job Centre,' said Dr Akande.

His wife corrected him with precision. 'The Employment Service Job Centre. The ESJ, as it's now called. Melanie was looking for a job.'

'She was trying to find work long before she finished her course,' said Laurette Akande. 'That was at Myringham. She graduated this summer.'

'The University of the South?' Wexford asked.

Her husband answered. 'No, Myringham University, the old Polytechnic that was. They're all universities now. She was studying music and dance, "Performance Arts", it's called. I never wanted her to do that. She got a good history A Level – why couldn't she have read history?'

Wexford thought he knew what the objection was to music and dance. 'They make such wonderful dancers', 'They have these great singing voices. . . .' How often had he heard those seemingly generous remarks?

Laurette said, 'You may or may not know that black Africans are the most highly educated members of British society. Statistics show that. In view of this, we have high expectations of our children, she should have been preparing herself for a profession.' She seemed suddenly to recollect that it wasn't Melanie's education or the lack of it that this crisis was about. 'Well, it doesn't matter now. There were no openings for her in what she wanted to do. Her father had told her there wouldn't be but they never listen. You'll have to retrain in business management or something, I said to her. She went to the ESJ and picked up a form and got an appointment to see a New Claims Adviser there at two-thirty on Tuesday.'

'So when did she leave here?'

'My husband had his afternoon surgery. It was my day off. Melanie took an overnight bag with her. She said she expected to get to Laurel's by five and I remember I said, don't count on it, having that appointment at two-thirty doesn't mean she'll see you then, you could easily wait an hour. She left here at ten past two to give herself plenty of time. I know that because it's a fifteen-minute walk to the High Street from here.'

What an admirable witness Laurette Akande

23

would make! Wexford found himself hoping she would never be called upon to be one. Her voice was cool and controlled. She wasted no words. Somewhere, under the accent of South East England, was a hint of the African country she had come from perhaps as a student.

'You had the impression she was going straight from the ESJ to this place in Myringham?'

'I *know* she was. By bus. She hoped to catch the four-fifteen, which was why I said that about having to wait to see the New Claims Adviser. She wanted to take my car but I had to say no. I needed it in the morning. I was due at the hospital by eight when the day shift starts.' She looked at her watch. 'I am today. The traffic at this hour makes a ten-minute journey into half an hour.'

So she was going to work? Wexford had waited for a sign of that anxiety Dr Akande had been so insistent his wife was prey to. There was none. Either she wasn't worried or she was under an iron control.

'Where do *you* think Melanie is, Mrs Akande?'

She gave a small light laugh, a rather chilling laugh. 'I very much hope she isn't where I think it most likely she is. In Euan's flat – room, rather – with him.'

'Melanie wouldn't do that to us, Letty.'

'She wouldn't see it as doing anything to *us*. She has never appreciated our concern for her security and her future. I said to her: Do you want to be one of those girls these boys get pregnant on purpose and are *proud* of it? Euan's already got two children with two different girls and he's not twenty-two yet. You know that, you remember when she told us about those children.'

They had forgotten Wexford was there. He coughed. Dr Akande said miserably.

'That's why she split up with him. She was just as

24

shocked and upset as we were. She hasn't gone back to him, I'm sure of that.'

'Dr Akande,' said Wexford, 'I'd like you to come down to the police station with me and report Melanie missing. I think this is a serious matter. We have to search for your daughter and keep on searching till we find her.'

Alive or dead, but he didn't say that.

There was nothing Caucasian about the face in the photograph. Melanie Elizabeth Akande had a low forehead, a broad, rather flat nose, and full, thick, protuberant lips. Nothing of her mother's classical cast of feature showed in that face. Her father was an African from Nigeria, Wexford now discovered, her mother from Freetown in Sierra Leone. The eyes were huge, her thick black hair a mass of tight curls. Wexford, looking at the photograph, made a strange discovery. Though she was not beautiful to him, he could see that by the standards of others, of millions of African people, Afro-Caribbean people and African Americans, she might be considered very lovely. Why was it always the white people who set the standard?

The missing persons form, filled in by her father, described her as being five feet seven, hair black, eyes dark brown, and gave her age as twenty-two. He had to phone his wife at the hospital to be reminded that Melanie weighed nine stone two (or 128 pounds) and had been wearing blue denims, a white shirt and a long embroidered waistcoat when last seen.

'You also have a son, I think.'

'Yes, he's a medical student at Edinburgh.'

'He can't be there now. Not in July.'

'No, he's in South East Asia. So far as I know. He went off in a car about three weeks ago with two friends. They were making for Vietnam, but of course they can't be there yet . . .'

'At any rate, his sister couldn't have gone to him,' said Wexford. 'I have to ask you this, doctor. What sort of terms were you and your wife on with Melanie? Were there disagreements?'

'We were on good terms,' the doctor said quickly. He hesitated and then qualified that statement. 'My wife has strict ideas. No harm in that, of course, and there's no doubt we had high expectations for Melanie, which perhaps she couldn't fulfil.'

'Does she like living at home?'

'She really doesn't have much choice. I'm not in a position to provide accommodation for my children and I don't think Laurette would much care for . . . I mean Laurette expects Melanie to live at home until she . . .'

'Until what, doctor?'

'Well, take this idea of retraining. Laurette expects Melanie to live at home while she does that and perhaps not move away until she's earning enough and responsible enough to buy somewhere for herself.'

'I see.'

She was with the boyfriend, Wexford thought. She had met him, according to her father, when they both found themselves in their first term at what was then Myringham Polytechnic, before such institutions were elevated to university status. Euan Sinclair came from the East End of London, had graduated at the same time as Melanie, though by then the quarrel with its anger and insults had divided them. One of Euan's children, now nearly two, had been born when he and Melanie had been going out together for over a year.

Akande knew his present address. He spoke as if it was written in bitterness on his heart. 'We've tried to phone him but the number is unobtainable. That means it's been cut off for non-payment of his bill, doesn't it?'

'Probably.'

'That young man is a West Indian.' Snobbery raised its head in these areas as well, did it? 'An Afro-Caribbean, as we're supposed to call them. Her mother sees him as someone who could potentially wreck Melanie's life.'

It was Detective Sergeant Vine who went to London to seek Euan Sinclair in his rented room in a Stepney street. Akande had told him he wouldn't be surprised if Euan was living there with one of the mothers of his children and perhaps the child as well. This would make it very unlikely that Melanie was there too but Vine didn't say so. Myringham Police had undertaken to send an officer round to the home of Laurel Tucker.

'I shall look in at the ESJ myself,' Wexford said to Burden.

'The what?'

'The Employment Service and Jobcentre.'

'Then why isn't it the ESAJC?'

'Maybe it's really Employment-Service-Job-Centre, all one word. I'm afraid that those civil servants who remodel our language have made Jobcentre into one word as they have "jobsearch".'

For a moment Burden said nothing. He was trying to read, with increasing incredulity, a PR handout from a company guaranteeing to make private cars thief-proof.

'It shuts them up in a metal cage. After two minutes it stops and nothing will start it. Then it makes these blood-curdling howls. Imagine that on the M2 at five-thirty, the obstruction, the safety hazard . . .' Burden looked up. 'Why you?' he said. 'Archbold could do that or Pemberton.'

27

'I daresay they could,' said Wexford. 'They go there often enough when someone's assaulted an admin officer or started taking the place apart. I'm going because I want to see what it's like.'

Chapter Three

It was going to be a fine day, if you could stand the humidity. The air was still, not so much misty as with a thick feel to it. You wanted to fill your lungs with fresh air but this *was* fresh air, all you were going to get. A hot sun was filtered through meshes of cloud behind which the sky must be a rich dark blue but which looked like a pale opal and was covered with an unmoving thready network of cirrus.

Fumes from traffic were trapped under the cloud ceiling and by the still air. Along the pavement Wexford found himself passing through areas where someone had stopped to talk while smoking. The smell that still hung there was of cigarettes, in one spot a French cigarette, in another a cigar. Though it was still early, not quite ten, a reek of stale seafood swung out from the fishmonger's. To pass a woman from whose skin came light floral scent or musky perfume was a pleasant relief. He paused to read the menu inside the window of the new Indian restaurant, the Nawab: Chicken Korma, Lamb Tikka, Chicken Tandoori, Prawn Biryani, Murghe Raja – all the usual stuff, but you might say that about roast beef and fish and chips. It all depended on the cooking. He and Burden could try it for lunch, when they had a moment. Otherwise, it would be take-away from the Moonflower Instant Cantonese Cuisine.

The Employment Service Jobcentre was this side of

29

the Kingsbrook Bridge, a little way down Brook Road between the Marks and Spencers foodstore and the Nationwide Building Society. Not a particularly sensitive location, Wexford thought, considering this for the first time. The people who came to sign on would be made to wince at anything which reminded them of burdensome mortgages and repossessed houses and hardly cheered by the sight of shoppers coming out of the doors on the other side with carrier bags full of food specialities they could no longer afford. Still, nobody who had a say in it had thought of that and perhaps the ESJ came there first. He couldn't remember.

A car park at the side – 'Strictly ESJ Staff Only' – had access into the High Street. Steps with chipped stone balustrades led up to double doors of aluminium and glass. Inside, the atmosphere smelt stale. It was hard to say what it smelt of, for Wexford could see two notices that forbade smoking ('Strictly Prohibited') and no one was disobeying. Nor was it the smell of bodies. If he were to be fanciful, and he decided he had better not be, he would have said it was the odour of hopelessness, of defeat.

The large room was divided into two sections; one area, the larger, was the Benefit Office, where you went to give proof of life, proximity and continuing unemployed status by signing on; the other offered jobs. On the face of it, an abundance of jobs. One free standing notice board advertised receptionists, another housekeepers and catering, a third shops, managerial, drivers, bar staff and miscellaneous. A closer look showed him that in all cases only the experienced need apply – references were required, CVs, qualifications, skills – yet it was obvious that only the young were wanted. None of the cards actually said, 'Up to age 30', but energy was stressed as a requirement, or a vigorous and youthful outlook.

People sat about on three rows of chairs. All must have been under sixty-five but the older ones looked more. The young ones looked particularly hopeless. The chairs they sat on were a neutral shade of grey and now he noticed there was a colour scheme here, a rather unfortunate combination of a buttery-cream shade, navy blue and this grey. At the end of each row of chairs, on the mottled carpet, stood a plastic houseplant in a plastic Grecian urn. Several doors at the side were marked 'Private' and one, that seemed to lead to the car park, 'Strictly Private'. They had a passion for strictness in here.

Apparently, when you arrived you took a card with a number on it from a kind of ticket machine. When your number and the number of one of the desks came up in red neon you went up and signed your claim. That was the way it looked, a bit like the doctor's. Wexford hesitated between the 'Jobseekers' counter (another new composite word) and the numbered desks. At each one of these someone stood or sat, discussing complications of his or her claim with a staff member. The grey and navy badge the one nearest to him wore on her blouse proclaimed her as Ms I. Pamber, Admin Officer.

The next desk was temporarily free. Wexford went up to Ms W. Stowlap, Admin Officer, and asked politely if he could see someone in authority. She glanced up, said gruffly, 'You have to wait your turn. Don't you know you're supposed to take a card from the machine?'

'This is the only card I have.' She had riled him. It was his warrant card he produced as he snapped, 'Police.'

She was a thin freckled woman with white eyebrows and blushing didn't become her. The pink tide spread to the roots of her pale ginger hair. 'Sorry,' she said. 'You'll want the manager – Mr Leyton, that is.'

While she was away finding him Wexford wondered what the reason could be for all this formality, the 'Ms' and 'Mr' stuff, the initials instead of Christian names. It seemed out of tune with contemporary attitudes. Not that he minded that, recalling the way Ben and Robin called everyone by first names, even Dr Crocker, nearly sixty years their senior.

Discreetly, not staring, he surveyed the people who waited. Quite a lot of women, at least half. Before his wife laid into him, calling him a sexist, a chauvinist and antediluvian as well, Mike Burden had been in the habit of saying that if all these married women didn't take the jobs the unemployment figures would be halved. A black man, someone vaguely South East Asian, two or three Indians – Kingsmarkham was becoming more cosmopolitan daily. Then, in the back row, he spotted the fat young woman who had been in the waiting room at the medical centre. Wearing red and green floral leggings and a tight white tee-shirt, she slumped in her chair with her legs apart, gazing at the poster which, under a drawing of a gaily coloured gas balloon, advertised the 'Jobplan Workshop' and advised candidates for it to 'give your jobhunting a lift'.

It was with unseeing eyes, Wexford thought, that she gazed. She looked as if sledgehammered into apathy, without thoughts, without even resentment, in utter despair. Today Kelly wasn't with her, the little girl who had run along the chairs and torn up magazines. Left with a mother or a neighbour probably, not, he hoped, in one of those toddler farms, where they strapped the infants into push-chairs in front of videos of rampaging monsters. Better that, though, than left alone. Next to her, in fact two empty seats away, a trim handsome girl provided a cruel contrast. Middle-classness stamped

32

her, from her long corn-coloured hair, shining clean and cut as evenly as a curtain hem, her white shirt and blue denim skirt to the brown loafers she wore. Another Melanie Akande, Wexford thought, a new graduate who had found a degree doesn't automatically confer a job . . .

'Can I help you?'

He turned round. The man was about forty, red-faced, black-haired, with big features, the kind who looks as if his blood pressure would be high. To his grey tweed sports jacket was pinned the badge with his name and status: Mr C. Leyton, Manager. He had a harsh grating voice, an accent from somewhere north of the Trent.

'Do you want to go somewhere private?'

Leyton asked the question as if expecting the answer 'no' or 'no, don't bother'.

'Yes,' said Wexford.

'What's all this about then?' He asked it over his shoulder as he led Wexford past the counter and the New Claims booths.

'It can wait till we're in your somewhere private.'

Leyton shrugged. The heavy-set bullet-headed man who stood outside the door moved off as they approached. The Benefit Office was more in need of a security guard than most banks and it was the regular haunt of members of the uniformed branch. Desperation, paranoia and indignation, resentment, fear and humiliation all breed violence. Most people who came here were either angry or afraid.

Rather late in the day the manager said, 'I'm Cyril Leyton.' He closed the door behind them. 'What's the trouble?'

'I hope there won't be any. I want you to tell me if a certain . . . er, claimant came here on Tuesday to see one of your New Claims Advisers. Tueday, July the sixth at two-thirty.'

Leyton curled his lip and put up his eyebrows. His expression would have been appropriate for the Head of MI5 when asked by some minion, a cleaner or driver perhaps, for access to top secret papers.

'I don't want documentation,' said Wexford impatiently. 'I only want to know if she came here. And I'd like to talk to the New Claims Adviser she saw.'

'Well, I . . .'

'Mr Leyton, this is a police investigation. I suppose you know I could get a warrant in a couple of hours. Is there any point in delaying things?'

'What's her name?'

'Melanie Akande. A, K, A, N, D, E.'

'If she came on Tuesday,' said Leyton grudgingly, 'it should be on the computer by now. Just wait a minute, will you?'

His manner was unfortunate, cold, sour, rebarbative. Wexford guessed that the greatest pleasure he got out of life was derived from putting spokes in wheels. What effect must he have on claimants? Perhaps he never saw them, perhaps he was too 'high up' (as Laurette Akande put it) for that.

The room was all grey, lined with filing cabinets. There was a grey chair like those the claimants sat on, a small grey metal desk and on it a grey telephone. The view from the window seemed a riot of colour, though it was only of the shoppers' pick-up bay at the back of Marks and Spencers. Cyril Leyton came in, holding a millboard with papers attached to it by an elastic band.

'Your Miss Akande came in for her appointment at two-thirty and brought back her ES 461. That's the form required by . . .'

'I know what it is,' Wexford said.

'Right. The NCA she saw – that is, New Claims Adviser – was Miss Bystock, but you can't talk to her, she's off sick.' Leyton unbent an inch. 'One of these viruses.'

34

'If she's off sick how do you know it was Miss Bystock Melanie Akande saw and not Mr Stanton?'

'Come on. Her initials are on the claim. See?'

Ostentatiously covering up everything but the bottom right hand corner of the sheet, Leyton showed Wexford the pencilled initials: A.B.

'Did anyone else see her? Any of the other NCAs? The administration officers?'

'Not that I know of. Why would they?'

Wexford said suddenly, with extreme sharpness, 'Don't ask me. It doesn't help to be obstructive.'

Leyton's mouth opened but no sound came.

'Mr Leyton, it is an offence to obstruct the police in their duties. Did you know that? Melanie Akande is missing from home. She hasn't been seen since she left this building. This is a very serious matter. I suppose you read the newspapers? You watch television? You know what happens in the world we live in? Have you some reason for jeopardizing this enquiry?'

The man went a darker red. He said slowly, 'I didn't know. I'd have been . . . well, I had no idea.'

'You mean that what I've been treated to is your normal manner?'

Leyton said nothing. Then he seemed to take hold of himself. 'I'm sorry. I'm under a lot of pressure here. Has . . . has something happened to her? This woman?'

'That's what I'm trying to find out.' Wexford showed him the photograph. 'Will you ask your staff, please?'

This time he waited outside that stuffy grey room. He thought of the hymn line: 'Frail children of dust. . . '. That room was like a cell spun and carved out of dust. He read the other posters, the one advocating work trials, whatever they were, and the one that asked employers: 'Do you always choose the right person to fill your vacancy?' He decided to fill his own vacancy by reading one of the leaflets which lay about.

It was curiously apposite. 'Be alert', it said. 'Be safe when jobseeking.' Inside he read, 'DO – tell a friend or relative where you are going and what time you expect to be back . . . arrange to be collected from the interview if it takes place outside working hours . . . find out as much as you can about the company before the interview, especially if there are no details in the job advert . . . make sure that the interview takes place at the employer's premises or, if not, in a public place. DON'T – apply for a job which seems to offer too much money for very little work . . . agree to continue the interview over drinks or a meal, even if it seems to be going very well . . . let the inter- viewer steer the conversation towards personal sub- jects that have nothing to do with the job . . . accept a lift home from the interviewer. . . .'

Melanie hadn't been offered a job, she hadn't been sent for an interview – or had she? Cyril Leyton came back with the admin officer labelled Ms I. Pamber, a dark-haired pretty girl with dazzling blue eyes, in her late twenties, wearing a grey skirt and pink shirt. None of the staff wore jeans, Wexford had noticed, everyone was dressed in a neat, rather outdated, way.

'I saw her, this girl you're looking for.'

Wexford nodded. 'Did you speak to her?'

'Oh, no. I'd no call to. I was on the counter. I just saw her go up and talk to Annette . . . er, Miss Bystock.'

'Can you remember what time that was?'

'Well, her appointment was for two-thirty and no one's allowed more than twenty minutes. I suppose it must have been twenty to three, something like that.'

'If she was able to see Miss Bystock on time. Was she? Or did she have to wait half an hour?'

'No, she couldn't have done. A Claims Adviser's last appointment is at three-thirty, and I know Annette had three to see after her.'

So Laurette Akande had been wrong about that. He asked Leyton for Annette Bystock's address. While the manager was away finding it, he said, 'Did you see her leave the building? Go out through those doors?'

'I just saw her talking to Annette.'

'Thank you for your help, Miss Pamber. By the way, tell me something, in these days of universal first names, why do you all have Ms or Mr and your surname and an initial on your name tags? It seems very formal.'

'Oh, it's not that,' she said. She had a charming manner, he thought, warm and just a touch flirtatious. 'Actually, I'm Ingrid. No one calls me Ms Pamber, not anyone. But they say it's for our protection.'

She looked up at him through long dark eyelashes. Her eyes were the bluest he had ever seen, the blue of a gentian or a Delft plate or a star sapphire.

'I don't follow.'

'Well, most clients are OK, I mean they're nice, most of them. But you do get some nuts – crazy people, you know? I mean, we had someone in here threw acid at Cyril – Mr Leyton, that is. He didn't hit him but he had a go. Don't you remember?'

Vaguely, Wexford did, though he'd been on leave at the time.

'Hopefully, there's very few that would do that. But if we had our full names on our tags, like "Ingrid Pamber", say, they could look us up in the phone book and . . . well, you might get someone who thought he was in love with you or someone – and

37

that's more likely – who hated you. You know, we've got jobs and they haven't, that's what it's about.'

Wexford wondered how many 'I. Pambers' there were in the Kingsmarkham and District telephone directory and guessed at just one. Still, as a safety measure keeping first names a secret was wise. The thought came to him that quite a lot of people might fancy themselves in love with Ingrid Pamber.

Another poster caught his eye, this one warning those seeking jobs not to pay anyone money for finding them work. The system seemed open to many abuses.

With Annette Bystock's address in his pocket, he went out and down the steps. In the half-hour since he had gone in there several young men had arrived to seat themselves on the stone balustrades, two of them smoking, the others staring vacantly at nothing. They took no notice of him. Lying on the pavement where someone, perhaps one of them, had discarded it, was an ES 461, the highly coloured questionnaire form. It was open at page three and when Wexford bent to pick it up he saw that the egregious question four: 'If you have not worked for the past twelve months, how have you spent your time?' had been answered. Carefully printed in the allotted space was the single word, 'Wanking'.

That made him laugh. He began trying to retrace what might have been Melanie Akande's footsteps on leaving the ESJ. According to Ingrid Pamber, she would have been in plenty of time for the three-fifteen bus to Myringham, no more than five minutes' walk away.

Wexford timed himself to the nearest bus stop. These periods of time were nearly always shorter than you anticipated and he found it took him, not five minutes, but three. However, there was no earlier bus she could have caught. He studied the timetable in its frame, somewhat vandalized, with a diagonal crack across the glass, but still readable. The buses went once an hour, on the first quarter. She would have had to wait at least twenty minutes.

It was during that sort of enforced waiting, he thought, that women accepted lifts. Would she have done that? He must ask the parents if she ever, for instance, hitched lifts. Wait, though, until Vine's report came in and there was some information from the Myringham end. Meanwhile, had anyone in the neighbourhood of this bus stop seen anything?

In the dry cleaners he drew a blank. You couldn't see the street from the interior of the wine shop. Its windows were too densely stacked with bottles and cans. He went into Grover's the newsagent. They were his newsagents, the shop that supplied his daily paper and had done for years. As soon as she saw him the woman behind the counter began apologizing for the recent late deliveries. Wexford cut her short, said he hadn't noticed, and anyway he didn't expect some schoolboy or schoolgirl to get up at the crack of dawn to bring his *Independent* by seven-thirty. He showed her the photograph.

Melanie Akande's being black was to their advantage. In a place where there were very few black people, she was known, remembered, even by those who had never spoken to her. Dinny Lawson, the newsagent, knew her by sight but, as far as she knew, Melanie had never been into the shop. As to bus queues, she sometimes noticed them and she sometimes didn't. It was Tuesday afternoon Wexford was talking about? One thing she could tell him was that no one, black or white, got on the three-fifteen to Myringham bus, no one at all.

'How can you be so sure?'

'I'll tell you. My husband said to me, it must have been Saturday or Sunday, he said it was a wonder they went on running that bus in the afternoons on account of no one went on it. Mornings, yes, specially the eight-fifteen and the nine-fifteen, and the ones that come back in the evening, they're busy. So I said, I'll keep an eye open and see. Well, we've kept the shop door open all day this week, it's been so hot, and I could see without even going to the door. And he was right, it's a fact, no one's got on the two-fifteen, the three-fifteen or the four-fifteen Monday, Tuesday or yesterday. My husband said to have five pounds on it and was I glad I didn't take him up on that . . .'

So she had disappeared somewhere between the Benefit Office and the bus stop. No, 'disappeared' was too strong a word – yet. No matter what she told her parents, perhaps she had never intended to take that bus. Perhaps she had arranged to meet someone as soon as her appointment with the New Claims Adviser was over.

In that case, was there a chance she had mentioned this to Annette Bystock? For all he knew, Annette Bystock might be one of those warm friendly people whose effect on others is to invite confidences, and confidences which have no apparent connection with the matter in hand. It was quite possible Annette had asked her if she'd be available for an interview that day and Melanie had said no, she was going to meet her boyfriend. . . .

Or there had been no meeting with a boyfriend, no confidences, nothing to confide, and Melanie had accepted a lift to Myringham from a stranger. After all, Dinny Lawson hadn't said there had been no one in the vicinity of the bus stop all afternoon, only that she had seen nobody get on the bus when it came.

Dora Wexford had got into the habit of preparing large quantities of quite elaborate food for her daughter and her daughter's family when they came to meals. Her husband had pointed out to her that though Neil and Sylvia were unemployed, they weren't poverty-stricken, they weren't on the bread-line, but this had little effect. He came home that evening just in time to share in the servings of carrot and orange soup before a main course of braised lambs' kidneys, spinach and ricotta cheese in filo pastry, new potatoes and french beans. Dessert spoons on the table indicated the arrival later of that rarity, that luxury that never happened when the two of them were alone, a pudding.

Pale weedy Neil ate hugely, as if for comfort. As Wexford joined them and sat down, he was describing to his mother-in-law his abortive visit to the Benefit Office. No payments could be made to him because, before losing his work, he had been self-employed.

'What difference does that make?' Wexford asked.

'Oh,' he explained quite carefully. 'As a self-employed person I didn't pay Class One National Insurance contributions during the two tax years prior to the tax year in which I'm making my claim.'

'But you paid them?'

'Oh, I paid them but in another class. He explained that too.'

'Who was it?' Wexford said. 'Ms Bystock or Mr Stanton?'

Neil goggled at him. 'How do *you* know?'

Enigmatically, 'I have my reasons.' Wexford relented. 'I was there today about something else.'

'It was Stanton,' Neil said.

Wexford wondered suddenly why Sylvia was looking so smug. Anxious not to put on weight, she had eaten the kidneys, refused the pastry and had now laid her knife and fork precisely down diagonally across her plate. A little smile lifted the

41

corners of her mouth. One after the other, Ben and Robin asked for more potatoes.

'You promise to eat every bit then.'

'*Problem yok*,' said Robin.

'So what are you going to do? They must do something for you.'

'Sylvia has to claim, if you can believe it. She was only part-time but she got in just enough hours to claim, so she's doing it for herself and me and the boys.'

Having told Ben to chew his food properly and not swallow in lumps, Sylvia said with undisguised triumph, 'I sign on every other Tuesday. It's A to K on Tuesdays, L to R on Wednesdays and S to Z on Thurdays. I get benefit for all of us. *And* they'll pay the mortgage. Neil hates me doing it, don't you, Neil? He'd rather I went out cleaning.'

'That isn't true.'

'It is true. I won't pretend I don't enjoy it because I do. How d'you think I feel after years of my husband telling me first that I wasn't capable of earning and then when I was that what I earned wasn't worth the trouble of working, it'd all go in tax.'

'I never said any of that.'

'It feels *great*,' Sylvia said, ignoring him. 'The whole lot of them depend on *me* now. All the money, quite a lot of it, will be paid to me personally. So much for sexism, so much for chauvinism . . .'

'They won't pay the mortgage,' Neil interrupted her. 'Almost everything you say is wildly inaccurate. They'll pay the *interest* on the mortgage and they're putting a ceiling on the amount of mortgage they'll pay up to. We shall put the house on the market.'

'We shall not.'

'Of course we shall. We have no option. We shall sell it and buy a semi in Mansfield Road – if we're lucky. That looks like Eve's pudding, Dora, one of my favourites. You don't improve the situation, Sylvia, by telling a pack of lies as a vindication of the rights of women.'

Ben said, 'You know men have Adam's apples, don't you?'

Silently blessing him for the distraction, Wexford said yes, he did know, he supposed everyone knew.

'Yes, well, d'you know why they're called that? I bet you don't. It's because when the snake gave Eve the apple she could swallow it all right but a lump of it stuck in Adam's throat and that's why men have got that bit sticking out . . .'

'If that story isn't rank sexism, I don't know what is. Are you ever going to eat up those potatoes, Robin?'

'No pasa nada.'

'I don't know what that means,' said Sylvia crossly.

'Come on, Mum. Can't you guess?'

Refusing pudding and coffee, Wexford went out into the hall to phone Detective Sergeant Vine.

It had taken Barry Vine a long time to find Euan Sinclair. He had only just got back from London. After he had eaten he was going to write his report. It would be on Wexford's desk by nine in the morning.

'Give me a résumé now,' said Wexford.

'I didn't find the girl.'

Vine had gone first to the address provided by Dr Akande. It was a fairly large Victorian house in the East End of London, occupied by three generations of the Sinclair and Lafay families. An old grand-mother, though domiciled there for thirty years, spoke only a version of the patois. Three of her daughters also lived in the house and four of their children, though not Euan. He had moved out some three months before.

43

Deeply distrustful of the police, the women spoke to him with a kind of laconic suspicion. Euan's mother Claudine who occupied the ground floor with her partner and father of her two younger children, a man called Samuel Lafay, the brother incidentally of the elder sister's ex-husband . . .

'Oh, get on with it,' Wexford said.

It was clear that Vine was expounding with relish on the complexities of this intricate family. He seemed to have enjoyed his day. After asking rhetorically why she should tell him anything about her son who was a good, clean-living and honourable man, an intellectual, Claudine Sinclair or Lafay had sent him to a council flat in Whitechapel. This turned out to be the home of a girl called Joan-Anne, mother of Euan Sinclair's daughter. Joan-Anne never wanted to see Euan again, if he came into a million she wouldn't accept a penny of it in child-support for Tasha, if he went on his knees to her she wouldn't, she had a good man now who had never been without so much as a day's work in his life. She gave Vine an address in Shadwell, home of Sheena ('poor cow, lets him walk all over her') who was the mother of Euan's son.

Euan had gone to sign on, Sheena told him. Thursday was his day. After signing on he usually went for a drink with some friends, but he'd turn up sometime, she couldn't really say when. No, Vine couldn't wait for him, she couldn't have that. The idea made her nervous, Vine could see, probably on account of the neighbours. The neighbours would have identified him in the mysterious way some people can always spot a policeman and they'd make a note of how many hours Vine spent in Sheena's flat. All this time Euan's son was screaming his head off in the next room. Sheena went to attend to him and came back with a handsome angry boy who

44

already looked too big for his diminutive mother to carry.

'Oh, stop your noise, Scott, stop your noise,' she said ineffectually, over and over. Scott roared at her and roared at the visitor. Vine left and went back at four.

Sheena and her son were still alone. Scott was still intermittently roaring. No, Euan hadn't been back. Phone her? What did he mean, phone her? Why would he? Vine gave up. Sheena gave Scott a bag of salt and vinegar crisps and stuck him in front of a video of what appeared to be *Miami Vice*. When he was quiet, Vine asked her about Melanie Akande but it was plain Sheena had never heard of her. While Vine probed a bit, Euan Sinclair came in.

Tall, handsome, very thin, Euan had the sort of looks that reminded Vine of Linford Christie. His hair was very short, a week's growth, Vine guessed, after a total shave. He walked with the peculiar grace of the young black man, all movement from the hips, the torso erect and still. But it was his voice that surprised Vine. Not Creole English, one generation removed, not East End Cockney, not Estuary but nearer Public School.

Wexford said, half-joking, half-serious, 'So you're a snob as well as a racist, Barry.'

Vine didn't deny it. He said he'd had the impression Euan Sinclair had taught himself to talk like that for some unknown reasons of policy. It suddenly struck him – for the first time – that Euan might deny knowledge of Melanie in Sheena's presence.

'That would have been the first thing I'd have thought of,' said Wexford.

'He didn't, though. That was the funny thing. I could see it was all news to her and she didn't like it. He couldn't have cared less.'

He'd seen Melanie the previous week. At the

Myringham graduation ceremonies. They had a talk and she agreed to meet him the following Tuesday in Myringham. By this time Sheena was staring at him with a kind of horror. Melanie was going to Laurel Tucker's party, Euan said, and he could come too.

Vine asked where they were meeting and Euan named a pub in Myringham. At around four. The Wig and Ribbon in the High Street opened from 11.00 am till 11.00 pm. She hadn't turned up, though Euan waited till five-thirty. At this point he saw a man he knew, another alumnus of Myringham University. The two of them got together, went to another pub and then another, and Euan spent the night sleeping on the floor in this man's room.

Sheena could contain herself no longer. 'You told me you were at your grandma's.'

He said to her, in the sort of voice a man uses to say it's raining, 'I lied.'

Sheena stalked to the door. Just before it closed behind her Euan called out, 'You'd better not leave me alone with him. I'm no baby-minder. That's women's work, right?'

'I'll check it out with this bloke he says he met,' said Vine, 'but I believe him. He gave me the fellow's name and address without turning a hair.'

'It looks as if Melanie never reached Myringham,' Wexford said. 'Something happened to deflect her in Kingsmarkham High Street. Somewhere on about two hundred yards of pavement. We have to find out what it was.'

Chapter Four

The Tucker Family, Laurel and Glenda Tucker, their father and stepmother, had little that was new to offer. They were plainly unwilling 'to get mixed up in anything'. It was true that Laurel had expected Melanie on the late afternoon of 6 July and had been displeased when it was clear she wasn't coming. But she hadn't been all that *surprised*. After all, they had quarrelled.

The detective sergeant from Myringham who had been asking the questions said, 'What was that about then?'

Laurel had been at the graduation ceremony, witnessed the meeting between Melanie and Euan Sinclair and seen the two of them go off together. Melanie phoned her next day, said she was thinking of getting back with Euan, he was lonely, there had been no one in his life since they split up, and she'd told him she'd bring him to Laurel's party on Tuesday. I don't want him, Laurel said, I don't like him, I never did. I'm not surprised he hasn't been seeing anyone else – who'd want him? Melanie said if Euan couldn't come to the party she wasn't coming either, and they had a row.

'She did tell her parents she was going to this party,' Burden said to Wexford. 'She was going to the Tucker house first and then on to this party.'

'Well, she wouldn't tell them she had a date with this Euan, would she? They can't stand him, haven't got a good word to say for him. Mother's something of a formidable woman, I'd almost say she'd be capable of locking a daughter up. By this time Melanie had obviously decided she wasn't going to the party. She was going to stick to what she'd said and not go if Euan wasn't also welcome. She was going to meet Euan in the Wig and Ribbon and there's not much doubt she meant to stay with him, spend the night with him.'

'Yes, but where? Not at this Sheena's place. People that age don't hire hotel rooms, do they?'

Wexford laughed. 'Not if they're living on the IS they don't.'

'The what?'

'Income Support. If Melanie thought about that aspect at all I expect she thought they'd go to Euan's mother's place in Bow. She'd very likely been there before. And next day she'd come home.'

'Amazing, isn't it?' said Burden, looking down his nose. 'They've got no jobs, they're living on what-d'you-call-it, IS, and they still splash out on drinks and dates with girls and God knows what for train fares.'

'It doesn't matter much, Mike, because we know she didn't go to London. She didn't even go to Myringham. She didn't meet Euan because Euan – ' Wexford had another look at Vine's latest report ' – spent the evening with someone called John Varcava in the Wig and Ribbon, the Wild Goose and Silk's Club before returning to Varcava's rented room in Myringham at three in the morning. It's all confirmed by a barman, a barmaid, the manager of Silk's and Varcava's landlady, who nearly came to blows with Varcava and Euan Sinclair over the mayhem they were making in her house in the small hours.'

'So what happened to Melanie in those few

minutes after she left the unemployment place? The last person she saw, according to you, was this Annette Bystock, the New Claims Adviser. Is there any point in talking to her?'

'She was off sick,' said Wexford. 'She may be back at work by now, though people don't usually go back on a Friday, they take the whole week. But what are we saying, Mike? That Melanie Akande confided the details of some secret appointment to a complete stranger? A woman she'd talked to for fifteen minutes and talked to surely only about filling in a form and job prospects? Come to that, what secret appointment? She'd already got one of those with Euan. Now she's having another with some other chap just an hour before she meets Euan?'

Burden shrugged. 'Well, you said all that. I didn't. My imagination hasn't travelled that far. All I'm saying is, we ought to talk to Annette Bystock, solely on the grounds that she was the last person to see Melanie. . . .' He hesitated.

'You were going to say "alive", weren't you?'

There but for the grace of God go I, was not a reflection Michael Burden was ever likely to quote. He neither said it to himself when he saw famine victims on television, nor if he passed the half dozen or so homeless who slept on the street in Myringham. He didn't say it now, entering the Benefit Office and contemplating the jobless who sat about waiting on the grey chairs.

That he wasn't among them had nothing to do with God's grace in his opinion, and everything to do with his own industry, determination and hard work. He was one of those who ask the unemployed why they don't get a job and the homeless why they don't find a place to live. If he had been in Paris in the 1780s he would have told the starving who begged for bread to eat cake. Now, wearing his immaculate beige trousers and new jacket of beige linen with a navy fleck – one thing, as Wexford sometimes said, no one would have taken him for a policeman – he contemplated the unemployed and reflected on what a hideous garment the shellsuit was. Marginally worse than the tracksuit. It had never occurred to him that these clothes are cheap, warm in cold weather and cool in hot, easy to wash, resistant to creases and very comfortable, and he didn't consider the matter now. He turned his attention to the administrative assistants behind their desks, deciding which one he should approach.

Jenny Burden said of her husband that if he had a choice, he would always enquire of a man rather than a woman, ask a man the way somewhere, go up to a male assistant in a shop, take the seat in a train next to a man. He hadn't liked that, he said it made him sound homosexual, but that wasn't what she meant at all. In the Benefit Office he had a choice, for behind the desks sat a man and three women. The man, however, had a brown skin and wore a label with the name Mr O. Messaoud. Burden, who hotly denied that he was a racist in any degree, nevertheless rejected Osman Messaoud on the grounds (of which he was only subliminally aware) of his skin colour and his name, and went up to freckled, ginger-haired Wendy Stowlap. She happened to be briefly free and this was the reason Burden would have given for choosing her.

'Is it about that girl who's missing?' she asked after he had enquired for Annette Bystock.

'Just routine enquiries,' said Burden blandly. 'Is Miss Bystock back yet?'

'She's still off sick.'

He turned away, almost colliding with Wendy Stowlap's next client, a big heavy woman in a red

50

shellsuit. She smelt powerfully of cigarettes. They can always afford to smoke, Burden said to himself. Two of the boys sitting on the stone balustrade were also smoking, their feet dabbling in a litter of ash and cigarette ends. Burden gave them a long severe look, drawing his brows together. His eyes lingered particularly on the black boy with the Rastafarian hair, a mountainous crest of matted dreadlocks, on top of which rested a woolly cap, knitted in concentric circles of colour. It was the sort of hat he called a tam-o'-shanter, as his father would have done and his grandfather before him.

The boys took absolutely no notice of him. It was as if his body was transparent and their eyes penetrated it to the stonework behind him, the pavement, the corner where Brook Road turned into the High Street. They made him feel invisible. With an angry shrug he went back to the car he had parked in the 'strictly private' area for ESJ staff only.

The address Wexford had given him was in south Kingsmarkham. It was formerly one of the best parts of the town where, in the late nineteenth century, the most prosperous of its citizens had built themselves large houses, each standing in an acre or two of garden. Most of them were still there but partitioned now, and their gardens 'infilled' with new houses and rows of garages. Ladyhall Gardens had come in for this treatment, but the Victorian relics were smaller and each one divided into two or three flats.

Someone had pretentiously named number fifteen Ladyhall Court. It was a gabled house on two floors, built of the 'white' brick which was the fashionable building material here in the 1890s. A screen of copper sycamores hid much of the ground floor from the road. Burden guessed there were two flats on each floor, the two at the rear accessible from a side door. Above the bell for the upper floor a card read:

John and Edwina Harris, and above the bell for the lower flat: Ms A. Bystock.

When there was no answer from Flat One, he rang the Harrises' bell. No answer there either. The front door had a lock at the top, a lock in the middle, and a brass knob, now tarnished black. On the off chance Burden tried the handle and to his surprise – and disapproval – it came open.

He found himself in a hallway with plaster scroll-work on the ceiling and uncompromisingly modern vinyl tiles on the floor. The staircase had an iron balustrade and grey marble steps. There was only one door, dark green with the figure 1 painted on it in white. The knocker was brass and so was the knob, but polished brass, and the bellpush bright as gold.

Burden rang the bell, waited. She might be in bed. If she was ill she might well be. He listened for sounds of movement, for footsteps or the creak of a floorboard. He rang the bell again. The little knocker was almost useless, it made a frenzied clack-clack, like a child trying to make its small voice heard.

Probably she was simply not answering the bell. If he was ill in bed, alone in the house, and some unexpected caller rang the bell he wouldn't answer it. There might be someone looking after her, of course, some neighbour perhaps, and that person would have a key.

He knelt down and looked through the letter box. Inside it seemed quite dark, darker than in the corridor. Gradually, through the small open rectangle, he made out a shadowy hallway with red fitted carpet, a small console table, dried flowers in a little gilded basket.

He stood up, rang the bell again, banged on the baby knocker, squatted down and called her name through the aperture: 'Miss Bystock!' and, louder, 'Miss Bystock! Are you at home?'

For one last time he called her name and then he went out of the house and round the side, pushing aside the sycamore branches with their leathery leaves that made everything so dark. This little window would be the kitchen, this one the bathroom. No sycamores here, only waist-high golden rod on either side of a concrete drive. Behind the last window by the side door the curtains were closed. For some reason he looked behind him, the way we do when we think we are being watched. On the opposite side of the street, in a 1900-ish house with a short front garden, someone was looking at him from an upstairs window. A face that looked as old as the house, crinkled, frowning, glaring.

Burden turned back to the window. He thought the drawn curtains a bit strange. How ill was she? Ill enough to need a darkened room to sleep in mid-morning? The thought came to him that perhaps she wasn't ill at all, that she was skiving off work and had gone out somewhere.

He wouldn't have been surprised if the old watcher at the window had come downstairs and crossed the road and tapped him on the shoulder. In the expectation of this he turned round once more. But the face was still there, its expression unchanged, and it was perfectly still, so much so that for a moment Burden asked himself if this was a real person or some sort of facsimile, a wooden cutout of a glaring and evil-countenanced observer, placed there by the occupier as some people keep a painted chipboard cat in their gardens to frighten real ones.

But this was nonsense. He squatted down and tried to see between the curtains but the gap was infinitesimal, the merest line. In defiance of what the watcher over the way might think or do, he knelt down on the concrete paving and tried to look under the hem of the curtains. Here was a gap of perhaps

53

half an inch between curtain hem and lower window frame.

It was dim in there. He couldn't see much. At first he could see scarcely anything. Then, as his eyes grew accustomed to the subfusc interior of the room, he made out the edge of a table, possibly a dressing table, the polished wooden foot of something on blue carpet, a segment of flowered material touching the floor. And a hand. A hand, which hung down against those printed lilies and roses, a white immobile hand, the fingers extended.

It must be made of china, of plaster, of plastic. It couldn't be real. Or it could be real and she asleep. What sort of sleep was maintained through all that shouting? Almost involuntarily, forgetting possible watchers, he drummed on the glass with his knuckles. The hand didn't move. The hand's owner didn't leap up with a cry.

Burden ran back into the house. Why had he never learned how to pick a lock? Opening this one would be child's play to a lot of men and women he encountered in a day's work. Doors in the movies cave in with ease at the pressure of a shoulder. It always made him laugh angrily when he saw actors on television run up against stout doors and send them crashing in at one shove. It was so silent too, the way they did it. He knew his own efforts would be noisy and very likely bring the neighbours. But it couldn't be helped.

He ran up against the door, applying his shoulder. It juddered and creaked but his action hurt him more than it hurt the door. He rubbed his shoulder, took a deep breath, and hurled himself at it – once and again and once more. This time he kicked it, more of a punch with his foot, and the door groaned. Another foot-punch – he hadn't kicked like that since on the soccer field at school – and the door split and flew open. He stepped over the broken wood and paused to get his breath.

The hallway was tiny. It turned the corner and became a passage. All five doors were shut. Burden went down it, guessed at the bedroom door, opened it and found a broom cupboard. Next to it must be the bedroom, its door not quite closed, half an inch ajar. First taking a deep breath, he pushed it open.

She lay as if asleep, her head on the pillow, her face turned into it and hidden by a mass of dark curly hair. One shoulder was bare, the other and the rest of her body covered by the bedclothes and the flowered quilt. From the naked shoulder extended her rather plump white arm with the hand he had seen, trailing almost to the floor.

He touched nothing, not the curtains, not the bedclothes, not that buried head, nothing but the hanging hand. One finger he put out to feel it, the back of it above the knuckles. It was stiffening as if frozen and as cold as ice.

Chapter Five

They filled the place, it was so small; the pathologist, the photographers, the scene-of-crime officers, everyone indispensable, each with a specific task. Once the windows had been photographed and the curtains drawn back it was better, and when the body was taken away most of them went with it. Wexford lifted the lower sash in the bay and watched the van bearing Annette Bystock's remains disappear in the direction of the mortuary.

There would have to be formal identification but he had identified her from the passport he found in a dressing table drawer. The passport was a newish one, in the dark red and gold binding of the European Union, issued just over twelve months before. It gave the holder's name as Bystock, Annette Mary, her status as a British Citizen and her date of birth, 22.11.54. The photograph was plainly of the dead woman, clearly identifiable, in spite of the effects on her face of strangulation, the swelling, the cyanosis, the tongue protruding between the teeth. Her eyes were the same. She had stared into the camera with almost the same degree of horrified apprehension as she had looked into her killer's face.

They were round dark eyes. Her hair was dark and fussy, a dense bush of it which must have made a wide frame for her face unless she had somehow confined it. When Burden found her she had been wearing a pink nightdress patterned with white flowers. Across the quilt had lain a white wool cardigan that had evidently done duty as a bedjacket. Thee were no rings on the hands, no earrings in her ears. On the left-hand bedside cabinet were her watch, gold with a black strap, a gold ring with a red stone, probably a ruby, that looked valuable, a comb and a half-empty bottle of aspirins; on the right-hand cabinet were a novel by Danielle Steel in paperback, a glass of water, a packet of throat pastilles and a Yale key.

A bedlamp stood on each cabinet, each one a simple white vase-shaped base with a pleated blue shade. The one on the right of the bed, farthest from the door, was intact. The other had a chip out of its base and its cord torn from the base. This cord, with plug still attached, had gone now, had been removed in a plastic bag by DC Pemberton, but when they first came into the bedroom it had been lying on the floor within inches of Annette Bystock's hanging hand.

'She's been dead at least thirty-six hours,' Sir Hilary Tremlett, the pathologist, had said to Wexford. 'I'll be able to tell you more precisely when I've had a closer look. Let me see, it's Friday, isn't it? On the face of it, I'd say she died on Wednesday night, certainly before midnight on Wednesday.'

He left before the van bearing the body was out of sight. Wexford closed the bedroom door.

'A confident killer,' he said. 'An experienced killer, I'd say. He must have been very sure of himself. He didn't bother to bring a weapon with him, he was sure he'd find one to hand. Everyone has electric leads in their home, but if by chance he couldn't find a suitable one, everyone has knives, heavy objects, hammers.'

Burden nodded. 'Or he was familiar with the place. He knew what was on offer.'

'Must it be a he? Or are you just being politically incorrect?'

Burden grinned. 'Old Tremlett may be able to help us there. I can't somehow imagine a woman breaking into a place and tearing a lead out of a lamp to strangle someone.'

'You're well known for having quaint ideas about women,' said Wexford. 'He or she didn't break in, though, did they? There's no sign of a break-in. They were let in or they had a key.'

'Someone she knew, then?'

Wexford shrugged. 'How's this for a scenario? She started to feel ill on Tuesday evening, went to bed, felt worse in the morning, so she phoned the Benefit Office to say she wasn't coming in and then she phoned a friend or a neighbour and asked them to fetch something in for her. Look at this.'

Burden followed him into the kitchen. It was too small to contain a table but on the narrow counter, on the left side, was a grocer's cardboard box, twelve inches by nine and about nine inches high. The items inside seemed untouched. On top of them lay a supermarket print-out, dated 8 July. Beneath it were a packet of cornflakes, two small pots of strawberry yogurt, a carton of milk, a small wholemeal loaf wrapped in tissue paper, a packet of pre-sliced Cheddar cheese and a grapefruit.

'So the friend that was shopping for her brought that in yesterday,' Wexford said. 'If the friend works, the likelihood is it was yesterday evening . . . Yes, Chepstow, what is it?'

The fingerprint man said, 'I haven't done in here yet, sir.'

'We'll clear out of your way then.'

'There's a key on the bedside table. Why not give the friend a key?' Burden asked as they moved into Annette Bystock's living room. 'The front door was unlocked when I got here. Did she leave her own front door on the latch? Why do that in this day and

58

age?' If Wexford winced Burden didn't notice. 'It's just inviting a burglar.'

'She couldn't give the friend a key if the friend wasn't there, Mike. Man hasn't yet mastered the technique of sending solid objects by phone, radio or satellite transmission. If she didn't want to get out of bed to let him or her in she could only leave the door on the latch. Once the friend had come she could hand over a key.'

'But someone else came in while the door was on the latch?'

'It looks like it.'

'We have to find the friend,' said Burden.

'Yes, I'm wondering if it was a neighbour or if she only made one phone call on Wednesday morning, if she killed two birds with one stone, so to speak. After all, Mike, who are our friends? Mainly, the people we were at school with or trained with or met at work. I think it's very likely the Good Samaritan who brought the yogurt and grapefruit works at the Benefit Office.'

'Karen and Barry are doing the neighbours now, but most of them are at work.'

Wexford had been standing at the window but now he turned round and surveyed the room. He looked at Annette Bystock's pictures on the wall, a bland and innocuous pen and ink drawing of a windmill, a bright watercolour of a rainbow over green hills; at her framed photographs, one in black and white of a girl of about three in a frilly dress and white socks, one of a couple in a suburban garden, the woman with her hair in sausage curls, her dress full-skirted and tight-waisted, the man in floppy grey flannels and pullover. Her mother as a child, Wexford guessed. Her parents newly married.

The furniture was a three-piece suite, a lacquered coffee table, a useless-looking two-tiered table, a bookcase which contained few books and whose middle shelves were used to display china animals. On the bottom shelf were perhaps twenty compact discs and the same number of cassettes. The red hall carpet extended to cover the floor of this room but otherwise the colour scheme was unexciting, mostly beige and brown. Her parents probably had a beige living room and a blue bedroom. There was nothing to show that Annette had been comparatively young, not yet forty, no break-away from convention, nothing minimally adventurous.

'Where's the television?' Wexford asked. 'Where's the video? No radio, no cassette player, no CD player? None of those?'

'That's funny. Maybe she didn't have them, maybe she was some sort of fundamentalist who didn't believe in those things. No, but wait a minute, she had CDs. . . . See that table there? The one with the two tiers. Don't you reckon there's been a TV on the top and a video underneath?'

You could see the marks, a rectangle of dust in the polished surface above and a slightly larger one below.

'It looks as if her invitation to the burglar was accepted,' said Wexford. 'I wonder what else she had. A computer maybe? A microwave in the kitchen, though it's hard to say where it would have fitted in?'

'She was killed for *that*?'

'I doubt it. If our perpetrator killed her for what she had in the flat, he'd have taken her watch and her ring. That ring looks valuable to me.'

'Or it could be that the TV and the video have gone off somewhere to be repaired.'

'Oh, sure, it could be. All sorts of things could be. There's been one single case recorded of successful self-strangulation, so she might be the second one.

And she sold the best part of her consumer goods first to pay for her funeral. Come *on*, Mike.'

Returning to the bedroom, now free for any kind of arbitrary examination, Wexford opened the cupboard door and, without comment, though Burden was behind him, eyed the garments inside. Two pairs of jeans, a pair of cords, cotton loons, several not very short miniskirts size twelve and two longer skirts size fourteen, which seemed to indicate that Annette had recently put on weight. Folded sweaters on the shelves, blouses, all of them ordinary, safe, quiet. Behind the other door hung a navy winter coat, beige raincoat, two jackets, one dark red, one black. Had she never dressed up, gone out in the evenings, been to a party?

Wexford picked the ring off the bedside cabinet and held it out on his palm to Burden. 'A fine ruby,' he said. 'Worth more than all your TVs and Nicam video-plusses and cassette players put together.' He hesitated. 'Which of us is going to be the first to ask the question?'

'It's been on the tip of my tongue ever since I knew she'd been murdered.'

'And mine.'

'OK,' said Burden, 'I will. Is there any connection between this death and the fact that she seems to have been the last person to have seen Melanie Akande alive?'

Edwina Harris came home while they were still there. She pushed the door open, entered the hall, saw Flat One sealed off with yellow tape and was standing staring when DS Karen Malahyde came out to her.

'Did I leave the door on the latch? I mean, I always do when I go out and nothing's ever happened.' She realized what she had said. 'What *has* happened?'

61

'Can we go upstairs, Mrs Harris?'

Karen broke it to her carefully. It was a shock but no more than that. She and Annette Bystock had been neighbours, not friends, never close. After a few minutes she was able to tell Karen that Annette's parents were dead, she had no brothers or sisters. She thought Annette had once been married but she knew no more than that.

No, she hadn't heard or seen anything untoward in the past few days. She lived in the upper flat with her husband and he hadn't heard anything or he would have told her. In fact, she hadn't known Annette was ill. She wasn't the friend who had brought in the groceries.

'Like I said, I wasn't her *friend*.'

'Who was?'

'She never had any boyfriends to my knowledge.'

'Women friends, then?'

But Edwina Harris couldn't say. She had only once been inside Flat One, but couldn't remember noticing whether or not Annette had television.

'But everyone has TV, don't they? She had a radio, a little white one. I know that because while I was in there she showed it to me. She'd spilt red nail varnish on it and she couldn't get it off, wanted to know what would get it off, and I said remover, but she'd tried that.'

'There's someone lives opposite,' Burden said. It was a bit awkward, he found he couldn't tell whether it was a man or a woman. 'A very old person,' he said carefully, and with equal tact, 'They look as if they'd see everything. Did they know Annette?'

'Mr Hammond? He's never been over here. He hasn't left that room for . . . well, it has to be three years.'

Edwina Harris wasn't prepared to identify the body. She had never seen a dead person and didn't want to start now. Annette had had a cousin some-where, she had heard her mention a cousin. Jane Something. A birthday card had come from this woman and the postman had put it in her box instead of Annette's. That was when Edwina Harris heard about the cousin, when she took the birthday card over to Annette.

It was Wexford who asked her about the front door to the house.

'It was never left unlocked overnight.'

'Are you sure?'

'Well, I'm sure I never left it unlocked.'

'Strange, isn't it?' said Burden, after they left her. 'Women in ground floor flats are supposed to be sleepless with dread about intruders. They have alarms, they have bars on all the windows – or that's what I read.'

'Appearance and reality,' said Wexford.

Some time later in the day they found Annette's cousin, a married woman with three children living in Pomfret. Jane Winster agreed to come to Kings-markham and identify the body.

Told what had happened, Cyril Leyton at first refused to believe. Incredulously, 'You're having me on,' he had said roughly when phoned, then, 'Is this some sort of trick?' Finally convinced, he repeated over and over, 'My God, my God. . . .'

Tomorrow would be Saturday, but in name only, as Wexford said to Burden. There wouldn't be any time off and all leave would be cancelled. Burden's remarks about women in ground floor flats reminded him of the meeting scheduled for Saturday night at Kingsmarkham Comprehensive. He wondered if he would still be able to take part. The talk he was planning he had given twice before at Women, Aware! meetings and had enjoyed speaking. He wouldn't miss it this time, not unless he absolutely had to; unless, for instance, someone had been arrested for this murder.

The young men – Wexford disliked the word 'youth' and refused ever to use it – were still sitting on the stone balustrade of the Benefit Office steps. Perhaps they weren't the same ones but they looked the same to him. This time he took particular note of them so that he would know them again: a boy with a shaven head in a grey tee-shirt; a boy in a black leather jacket and tracksuit bottoms with rats' tail hair tied back in a ponytail; another very short one with fair curly hair and a black boy with dreadlocks and one of those big floppy knitted caps. Assessing them like this, he realized what he had done, what he had told Burden racists did, so he changed the description to: a *boy* with dreadlocks and a knitted cap.

They looked at him with indifference, or three of them did. The one with the ponytail didn't look at him at all. For all that, he expected some muttered remark as he passed them, an insult or a quip, but there was nothing. He went up the steps to find the door locked but a young girl coming towards him behind the glass to open it.

He hadn't seen her before. She was small with pointed features and reddish hair, the label pinned to her black tee-shirt identifying her as Ms A Selby, Admin Assistant. He said good afternoon to her and something about being sorry to detain them all like this after hours, but she was too shy to reply. He followed her between counters to the back where she opened a door marked not only 'Private' but 'Keep Out' as well.

He hadn't intended it to be like this. Cyril Leyton – for it was surely he who had fixed this up – was evidently a headmaster *manqué*. The chairs, normally

64

those on which clients waited to sign on, were arranged in five rows with grey metal tables in front of each. On these chairs the staff sat. There were more of them than Wexford had realized. He saw to his rather horrified amusement that Leyton had seated them according to rank: the two supervisors, the remaining New Claims Adviser and all Executive Officers, in the first row; administrative officers behind; then the administrative assistants, those who worked on the switchboard, saw to the post, operated the copier, at the back. In the last row, on the extreme left, possibly the seat of the lowliest, was the bullet-headed security officer.

On each table, in front of each member of staff, was a notepad. All that was lacking, Wexford thought, was a blackboard – and perhaps a ferrule for Leyton to hold and use for rapping knuckles. The manager looked busy and important, enjoying himself now the first shock was past. His red face was shiny. Since Wexford had last seen him he had had his hair cut cruelly short and the clippers had left an angry-looking crimson rash on his neck.

'All present and correct, I trust,' he said.

Wexford merely nodded to him. Ridiculous as this regimentation was, the notepads might be useful. So long as they understood they weren't to write down what *he* said but what *they* knew.

'I'll try not to detain you long,' he began. 'You'll all have heard by now of Miss Bystock's violent death. It will be on our local television news at six-thirty and in the papers tomorrow so there's no reason why I shouldn't tell you now that it was a case of murder.'

From somewhere in the audience he heard the sound of an indrawn breath. It might have come from Ingrid Pamber, whose blue eyes were fixed earnestly on him, or the wispy fragile blonde sitting next to her who must have been twenty-five but

65

looked no more than fifteen. Her label was too far away for him to read. In the row in front of them Peter Stanton, the other New Claims Adviser, sat like an important young executive at a seminar, one long elegant leg crossed over the other, ankle on knee, his elbows on the chair arms, his head flung back. He was very good looking in a dark brooding way and he seemed to be enjoying himself.

'She was murdered in her own home, Ladyhall Court in Ladyhall Avenue. We don't yet know when. We shan't know until the postmortem is over and the other forensic tests have been done. We shan't know how she died or when or why. But as far as that goes the help of the people who knew her will be invaluable to us. Miss Bystock had very little family, few friends. The people she knew are the people she worked with and that means *you*.

'One of you or several of you may between you have all the information we need to find Miss Bystock's killer and bring him – or her – to justice. Your cooperation will be invaluable. I should like you all to agree to be interviewed by my officers tomorrow, either in your own homes or at Kingsmarkham Police Station if you prefer. Meanwhile, if any of you has anything to tell me now, anything that might be important or urgent, I shall be in Mr Leyton's office for the next half-hour and I'd be grateful if you'd come to me there and pass this information on. Thank you.'

Cyril Leyton said importantly as they walked into the little grey office, 'I can tell you anything you want to know. There's not much goes on here that I don't know about.'

'I've already told everyone that if they have something to tell me that's urgent they should do it now. Have you anything to tell me?'

Leyton grew redder. 'Well, no, not specifically, but I . . .'

'What time did Miss Bystock phone on Wednesday to say she wouldn't be coming in? Can you tell me that?'

'I? No, *I* can't. I'm not a switchboard operator. I can find someone who will . . .'

'Yes, Mr Leyton,' Wexford said patiently, 'I'm sure you can, but all your staff will be questioned tomorrow. Didn't you hear me say that? I'm asking you what *you* can tell me.'

Leyton was saved from answering by a tap on the door. It opened and Ingrid Pamber came in. Wexford, who always noticed – as most men do notice – if a woman is specially good looking, had taken good note of this girl. Her looks were the kind that most appealed to him, the fresh wholesomeness of her, her glossy dark hair sleekly held back by a barrette, her fine features and smooth pink and white skin – what his father would have called her 'complexion' – her shapely figure that was slim but a long way from today's anorexic ideal. The clothes she wore were in his opinion the most flattering to any pretty woman: a short straight skirt, a clinging knitted sweater – in this case cream cotton and short-sleeved – low-cut shoes with heels, as unlike a man's shoe as could be.

She levelled at Wexford a rueful smile that was almost laughter through tears. It looked natural but he thought it was calculated. Her eyes were the kind whose irises are such a strong colour that they seem to shed their own blue light.

'I was – I was looking after her,' she said. 'Poor Annette, I was taking care of her.'

'You were friends, Miss Pamber?'

'I was her only friend.'

Ingrid Pamber said it quietly but dramatically. She sat down opposite Wexford, and sat with care, but her skirt was too short not to rise six inches above her

67

knees. The sideways attitude she sat in, knees and ankles close together, seemed designed to show off a woman's legs to best advantage – but a modest woman's, not the Hollywood starlet kind who crosses one leg over the other, extending the toe in its high-heeled shoe. He thought he understood Ingrid Pamber as a girl whose sexual success depended on a contrived reserve, discreet revelations, an almost shy appeal. In another age she would have managed excellently the manipulation of petticoats to give a sight of ankle or the handling of a shawl that when it slipped allowed a glimpse of cleavage.

'It was you who took the call from Miss Bystock on Wednesday morning?'

'Yes. Yes, it was. She asked the switchboard to put the call through to me.'

'Which was most improper,' said Leyton. 'I shall be speaking to Mr Jones and Miss Selby about that. The call should have come to me.'

'I told you about it,' said Ingrid. 'I told you within about thirty seconds.'

'Yes, maybe, but that's not the . . .'

'Mr Leyton,' Wexford said, 'I'd be grateful if you'd leave us. I'd like to talk to Miss Pamber alone.'

'Look here, this is my office!'

'Yes, I know, and very obliging it is of you to let me use it. I'll see you later.'

Wexford got up and opened the door for Leyton. He had scarcely gone through it before Ingrid Pamber giggled. One of the hardest things we are ever called on to do is feign sorrow when we are happy or pretend happiness when we are in grief. Ingrid remembered too late that, as Annette's only friend, she was supposed to be sad. She looked down, biting her lip.

He waited a moment, then asked her, 'Can you tell me what time this call came?'

'It was nine-fifteen.'

'How can you be so sure of the time?'

'Well, we start at nine-thirty and we're supposed to be in by nine-fifteen.' She opened her eyes wide as she looked at him and he felt the force of that blue beam. 'I've been getting in a bit late lately and . . . well, I was pleased with myself for making it on time. I'd looked at the clock and seen it was nine-fifteen and at that moment the call from Annette came for me.'

'What did she say, Miss Pamber?'

'That she thought she had a bug and felt awful and wouldn't be in and I was to tell Cyril. And she said would I take her in a pint of milk on my way home from work, that was all she wanted, she couldn't eat anything. She said she'd leave the door on the latch for me. It's the kind of door that's got a handle like a door . . . well, an inside-door if you know what I mean.'

Wexford nodded. This then was the friend he had guessed at.

'So I said I would and the minute I put the phone down a man phoned and asked for her. He didn't give his name but I knew who it was.' She gave him a sidelong look, rather a rogueish look. 'Anyway, I said she was at home ill.'

'And you did take her the milk?'

'Yes. It was about five-thirty I went in.'

'She was in bed?'

'Yes, she was. I was going to stay for a bit, have a chat, you know, but she said not to come too near in case I caught it. She'd made a list of things she wanted me to get her next day and I took that with me. She said she'd give me a ring at work in the morning.'

'Did she?'

'No, she didn't but it didn't matter.' Ingrid Pamber

69

seemed quite unaware of what she was saying. 'I'd got her list. I knew what she wanted.'

'So she'd given you a key?'

'Yes, she had. I got the things, cornflakes and grapefruit and stuff, and I went in with them at the same time last evening. I left them in the box. I thought she'd put them away.'

'You didn't go in to see her?'

'Last evening? No, I didn't. I couldn't hear anything. I thought she must be asleep.'

He detected the guilt in her voice. Friend she might have been but she hadn't wanted to be bothered with Annette the night before, she had been in a hurry, so she had dumped the box of groceries and left without looking into the bedroom. . . . Or wasn't it like that at all?

'Now when you left the flat on Wednesday evening you had a key, so of course you didn't leave the front door on the latch? It was locked behind you?'

'Oh, yes.'

How blue her eyes were! They seemed to grow bluer, to become neon-like, day-glo peacock eyes, as they gazed earnestly into his. 'So when you returned on Thursday evening, last evening, you found the door locked and let yourself in with your key?'

'Oh, yes. Absolutely.'

He switched to another subject. 'I suppose Miss Bystock had television? A video?'

'Yes.' She looked surprised. 'I remember when she bought the video. It was around last Christmas.'

'Now when you went there on Wednesday and yesterday, did you see the television set?'

She hesitated. 'I don't know, I . . . I'm sure I saw it on Wednesday. Annette said to draw the curtains as I was leaving. She wanted the curtains drawn to stop the sun fading the carpet or something. Funny, wasn't it? I'd never heard of that before. Anyway, I did draw them and I saw the TV and the video.'

He nodded. 'And yesterday?'

'I don't know. I didn't notice.' In too much of a hurry, Wexford thought, in and out, no messing. Something in his look seemed to touch her. 'You don't mean . . . she was dead then, she was already dead . . . you can't mean that!'

'I'm afraid she was, Miss Pamber. It looks very much as if she was.'

'Oh, God, and I didn't know. If I'd gone in there. . . .'

'It would have made no difference.'

'They didn't . . . they didn't kill her for a telly and a video?'

'It wouldn't be the first time such a thing has happened.'

'Poor Annette. That makes me feel terrible.'

Why did he have the distinct impression she didn't feel terrible at all? She spoke the conventional words in the conventional way and her face wore a conventional mask of woe. But those eyes danced with life and vitality and happiness.

'The man who phoned here and asked for her? Who did you think that was?'

She lied again. He marvelled that she thought he couldn't tell. 'Oh, just a friend, one of her neighbours actually.'

'Who did you think it was, Miss Pamber?' he said.

She looked him straight in the eye. 'I don't know, I honestly don't know.'

'You knew who it was just now and now you don't? I'll ask you again tomorrow.'

The light inside her head had gone out. He watched her go, leave the room, let an indignant Leyton back into it. She had lied a great deal, he thought, and he could pinpoint the moment at which the lying began: it was when he first uttered the word 'key'. He looked beyond the greyness at Marks and Spencers loading bay, at a bright green carrier bag the summer wind was tossing to and fro. A woman was lifting carriers from a trolley into her car boot. She belonged to the same type as Annette, dark, stocky with an hourglass figure, a high colour, excellent legs. Why had Ingrid lied about the man who phoned? Why had she lied about the key? And in what respect had she lied?

She had been dead while Ingrid was in the flat on Thursday evening. Ingrid had locked the door behind her. Who then had unlocked it during the night before Burden arrived?

Chapter Six

Those who had jobs and went to them every day were the lucky ones. Looking back a few years, Barry Vine wondered what he would have thought of such a sentiment then. It was true today, no denying it. He was surprised when he found that the occupants of Flat Three and Flat Four in Ladyhall Court all had work.

The Greenalls, however, had not been at their jobs during the previous week; they had been away on holiday, returning home some five hours after the discovery of Annette's body. The occupant of Flat Four, Jason Partridge, a solicitor just six months over the Law Society's exams, had lived there for only a matter of weeks and could not remember ever having seen Annette. Vine, who knew all about how seeing policemen as younger and younger was a sign of middle age, wondered what it meant when solicitors looked like A Level candidates.

On the opposite side of Ladyhall Gardens were an old house divided into three flats, three red brick bungalows and an empty site where six houses like the old one had been demolished. The new ones would be in nineties' trend, a Portmeirion-like arrangement of a Gothic weatherboard house at angles to a brick house, joined to a plaster-rendered Georgian house, all the roofs at different levels, all the windows different shapes. So far only the foundations were there, the 'infrastructure' and walls built to a height of six feet. That limited those likely to have had a view of Ladyhall Court to the bungalows and the old house.

It was Saturday, so the occupants of the bungalows were at home. Vine talked to a youngish couple, Matthew Ross and his partner Alison Brown, but neither of them had so much as looked out of their front windows on the night of 7 July. They knew nothing of Annette Bystock and could not remember ever having seen her.

Next door was shared by two women, Diana Graddon in her mid-thirties, and Helen Ringstead twenty years older. Mrs Ringstead was lodger rather than friend. Diana Graddon couldn't have afforded to live there without her contribution, she frankly said, though since she had lost her own job the Social Security paid her rent. She had once known Annette well. In fact, it was she who, about ten years before when herself a newcomer to Ladyhall Avenue, had told Annette of the flat for sale on the other side of the street.

'We'd lost touch, though,' said Diana Graddon. 'She dropped me, as a matter of fact. I don't know why. I mean, it was silly really, living opposite and all that, but she never seemed to want to know me after she came here.'

'When did you last see her?'

'It must have been Monday. Last Monday. I was going away for a few days. I saw her coming home from work as I was going to get the bus. We just said hallo, we didn't really speak.'

She had been away from home until the previous morning, the Thursday morning. Helen Ringstead said she never noticed who came and went across the road.

The wrinkled face that Burden had for a wild

moment thought might be a mask or a cutout belonged to a man of eighty-seven called Percy Hammond. It was four years, not three, since he had come down the stairs from his first-floor flat, and most days he remained in the bedroom that over-looked Ladyhall Avenue. Meals-on-wheels were brought to him and twice a week a home help came in. For thirty years he had been a widower, his sons were dead, and his only friend was the tenant of the ground floor flat who, though eighty and blind, made her way upstairs to visit him every day.

It was she who let Burden in. Having introduced herself as Gladys Prior, asked him for his name twice and then made him spell it, she walked up the stairs ahead of him, sure-footed on the treads, her hand touching the banister more from convention than for support. Percy Hammond was in a chair by the window, staring into an empty street. The face that was dinosaur-like in close-up was turned on Burden's and its owner said, 'I've seen you somewhere before.'

'No, you haven't, Percy. You've made a mistake there. He's a police detective that's come to make enquiries. He's called Burden, Inspector Burden, B,U,R,D,E,N.'

'All right. I don't want to write to him. And I *have* seen him before. What do you know? You can't see at all.'

This on the face of it cruel taunt seemed to amuse rather than distress Mrs Prior. She sat down, giggling. 'Where have I seen you?' said Percy Hammond. 'Now *when* have I seen you?'

'Yesterday morning, over on the other . . .' Burden began but was interrupted.

'All right, don't tell me. Don't you know a rhetorical question when you hear one? I know who you are. You were trying to break into the house, or that's what I thought. Yesterday morning. Ten, was it? Or a bit later – eleven-ish? I'm not as good on time as I used to be. I don't suppose you were breaking in, *looking* in, more likely.'

'Of course he wasn't breaking in, Percy. He's a *policeman*.'

'You're naive, Gladys, that's what you are. I suppose Inspector B,U,R,D,E,N was looking through the curtains at our murder.'

That was one way of putting it, if somewhat cold-blooded. 'That's right, Mr Hammond. I really want to know, not if you saw me, but if you saw anyone else. I think you watch the street from your window quite a bit, don't you?'

'Never leaves that window all blessed day long,' said Mrs Prior.

'And how about the night?' said Burden.

'It's light at night this time of the year,' Percy Hammond said, a gleam of pleasure in his hooded eyes. 'Doesn't get dark till ten and it starts getting light again at four. Generally, I get in my bed at ten and out of it at half-past three. That's as long as I can sleep at my age. And when I'm not in my bed I'm at my window, I'm at my watching place. Do you know what Mizpah means?'

'I can't say I do,' said Burden.

'The watching place that overlooked the Plain of Syria. You youngsters don't know your Bible, more's the pity. This window is my Mizpah.'

'And have you seen anything on the . . . er, Plain of Syria these past two nights, Mr Hammond?'

'Not last night but the night before . . .'

'Two tom cats came knocking at the door!' crowed Mrs Prior, laughing.

Percy Hammond ignored her. 'A young chap came out of Ladyhall Court. I'd never seen him before, I knew he didn't live there. I know them all by sight, the ones that live there.'

'What time would that have been?'

'It was dawn,' said Percy Hammond. 'Four. Maybe a bit later. And I saw him again, I saw him come out carrying something, like a big wireless set.'

'Wireless set!' said Gladys Prior. 'I may not have my sight but I do move with the times. They call them tellies and radios.'

'He went in again and came out with something else in a box. I couldn't see what he did with it. If he had a car it was parked round the corner. I thought to myself, he's moving house for someone, getting it done early before the traffic gets bad.'

'Could you describe him, Mr Hammond?'

'He was young, about your age. About your height. Had quite a look of you. It was still darkish, you know, the sun wasn't up. Everything looks black and grey at that hour. I couldn't tell you the colour of his hair . . .'

'He gets confused,' said Mrs Prior.

'No, I don't, Gladys. As I said, it was about four-thirty to five, and I saw him come out and go in again and come out, carrying these boxes, a young chap of maybe twenty-five or thirty, six feet tall, at least six feet.'

'Would you know him again?'

'Of course I would. I'm an observant man. It may have been dark but I'd know him anywhere.'

Percy Hammond turned on Burden the fierce scowl, downturned mouth and heavy dewlaps that was his normal expression, an intense gleam in his saurian eyes.

'Women, learn to be streetwise,' the programme text began. 'Come and hear what the experts have to say about making yourselves aware. In your car, walking home alone after dark, in your home. Do you know what to do if attacked in the street? Can you protect

77

yourself if your car breaks down on the motorway? Can you defend yourself against rape?'

It listed the speakers: Chief Inspector R. Wexford, of Kingsmarkham CID, to talk on 'Crime on the Streets and in Your Home'; PC Oliver Adams on 'Driving Alone and Safe'; WPC Clare Scott, the Rape Adviser, on 'Changed Attitudes to Reporting Rape'; Mr Ronald Pollen, Self-Defence Expert and Judo Black Belt, to show his enthralling and informative video and talk on 'How to Fight Back'. Questions would be invited from the audience which the team of experts would answer. Organizer: Mrs Susan Riding, President, Kingsmarkham Women Rotarians; Chairperson, Mrs Anouk Khoori.

'Have you ever heard of a woman called Anouk Khoori? Curious name, isn't it? Sounds Arabic.'

Dora didn't hesitate. 'Oh, Reg, you never listen to me. I told you all about her coming to the Women's Institute and talking about women's lives in the United Arab Emirates.'

'There you are, I was right. She is an Arab.'

'Well, she doesn't look like one. She's a blonde. Very good looking in a showy sort of way. Very rich, I should think. Her husband owns a lot of shops, Tesco or Safeway or something. No, it's not those, it's Crescent. You know the ones, they're springing up everywhere.'

'You mean those supermarkets you see from motorways that look like palaces from the Arabian nights? All pointed arches and moons on the roof? What's she got to do with not getting raped or mugged? Is she going to tell the women to wear the veil?'

'Oh, she's just there because she wants to get herself in the public eye. She and her husband have built a vast new house where Mynford Old Hall used to be. She's standing for the Council in the by-

78

election. They say she'd like to get into Parliament, but she can't surely, she isn't even English.'

Wexford shrugged. He didn't know and cared less. The task ahead of him, the immediate task, he dreaded and would have avoided if he could. On the way he was going to meet Burden in the Olive and Dove for a drink, but after that – it could be postponed no longer – the Akandes.

The Olive stayed open from and until all hours now. You could drink brandy at nine in the morning if you wanted to, and a surprising lot of European visitors did want to. Instead of being cleared out pell-mell at two-thirty you could drink on through the afternoon and evening till the Olive finally closed its bars at midnight. It was ten past eleven when Wexford got there and found Burden sitting outside at a table in the shade.

There were almost too many tubs, barrels, vases and hanging baskets spilling out fuchsias and geraniums and other unnameable brilliant flowers. But all were scentless and the air smelt of petrol fumes and also of the river, its waters low from drought and scummed with algae. A few yellow leaves had fallen on to the table. In July they were too early for the autumnal shedding but their presence warned that autumn would come.

Burden had a half of Adnams in a tankard that the Olive called a jug. 'I'll have the same,' said Wexford. 'No, I won't, I'll have a Heineken. I need some Dutch courage.' Returning with it, Burden said, 'The old man definitely saw someone. Those trees don't block the view from up there. He saw the thief of the TV and the video.'

'But not Annette's killer?'

'Not if it was four-thirty in the morning. Annette had been dead five hours by then. He says he'd know him again. On the other hand, he says the man he saw was about my age and then that he was between twenty-five and thirty.' Burden looked down modestly. 'Of course, it wasn't very light.'

'I don't suppose it was, Dorian.'

'Yes, well, you may laugh, but if this character looks like me we may be getting somewhere.'

'It's a killer we want, Mike, not a burglar.' The sun had moved round and Wexford shifted his chair into the shade. 'So – Melanie Akande, where does she come into it?'

'We haven't looked for her body.'

'Where would you start, Mike? In the High Street here? In the cellars of the Benefit Office? If it has a cellar, which I doubt. On British Rail's inter-city line to Victoria?'

'I talked to those layabouts, you know, the ones who hang about outside the Benefit Office. They're always there, always more or less the same ones. What attracts them to the place? They only have to sign on once a fortnight but they're there every day. It would be different if they went inside asking about jobs.'

'Maybe they do.'

'I doubt it. I very much doubt it. I asked them if they'd ever seen the black girl. You know what they said?'

Wexford made a guess. ' "I don't know, I might have." '

'Exactly right. That's what they said. I tried to get them to cast their minds back to last Tuesday. Correction, what *passes* for minds with people like that. The way they went about it, I mean the *process*, it was like three very old men trying to recall something. It went something like this, "Well, yeah, man, that was the day I like, you know, I come here early on account of me mum was, you know, going to . . ." mumble, mumble, scratch scalp, and then the next one says, "no, man, no, you got it all wrong, that was Tuesday 'cos I said like . . ." '

'Spare me.'

'The black one, the one with the hair in sort of plaits, only not, sort of matted up, he's the worst, he sounds brain-damaged. You know you can have senile and juvenile diabetes? Well, d'you reckon there's such a thing as juvenile Alzheimer's?'

'I suppose they knew nothing about her?'

'Not a thing. You could have a girl abducted on those steps by three characters from *Jurassic Park* and they wouldn't notice. All I got was that the one with the ponytail says he thinks he saw a black girl on the other side of the street on *Monday*. I'll tell you something, we aren't going to find anyone who saw Melanie after she left the Benefit Office. We'd have done so by now if we were going to. All we've got is the connection between her and Annette Bystock.'

The sun had moved round. Wexford pushed his chair into the shade. 'But what exactly is that connection, Mike?'

' "Exactly" is what I don't know. "Exactly" is what Annette was killed for, to stop her telling. It's obvious, isn't it? Melanie told her something before she left on Tuesday afternoon and whatever it was was overheard. Either that, or some meeting was arranged which the killer of both girls decided must not at all costs take place.'

'You must mean overheard by someone in the Benefit Office, an employee.'

'Or a client,' said Burden.

'But what was it that was overheard? What sort of thing?'

'I don't know and for our purposes it basically doesn't matter. The point is that whoever heard it was worried by it, more than that, felt that his or her life or liberty was endangered by it. Melanie had to die and, because she had passed this secret on, the woman to whom it was spoken had to die too.'

'D'you want another one? The other half for the road before we walk round and see them?'

'*We*?'

'You're coming with me.' Wexford fetched their drinks. When he came back with them he said, 'When someone mentions terrible secrets to me I always need to be given some inkling of what they might be. I'd like an example. You know me, I always want examples.'

They were no longer alone. A number of the Olive's clientele were finding it more pleasant out in the open air. A touring American with a camera posed the other members of his party at a table under a sunshade and began taking shots of them. Wexford moved his chair again.

'Well, this man she was going to meet,' Burden began. 'I mean, she could have told Annette his name.'

'She was going to meet *another* man? That's the first I've heard of it. What was he, a white slaver?'

Burden looked genuinely puzzled. 'A what?'

'Before your time. You've really never heard the term?'

'I don't think so.'

'It must have been used at the beginning of the century and maybe a bit later. A white slaver was a sort of pimp, specifically one who procured girls for prostitution abroad.'

'Why "white"?'

Wexford felt himself approaching dangerous ground. He lifted the 'jug' to his lips and as he did so blinked at the sudden flash. The photographer – not the same one – said something that might have been 'thanks' and dived back into the Olive.

'Because slaves were always thought of as black. It

wasn't that long after emancipation in the United States. The girls were taken against their will, I suppose, like slaves, and forced into servitude abroad, again like slaves, only it was brothels for them. Buenos Aires was the favourite place in the popular imagination. Shall we go? Akande's surgery will be over by now.'

It was and he was back at home. The days gone by had aged him. Hair doesn't turn grey in a matter of days from shock or anxiety, whatever the sensation merchants may say, and Akande's was the same as it had been on Wednesday, black with a white sprinkling at the temples. It was his face that had become grey, drawn and gaunt, all the protrusions of the skull showing.

'My wife is at work,' he said as he showed them into the living room. 'We've tried to carry on as usual. My son phoned us from Malaysia. We didn't tell him, there seemed no point in spoiling his trip. He would have felt he had to come home.'

'I'm not sure that that was a good idea.' Wexford noticed what he hadn't noticed before, a framed photograph of the whole family. It stood on the bookcase and it was obviously a studio portrait, posed and rather formal, the children dressed in white, Laurette Akande in a low-cut blue silk dress and gold jewellery, looking beautiful and very unlike a ward sister. 'He might have been able to help. His sister may have confided in him before he went away.'

'Confided what, Mr Wexford?'

'Possibly that there was a man in her life apart from Euan Sinclair.'

'But I'm sure there wasn't.' The doctor sat down and fixed Wexford with his eyes. He had a rather disconcerting way of doing this. Wexford had noticed it when their roles were reversed, when he so to speak was the client and the other man the omniscient adviser, and in his surgery, confronting each other across the doctor's desk, Akande's black penetrating eyes had stared deep into his own. 'I'm sure she had never had any boyfriend but Euan. Apart, that is, from – I'm not quite sure how to say this . . .'

'Say what, Dr Akande?'

'My wife and I . . . well, we wouldn't care for the idea of Melanie taking up with a . . . well, a white man. Oh, I know things are changing every day, they don't even use words like "miscegenation" any more and, of course, there was no question of *marriage* but still . . .'.

Wexford could imagine Sister Akande being as magisterial about this as any county gentlewoman whose daughter was attracted by a Rastafarian. 'Melanie had a white boyfriend, doctor?'

'No, no, nothing like that. It was just that his sister was at the college too, that was how Melanie met him, and she told us they'd had a drink together – with the sister. I mention him because he's the only other boy Melanie told us about apart from Euan. Laurette said at once that she hoped Melanie wouldn't get to know him better and I'm sure Melanie never did.'

How much did he know, this parent, of his children's lives? How much does any parent know? 'Melanie didn't meet Euan last Tuesday evening,' Wexford said. 'That's been established beyond doubt.'

'I knew she didn't. I knew it. I told my wife she'd too much sense to go back to that boy who had no respect for her.' Akande seemed calm but his hands gripped the arms of his chair and the knucklebones showed white. 'Do you . . .' he began. 'Do you have any news for me?'

'We've nothing specific, sir.' Wexford read a lot into that emphatic 'sir', probably a good deal more than Burden was aware of. He heard in the stress a real effort on the inspector's part to treat this man just as he would any other man in the doctor's position. And he could tell that Burden, who had encountered very few black people, was ill-at-ease, not at a loss but nervous, unsure how to proceed. 'We've done all we can to find your daughter. We've done everything that's humanly possible.'

The doctor must have thought, as Wexford did, that this was meaningless. His knowledge of psychology, and perhaps of white men, enabled him to see through Burden. Wexford thought he could detect the ghost of a sneer on Akande's unhappy face. 'What are you trying to say to me, Inspector?'

Burden didn't like that 'trying'. There had been a faintly sarcastic emphasis on the participle. Wexford took over, rather too hastily.

'You must prepare yourself, Dr Akande.'

His short bark of laughter was shocking in that context. It was a single 'Ha!' and then it was gone, the doctor's face wretched again – worse than wretched now, distraught. 'I am prepared,' he said in a stoical voice. 'We are prepared. You're going to tell me to accept that Melanie must be dead?'

'Not quite that. But, yes, there's a very strong probability.'

Silence fell. Akande put his hands into his lap and forced himself to relax them. He gave a heavy, profound sigh. To his horror, Wexford saw a tear fall from each of those tragic eyes. Akande was un-embarrassed. He removed the teardrops with the forefingers of each hand, wiping them across his cheeks, then contemplating the fingertips with bent head.

To keep his face hidden, without looking up, he

said quietly, in an almost conversational tone. 'There is something I've wondered about. Since I saw the television news last evening and read this morning's paper. The murdered woman in Ladyhall Avenue, her name is the same as the one Melanie had her appointment with last Monday: Annette Bystock. The paper called her a civil servant and I suppose that's what she was. Is it a . . . coincidence? I've wondered if there could be a connection. As a matter of fact, I was awake all last night thinking about it.'

'Melanie had no previous knowledge of Annette Bystock, doctor?'

'I'm sure she didn't. I remember her exact words. "I have to see the New Claims Adviser at two-thirty," she said, and then, a while later, "a Ms Bystock," she said.'

Wexford said gently that the doctor had not told him that before. Mrs Akande hadn't told him that on the single occasion he had talked to her.

'Maybe not. It came back to me when I saw the name in the paper.'

Wexford deeply distrusted evidence which 'came back to' witnesses when they saw a name in the paper. Poor Akande said he was prepared, he could accept, but he hoped just the same. Hope may be a virtue but it causes more pain, Wexford thought, than despair. He considered asking the doctor if he knew of anything Melanie might have said to Annette Bystock that would have put both their lives in jeopardy, and then he thought how pointless such a question was. Of course Akande didn't know.

He said instead, 'What is the name of this white boy she had a drink with?'

'Riding. Christopher Riding. But that was months ago.'

Akande, seeing them to the door, struggled not to say it. He lost the fight, wincing before he spoke. 'Is

there any . . . is there the slightest hope she may be
. . . still alive?'

Until we find her body we can't regard her as dead.
Wexford didn't use those words. 'Let's just say you
must prepare yourself, doctor.' He couldn't give
hope, knowing almost for sure that in a day or two he
would snatch it away again.

The women filled the school hall, at least three
hundred of them. With ten minutes still to go before
the meeting started, they were still arriving and one
of the organizers was bringing in more chairs.

'It's not us they're coming for,' Susan Riding
whispered to Wexford. 'Don't flatter yourself. And
finding out how to blind and maim a rapist is only
part of it. No, they've come for *her*. To see *her*. It was a
good move getting her in the chair, wasn't it?'

Wexford looked across the platform at Anouk
Khoori. He had a feeling he had seen her somewhere
before, though he couldn't remember where.
Perhaps it had only been a photograph in a paper.
She was a big fish in a small pond, he thought, on her
way to becoming Kingsmarkham's First Lady.
Presumably, that suited her. If it was true that most
of these women had come for a sight of her in the
flesh, to see what she wore and hear how she talked,
their aspirations were not high. In her small way she
was like one of those international celebrities whose
pictures are always in the papers, whose names are
household words and who are favourites for TV chat
shows, but of whom it would be hard to say what
they *did* and impossible to know what they had
achieved.

'She doesn't look Middle Eastern,' he said and
immediately wondered if that was a racist remark.

Susan Riding only smiled. 'Her family are from
Beirut. Anouk is a French name, of course. We knew

87

them slightly when we were in Kuwait. His young nephew needed a minor op and Swithun did it.'

'They left because of the Gulf War?'

'*We* did. I don't think they ever left. They've a house there and one in Menton and an apartment in New York, or so I've heard. I knew they'd bought Mynford Old Hall so I plucked up my courage and asked her if she'd do this and she was charming about it. Swithun's here, by the way, and it looks as if he's going to be the only man down there. Still, he won't mind, he takes that sort of thing in his stride.'

Wexford spotted the paediatric surgeon sitting one row from the back, looking as urbane as his wife had suggested he would be. Why was it that when women sat with their legs crossed they rested calf on kneecap but when men did it they placed ankle on femur? Out of modesty in the women's case, presumably, but that wouldn't apply now they wore trousers all the time. Swithun Riding was sitting with his ankle on his femur and clasping it with a long elegant hand. Next to him sat a girl with corn-coloured hair so like him she must be his and Susan's daughter. Wexford recognized her. The last time he saw her she had been waiting to sign on at his first visit to the Benefit Office.

'Your son couldn't bring himself to give his father moral support?' said Wexford.

'Christopher's away for a week. He went off to Spain with a bunch of friends.'

So much for another tentative theory.

Across the room Mrs Khoori laughed, a long musical peal. The man she was talking to, an ex-mayor of Kingsmarkham, smiled at her, evidently already smitten. She gave him a light pat on the arm, a delightful and strangely intimate gesture, before moving back behind the table to the central chair.

There, she adjusted her microphone with the ease of someone accustomed to public speaking.

'I'll introduce you,' said Susan Riding.

Wexford expected an accent but there was none, only the faintest French intonation, the ends of her sentences rising instead of falling. 'How do you do?' She held his hand a little longer than was necessary. 'I knew I should meet you here, I felt it.'

Not surprising, he thought, since his name as a speaker was in the programme. He was a little disturbed by her eyes, which seemed to be assessing him, calculating something about him. It was as if she was speculating how far she could go with him, at what point she would need to draw back. Oh, nonsense, imagination . . . They were black eyes, and that must be what disconcerted him, such dark eyes in contrast to that creamy-olive skin and very fair hair.

'Are you going to tell us poor creatures how to fight big strong men and protect ourselves?'

Anyone less like a poor creature it would be hard to find. She was at least five feet nine, her body sinuous and strong in the pink linen suit, arms and legs muscular, her skin glowing with health. On the hand he hadn't held was a huge rock of a diamond, a single uncluttered stone on a platinum band.

'I'm not a martial arts expert, Mrs Khoori,' he said. 'I shall be leaving that to Mr Adams and Mr Pollen.'

'But you are going to speak? I shall be *so* disappointed if you aren't going to speak.'

'A few words.'

'Then you and I must have a chat afterwards. I'm worried, Mr Wexford, I am seriously worried about what is happening to us in this country, child murders, all these poor young girls assaulted, raped and worse. That's why I'm doing this, to do what I can in my small way to . . . well, turn the tide of crime. Don't you think we each and every one of us ought to do that?'

He wondered about that 'us'. How long had she been living here? Two years? He wondered if he was being unreasonable, resenting her claims to Englishness while he honoured Akande's. Her husband was an Arab multi-millionaire. . . . He was saved from making any reply to her earnest, though oddly vague, remarks by a whispered, 'Anouk, we're ready to start,' from Susan Riding.

With great confidence Anouk Khoori stood and surveyed her audience. She waited for their silence, their total silence, holding up her hands, the great ring catching the light, before she began to address them.

An hour later, if he had been asked to give a résumé of what she had said, he couldn't have recalled a word of it. And at the time he was aware that she had that great gift, on which so many politicians have founded their success, of being able to say nothing at length and in a flowing sequence of polysyllabic fashionable words, of talking meaningless nonsense in fine mellifluous phrases with absolute self-confidence. From time to time she paused for no apparent reason. Occasionally she smiled. Once she shook her head and once she raised her voice on an impassioned note. Just when he thought she would go on for half an hour, that nothing but physical force would stop her, she ceased, thanked her audience and, turning to him graciously, began to introduce him.

She knew a lot about him. Wexford heard, to his amusement rather than dismay, his whole *curriculum vitae* reeled off. How did she know he had once been a copper on the beat in Brighton? Where did she find out he had two daughters?

He got to his feet and talked to the women. He told

them they must learn to be streetwise but told them too that they must cultivate a balanced attitude to what they heard and read about crime on the streets. With a glance of mild displeasure at the *Kingsmarkham Courier* reporter, taking notes from the front row, he said that newspapers were to blame for a great deal of the hysteria over crime in this country. An example would be an account he had read recently of pensioners in Myfleet afraid to leave their homes for fear of the mugger who stalked the village and was responsible for numerous attacks on women and elderly people. The truth, on the other hand, was that one old lady, walking home from the bus stop at 11.00 pm, had had her purse snatched by someone who asked her the way. They must be sensible, avoid taking risks, but not become paranoid. In the rural areas of the police district the chances of a woman being attacked in the street were ninety-nine per cent against, and that they should remember.

Oliver Adams spoke and then Ronald Pollen. A video was shown in which actors simulated an encounter on the street between a young woman and a man with a stocking over his face. When grasped from behind, her attacker's hands at her waist and her throat, the actress showed how to draw the high heel of her shoe down the man's calf and grind it into his instep. This drew delighted cheers and clapping from the audience. They recoiled a little from a demonstration of how to stick your thumbs in an assailant's eyes but shocked gasps soon became sighs of pleasure. Everyone, Wexford decided, was enjoying herself a lot. The atmosphere became grimmer when WPC Clare Scott began to talk about rape.

How many of these women, if raped, would report it? Half, maybe. Once you could have said no more than ten per cent.

Things had changed for the better, but he still wondered if the pictures now coming up on the screen of the comfortable 'suite' at the new Rape Crisis Centre in Stowerton would go far in enticing women to be open about the only crime in which authority often treated the victim worse than the perpetrator.

They were applauding now. They were writing down their questions for the four speakers. In the sea of faces he spotted Edwina Harris and, a dozen seats along from her, Wendy Stowlap. A quarter of an hour, he thought, and he could go home. There was no way he was going to become involved in a chat with Anouk Khoori about crime waves and dangerous Britain.

The first question was for PC Adams. Suppose you hadn't a car phone and your car broke down after dark on an A road where there were no roadside phones? What should you do? After Adams had done his best to answer this WPC Scott, the rape adviser, was asked a difficult question about so-called 'date rape' from someone who sounded like a victim. Clare Scott did her best to answer the unanswerable and Mrs Khoori, having opened the next folded paper, handed it to her. The rape adviser read it, shrugged and after a small hesitation handed it to Wexford.

He read the question aloud. 'If you know a member of your family is a rapist, what should you do?'

There was a sudden silence. Women had been whispering to each other, one or two at the back were gathering their things preparatory to leaving. But now all was still. Wexford saw Dora's face in the second row from the front with Jenny beside her. He said, 'The obvious answer is, tell the police. But you know that already.' He hesitated, then said in a strong voice, 'I would like to know if this question is simply academic or if the member of the audience who wrote this had a personal reason for asking.'

Silence. It was broken by three women in the back row leaving. Then someone broke into prolonged coughing. Wexford persisted.

'You've been told you remain anonymous when you ask these questions, but I should like to know who asked this one. Outside the hall, behind the stage here, there's a door marked Private. I'll be inside that door for half an hour after the meeting with WPC Scott. You only have to come round the side of the hall and knock on that door. I very much hope you will.'

After that there were no more questions. The youngest girl pupil at Kingsmarkham Comprehensive came up to the stage and presented Mrs Khoori with a bouquet of carnations. She thanked her effusively, she bent over and kissed her. The audience began filing out, some lingering in groups to talk over what had been discussed.

Although smoking was banned from the hall, Anouk Khoori was evidently unable to wait a minute longer for a cigarette. When Wexford saw her put the kingsize to her lips and bring the lighter to it, he remembered who she was. He recognized her. She had looked very different then, in her tracksuit and without make-up, but there was no doubt she was the woman in the medical centre who had come to see Dr Akande about some malady suffered by her cook.

He walked out into the car park, saw Susan Riding step into a Range Rover, Wendy Stowlap toss her holdall into the boot of a tiny Fiat, and then he retreated by the side door into the room at the back, a storeplace for chairs and trestle tables. Clare Scott unfolded a couple of chairs, he sat on one and she on the other. A clock on the wall with a large face and a loud tick gave the time as five past ten. He and Clare talked about the morality of betraying family members in aid of the greater good, whether one never should but keep silent out of loyalty or whether one always should and whether there were exceptions. They talked about the heinousness of rape. Perhaps it was right to betray the perpetrator only in the case of a crime of violence. You wouldn't report your wife's shoplifting, would you? The time went by and no one knocked at the door. They gave it another five minutes, but when they came out of the room at twenty to eleven the hall was empty. There was no one outside. The place was deserted.

Chapter Seven

His face looked back at him from the front page of the Sunday paper, a so-called 'quality' Sunday paper. And not only his face. The photograph showed himself and Burden at the table outside the Olive and Dove, only there wasn't much of Burden. Burden would be unrecognizable except to those who knew him well. His, on the other hand, was an excellent likeness. He was smiling . . . well, laughing, to tell the truth, as he raised to his lips the brimming tankard of Heineken. In case there was any doubt, the caption said: *Wexford hunts Annette's killer*, and underneath was the legend: *Chief Inspector in charge of Kingsmarkham murder has time to relax with a pint*.

There hadn't been a moment, he reflected bitterly, when his thoughts hadn't been occupied with Annette Bystock and her death. But to whom could he tell that without seeming absurdly defensive? He could do nothing but pretend he didn't care and thank God the Deputy Chief Constable bought *The Mail on Sunday*.

Things were not improved by the arrival of Sylvia with Neil and the boys. His daughter, having forgotten which newspaper he took, had brought her own copy of the offending one to show him on the grounds that he would 'want to see it.' And no amount of arguing on the part of her mother and her husband could persuade her that there was any irony in the caption. In her eyes it was 'nice', the best photograph she had seen of her father in years and did he think the newspaper would let her have a copy?

Sylvia dominated the conversation at lunch. She was fast becoming an expert on the provisions made by government for its jobless citizens and their dependants. Wexford and Dora had to listen to a lecture on Unemployment Benefit and who was entitled to it, the differences between it and Income Support, and the amenities of something called a 'Job Club' which she was engaged in pulling strings for Neil to join.

'They have all the main newspapers there and free use of the phone, which has to be taken into consideration. And they supply envelopes and stamps.'

'Sounds a breeze,' said her father sourly. 'Somebody once took me to lunch at the Garrick and there weren't any free stamps there.'

Sylvia ignored him. 'After he's been unemployed another three months he can go on a training course. A TFW course might be best. . . .'

'A *what*?'

'Training For Work. And I think I might do one for computers. Robin, be a love, and get the leaflets from my handbag, will you?'

'*Nitcho vo*,' said Robin.

Unable to bear another run-through of the most boring brochures he had ever seen in his life, Wexford made an excuse and resorted to the living room. Sport dominated the television programmes and he baulked at switching to the news in case, mysteriously, his own portrait had found its way to the screen. It was paranoia but he knew no way of conquering it. He even speculated if it could be a journalist's revenge for what he had said the previous night about the press fomenting people's fears of violence.

He was still smarting, though less painfully, when he came into his office very early next morning. His team's reports were already on his desk and no one was going to say a word about that photograph. Burden had seen it. That particular newspaper wasn't his choice but Jenny's.

'Funny how you get used to it,' Wexford said. 'I mean the way the passage of time eases things. I don't feel as bad about it today as I did yesterday, and tomorrow I won't feel as bad as I do today. If only we could live by that instead of just coming to the knowledge afresh each time, if we could be aware at the time that it's not going to matter a lot after a couple of days, life'd be a lot easier, wouldn't it?'

'Hm. You are what you are and that's about it. You can't change your nature.'

'What a depressing philosophy.' Wexford began going through the reports. 'Jane Winster, the cousin, identified the body. Not that there was much doubt. We should get something from old Tremlett today or maybe tomorrow morning. Vine interviewed Mrs Winster at her home in Pomfret but he doesn't seem to have learned much. They weren't close. So far as she knows, Annette had no boyfriends and, oddly, no close woman friend. It sounds a very lonely life. Ingrid Pamber seems to have been the only person she was friendly with.'

'Yes, but would the Winster woman know? She hadn't seen Annette since April. That would be understandable if she lived in Scotland, say, but she lives in *Pomfret* and that's all of three miles. They can't have liked each other much.'

'Mrs Winster says, I quote, "I had my own family to think about". They spoke to each other on the phone. Annette always went to them on Christmas Day and was apparently with them when they

97

celebrated a twentieth wedding anniversary. Still, as you say, it's a bit distant.' He worked through the pages, pausing occasionally to read something twice. 'He also saw that Mrs Harris we talked to – remember? Edwina Harris, the woman upstairs? She heard nothing at night, but she admits she and her husband are heavy sleepers. Another thing she insists on is that she never saw any friend call on Annette or Annette leave the building or come into it with someone accompanying her.

'Neither of the supervisors at the Benefit Office, that's Niall Clarke and Valerie Parker, seems to know anything about Annette, her private life, that is. Peter Stanton – he's the other new claims adviser, the one who looks like the young Sean Connery – he seems to have been very open with Pemberton, told him he took Annette out a couple of times. And then Cyril Leyton told him it wouldn't do. He didn't want staff getting into "intimate relationships".'

'And Stanton accepted that?'

'It doesn't sound as if he was bothered. He told Pemberton they hadn't much in common, whatever that means. Hayley Gordon, she's the young admin officer, the fair one, she hardly knew Annette, she's only been on the staff a month. Karen saw Osman Messaoud and Wendy Stowlap. Messaoud was very nervous. He was born and brought up in this country but he's uneasy around women. He told Karen he didn't want to be interviewed by a woman, he wanted, again I quote, "a police*man*" and he said if Karen questioned him about a woman, Annette that is, his wife would be suspicious. However, he seems to know less than nothing about Annette's life outside the Benefit Office.

'Apart from Ingrid Pamber, Wendy Stowlap appears to be the only member of staff to have been to Annette's flat. She herself lives fairly near, in

Queens Gardens. It was a Sunday and she wanted someone to witness a document – doesn't say what kind of document – something she apparently didn't want the neighbours to know about, so she took it round to Annette. Annette was watching a video and told Wendy she'd just bought a new video recorder, some special kind that you punch a code into. That was six or seven months ago. All this circumlocution seems just to prove she did in fact have a video. Now let's have a look at what Barry has to say about Ingrid Pamber . . .'

But at that moment Detective Sergeant Vine came into the room. Vine wasn't really a short man but he looked short beside Wexford, and Burden too towered above him. He had the extraordinary combination of red hair on his head and dark hair on his upper lip. If he was in Barry Vine's shoes, Wexford had often thought, he'd shave off that moustache. But Vine – though this was unexpressed – seemed to enjoy the bicoloured effect, appearing to believe it gave him distinction. He was sharp and watchful and clever, a man with a prodigious memory that he crammed with all kinds of information, useful and otherwise.

'Have you looked at my report yet, sir?'

'I'm reading it now, Barry. This Ingrid really was Annette's only friend, wasn't she?'

'Not exactly. How about this married man?'

'What married man? Ah . . . wait a minute. Ingrid Pamber told you Annette had confided in her she'd been having an affair for the past *nine years* with a married man?'

'That's right.'

'Why didn't she tell me this on Friday?'

Vine sat down on the edge of the desk. 'She said she'd lain awake all night, wondering what was the right thing to do. She'd promised Annette faithfully, you see, that she'd never tell.'

The man who had phoned the Benefit Office, Wexford thought, the man Ingrid had said was a neighbour. 'All right. Yes, I can imagine. Spare us the schoolgirl heart-searching, will you?'

Vine grinned. 'I gave her the usual stuff, sir. Annette's dead, promises to a dead person weren't valid, didn't she want to help find whoever killed her, all that. She told me a bit and then she said she'd tell you. I mean, she'd only tell you.'

'Really? What have I got that you haven't, Barry? Must be age.' Wexford concealed the mild embarrassment he felt by pretending to read from the report. 'We'll gratify her, shall we?'

'I thought you'd say that, so I asked her if she'd be at the Benefit Office, but no, she won't be. She starts two weeks' leave today and she and her boyfriend can't afford to go away. She'll be at home.'

Burden stepped over the yellow scene-of-crime tape, unlocked the door of the flat and went inside. Starting at the living room, he walked from room to room, slowly studying every object, looking out of the window into reddish-brown foliage, the concrete drive, the red brick side of the house next door. He took down what few books there were and shook their pages in case there were sheets enclosed, but with no particular purpose in mind. In the living room he looked carefully at Annette Bystock's music on a shelf of the bookcase, the compact discs for the missing CD player, the cassettes for the missing cassette player which was also a radio.

Her taste seemed to have been for popular classics and country. *Eine Kleine Nachtmusik*, Bach's *Mass in B Minor* – Burden had heard that this was among the top sellers in classical music – highlights from *Porgy and Bess*, a complete *Carmen Jones*, Beethoven's *Moonlight Sonata*, Natalie Cole's album *Unforgettable*,

Michelle Wright, k.d. lang, Patsy Cline. . . . Without Wexford breathing reproof over his shoulder, Burden was quick to notice that Natalie Cole was a black woman and *Porgy and Bess* and *Carmen Jones* operas about black people. Was that significant?

He was trying to find points of connection between Annette and Melanie Akande. There was no desk in the flat. The dressing table up against the bedroom window had served as a desk. Her passport had been taken away. Burden looked at the other papers in the drawer. They were contained in one of those folders made of clear plastic: certificates showing Annette's O and A Level results, a certificate or diploma showing that she had gained a Bachelor of Arts pass degree in Business Studies at Myringham Polytechnic. That was where Melanie Akande had completed her education, only they called it Myringham University now. Burden looked at the date – 1976. Melanie was only three in 1976. Yet there might be a link there. . . .

Edwina Harris had told them she thought Annette had once been married. There was no marriage certificate in the top drawer. Burden tried the bottom one and found a decree of divorce, dissolving the marriage of Annette Rosemary Colegate née Bystock, and Stephen Henry Colegate, the divorce having been made absolute on 29 June, 1985.

No letters. He had hoped for letters. A brown envelope, eight inches by five, contained a photograph of a man with a high forehead and dark curly hair. Under it was a stack of pamphlets instructing purchasers how to operate a Panasonic video recorder and an Akai CD player. The middle drawer held underclothes. He had already had a good look at the clothes in the wardrobe when he and Wexford came here on Friday. They were safe, dull clothes, the sort bought by a woman who can afford few and must put warmth and comfort before style. Therefore the underclothes surprised him.

They weren't quite what Burden would have called indecent. There were no bras with cut-outs, no crotchless pants. But all the – lingerie, he supposed, was the word – all of it was black or red and most of it transparent. There were two suspender belts, one black, one red, ordinary black bras and black platform bras, one strapless; a thing he called a corselet but Jenny said was a 'bustier' in red satin and lace, several pairs of black stockings, plain, fishnet and lacy, red and black knickers the size of the bottom part of a bikini and a kind of body stocking of black lace.

Had she worn that stuff under those jeans and sweaters, that beige raincoat?

Instead of clearing, as the meteorologists had said it would, the summery mist thinned and turned to rain. A grey drizzle began to fall and cool things down. Vine, driving the car, began speculating as to why rain in England is always cold while in other parts of the world it is warm and why, which he said was more to the point, it doesn't warm up again here afterwards as it does abroad.

'Something to do with being an island, I expect,' said Wexford abstractedly.

'Malta's an island. When I was there on holiday last year it rained but the sun came out afterwards and we were dry in five minutes. Did you see that picture of yourself in the paper yesterday?'

'Yes.'

'I cut it out to show you but I seem to have mislaid it somewhere.'

'Good.'

Vine said no more. They drove in silence to Glebe Lane where Ingrid Pamber lived in two rooms over a pair of lock-up garages with her boyfriend Jeremy Lang. Vine gave it as his opinion that as it was the first day of her holiday and only ten to ten in the morning she would still be in bed.

The neighbourhood was one of the charmless areas of Kingsmarkham. All you could say for it was that beyond the shabbiness, the waste ground and squat buildings, green hills rose skywards, topped with tree rings and behind them the sweep of downs. The district was vaguely commercial or industrial, some of the little houses converted to business premises, a good many buildings of the small factory or workshop kind. Gardens had become yards filled with used cars, scrap iron, oil drums, unidentifiable metal parts. The garages had one door painted black, the other green. At the side, approached by a narrow passage between chain link fencing, was the front door to the flat. There was no shelter from the rain. Vine rang the bell.

After rather a long time, during which there was some banging about and creaking from the upper floor, feet drummed on the stairs and the door was opened by a young man with wild black hair wearing nothing but black-framed glasses and a bath towel round his waist.

'Oh, sorry,' he said when he saw them. 'I thought you were the post. I'm expecting a parcel.'

'Kingsmarkham CID,' said Wexford, who wasn't usually so brusque. 'To see Miss Pamber.'

'Oh, sure. Come up.'

He was a small man, no more than five feet six, and fine-boned with it. The girl was no doubt, as Vine had predicted, still in bed. He closed the door behind them with perfect trust.

'You're Mr Lang?'

'That's me, though I'm mostly known as Jerry.'

'Mr Lang, are you in the habit of letting strangers into your home without question?'

103

Jeremy Lang peered at Wexford and pushed his right ear at him as if he had been addressed inaudibly or in a foreign language. 'You're police, you said.'

Neither Wexford nor Vine said anything. Each produced his warrant card and held it under Lang's nose. He grinned and nodded. He began to go upstairs, gestured to them to follow him, suddenly yelling at the top of his voice: 'Hey, Ing, you going to get up? It's the cops.'

Upstairs was a surprise. Wexford hardly knew what he had expected, but not this pleasantly furnished clean room with a big yellow sofa, blue and yellow floor cushions on a big brightly coloured woven mat, the walls entirely concealed under draped lengths of cloth, posters, and a huge faded tapestry bedspread. Everything had obviously been perks from a parent or else bought very cheaply but it made a harmonious and comfortable place to be. Houseplants in a yellow-painted wooden trough filled the floorspace between the windows.

The door to the bedroom opened and Ingrid Pamber came out. She too wasn't yet dressed but there was nothing frowsty about her, nothing to suggest she had just risen from a long lie-in. She wore a dressing gown or robe of white broderie anglaise that came to her knees. Her small shapely feet were bare. The satiny dark hair, which had been confined by a barrette when Wexford had talked to her on Friday evening, was now held back by a red Alice band. Without make-up her face was even prettier, the skin glowing, the blueness of her eyes startling.

'Oh, hallo, it's you,' she said to Wexford, sounding delighted to see him. On Vine she bestowed a friendly smile. 'Would you like some coffee? If I ask him very nicely, I'm sure Jerry will make us some coffee.'

'Ask me nicely then,' said Jeremy Lang.

She gave him a kiss. A highly sexual kiss, Wexford thought, in spite of being planted in the middle of his cheek and with closed lips. The kiss lingered, she withdrew her mouth an inch, whispered, 'Make us some coffee, my love, please, please. And I'm going to have a huge breakfast, two eggs and bacon and sausages if we've got any and – yes, fried potatoes. You'll cook it for me, won't you, angel? Please, please, mmm?'

Vine coughed. He was exasperated rather than embarrassed. Ingrid sat down on a floor cushion and gazed up at them. She was, Wexford thought, immeasurably more confident and in control here, on her home ground.

'I've already told him a bit of it,' she said, glancing at Vine. 'I've saved the important part for you. It's an amazing story.'

'All right,' Wexford said, and in the manner of Cocteau to Diaghilev, 'Astound me.'

'I never told anyone before, you know. Not even Jerry. I think people should keep their promises, don't you?'

'Certainly they should,' Wexford said. 'But not beyond the grave.'

Ingrid Pamber evidently enjoyed this kind of conversation. 'Yes, but if you'd promised somebody something and they died it wouldn't be right to break your promise and tell their children, would it? Not if it affected their children? I mean, it might be something about them that would ruin their lives.'

'Let's not get on to moral philosophy now, Miss Pamber. Annette Bystock hadn't any children. She had no relatives apart from a cousin. I'd like to hear what she told you about this love affair she was having.'

'He might be affected though, mightn't he?'

'Who do you mean?'

'Well, Bruce. The man. The man I told *him* about.' She pointed a forefinger at Vine.

'Leave that to me,' said Wexford. 'I'll worry about that.'

Jeremy Lang came back with coffee in three cups and on a plate, like a waiter in certain kinds of restaurant displaying to clients the raw materials of their meal, two eggs still in their shells, two rashers of bacon, three pork sausages and a potato.

'Thank you.' Ingrid looked into his eyes and said it again, 'Thank you, thank you, that will be lovely,' the words apparently having some special or secret meaning for the two of them, for the effect on him was to make him roll his eyes while she began to giggle. Wexford coughed. He could manage to get a good deal of reproach into a cough. 'Oh, sorry,' she said, and she stopped laughing. 'I must be good. I shouldn't laugh. I'm really very very sad about poor Annette.'

'How long had you known her, Miss Pamber?' Vine asked.

'Since I started working for the ES three years ago. I've *told* you all this. I was a teacher before that, only I wasn't much good. I couldn't get on with the kids and they hated me.'

'You didn't tell me that,' said Vine.

'Well, it's not exactly relevant, is it? I had a place quite near where Annette lived. That was before I met Jerry.' She cast Jeremy Lang a loving look and pursed up her lips in a kissing shape. 'We used to walk home together, Annette and I, and sometimes we'd have a meal somewhere. You know, if we didn't feel like cooking or getting anything in. I went to her flat once or twice but she came to mine much more and I just had a room. I got the feeling she didn't like asking people to her place.

106

'Then . . . well, I met someone and we started – '
A rueful look this time for Jeremy, who returned it with a pantomime frown. 'We started going about. I didn't live with him or anything,' she added, not making clear what 'anything' might signify. 'That was what made Annette tell me, I think. Or it might have been that one evening when I did go into her place and while I was there the phone rang and it was *him*. That was when she made me promise not to tell anyone what she was going to tell me.

'She'd been so jumpy before the phone rang. I'd guess he'd promised to phone at seven and it was nearly eight. She grabbed that phone like it was . . . well, a matter of life and death. Afterwards she said, "Can you keep a secret?" and I said of course I could and she said, "Well, I've got someone too. That was him," and then it all came out.'

'His name, Miss Pamber?'

'Bruce. His name's Bruce. I don't know Bruce *What*.'

'This was the man you thought had phoned the Benefit Office after Miss Bystock phoned to say she wouldn't be coming in?'

She nodded, untroubled by that earlier lie.

'You know where he lives?' Vine asked.

'My boyfriend and me, we were going to Pomfret one day and we gave Annette a lift. She was going to see her cousin. It was sort of Christmas, the day before Christmas Eve, I think. Annette was sitting in the back and as we passed this house she tapped on my shoulder and said, "Look at that, that house with the window in the roof, that's where you-know-who lives." That was what she said, "you-know-who".

'I don't know the number. I could show you.' Furious faces of discouragement made by Jeremy weren't lost on Wexford. Ingrid saw them and sighed happily. 'I could describe it. I will. You mustn't make silly faces, lovey. Now run away and cook my breakfast.'

'What did you do with the key to Miss Bystock's flat,' Wexford asked, 'when you left on Thursday?'

She answered promptly – too promptly.

Sitting in the car outside number 101 Harrow Avenue, a biggish Victorian house on three floors to which a fourth had been added with a dormer window in the mansard roof, Wexford gave Burden an account of what Ingrid Pamber had told him. They had already been to the house and found no one at home. It was about as far from the street in which Annette lived as was possible and still be in Kingsmarkham. The electoral roll had shown its occupants to be Snow, Carolyn E., Snow, Bruce J., and Snow, Melissa E. Wife, husband and grown-up daughter, Wexford guessed. No hint, of course, was given in the list of those eligible to vote as to how many other children the Snows might have.

'She'd been having this affair with him for nine years,' Wexford said. 'Or so she told Ingrid Pamber, and I can't think of any reason why even a liar like her should lie about that. It was one of those situations in which the married man tells his mistress he'll leave his wife for her as soon as the children are off their hands. Nine years ago Bruce Snow's youngest child was five, so you could say if you were a cynic like me that he was on to a good thing.'

'Right,' said Burden in a heartfelt way.

Wexford cast up his eyes. 'Wait for it. It gets better. They had to meet somewhere but he never took her to an hotel, he said he couldn't afford it. After that trip past the house in the boyfriend's car Ingrid asked her what Bruce had given her for Christmas and Annette said nothing, he never gave her anything, she'd never had a present from him. He needed everything he had for his family. Mind you, according to Ingrid, Annette wasn't resentful, she never criticized him. She *understood*.'

'I take it that after the first confidings there were more on other occasions?'

'Oh, yes. Once she'd started there was no stopping her. It was Bruce this and Bruce that whenever she and Ingrid were alone together. I imagine it was a relief to the poor woman to have someone she could talk to.' Wexford took another look at the house, at the signs of prosperity about it, the evidently recent rooftop extension, the new paint, the satellite dish outside an upper window. 'As I said,' he went on, 'Snow never took her to an hotel and of course they couldn't go to his house. She had her flat but he refused to go there. Apparently, there was some friend or relative of his wife living opposite. So he summoned her to his office after hours.'

'You're joking,' said Burden.

'Not unless Ingrid Pamber is and I doubt if she'd have the imagination. Snow never wrote to her, which is why we found no letters. He gave her nothing, not even a photograph of himself. He phoned, at appointed times, "when he could". But she loved him, you see, and that was why all that was OK, was reasonable in her eyes, was prudent. After all, it would only go on so long as the children were young.'

Burden used his small son's currently favourite word, 'Yuck!'

'I couldn't put it better myself. When he wanted to meet her, or let's say when he wanted his bit on the side . . .' Wexford ignored Burden's pained expression, 'he'd ask her to come to his office. He's an accountant with Hawkins and Steele.'

'Is he now? In York Street, aren't they?'

'In one of those very old houses that overhang the street. The back way has access into Kiln Lane, that sort of alley that comes out in the High Street the other side of St Peter's. There's never a soul about down there after the shops close and Kiln Lane is just an alley between high walls. Annette could sneak down there and he'd let her in by the back door. The best part of this – or the worst part, depending on how you look at it – is that he explained his choice of venue by saying that if his wife phoned the office he'd be there to answer it and she'd know he was working late.'

Lights were coming on in the houses but 101 remained in darkness. Wexford and Burden left the car again and walked up the drive. A side gate was unlocked and they went into the rear garden, a large area of lawn and shrubs whose end was lost in a cluster of tall trees, darkening as the dusk came.

'She did that for nine years?' said Burden. 'Like a call girl?'

'A call girl would expect a bed, Mike, and probably a glass of something stimulating. Call girls, I'm told, expect bathrooms. And very definitely to get paid.'

'It explains the underwear.' Burden described what he had found at the flat in Ladyhall Court. 'She'd always be ready for him. I wonder what's going through his mind now?'

'Is he the guy in the photo, d'you think? What I'm wondering is if he's away on holiday.'

'He won't be, Reg. Not if his youngest is only fourteen. He'll wait for the school term to end and that won't be for a couple of weeks.'

'We have to see him and soon.'

Burden considered. 'What makes you say this Ingrid's a liar?'

'She told me she left the key Annette gave her behind in the flat after she left on Thursday. If she did, where is it?'

'It was on the bedside table,' said Burden promptly.

'No, it wasn't, Mike. Not unless she was lying when she said there were two keys there on Wednesday. One of those statements of hers has to be a lie.'

Chapter Eight

Only two samples of fingerprints had been found in Annette Bystock's flat. Most were those of Annette herself, the other set of women's prints, on the surface of the grocer's box, the kitchen door, the front door and the hall table, were those of Ingrid Pamber. Not another print had been found in the whole place. It seemed as if Annette's home had not only been her castle, it had been the cell where she passed her solitary confinement.

The thief of the electronic equipment had worn gloves. Her killer had worn gloves. Bruce Snow had never set foot or finger inside the home of the woman who had been his mistress for nearly a decade. No friend, apart from Ingrid, had come there. It was likely, Wexford thought, that Annette had discouraged potential friends. Such visitors might overhear one of her conversations with Snow, might betray her; more to the point as she saw it, might by some indiscretion destroy Snow's carefully planned cover. So, for love's sake, she lived this lonely life. It was the saddest story. . . .

The one friend she had she must have trusted to be discreet. And if Ingrid was to be believed her trust was not misplaced, for Ingrid had told no one until after Annette was dead. It seemed that her death had occurred about seven months after she had first confided in Ingrid, so it was hardly likely to be the result of her divulging the secret or divulging more details.

Wexford sighed. Annette had died in the region of thirty-six hours before Burden found her body on Friday morning. Not earlier than 10.00 pm on the Wednesday and not later than 1.00 am on the Thursday. By the time Ingrid Pamber went into the flat at five-thirty on Thursday, Annette had been dead for a day and half a night. Death was due to strangulation with a ligature, in this case a length of electric lead. He knew that already and such medical details were always incomprehensible. Tremlett offered his opinion that a strong woman might have been the perpetrator. Until her death Annette had been a normal healthy woman with no distinguishing marks, not a scar on her body, no peculiarities or minor deformities. She was of normal weight for her height. There was no disease of any kind present.

The flat had been clean but still a considerable amount of hairs and fibres had been gathered from the bed, the bedside tables and the floor. How helpful it would be, Wexford thought as he often did, if one of the investigating officers had picked up a spent cigarette end in the vicinity of the body, as happened in detective stories. Or if a button torn from the killer's jacket, and obligingly retaining a fragment of tweed on its shank, had been found clutched in poor Annette's lifeless hand. Such clues never came his way. Of course it was true that nobody goes anywhere without leaving a vestige of himself behind and taking a vestige of where he has been away with him. That was only useful if you had a clue who and where he might be. . . .

He was leaving for the local studios to make his television appeal for help from the public when his phone rang. The switchboard said it was the Chief Constable for him, calling from his home in Stowerton.

Freeborn, a cold man, always went straight to the

heart of things. 'I don't want to see pictures of you carousing.'

'No, sir. It was unfortunate.'

'It was more than that, it was bloody disgraceful. And in a *good* newspaper too.'

'I can't see it would have been any better in a tabloid,' said Wexford.

'Then that's just one of the many things you ought to see and don't.' Freeborn went on for quite a long time about the need to catch Annette's murderer fast, about the increase in violent crime, about this lovely, safe, once secure, place in which they lived, quickly becoming as dangerous as some inner suburb of London. 'And when you go on TV try not to have a glass in your hand.'

They allowed him only two minutes and that, he knew, would be cut to thirty seconds. Still, it was better than nothing. His appeal would call forth from a public who longed to be important its imagined and fantasized sightings of a killer in the vicinity of Ladyhall Road, confessions to the crime, offers from clairvoyants, claims to have been at school with Annette, at college with her, to have been her lover, her mother, her sister, to have seen her in Inverness or Carlisle or Budapest after she was dead and, perhaps, one genuine and valuable piece of information.

He got to bed late. But he was up early just as the post came. Dora came down in her dressing gown to get his breakfast, an affectionate but unnecessary move as he was only having cereal and a piece of bread.

'One letter and it's for both of us. You open it.'

Dora slit the envelope and drew out a card, deckle-edged.

'Goodness, Reg, she must have taken a fancy to you.'

114

'Who must? What are you talking about?' Strange that his thoughts ran straight to pretty Ingrid Pamber.

'Invitations to this party are like gold dust, Sylvia says. She'd *love* to go.'

'Let's have a look.' What a fool! Why did he take these fancies into his head at his age? He read aloud what was on the card. ' "Wael and Anouk Khoori request the pleasure of the company of Mr and Mrs Reginald Wexford at a Garden Party at their home, Mynford New Hall, Mynford, Sussex, on Saturday, July 17th, at 3pm." ' At the foot of the card was the addendum: 'In aid of CIBACT, the Cancer in Babies and Children Trust'. 'They're not giving us much notice. It's the thirteenth today.'

'No, well, that's what I mean. We obviously weren't on the guest list. And then she took a shine to you last Saturday night.'

'I bet Freeborn's on the list,' Wexford said gloomily. 'Everyone will be expected to fork out at least a tenner, which is a bit of a nerve when you consider Khoori's a millionaire. He could underwrite this CIBACT himself without fund-raising bonanzas. Anyway, it doesn't matter since we shan't go.'

'I should like to go,' Dora said as her husband disappeared out of the door. She called after him, 'I said I should like to go, Reg.'

There was no answer. The front door closed quietly.

The inquest on Annette Bystock opened at 10.00 am and was adjourned pending further evidence at ten past. Jane Winster, who was Annette's cousin, though not attending it, was waiting for Wexford when he got back to the police station. Somebody – some fool, he thought – had put her in one of the bleak interview rooms where she sat on a tubular

115

metal chair in front of the chipboard table, looking puzzled and a little alarmed.

'You have something you want to tell me, Mrs Winster?'

She nodded. She looked about her, as well she might, at the cream-painted brick walls, the uncurtained window.

'Come upstairs to my office,' he said.

Someone's head ought to roll for this. What did they take her for, this small middle-aged woman buttoned up in her raincoat, a damp scarf tied round her head? A shoplifter? A bag-snatcher? She looked like a school dinner lady who could have done with a good helping of what she purveyed. Her face was thin and pinched, her hands bony and veined, prematurely aged.

Once in the comparative comfort of his office, carpeted and with seats that were almost armchairs, he expected her to complain of her treatment, but she only gave the room the same wary look. Perhaps all new places overawed her, so sheltered and circumscribed was her life. He asked her to sit down and he repeated what he had said to her downstairs. For the first time she spoke, having seated herself on the edge of the chair, her knees pressed together.

'The policeman who came, there was something I forgot to tell him. It was a bit . . . I mean, I was. . . .'

Vine's briskness had intimidated her, he supposed. 'It doesn't matter, Mrs Winster. You've remembered now, that's the main thing.'

'It was a shock, you see. I mean, we weren't . . . well, we weren't close, Annette and me, but . . . well, she was my *cousin*, my own auntie's daughter.'

'Yes.'

'And having to go to that place and see her . . . well, dead like that, that was a shock. I've never had to do anything like that before and I. . . .'

116

A woman who left sentences unfinished through self-doubt and perhaps uncertainty that anyone would ever take her seriously. He realized that all this was in the nature of an apology. She was apologizing for having emotions.

'I did tell him we phoned each other. I mean, I said we spoke on the phone but he was . . . well, he was more interested in when I'd last seen her. I hadn't seen her since she came to our wedding anniversary, and that was April, April the third.'

'But you had spoken on the phone?'

She was going to need a lot of prompting and of the kind Vine wasn't the man to give. She looked at him appealingly.

'She phoned me on the Tuesday before she . . . last Tuesday, I mean. . . .'

The day Melanie Akande spoke to her. 'Was that in the evening, Mrs Winster?'

'In the evening, about seven. I was getting my husband's meal on the table. He doesn't . . . well, he doesn't like to be kept waiting. I was a bit surprised she phoned but then she said she wasn't feeling too good, she thought she'd go to bed early . . .' Mrs Winster hesitated. 'My husband . . . well, my husband was making signs to me, so I put the phone down for a minute and he said – I know you'll think this sounds awful . . .'

'Please go on, Mrs Winster.'

'My husband – it's not that he didn't like Annette, it's really that's he doesn't care for any outsiders. Our own family's enough for us, he always says. Of course, Annette *was* family in a way but he always says cousins don't count. He said to me, I mean when Annette was on the phone, he said, don't get involved. If she's ill she'll expect you to go over there getting her shopping and all the rest of it. Well, I suppose she did expect that, that's why she phoned,

117

and I felt awful saying I was busy, I couldn't talk then, but I have to put his wishes first, don't I?'

If this was all, he was wasting his time. He had to be patient. 'You rang off?'

'Well, no. Not at once. She said, could she call me back later? I didn't know what to say. Then she said there was something else, something she wanted to ask me about, maybe ask Malcolm too – Malcolm's my husband – it was whether she ought to go to the police.'

'Ah.' This was it then. 'She told you what this was about?'

'No, because she was going to call me back. But she didn't.'

'You didn't phone her?'

Jane Winster flushed. She looked defiant. 'My husband doesn't like me making unnecessary phone calls. And it's up to him, isn't it? He earns the money.'

'Tell me exactly what your cousin said to you about going to the police.'

Wexford was beginning to understand Vine's impatience with her as a witness, even understand whoever it was who had incarcerated her in that grim interview room. His sympathies were fast diminishing. Here was just another person who had rejected Annette Bystock. She was fidgeting with her handbag, pursing her lips; a woman, he guessed, who though an expert at putting herself down would deeply resent anyone else's criticism.

'I can't do the exact words, or I don't . . . well, it was something like, "There was something happened through work and I think maybe I should go to the police but I want to see what you think and maybe Malcolm too." That was all.'

'You mean "at" work, don't you?'

'No. "Through work" is what she said.'

'You never spoke to her again?'

'She never phoned back and I. . . . No, I . . . I hadn't any call to speak to her.'

He nodded. Her cousin having failed her, Annette had called on the slightly more sympathetic Ingrid to come in, do her shopping, pay her the small attentions needed by someone with 'the falling sickness'. As for the police, she had changed her mind, or more likely, postponed the phone call she should have made until she was better. But she was never better, she was much much worse and it was too late.

'Did your cousin ever mention a man called Bruce Snow?'

She looked up with indifference. 'No. Who's he?'

'You'd be surprised to learn he was a married man Miss Bystock had been in a relationship with for several years?'

Jane Winster was more shocked than she had been by her cousin's death, more shocked than when she saw Annette's dead face in the mortuary. 'I'll never believe that. Annette would never have done a thing like that. She wasn't that sort of person.' Astonishment had made her articulate. 'My husband would never have had her in the house if there'd ever been a suspicion of any of that. Oh, no, you've got it wrong there. Not Annette, Annette wouldn't have done that.'

When she had gone, Wexford had a call put through to Hawkins and Steele and asked to speak to Mr Snow. Waiting while a tape played 'Greensleeves', he thought about Snow and wondered how appalling a shock hearing who was calling him would be. Annette, after all, had been found dead on the previous Friday, it had been on television on Friday, in the papers on Saturday. But no one knew of their liaison except Annette and himself, did they? And Annette was dead. He must think he had got

119

away with it. Got away with exactly what, though, Wexford asked himself.

'Mr Snow is on his other line. Will you hold?'

'No, I won't. I'll call back in ten minutes. You can tell him it's Kingsmarkham Police.'

That should stir him up a bit. Wexford wouldn't have been surprised if Snow had called back himself, unable to wait to know the worst, but no call came. He gave it a quarter of an hour before dialling the number again.

'Mr Snow is in a meeting.'

'Did you give him the message?'

'Yes, I did, but he had this meeting straight after he came off the phone.'

'I see. How long will this meeting last?'

'Half an hour. Mr Snow has his next meeting at eleven-fifteen.'

'Give him another message, will you? Tell him to cancel his other meeting as Chief Inspector Wexford will see him in his office at eleven.'

'I can't possibly . . .'

'Thank you.' Wexford put the phone down. His temper had started to rise. He remembered his blood pressure. Then he had a good idea which made him laugh to himself before he picked up the phone again and asked DS Karen Malahyde to come up and see him.

Karen Malahyde was very much the new woman. Young, fairly good-looking, she did little to enhance her looks. Her face was always without make-up of any kind, her fair hair was very short as were her fingernails. Many with fewer advantages than she had made themselves into beauties. She could do nothing, however, to disguise the excellence of her figure. Karen was a beautiful shape and had the sort of long legs that looked as if they started at her waist. She was a feminist and almost a radical one, a good

120

police officer but one who had sometimes to be cautioned not to lean too hard on men or favour women.

'Yes, sir?'

'I want you to come with me on a visit to a gallant lover.'

'Sir?'

Wexford told her some of Annette Bystock's love story. Instead of castigating Snow as a bastard, which was what he expected, she said rather gloomily,

'These women are their own worst enemies,' and then, 'did he kill her?'

'I don't know.'

They entered the old house by the front door in York Street. Inside it was poky and low-ceilinged but authentically ancient, the kind of place that is generally said to be full of character. There was no lift. The receptionist left her desk and took them upstairs, up a narrow creaking oak staircase, winding to a passage at the top. She knocked on a door, opened it and said rather cryptically,

'Your eleven o'clock appointment, Mr Snow.'

The man in the photograph Burden had found came up to them with outstretched hand. Wexford pretended not to have seen it. For a moment he thought Snow hadn't been told who his callers were. Surely if he had known he could hardly have been so confident, would hardly have smiled so winningly.

'I'm happy to tell you it's turned up,' he said.

They were evidently at cross-purposes but how and why Wexford couldn't tell. He thought that if he didn't keep a watch on himself he might start enjoying this. It was going to be good.

'What has turned up, sir?'

'My driving licence, of course. There were five places it could have been, I looked in them and there it was in the fifth and last.' Snow realized that something was wrong but he was only disconcerted, not fearful. 'I'm sorry. What did you want to see me about?'

Karen was looking offended at being taken for a traffic cop. Wexford asked, 'What do you *think* we want to see you about, Mr Snow?'

A wariness in his eyes showed that realization was dawning. He put up his eyebrows, his head a little on one side. He was a tall thin man, his bushy dark hair greying, not good-looking but with an air of distinction. Wexford thought he had a mean mouth. 'How should I know?' he said in a voice that was a little shriller than it had been.

'May we sit down?'

Karen, when she was seated, couldn't help showing a lot of leg. Even in those awful brown lace-ups with their Cuban heels, her legs were spectacular. Snow gave them a swift but significant glance.

'I'm surprised you don't know why we've come, Mr Snow,' Wexford said. 'I'd have thought you'd be expecting us.'

'I was. I told you, I thought you were here because I couldn't produce my licence when I was stopped on Saturday.' He knew, Wexford could tell. Was he going to brazen it out? Snow's fingers fidgeted with objects on his desk, straightening a sheet of paper, replacing the cap on a pen. 'So what is it then?'

'Annette Bystock.'

'Who?'

If it hadn't been for those restless fingers, now busy with the telephone lead, those eyes that held a gleam of real panic, Wexford might have doubted, might have thought the dead woman a paranoid fantasist, Jane Winster an oracle and Ingrid Pamber queen of the liars. He glanced at Karen.

'Annette Bystock was murdered last Wednesday,'

said Karen. 'Don't you watch television? You haven't seen the papers? You and she had a relationship. You'd been having a relationship with her for nine years.'

'I *what*?'

'I think you heard me, sir, but I don't mind repeating it. You had been having a relationship with Annette Bystock for . . .'

'That is absolute nonsense!'

Bruce Snow got to his feet. His thin face had gone a dark red and a pulse beat in a bluish vein on his forehead.

'How dare you come into my office and make these totally false suggestions!'

For some reason Wexford thought suddenly of Annette coming here, hiding in the alley, tapping on the back door, being brought up that winding stair by Snow to this office where there wasn't even a couch, where there was not the means to produce a drink or even a cup of tea. The phone was there, though, in case his wife called him.

He got up and Karen, taking her cue from him, also rose to her feet.

'No doubt it was a mistake coming to your office, Mr Snow,' he said. 'I apologize.' He watched Snow relax, breathe again, gather up his energy for a final blustering. 'I'll tell you what we'll do. We'll come to your home this evening and talk about it there. Shall we say eight? That'll give you and your wife a chance to have your evening meal first.'

If it hadn't worked it would have shown he was wrong, one or both of the women were fantasists, he'd imagined every sign he'd detected in Snow, and he'd be for the high jump. Freeborn would like this a lot less than newspaper photographs of merry-making.

But it worked.

Snow said, 'Sit down, please.'

'Are you going to tell us about it, Mr Snow?'

'What is there to tell? I'm not the first married man to have a girlfriend. As it happens, Annette and I had decided to break up. It was over.' Snow paused, cleared his throat. 'There is no point in my wife's knowing now. I may as well tell you I went to great lengths to conceal my relationship from my wife. I was anxious not to cause her pain. Annette understood that. Our relationship was, not to put too fine a point on it, purely physical.'

'Then you never intended to leave your wife and marry Miss Bystock once your youngest child was off your hands?'

'Good heavens, no!'

Karen said, 'Where did you meet, Mr Snow? At Miss Bystock's home? At an hotel?'

'I can't see that that's relevant.'

'Perhaps you'd answer the question just the same.'

'At her home,' said Snow uncomfortably. 'We met at her home.'

'That's odd, sir, because we didn't find any fingerprints in Miss Bystock's flat apart from her own and those of a woman friend. Perhaps you wiped surfaces clean of prints.' Karen seemed to rack her brains. 'Or – yes, that would be it – you wore gloves.'

'Of course I didn't wear gloves!'

Snow was growing angry. Wexford watched the beating pulse, the bloodshot eyes. Had he no grief for Annette Bystock at all? After all that time was there no sorrow, no nostalgia even, no regret? And what did the man mean with his 'purely physical' relationship? What did anyone ever mean? That there had been no words exchanged, no endearments, no promises? One at least he had extracted from the dead woman, that she tell nobody. She had very nearly kept it.

'When did you last see her?'

'I don't know. I'll have to think. A few weeks ago, I think it was a Wednesday.'

'Here?' said Karen.

He shrugged, then nodded.

Wexford said, 'I'd like you to tell me where you were between 8.00 pm and midnight last Wednesday. Wednesday, July the seventh.'

'At home, of course. I've always got home by six.'

'Except when you were meeting Miss Bystock.'

Snow winced and coughed as if screwing up his face was a normal preliminary to clearing his throat. 'I got home by six last Wednesday and I stayed at home. I didn't go out again.'

'You spent the evening at home with your wife and – your children, Mr Snow?'

'My elder daughter doesn't live at home. The younger one, Catherine, she's . . . well, she's not often in in the evenings . . .'

'But your wife and your son were with you? We shall need to talk to your wife.'

'You can't bring my wife into this!'

'You have brought her into it yourself, Mr Snow,' Wexford said quietly.

Bruce Snow's 11.15 appointment had been cancelled and now he was obliged to postpone the one he had with a Tax Inspector at 12.30. Wexford didn't think his misery had anything to do with guilt, or rather, with any responsibility for Annette's death. It was terror, the fear of his orderly world falling to pieces. But he couldn't be sure.

'Now you last saw Miss Bystock on a Wednesday some weeks ago. How many weeks, sir?'

'Do you really want me to be precise about it?'

'Certainly I do.'

'Three weeks, then. It was three weeks.'

125

'And when did you last talk to her on the phone?'

Snow didn't want to admit it. He screwed up his eyes like someone in a smoky room. 'It was Tuesday evening.'

'What, the Tuesday before her death?' Karen Malahyde was surprised. 'Tuesday the sixth?'

'I phoned her from here,' Snow said in a rush. 'I phoned her from this office just before I went home.' He rubbed his hands together. 'To make a date, if you must know. For the next night. God, this is my private life you're putting on the line. Anyway, it wasn't important, there was nothing, she just said she wasn't well. She was in bed. She'd got flu or something.'

'Did she mention a girl called Melanie Akande? Did she say anything about giving information to the police?'

This gave Snow a sort of hope. Here was something else. The heat had, at least temporarily, gone off his long and suddenly reprehensible affair with Annette. But he gave a heavy sigh.

'No, I don't – wait a minute, did you say Akande? There's a doctor called that in the same practice as my doctor. Coloured chap.'

'Melanie is his daughter,' said Karen.

'Well, what about her? I don't know anything about her. I don't know him, I didn't know he had a daughter.'

'Annette did. And Melanie Akande has disappeared. But no, of course not, Annette wouldn't have mentioned anything to you because yours was a purely physical relationship, you said, conducted in silence.'

Snow was too wretched to lash back. He did ask when Wexford intended to speak to his wife.

'Oh, not yet, Mr Snow,' Wexford said. 'Not today. I'll give you a chance to tell her yourself first.' He

126

dropped the faintly bantering tone and became serious. 'I suggest you do that, sir, at the first possible opportunity.'

William Cousins, the jeweller, took a good look at Annette Bystock's ring, pronounced it a fine ruby and valued it at two thousand, five hundred pounds. Give or take a little. That was around the sum he would be prepared to pay for such a ring if it was offered to him. He could probably sell it for much more.

Tuesday was one of Kingsmarkham's two market days, the other being Saturday. As a matter of routine, Sergeant Vine cast his eye over the goods for sale on the stalls in St Peter's Place. The stolen stuff either turned up here or at the car boot sales in gardens or on waste ground that had become a regular weekend feature. He generally went round the stalls first, then headed for the sandwich bar to collect his lunch.

Leaving Cousins's, he began his investigation of the market and on the second stall he looked at saw for sale a radio-cassette player. It was made of a hard white plastic substance and across the top of it, just above the digital clock, was a dark red stain someone had tried in vain to eradicate. For a moment or two Vine thought the stain was blood, and then he remembered.

Chapter Nine

The worst thing, Dr Akande told Wexford, was the way everybody asked them if there was any news of their daughter. All his patients knew and they all asked. At last, unable to keep the truth from him any longer, Laurette Akande had told her son when he telephoned from Kuala Lumpur. Immediately he said he would come home. As soon as he could get a cheap flight he would come back.

'The death of that other girl made me believe Melanie must also be dead,' Akande said.

'I should be raising false hopes if I told you not to think that way.'

'But I've told myself there's no connection. I have to keep hoping.'

Wexford had come to them as he did most mornings on his way to work or evenings on his way home. Laurette, changed out of her navy and white uniform into a linen dress, impressed him with her handsome looks, her dignified demeanour. He had seldom seen a woman with a straighter back. She showed less emotion than her husband, was always under control, cool, steady-eyed.

'I wonder if you can tell me what Melanie did the day before she . . . disappeared,' he said. 'On the Monday. What did she do that day?'

Akande didn't know. He had been at work but it was Laurette's day off. 'She wanted a lie-in.' Wexford got the impression that here was a mother who disapproved of staying in bed late. 'I got her up at ten. It's no good getting into those habits if you want to get on in life. She went down to the shops, I don't know what for. In the afternoon she went for a run – you know, jogging that they all do. She always took the same route, Harrow Avenue, Eton Grove, uphill all the way, horrible in this heat, but it would have been pointless saying so. The world would be a better place if they thought as much about their responsibilities as they do about their figures. My husband came home, we had our meal, the three of us . . .'

'She talked about getting a job,' said the doctor, 'about this appointment she had and the possibility of getting a grant to do business training.' He made an effort at a laugh. 'She got cross with me because I said she'd have to think about working her way through college the way they do in America.'

'Well, we couldn't afford to pay,' Laurette said sharply. 'And she'd had one grant. It wasn't as if her first degree was any good, they do take that into account, I told her. She got sulky about it. We all watched some television. She phoned someone, I don't know who, possibly that Euan, God forbid.'

'My wife,' said Dr Akande, in almost reverential tones, 'had a degree in physics from University College, Ibadan, before she studied nursing.'

Wexford was beginning to pity Melanie Akande, a seriously pressurized young woman. The irony was that it looked as if she had had no more chance of escape from forcible education than a Victorian girl had from its denial. And like that Victorian, she was obliged to live at home for an unforeseeable future.

He referred back to her afternoon's jogging. 'She told you nothing of what she had seen while she was out, anyone who had spoken to her, anything at all?'

'She didn't tell us anything,' said Laurette. 'They

129

don't. They're experts at that. You'd think she'd taken a course in secrecy.'

Wexford got into the car, driving himself, but instead of heading for home, took the Glebe Lane direction. Asking himself if it was possible either of the Akandes was responsible for Melanie's disappearance, perhaps Melanie's death, he had to face the chance that it was. But he still went and talked to them. To allege that Akande might be guilty of such a crime was to presuppose him mad or at least a fanatic. The doctor appeared neither of those things and not at all obsessed about Euan Sinclair's association with his daughter. Wexford had never checked out Akande's alibi, hardly knew if he *had* an alibi. But he could see that there was one car Melanie would have got into while she was on her way from the Benefit Office to the bus stop – her father's.

Then had Akande lied? As Snow had, as surely Ingrid Pamber had? It was strange how he knew she had been lying without knowing what she was lying about. He drove into Glebe Lane, over the cobbles. She came down to let him in and said she was at home alone. Lang had gone to see his uncle, a strange excuse that immediately made Wexford suspicious, though he hardly knew of what. Her eyes met his. It spoke of a sublime self-confidence, or an ability to lie effectively, when someone could look you so boldly in the eye and hold the gaze. She wore a long patterned skirt, blue with paler blue flowers, and a silk sweater. Her dark shiny hair was twisted up on top of her head.

'Miss Pamber, you'll think I have a bad memory but I wonder if you'd tell me all over again just what happened when you called on Miss Bystock last Wednesday? When you took her a pint of milk and she asked you to fetch her some shopping on the following day?'

'You haven't really got a bad memory, have you? You're just testing me to see if I'll say the same things.'

'Perhaps I am.'

The blue she wore made him think all blue-eyed women should wear that shade. She was an ornament to the room so that it seemed to need no other. 'I bought the milk at the corner shop where Ladyhall Avenue crosses Lower Queen Street. Did I say that before?' She must know she hadn't. He said nothing. 'It's easy to park there, you see. It was just a bit after five-thirty when I got to Annette's. The front door to those flats has been unlocked every time I've been there – I don't think that's very secure, do you?'

'Evidently not.'

'I think I said Annette had left her door on the latch. I put the milk straight in the fridge and then I went into the bedroom. I knocked on the door first.' All these details were being given to tease him. He realized that but didn't mind. Any detail, however small, might be relevant in a case like this. 'She said, "Come in". I think she said, "Come in, Ingrid". I went in and she was in bed, sort of half-sitting up, but she looked quite ill. She said not to come near her because she was sure she was infectious, but would I get her the things on this list she'd made. It was a loaf and cornflakes and yogurt and cheese and grapefruit and more milk.'

Wexford listened, deadpan. He didn't move.

'She had two keys on the bedside table. She gave me one – that was the nearest I got to her, I really didn't want to catch it – and she said, now you'll be able to let yourself in tomorrow. So I said I would, yes, I would, and I'd get the things and to get well soon, and she said would I draw the curtains in the living room on my way out. So I did that and I called out goodbye and . . .' Ingrid Pamber looked at him ruefully, her head on one side, 'I may as well come out with it. You're not going to eat me, are you?'

Had he looked as if he wanted to? 'Go on.'

'I forgot to lock the door after me. I mean, I left it on the latch like it was. I just *did*. It was awful of me, I know, but it's easy to do with those sort of doors.'

'So the door was left unlocked all night?'

Before replying, she got up, walked across the room and felt for something behind the books on a shelf. Over her shoulder she smiled at him. Wexford repeated what he had said.

'I suppose so,' she said. 'It was locked when I got there on Thursday. Are you very very angry with me?'

She hadn't seen. She had no realization of what she had done. Her eyes were warm and full of happy light as she handed him Annette Bystock's key.

Carolyn Snow was out. She was taking her son Joel to school, the cleaning woman told Wexford. He decided to take a walk round the block, though 'block' was not the word for it. 'Park' would have been better or 'enclave'. The Snows' house, though twice the size of Wexford's own, was one of the smallest in this neighbourhood. Houses seemed to get bigger and be farther apart as he reached the corner and turned into Winchester Drive. He couldn't remember the last time he was in this part of Kingsmarkham, it must have been years, but he did now recall that he was in the vicinity of the route Laurette Akande said her daughter took when she went running.

The hallmark of desirability in dwelling places is when a suburb looks like a stretch of woodland and no houses are visible, where there are no gates and all that shows that people live somewhere in there are the letter boxes, discreetly positioned in gaps in the hedge. It was very high up, a green thickly treed ridge, beyond which, far below, he could catch glimpses of the winding Kingsbrook. In Winchester Drive green lawns terminated in high hedges or low walls at the pavement and, because you knew it must be there, you fancied you caught the faintest glimpse of mellowed brick between the great grey beech trees, the delicate silver birches and the branches of a majestic cedar.

The presence of two people on one of these lawns, a woman with a basket of shiny dark red fruit, a young man a little over twenty putting a ladder up against a cherry tree, did a little more to damage this image of wooded countryside. Wexford was surprised to identify the woman as Susan Riding, though he hardly knew why he should be. She must live somewhere and was reputed to be well-off. The boy was startlingly like his father with the same straw-coloured hair and Nordic looks, the high forehead, blunt nose, long upper lip.

Wexford said good morning.

She came a little way towards him. If you didn't know who she was and had encountered her away from her own environment, you would have taken her for one of the dossers who slept on Myringham High Street. She wore a cotton skirt with half the hem coming down and a tee-shirt that must have originated with one of her children, for 'University of Myringham' was printed across the faded red material. An elastic band held back her greyish frizzy fair hair.

He thought how her smile transformed her. In an instant she was almost beautiful, beggarwoman into earth mother.

'The birds take most of our cherries. I wouldn't mind if they ate them but they just pick a bit out and drop the rest on the ground.' The boy had gone up the tree, his back towards them, but she introduced

133

him just the same, 'My son, Christopher.' He took absolutely no notice. She shrugged as if this was no more than she had expected. 'You really need to be bird scaring from morning till night. We did last year but I had help then. How do people get staff in this country?'

'I understand it's difficult.'

'Do it yourself is what you're saying, isn't it? That's not so easy when you've got six bedrooms and four children all living at home most of the time. My au pair's just left me too.'

Christopher suddenly let out a string of startling obscenities and the wasp that had been annoying him zoomed out of the tree and headed for Susan Riding. She ducked, flapped at it with her hand.

'I *hate* them. Why on earth did God make wasps?'

'To clean it up, I suppose.' Her puzzled face made him explain. 'The earth.'

'Oh, yes. I really must thank you for giving up your Saturday night to us vulnerable women. I have written to you but I'm afraid I didn't post the letter till this morning.'

'Come on, Mum,' said the boy in the tree. 'We're supposed to be picking the buggers.'

Wexford called out to him, 'Do you know a girl called Melanie Akande?'

'*What?*'

'Melanie Akande. You once had a drink with her. Perhaps you saw her more than once.'

Susan Riding laughed. 'What is this, Mr Wexford? An interrogation? Is that the girl that's missing?'

Christopher came down the ladder. 'Is she missing? I didn't know.'

He was at least as tall as Wexford. His hands were big and his feet were big, his shoulders ox-like.

'Melanie disappeared last Tuesday afternoon,' Wexford said. 'Had you seen her recently?'

'Not for months. I went away last Tuesday morning. I can give you the names of the people I went with if I need an alibi. You can see my air ticket or what remains of it.'

'Christopher!' said his mother.

'Well, why ask me? I'm the last person. Can I get on with picking these cherries now?'

Wexford said goodbye and walked on. At the corner he looked back and between a gap in the trees could see the house quite clearly, the back of an Italianate villa, white walls, green roof, a tall turret. He could even see the bars on the ground floor windows. Well, Susan Riding was a Woman, Aware! woman, one who would no doubt be prudent. The place looked as if it contained a lot worth stealing. He turned into Eton Grove and went back down the hill. The Riding house was momentarily clearly visible from the road and then, suddenly, it disappeared behind a dense plantation of shrubs in white blossom. He stepped back to look at it once more and lingered for a while before turning left back into Marlborough Gardens and walking the few hundred yards to Harrow Avenue.

Donaldson in the driving seat of the parked car was reading the *Sun* but folded it up when he saw the boss. Wexford read his own paper for ten minutes. A young man with a camera hung round his neck appeared from round the corner and Wexford put his paper away, although this passer-by was clearly not interested in photographing him, hadn't even noticed him or taken his camera from its case.

'I'm getting paranoid.'

'Sir?'

'Nothing. Ignore me.'

The car suddenly appeared from nowhere, driven much too fast, sweeping into the drive of 101 and coming to a stop with a squeal of brakes. He had a good look at her as she left the car and went quickly to the front door, her doorkey on the same ring as the car keys. She was a tall slim woman, fairish, wearing black trousers and a sleeveless top. Two minutes after she had gone inside he went up to the front door and rang the bell. She answered it herself. She was younger than he had expected, probably forty but looking less. It struck him that she looked a lot younger than poor Annette.

No wedding ring. That was one of the first things he noticed and saw too that she had been used to wearing a ring, for there was a band of white skin on that brown finger.

'I've been expecting you,' she said. 'Won't you come in?'

Her voice was cultivated, pleasant, with the sort of accent associated with a select girls' boarding school. Wexford was suddenly and surprisingly aware of how very attractive she was. Her hair was so cut as to transform it into a cap of flaxen coloured feathers. She wore no make-up and her skin was good, smooth, light golden brown, only faintly lined about the eyes. The top she wore was the same sea-blue as her eyes and the brown arms it exposed might have been those of a young girl.

He began to ask himself why a man who had this at home, legitimately and honourably, would chase after Annette, but he knew such questions were always vain. Some of it was due to the legitimate and honourable being less attractive than the illicit and forbidden, and some of it to a strange lusting after the sordid and the naughty, after soft porn made flesh. He would guarantee, for instance, that Mrs Snow didn't wear see-through black and scarlet camisoles, but Calvin Klein briefs and Playtex sports bras.

She took him into a large living room with a green velvet carpet, enough sofas and armchairs to accommodate twenty people, and a fireplace of Cotswold stone with a copper hood over it. It was clear she knew why he had come and that she had her answers ready. She was confident but grim, her movements deliberate, her expression fixed and resolute.

He said carefully, 'I am sure your husband has told you he has been questioned in connection with the death of Annette Bystock.'

She nodded. She put her elbow on the arm of her chair and rested her cheek against her hand. It was a pose of controlled exasperation.

'That evening, Wednesday, July the seventh, your husband spent the evening at home with you and your son? Is that correct?'

She delayed answering so long that he was on the point of repeating what he had said. Her reply, when it came, was stiff and cold. 'Whoever gave you that idea? Did he tell you that?'

'What do you mean, Mrs Snow? That he wasn't here?'

The sigh she gave was as heavy and deliberate as the inhaling and exhaling prescribed for the exerciser, a deep intake of breath, a full expulsion of breath.

'My son wasn't here. He, my son, Joel, was upstairs in the playroom. He always is in the week evenings, he has a lot of homework, he's fourteen. We often don't see him between the time he has his meal and bedtime – and sometimes not then.'

Why was she telling him all this? No one was accusing the boy of the crime.

'So you and your husband were alone together? In here?'

'I asked who gave you that idea? My husband wasn't here.' Her expression became unearthly, dreamy, she seemed to gaze into the middle distance as if looking at a perfect sunset, her lips just parted.

Suddenly she turned on him. 'He often wasn't on a Wednesday. He worked late on Wednesdays, or didn't you know?'

This was not at all what he had expected. If he hadn't been at home with his wife, why had Snow mentioned her? If his dearest wish was to keep the knowledge of his affair with Annette secret from her, why had he produced his wife as his alibi? Surely because he had no choice . . . the last thing he wanted to do was enlighten Carolyn Snow himself as to her husband's philandering, but it looked as if he would have to. Snow then had chickened out, had lost his nerve, had evaded confession. Or had he?

'Mrs Snow, you have been told of your husband's relationship with Annette Bystock?'

No one can whiten under a tan, but her skin contracted and aged her. It hadn't been a revelation, though. 'Oh, yes. He told me.' She stopped looking at him. 'You understand that I didn't know until yesterday – no, the day before yesterday. I was in the dark, I'd been kept in the dark.' A little cold laugh summed up her feelings about such men as Snow, their values, their cowardice. 'He had to tell me.'

'And asked you perhaps to tell me you were with him last Wednesday?'

'He didn't ask me anything,' she said. 'He knew better than to ask for favours.'

There was nothing more to say for the moment. It was all very different from what he had anticipated. Until this moment he had never seriously considered Snow as a suspect, as a candidate for murderer. After all, Snow hadn't been inside the flat at Ladyhall Court. But by that reckoning no one had been in the flat except Annette herself and Ingrid Pamber. There had been no evidence of Edwina Harris's visit or, more to the point, of the thief who came in at some point and took the television, the video and the radio-cassette player. If that thief had worn gloves, so might Bruce Snow have done.

He had spoken to Annette on the Tuesday evening but he might have been lying when he said she told him she was ill and couldn't meet him the following night. She loved him, she never refused him, she put him first. It was one thing not to go to work, to tell Ingrid she would need shopping done for her, but quite another to cancel a longed-for meeting with Snow on the dubious grounds that she might still be ill twenty-four hours later.

But they always met in Snow's office. Always except for just this once? I'm not well enough to go out, she had perhaps said, but you could come here – won't you just for once come here? And he had agreed, had gone there, had stayed and stayed, and quarrelled with her at last and killed her. . . .

Bob Mole had no intention of telling Vine where the radio came from. All he would say at first was that it had been among a job lot saved from a fire. That there were no burn marks on it meant nothing. These rugs, for instance – had Vine even bothered to look at them? – weren't burnt. The three dining chairs weren't burnt. There was plenty of stuff that was and no one was going to buy that from a stall. What did he think, the public were daft?

Where did that stain come from, Vine wanted to know. Bob Mole couldn't account for it. Come to that, why should he account for it and what was Vine getting at? When Vine told him, things changed. It was the word 'murder' that did it, specifically the murder of Annette Bystock, Kingsmarkham's own local murder that was in the daily papers and even on telly.

'It was hers?'

'Looks very much like it.'

139

Bob Mole, who had gone putty colour, curled back his upper lip. 'Not blood, is it?'

'No, it's not blood.' Vine wanted to laugh but didn't. 'It's red nail varnish. She spilt it. Now tell me where you got it from.'

'It's like I said, Mr Vine. It was what come out of this fire.'

'Sure. I heard you. But who was it rescued it from the flames and put it in your sticky hands?'

'My supplier,' said Bob Mole as if he were a respectable retailer talking about a wholesaler of nationwide repute. 'You're sure it's hers, this Annette that's dead?' He dropped his voice on the name and looked from side to side.

'There's a TV and a video too,' said Vine.

'I never got them, Mr Vine, and that's the absolute honest truth.' With another glance to the right and one to the left, Bob Mole leaned towards Vine and whispered, 'They call him Zack.'

'Does he have another name?'

'If he does I don't know it, but I can tell you where he lives.'

Not an address but a description of a place. Bob Mole didn't know the address. His directions were to go all the way down to the bottom of Glebe Lane, turn down that passage by that place, that sort of church the Methodists used to have but was now a sort of store, go round the back of the used car dump and he lives in the furthest away of the two cottages facing Tiller's paintbrush works.

When Burden heard about it he went on the hunt for Bob Mole's supplier himself, taking Vine with him. He expected something like Ingrid Pamber's place but this back corner of Kingsmarkham made hers look like a smart mews. Confusion could hardly have arisen as to which cottage Zack lived in as the nearer to the lane of the two was derelict, its door and

140

windows boarded up. It scarcely seemed like a dwelling house any longer, but more a shed for neglected animals, a dirty brownish hut, the broken tiles on its roof yellow with stonecrop.

Zack's wasn't much better. Years ago someone had put a pink undercoat on the front door, never painted on top but apparently wiped a brush laden with different coloured paints against its surface. Perhaps this was the work of an employee at the little factory opposite. A broken window had been mended with masking tape. From a rickety trellis hung the tendrils of a climbing plant that had apparently died some years before.

'The council should do something about this dump,' Burden said crossly. 'What do we pay our rates for, I should like to know.'

The young woman who came to the door was thin and pale, no taller than a child of twelve. She carried on one puny hip a boy of about a year who was crying loudly.

'Yes, what is it?'

'Police,' said Vine. 'Can we come in?'

'Oh, shut up, Clint,' she said to the child, shaking him in a half-hearted way. She looked with a kind of apathetic distaste from Barry Vine to Burden and back again. 'I'll want to see some identification before I let you in.'

'Who are *you*, then?' said Vine.

'Kimberley. Ms Pearson to you. He's not here.'

Warrant cards were produced and she scrutinized them as if to check they weren't forgeries. 'Look at the funny photo of the man, Clint,' she said, pushing the child's head nearly into Vine's chest.

When Clint understood he couldn't have the pictures he began crying even more loudly. Kimberley moved him to her other hip. Burden and Vine followed her into what Burden afterwards called one of the worst tips he'd ever been into. Analyzing the smell, he declared it to be compounded of soiled napkins, urine, fat that chips had been cooked in fifty times, meat kept too long without a refrigerator, cigarette smoke and canned dog food. The linoleum that covered the floor was worn into holes and covered with sticky, hairy patches and dark ring marks. Ashes from last winter's fires were tumbled about the grate which was piled high over them with waste paper and cigarette ends. Two deckchairs faced a huge television set. It was too large to have been Annette's but the video recorder next to it might have been hers.

Kimberley put the child into one of these chairs and gave him a bag of crisps which she produced from one of the many cardboard grocer's boxes that stood about and served as cupboard, sideboard and larder. Another box provided her with a packet of Silk Cut and matches.

'What d'you want him for?' she said, lighting her cigarette.

'This and that,' said Vine. 'Maybe something serious.'

'What's serious mean?' said Kimberley. She had the very pale green eyes of a white cat. Her skin and hair were luminous with grease. 'He never done nothing serious.' She corrected herself. 'He never done nothing.'

'Where is he?'

'It's his signing-on day.'

All ways, as Wexford had thought, led back to the Benefit Office.

'Where did the video come from, Miss Pearson?' Burden asked, refusing to have any truck with that 'Ms' stuff.

'My mum give it me.' Her answer came quick as a

142

flash. That, of course, meant nothing. 'And it's Mrs Nelson.'

'I see. Miss Pearson to him and Mrs Nelson to me. That his name, is it? Nelson?'

She didn't answer. Having finished the crisps, Clint set up a renewed roaring. 'Oh, piss off, Clint,' she said. Taken from his deckchair and placed on the floor, he crawled over to one of the grocer's boxes, pulled himself into a standing position and began removing its contents, item by item. Kimberley took no notice. Apropos of nothing that had gone before, she said, 'They're going to pull it down, this place.'

'Best thing they can do,' said Vine.

'Oh, yes, sure, it's the best bloody thing they can do. What's going to happen to us? You don't think of that, do you, when you say . . .' she mimicked his voice in an exaggerated way, ' "it's the best thing they can do".'

'They'll have to re-house you.'

'You want to bet? In a bed and breakfast maybe. If you want to be re-housed you have to do it yourself. One thing you can say for this dump, the DSS pay the rent. He'll lose that, won't he? He's not had a job in months.'

Outside, Burden inhaled the air, somewhat contaminated though it was with the fumes from paint-brush manufacture. 'Doesn't stop them having kids, does it, being out of work? You'll notice they can always afford to smoke.'

If I lived in that midden I'd smoke myself to death, thought Vine, but he didn't say it aloud.

'Did you see them in the paper, it'd have been around last Christmas? I remember the name, Clint. He had something wrong with his heart and they operated on it at Stowerton Infirmary. There were pictures of him and Kimberley Pearson all over the *Courier*.'

But Burden couldn't remember. He was sure that somehow they would miss Zack Nelson, that he was a genius at slip-giving. Kimberley had no phone, even if it was possible to phone people waiting to sign on. Burden didn't know whether it was or not and he was sure Vine didn't. But when they came into the Benefit Office, Zack was still there.

He was one of a dozen people waiting, sitting on the grey chairs. Burden had made what he thought was an intelligent guess at which one of the seven or eight men he was and got it wrong. The first person he approached, a boy of perhaps twenty-two with a blond crewcut, three rings in each ear and one in a nostril, turned out to be a John MacAntony. The only other man who could possibly be Zack Nelson admitted it first with an exaggerated shrug, then a nod.

He was tallish and of all the men in there, in the best condition. It looked as if he worked out with weights, for his body was lean and hard and he had no need to flex his bare arms to show the large round muscles that stretched the sleeves of a dirty red polo shirt. His long hair, as greasy as Kimberley's, was plaited for an inch or two before being tied with a shoelace. Inside the open neck of his shirt, under the fuzz of dark hair, could be seen the greenish-blue, red and black inks of an elaborate tattoo.

'A word,' said Burden.

'It'll have to wait till my number comes up,' said Zack Nelson without irony.

Burden was baffled, then saw that he referred to the neon signs that hung from the ceiling. When the number on his card appeared he would go up to a desk to sign on.

'How long is that going to be, then?'

'Five minutes. Maybe ten.' Zack made the sort of face at Vine that he himself had made when he smelt the inside of the cottage. 'What's the hurry?'

144

'No hurry,' said Burden. 'We've got plenty of time.'

They moved away and sat on a pair of grey chairs. Burden fingered one of the leaves of the houseplant in the tub next to him. It had the faintly sticky, rubbery texture of polythene.

Vine said in a low voice. 'He looks like you, you know. I mean, if you grew your hair and didn't wash much. He might be your young brother.'

Incensed by this, Burden said nothing. But he remembered what Percy Hammond had said, that the man he had seen in the night coming out of Ladyhall Court looked like him. If it was true, and here was Vine absurdly confirming it, it said a lot for the old man's powers of observation. It meant that the old man could be trusted.

He looked about the big room. Behind the counter were Osman Messaoud, Hayley Gordon and Wendy Stowlap, this last apparently suffering from an allergy, for she kept wiping her nose on a succession of coloured tissues pulled from a box in front of her. All were occupied with clients. Cyril Leyton stood outside the door of his office deep in conversation with the security officer.

Messaoud's client finished her business and moved away from the desk. A number came up in red neon and the boy with the rings in ears and nose went up. You couldn't see the New Claims Officers from where Burden sat, only the sides of their booths. He got up and began walking about, apparently aimlessly, but avoiding confrontation with Leyton. The new claims officer sitting in the booth next to Peter Stanton's must be a replacement for Annette, but was too far away for Burden to read the name tag he wore. In the light of increased knowledge, Burden made a mental note to subject Stanton to a second interview. After all, the man had admitted to taking Annette out. Was she, in his company, trying to find herself a better option than Bruce Snow? And if so, what had gone wrong?

He was alerted by a woman shouting and he turned round. This was the first instance of 'trouble' there had been since they began calling at the Benefit Office. The woman, fat and unkempt, was complaining to Wendy Stowlap about a lost giro and Wendy seemed to be checking on the computer screen that it had been sent to her. The answer wasn't apparently acceptable and the torrent of complaint became a stream of abuse, culminating in a yell of, 'You're a whore!'

Wendy looked up, unmoved. She shrugged. 'How did you know?'

There came a faint snigger from Peter Stanton who was passing the counter on his way to pick up a leaflet. The woman turned her invective on him and there was a moment when Burden considered intervening. But the staff seemed competent to deal with verbal abuse, and the woman soon deflated.

Zack Nelson's number appeared in red neon at last and he went up to Hayley Gordon. Vine thought her a little like Nelson's girlfriend Kimberley to look at, only cleaner and better dressed and – you had to face it – better fed. Zack would get – what? Nothing here, of course, but when his giro arrived he would collect from the post office unemployment benefit for himself of around forty pounds and the DSS would provide the Income Support for Kimberley and Clint – or did Kimberley herself collect Clint's Child Benefit? It was always the mother, wasn't it? Vine had to confess he didn't know. But no doubt they didn't live in poverty because they liked it.

These were private thoughts which would not affect his attitude to Zack who was a thief, he reflected, and a villain. They weren't permitted to arrest him in here, not unless requested to do so by the ES staff. 'We'll talk in the car,' he said when Zack returned, having assured himself of support for another fortnight.

'About what?'

'Bob Mole,' said Burden, 'and a radio with blood on it.'

It was, as he said to Wexford later, as easy as taking peppermints from a baby who didn't like them. 'That was never blood,' said Zack. He realized immediately what he had said, rolled his eyes and clapped one hand over his mouth.

'Why not blood?' said Vine, leaning close.

'She was strangled. It was on telly. It was in the papers.'

'So you admit you were in Annette Bystock's place, that the radio was hers?'

'Look, I . . .'

'We'll go back to the police station, Sergeant Vine. Zack Nelson, you need not say anything in answer to the charge but anything you do say will be taken down and may be given in evidence . . .'

Chapter Ten

'Not with murder?' said Zack in the interview room.

Wexford didn't answer. 'What *is* your name, anyway? Zachary? Zachariah?'

'You what? No, it's fucking not. It's Zack. There was some singer called his son Zack what is where my mum got it from. OK? I want to know if you're charging me with murdering that woman.'

'Tell us when you went into the flat, Zack,' said Burden. 'It was the Wednesday night, was it?'

'Who says I ever went in the flat?'

'She didn't bring that radio round to you and give it to you for a birthday present.'

This was a lucky shot on Wexford's part, not even intelligent guesswork. If it had been December instead of July he would have said 'Christmas present.' Zack stared at him in a kind of horror, as he might have at some clairvoyant possessed of proven supernatural powers.

'How d'you know Wednesday was my birthday?'

Wexford held back his laughter with difficulty. 'Many happy returns. What time was it you went into the flat?'

'I want my lawyer,' said Zack.

'Yes, I expect you do. I would in your position. You can phone him later. I mean, you can find one later and phone him.' Zack gave him a suspicious glare. Wexford said, 'Let's talk about the ring.'

'What ring?'

'A ruby ring worth two grand, give or take a bit.'

'I don't know what you're talking about.'

'Was she dead, Zack, before you took that ring off her finger?'

'I never took no ring off her finger! It wasn't on her finger, it was on the table!' Once more he had dropped himself in it. 'Fuck it all,' he said.

'You'd better start at the beginning, Zack,' said Burden. 'Tell us all about it.' Silently he blessed the recording device which had all this on tape. There was no arguing with it.

Zack made a few more attempts at argument before caving in. Finally he said, 'What's in it for me if I tell you what I found in there and what I saw?'

'How about you come up in court tomorrow instead of Friday, you only get one night in a cell and Sergeant Camb'll bring you a Diet Coke for a nightcap.'

'Don't give me that crap. I mean, if I tell you what I know I could help you find her killer.'

'You'll do that anyway, Zack. You don't want a charge of obstructing the police as well as burglary.'

Zack, who had an impressive record of petty offences, the computer had informed Wexford, knew all about it. 'It wasn't burglary. It wasn't dark. I never did no breaking and entering.'

'A figure of speech,' Burden said. 'I suppose you found the door unlocked and just walked in?'

A cunning look came into Zack's face, making it slightly lopsided. There was something sinister about him, something called evil. His eyes narrowed. 'Couldn't believe me eyes,' he said, his tone becoming conversational. 'I tried the handle and the door came open in me hand. I was amazed.'

'I'm sure. Carrying housebreaking tools, were you, just on the off-chance? What did you mean just now when you said it wasn't dark?'

'It was five in the morning, wasn't it? It'd been light an hour.'

'Up with the lark, were you, Zack?' Burden couldn't help grinning. 'You always an early riser?'

'The kid woke me up and I couldn't get back to sleep. I went out in the van to clear me head. I was just passing sort of slow – keeping in the speed limit, right? – and the front door was open, so I reckoned I'd pop in and see what was going.'

'D'you feel like making a statement, Zack?'

'I want my lawyer.'

'I tell you what, you make a statement and then we'll get the Yellow Pages and find you a lawyer. How's that?'

Zack yielded quite suddenly. He seemed to collapse without warning. One moment he was truculent, the next he had given in. 'I don't mind,' he said and gave a huge yawn. 'I'm dead tired. I don't never get enough sleep, not with my kid.'

At approximately five am on Friday, 9 July – Zack Nelson's statement ran – I entered Flat 4, 15 Ladyhall Avenue, Kingsmarkham. I had no housebreaking tools and did not break the door or the lock. I was wearing gloves. The front door was unlocked. It was not dark. The curtains were drawn in the living room but I could see. I saw a television set, a video recorder, a CD player and radio-cassette player, and these I removed from the flat, making two trips to do so.

I came back to the flat and opened the door to the bedroom. To my surprise there was a woman in the bed. At first I thought she was asleep. Something in her attitude made me suspicious. It was the way her arm was hanging. I approached nearer but did not touch her, as I could see that she was dead. On the table by the bed was a ring and watch. I did not touch these but left the flat quickly, making sure the door was locked behind me.

I put the television set, the video recorder and the radio-cassette player into the van I had loaned from my girlfriend's father and drove home. I am a dealer in secondhand electronic equipment. I had some of the said equipment salvaged from a factory fire and, included as one lot with some of the salvaged goods, I sold the radio-cassette player to Mr Bob Mole for the sum of seven pounds. The television set and video recorder are at present in my home at 1 Lincoln Cottages, Glebe End, Kingsmarkham.

'I like the virtuous touch about locking the door behind him, don't you?' Wexford said when Zack had been taken to one of the only two cells Kingsmarkham Police Station possessed. 'At least it explains how the door came to be locked when you got there. If anyone from the Employment Service reads an account of tomorrow's proceedings in the magistrates' court, Zack's going to lose his UB. The *Courier* will describe him as a dealer in electronic goods.'

'He won't need it where he's going,' Burden said.

'No, but Kimberley and Clint will. I don't know what happens in a case like this. Do they cut off his dependants' Income Support? Still, he'll not get more than six months and he'll serve four and a bit.' Wexford hesitated. 'You know, Mike, there's something odd in all this, there's something I don't like.'

Burden shrugged. 'Like him finding the door unlocked and the place all open for him? Like him not taking the ring?'

'Well, yes, but not that so much. The front door to the house is usually unlocked and we know Ingrid

Pamber left Annette's door unlocked. He says he was afraid of taking a ring and a watch that lay beside a dead body and I believe him. What bothers me is his apparently not knowing anything about the flats or their occupants before going in there. According to him, he just slipped in without bothering to shut the door behind him. He couldn't sleep, but he didn't go out on foot, he went out in his *van*. He just happened to be wearing gloves. In a heatwave in July? According to him, he had no housebreaking tools with him, yet how many people could he count on having feckless friends and leaving their front door unlocked overnight?'

'There are only two flats in there,' Burden said. 'He'd nothing to lose. All he had to do was try Annette's door and then go upstairs and try the Harrises'. If they were both locked he was no worse off than he had been.'

'I know. That's what he says himself. Piece of amazing luck for him, wasn't it, that the first door he tried was unlocked?'

'Maybe it wasn't the first door.'

'He says it was. So we come to the next odd thing. If what he says is true, he had no means of knowing whether there was anyone in the flat or not. What are we to think? That because he'd seen from outside – and remembered, calculated, worked it out – that all the curtains in Flat One were closed, then discovered that the front door was unlocked, he concluded there was no one at home? That would be on the theory that no one would stay in a place overnight with the front door unlocked, but they might go away and forget to lock it. It's all a bit tenuous.'

'He was taking a risk, certainly. But all burglary is risky, Reg.'

Wexford looked unconvinced. He always delved into human motive and the peculiarities of human nature while Burden concentrated on the facts, seldom disputing them however bizarre they might appear. As he made his way back to the Benefit Office, on foot this time, Burden thought of something Wexford had once said to him about Sherlock Holmes, how you couldn't solve much by his methods. A pair of slippers with singed soles no more showed that their wearer had been suffering from a severe chill than that he had merely had cold feet. Nor could you deduce from a man's staring at a portrait on the wall that he was dwelling on the life and career of that portrait's subject, for he might equally be thinking how it resembled his brother-in-law or was badly painted or needed cleaning. With human nature you could only guess – and try to guess right.

He caught Peter Stanton on his way out to lunch.

'Can we have a chat?'

'Not if it stops me eating.'

'I have to eat too,' Burden said.

'Come out this way.' Stanton took Burden out through the door marked 'Private' that led into the car park. It was a short cut to the High Street.

His wife or Wexford would probably have described the man as Byronic. He had those dark piratical good looks women are said to find so attractive, the handsome features allegedly ravaged by dissipations, the dark wavy hair that by Burden's own exacting standards was tousled, the gleam in the eye that may denote a penchant for cruelty or merely greed. Stanton wore a linen suit, stone-coloured and very crumpled, and his tie, which Leyton probably insisted he wear, was loosely tied under the collar of a not very clean shirt whose top button was undone. If it is possible to walk in a laid-back manner, Stanton did so, slouching along, his hands deep in the misshapen pockets of his baggy trousers. At the doorway of a sandwich bar with four empty tables pushed against the wall opposite the food counter, he paused and cocked a thumb.

'I usually come here. OK?'

Burden nodded. The last time he had been in one of these places, of which Kingsmarkham now had three, he had eaten 'prime freshwater shrimps' and the resulting gastro-enteritis had laid him low for three days. So when Stanton picked a prawn salad sandwich he stuck austerely to cheese and tomato. He watched without comment while Stanton emptied the contents of a hip flask into his glass of Sprite.

'I want to ask you about the kind of things you say to your clients.'

'Not half what I'd like to.'

Rather coldly Burden said, 'Specifically, I want to know the kind of thing Annette might have said to Melanie Akande.'

'What do you mean exactly?'

'I mean, what happens when a new client brings back a form – is it called an ES something? – and gets given a signing-on day and so on?'

'You want to know what she'd have said to the girl and advised her and all that?'

Stanton sounded deeply bored. His eyes had wandered to the young woman assistant who now emerged from the back regions to join the man behind the counter. She was about twenty, blonde, tall, very pretty, wearing a white apron over a scoop-necked red tee-shirt and the kind of very short tube skirt that is as tight as a bandage.

'Just that, Mr Stanton.'

'OK.' Stanton took a swig of his Sprite cocktail. 'Annette'd have taken a look at the ES 461, seen she'd filled it in right. There are forty-five questions to be answered in all and it's complicated till you know how. Let's say it's . . . well, uncommon for a client to get it right first time on his own. On *her* own, I should say. They've got a funny taste, these prawns, sort of fishy.'

'Prawns *are* fish,' said Burden.

'Yeah, but you know what I mean, sort of strong, like the smell of outside a fishmonger's. Do you reckon I ought to eat them?'

Burden didn't reply. 'Go on about what Annette would have said to her.'

'There's often something a bit off about the food here but the crumpet makes up for it. That's why I go on coming, I suppose.' Stanton caught Burden's basilisk eye. 'Yes, well, once she'd got the form straightened out she'd have given the client, Melanie What's-her-name, a signing-on day. It's alphabetical, that. A to K Tuesdays, L to R Wednesdays, S to Z Thursdays. No one signs on on a Monday or a Friday. What did you say she was called? Akande? She'd have had Tuesday. Once a fortnight on a Tuesday.

'Then Annette'd have explained about how signing-on is to prove you're still in the land of the living, haven't buggered off somewhere or died, that you're available and actively seeking work, and she'd have said how once you've signed on your giro'll be sent to you. That goes to your home address and you cash it at your post office or you can pay it into your bank if you want. Annette'd have explained all that. Then, I suppose, she'd have asked Melanie if she'd any questions. Melanie'd only have a maximum of twenty minutes with Annette, there wouldn't have been time for much.'

'Suppose she'd had a job to offer Melanie? Could she have had? What would have been the procedure?'

Stanton yawned. He had left his second sandwich

uneaten. He was now dividing his eye contact between the girl in the bandage skirt and a sandwich maker who had appeared from some nether region. This woman had waist length mahogany-coloured hair and appeared to be wearing nothing but a white chef's cap and a white cotton coat whose hem reached to two inches below her crotch. At a cough from Burden he dragged his stare away, sighing softly. 'There aren't jobs, you know. They're thin on the ground. I suppose Annette just might have had something suitable for this Melanie, client with a degree. Well, once in a blue moon she might have had something.'

'What, in a ledger? A file?'

Stanton gave him a pitying look. 'She'd have run it up on the computer.'

'And if she'd had anything to offer Melanie, what then?'

'She'd have phoned the employer and made an appointment for Melanie for an interview. She didn't, you know,' Stanton said unexpectedly. 'I can tell you that for a fact. Both the New Claims Advisers have the same stuff on their computers and there wasn't anything remotely suitable for a girl of twenty-two with a performance arts degree. You can check it out if you want but I can tell you there wasn't.'

'How did you know her degree was in performance arts?'

'She told me while I was raping and strangling her, of course.' Stanton must have remembered that there is such an offence as wasting police time. He said sullenly, 'Oh, come on. I read it in the paper.'

Burden fetched himself a cup of coffee. 'And that would have been all?' he said. 'No advice? You're advisers, aren't you?'

'That *is* advising, telling her how to sign on, explaining about her giro. What more d'you want?'

Hope had sprung for a moment in Burden's heart. A scenario had begun to take shape of Melanie leaving the Benefit Office on her way to a job interview, from which she had never returned. Only Annette knew where she had gone and why and, absolutely to the point, whom she had gone to see. But his carefully crafted playlet had quickly fallen apart and when he asked Stanton if he could imagine anything confidential, secret or sinister Melanie might have said to Annette, something that was a police matter, he wasn't surprised that the man made a dismissive gesture and shook his head.

'I ought to be getting back.'

'All right.' Burden got up.

'I've got a performance arts degree myself,' Stanton suddenly remarked apropos of nothing. 'No doubt that's why I remember she had. All set to be a great actor, I was, a second Olivier and a bloody sight better looking. That was me fifteen years ago and to this favour have I come.'

Bored by this, unsympathetic, Burden said as they went out into the street, 'Did anyone ever threaten her?'

'Annette? In the office? Bless your policeman's helmet, if you had one, they threaten us all the time. *All the time*. It's worse on the desks. Why d'you think we have a security officer? Ninety-nine per cent comes to nothing, it's vague promises to "get us". Some of them accuse us of keeping their giros for ourselves, losing their ES 461s on purpose, that sort of thing. And then they're going to "get" us or "cut" us.

'Then there's fraud. They know they've been signing on in three or four different names and they think we've reported them to the DSS fraud inspectors, so they're going to get us for that. . . .'

Now Burden recalled Karen Malahyde once being

called out to an 'incident' at the Benefit Office, on another occasion Pemberton and Archbold had gone. It hadn't meant much to him at the time. He said suddenly to Stanton, 'You took her out once or twice?'

'Annette?' Stanton became guarded, cautious. 'Twice, to be precise. It was three years ago.'

'Why twice? Why no more? Did something happen?'

'I didn't screw her, if that's what you mean.' Stanton, who had been slouching along, taking long strides, moving slowly, now stopped altogether. He stood indecisively in the middle of the pavement, then sat down on the low wall that bordered an estate agent's courtyard and took a packet of cigarettes out of one of the baggy pockets. 'Cyril the Squirrel called me into his office and said it had to stop. Relationships between staff members of opposite sexes were bad for the image. I asked him if he meant it would be all right for me to fuck Osman but he just said not to be filthy and that was that.'

Burden's look was eloquent of heartfelt agreement with Leyton for once, but he said nothing.

'Not that I was all that sorry.' Stanton took a long draw on his cigarette and expelled the smoke in two blue columns out of his nostrils. 'I wasn't keen on being used as a – how shall I put it? – I don't know, but what it amounts to is she only wanted me around to make this guy she'd got jealous so he'd leave his wife and marry her. Some hopes. She actually told me that, about how she'd tell this chap that I was keen on her and if he didn't want to lose her he'd best get his act together. Charming, wasn't it?'

'You went to her flat?'

'No, I never did. I went to the cinema with her, met her there and we had a coffee after. The next time it was just drinks in a pub and a pizza and we went for a

158

drive in my car. We parked out in the country and there was a bit of how's-your-father but nothing over the top and after that Cyril the doorman put his spoke in.'

They walked back to the Benefit Office together and Burden followed him in. He was talking to the security officer, asking if he could remember any specific threats being made to Annette, when a shrill scream from Wendy Stowlap's counter made him jump and spring to his feet.

'I told you I'd scream if you said that just once more,' the woman shouted. 'If you say that again I'll lie on the floor and scream.'

'What else can I say? You can have dental treatment free if you're on Income Support but you can't get your osteopath's bill paid.'

The woman, who was well dressed and spoke in a ringing actor's voice, got down on the floor, lay on her back and began screaming. She was young and her lungs were strong. The screaming reminded Burden of the noise three-year-olds sometimes make in supermarket aisles. He walked over to her, the security man following. Wendy was leaning over the counter, waving a blue and yellow leaflet with the title 'Help Us to Get It Right and How to Complain'.

'Come along now,' said the security officer. 'Up you get. This won't do, all this noise.'

She screamed harder. 'Stop that,' said Burden. He stuck out his warrant card six inches from the screaming face. 'Stop. You're causing a breach of the peace.'

It was the card which did it. She was middle-class and therefore awed by the police and the suggestion she might break the law. The screaming dropped to a whimper. She got awkwardly to her feet, snatched the leaflet from Wendy's hand and said bitterly to her, 'There was no need to call the police.'

Husband and wife sat side by side, but not too close to each other, in front of the desk in Wexford's office. He didn't want to frighten Carolyn Snow – not yet. Frightening, if needed, would come later. Meanwhile, though the room was hardly equipped as a recording studio, Detective Constable Pemberton was there with an efficient enough device if it was required.

They had arrived separately two minutes apart. And Carolyn Snow quickly explained that they *were* apart, she retaining the house in Harrow Avenue – 'It's my children's *home*' – the husband she had thrown out resorting to an hotel room. Wexford noticed that Bruce Snow was wearing yesterday's shirt. He looked as if he hadn't shaved. Surely his wife hadn't shaved him as well as laundering his clothes and running round at his beck and call?

'We have to clear up this matter of what you were both doing last Wednesday evening, July the seventh. Mr Snow?'

'I've already told you what I was doing. I was at home with my wife. My son was at home too. He was upstairs.'

'Not according to Mrs Snow.'

'Look, this is rubbish, this is all nonsense. I got home at six and I was all evening at home with my wife. We had a meal at seven, the way we always do. My son went upstairs after that, he had an essay to write for his history homework. The War of the Spanish Succession, it was.'

'You have a good memory, Mr Snow, considering you didn't know you'd have to remember.'

'I have been racking my brains, haven't I? I've thought of nothing else.'

'What did you do all evening? Watch television? Read something? Telephone anyone?'

160

'He didn't have a chance,' said Carolyn nastily. 'He went out at ten to eight.'

'That is a damned lie!' said Snow.

'On the contrary, you know it's true. It was *your* Wednesday, wasn't it? The Wednesday evening every couple of weeks you spent bonking that prostitute on your office floor.'

'Nice language, thank you, that really becomes you, that terminology. A man can take real pride in hearing his wife talk like that, like someone off the streets.'

'Well, you'd know all about those, wouldn't you? First-hand experience. And I'm not your wife, not any more. Two years, just two years, and you'll have to say "my ex-wife", you'll have to explain you're living in a bedsit because your "ex-wife" took you to the cleaners, took the house and the car and three-quarters of your income . . .' Carolyn Snow's normally quiet gentle voice was rising ominously, vibrating with anger, 'just because you were hooked on poking that fat floozie through her red knickers!'

For God's sake, thought Wexford, how much of it has he told her? Everything? Because he thought absolute total confession was his only chance? He gave an admonitory cough which nevertheless failed to stop Snow rounding on his wife and shouting, 'You shut your mouth, you frigid cow!'

Slowly Carolyn Snow rose to her feet, her eyes fixed on her husband's face. Wexford acted. 'Stop this, please. At once. I can't have a matrimonial fracas in here. Sit down, Mrs Snow.'

'Why should I? Why should I be made into some sort of guilty party? I've done nothing.'

'Ha!' said Snow, and he repeated it, reinforced with bitterness, 'Ha!'

'Very well,' said Wexford. 'I thought you might be more comfortable talking to me in here but I see I was wrong. We'll go down to Interview Room Two, DC Pemberton, and with your permission – ' he looked rather sourly at the Snows, making their permission sound like a formality ' – the rest of this interview will be recorded.'

It was rather different down there, some distant resemblance to a prison cell being achieved by white-painted walls of unrendered brick and a window set high up under the ceiling. The electronic devices lining the wall behind the metal table Wexford sometimes thought, and thought uneasily, suggested, if not a torture chamber, the kind of place where they kept you standing all night under bright lights.

On the way down he asked Snow, in seemingly casual fashion and out of earshot of his wife, if it was a fact that a friend or relative of theirs lived in Ladyhall Avenue within sight of the flats. Snow denied it. It wasn't true, he said, and he had never told anyone it was.

In the interview room he placed the Snows opposite each other and seated himself at one end. Burden, back from the Benefit Office, took the other. The austerity of the room, its grimness, quietened Carolyn, as he had known it would. Once in the lift, she had kept up a continuous jibing and carping at her husband while he stood with his eyes shut. Down here she was silent. She smoothed the fair hair back from her forehead and pressed fingers to her temples as if her head ached. Snow sat with folded arms, his chin sagging against his chest.

Wexford spoke into the device. 'Mr Bruce Snow, Mrs Carolyn Snow. DCI Wexford and DI Burden present.' He said to the woman, 'I should like you to tell me exactly what did happen on the evening of July the seventh, Mrs Snow.'

She gave her husband a sidelong look, deliberate and calculating. 'He came home at six and I said, not working late tonight? I'm going back to the office after I've eaten, he said . . .'

'A lie! Another filthy lie!'

'Please, Mr Snow.'

'Joel said he might want his father to give him some help with this essay he had to do and his father said, too bad because I'm going out . . .'

'I did not say that!'

'Because I'm going out, and he did go out. At ten to eight. I didn't suspect anything, mind you, not a thing. Why should I? I trusted him. I do trust people. Anyway, I phoned the office. Joel did want help. I said, we'll phone Dad and you can ask him on the phone. But there wasn't any answer. Not that I had any suspicions even then. I thought he just wasn't answering. I was in bed by the time he got home. It was after half-past ten, nearer eleven.'

'Oh, let her rave.'

'I'm a truthful person, he knows that. Whereas we know the lies *he* tells. Working late! Did you know he screwed her in the office so that if I phoned he'd be there to answer? If she hadn't got her just deserts, getting herself murdered, I could almost feel sorry for the poor fat bitch.'

'May I remind you,' Wexford said wearily, 'that, with your permission, this conversation is being recorded, Mrs Snow?'

'What do I care? Record it! Put it over the public address system all down the High Street! Let them all know, I'll tell them anyway, I've told all my friends. I've told my children, I've let them know what a bastard their father is.'

After they had gone, Burden put on a grave face and shook his head. 'Amazing, isn't it?' he said to Wexford. 'You'd call her a real lady if you met her

163

socially, quiet, well-mannered, refined. Who'd have thought a woman like that would even know that sort of language?'

'You sound like a policeman in a detective novel circa 1935.'

'OK, maybe I do, but doesn't it surprise you?'

'They get it out of modern fiction,' said Wexford. 'Nothing to do all day but read. Are we getting anywhere with Stephen Colegate?'

'Annette's ex-husband? He lives in Australia, he's married again, but his mother's in Pomfret and she's expecting him home for a visit on Sunday with his two kids.'

'Have someone check that he really was in Australia, will you? What happened to Zack Nelson?'

'Remanded in custody to the Crown Court. Why are you looking like that?'

'I'm thinking of Kimberley and the child.'

'You don't want to worry about that Kimberley,' said Burden, 'She'll know more about claiming benefit than Cyril Leyton does. She's the kind that's got an honours degree in Income Support.'

Wexford laughed. 'I'm sure you're right. That Snow woman's worn me out.' He hesitated, thought. ' "Oh, I am going a long way off, to the island valley of Avilion, where I will heal me of my grievous wound." '

'Blimey,' said Burden. 'And where might that be?'

'Home.'

Chapter Eleven

I told her we wouldn't be buying any oriental rugs,'
Dora said, 'and I was thinking, chance would be a
fine thing, though I didn't say that. Of course, she's
quite right, these things are evil and wrong, but it's
just that she always throws herself heart and soul
into every new project.'

Sheila Wexford had become a life member of
Anti-Slavery International. On the phone that
evening, just before Wexford got in, she had urged
her mother not to buy Middle Eastern or oriental
rugs, for these, she said, might well have been
woven by children of eleven or twelve or younger.
Girls in Turkey went blind from the close work in
ill-lit rooms. Children were obliged to work fourteen
hours a day and because their parents had put them
to this industry as payment of a debt, received no
wages.

'I suppose she'll be off to Turkey to see for herself?'
said Wexford.

'How did you know?'

'I know my daughter.'

'Why "international", anyway?' enquired Sylvia
in a querulous tone. 'International's an adjective.
What's wrong with society or association?'
Wexford's reference to Sheila as 'my daughter'
instead of 'my younger daughter', thus implying in
her estimation that he had only one, was what had

set her off, he knew. Much she cared about adjectives. 'Sheila wouldn't notice but it's as bad as "collective",' she said and glared at her father.

He was swift to make amends, appending to his question a rare endearment. 'Any sign of a job, darling?'

'Nothing. Neil's got himself into a workshop that could lead to a retraining programme. That's another awful word, "workshop".'

'And "creditable" for "credible",' said her father. It was the kind of conversation he usually had only with Sheila. 'And "gender-related" for male and female and "health problem" for "ill".'

Sylvia was happy again. 'Kanena provlima, which my son tells me is Greek for his favourite phrase. One good thing about being unemployed is I'll be home with them for the summer holidays. School breaks up next week.'

It was pouring with rain and Glebe End was awash. With no drainage or what there was long dysfunctional, Lincoln Cottages appeared as if floating on a swamp. A great sheet of water engulfed the brick path and came halfway up the tyres of an ancient van, the rear doors of which stood open. A black plastic dustbin bobbed lightly on a puddle by the front door.

Barry Vine had a look inside the van at a damp-looking mattress and an armchair with no seat cushion while Karen Malahyde knocked on the door. It took Kimberley several minutes to come and open it.

'What d'you want?'

'The stuff your boyfriend nicked,' said Vine.

She shrugged her thin shoulders but she opened the door wider and stood back. Clint was sitting in a

166

high chair, covering his face and the upper part of his body with a glutinous brown mess from a bowl with a crack in it. The high chair, painted white with pictures of rabbits and squirrels, was quite a respectable piece of furniture, gift perhaps of a comparatively affluent grandparent.

Cocking a thumb back the way he had come, Vine said, 'Moving out?'

'What if I am?'

'You gave us to understand you hadn't a hope of being rehoused.'

Kimberley picked up a dirty rag from the top of one of her cardboard boxes and began rubbing at Clint's face with it. The child yelled and struggled. Vine went upstairs and fetched the television set. Karen carried the video out to the car. Lifting Clint on to the ground, Kimberley said, volunteering information for once, 'My nan died.'

Not knowing what to make of this, Vine, who hadn't an unpleasant nature, said, 'I'm sorry to hear that,' and then, because he had cottoned on, 'You mean you've come in for her place or what?'

'That's it. Got it in one. My mum don't want it. She says we can have it.'

'When did this happen then?'

'What, my nan dying or my mum saying we could have her place?' She didn't wait for an answer. 'Mum come round Wednesday and I told her about Zack, so she said, you can't stay here, and I said, too right we can't, and that was when she said, you better move in your nan's place. Satisfied?'

'It has to be a change for the better.'

'Clint,' said Kimberley, 'you leave them bottles alone or you'll get a smack you won't like.'

A father and a conscientious one, Vine disapproved of corporal punishment, he had what he called a 'thing' about it, and Clint was very young.

'Is he OK?' he said.

'What d'you mean, OK? You mean he shouldn't be living in this dump? Right, I couldn't agree more. He's moving out, in't he? You a social worker now, are you?'

'I mean,' said Vine, 'is he quite recovered from that op he had?'

'For God's sake, that was a year ago.' She was suddenly furiously angry, her face bright red, her shoulders and arms trembling. 'What the fuck's it got to do with you? Of course he's recovered – look at him. He's bloody marvellous, he's *normal*, he's like he was born that way. Can't you *see*?' She shivered. 'Why don't you and her just take the stuff and fuck off?'

She slammed the door behind them. Vine put his foot in the puddle and cursed.

'I've got another child to see,' Karen said in the car. 'But I'm questioning this one, God help me.'

Wexford found it odious, the whole thing, the idea of asking a young boy for information about his own father. It reminded him, by a roundabout route, of the question he had been handed at the Women, Aware! meeting. Having Karen, a nice-looking young woman with a no-nonsense manner, interview Joel seemed the best way. Presumably, her well-known abrasiveness when questioning men wouldn't extend to boys of fourteen.

He went with her and talked to the mother while she sat with Joel in the quaintly named playroom, a place where there was nothing to play with but plenty of equipment conducive to study. Joel had an impressive collection of textbooks and dictionaries, a computer and a recording device. The posters on the walls were the educational kind, the life of a tree, the human digestive system, a climate map of the world.

Joel looked like his father, dark, thin, already tall, but had his mother's cool manner. Perhaps he too was capable of violent eruptions. He spoke to Karen before she had a chance to speak to him.

'My mother has told me what you've come for. It isn't any good asking me because I don't know.'

'Joel, I only want you to tell me if you were aware of your father going out just before eight. Were you in this room?'

The boy nodded. He seemed relaxed but his eyes were wary.

'You were in this room which is over the garage? If a car went out you'd hear it.'

'My mother keeps her car in the garage. His always stands out.'

'Even so. You've got good hearing, haven't you? Or were you concentrating very hard on your essay?' She had noticed that when the chance came he had not referred to Snow as 'my father'. She took the plunge. 'Your mother has told you what all this is about?'

'Please,' he said. 'I'm not a child. He's been committing adultery and now his woman's been murdered.'

Karen blinked. She was seriously taken aback. She took a deep breath and started again on the car, the garage, the time. Downstairs, Wexford was asking Carolyn Snow if she would care to amend the statement she had made concerning her husband's movements on the evening of 7 July.

'No. Why should I?' She wore no make-up. Her hair looked as if she hadn't washed it since she found out about Annette Bystock. If her clothes were expensive and in good order this was probably because she had no others. She said suddenly, 'There was another one before her, you know. A Diana something. But she didn't last long.' She put

169

her hand up to her hair. 'Is it true that a wife can't give evidence against her husband?'

'A wife can't be *compelled* to give evidence against her husband,' said Wexford. 'It's not the same thing.'

She thought about this and what she thought seemed to please her. 'You won't want to talk to me again, will you?'

'We might. It's a possibility. Not thinking of going away anywhere, I hope?'

Her eyes narrowed. 'Why do you ask?'

He could tell she was thinking of it. 'The schools break up next week. I don't want you going away at present, Mrs Snow.' At the front door he paused. She was standing behind him but left him to open the door himself. 'You have a relative living in Ladyhall Avenue, I believe?'

'No, I haven't. Where did you get that idea?'

He wasn't going to tell her that it had come from her husband or that this person's place of residence was his reason for not going to Annette's flat. 'A friend, then?'

'No one.' She shook her head fiercely. 'My family come from Tunbridge Wells.'

He left, thinking that if Annette had threatened to expedite a marriage between herself and Snow by divulging all to Carolyn, that would be Snow's motive for murder. Carolyn's reaction to learning of her husband's sustained infidelity was all too evident now. She was as unforgiving and as vindictive as Snow had expected her to be. And he would know; there had been another before Annette.

On the other hand, he might have gone round to Ladyhall Court on that Wednesday evening to beg Annette not to tell. He might have promised her all sorts of concessions. Taking her out to dinner occasionally would have been a start, Wexford

170

thought. Or a holiday somewhere with her or just giving her a present. None of it had worked. Nothing else would do but that he leave Carolyn and come to her. They quarrelled, he tore the lead of the bedside lamp out of the wall and strangled her. . . . It was that tearing the electric lead part that didn't ring true, Wexford thought. It would have taken some strength. In the heat of rage, wouldn't he have put his bare hands round her throat?

He crossed the pavement to his car where Karen already waited at the wheel, the only exercise he would get that day. Dr Crocker, and lately Dr Akande, had told him he should walk more (the best kind of cardiovascular exercise, they both intoned) and he was wondering whether to tell Karen to take the car back alone and leave him to do the mile or two on foot, when he saw the doctor coming towards him. Wexford was immediately aware of that craven reaction which makes us want to pretend we haven't seen someone, makes us cross the road and keep our eyes averted, when the prospective encounter may involve reproach or recrimination. He had committed no offence against Dr Akande; on the contrary, he had done everything in his and his force's power to find the doctor's missing daughter, but in spite of this he felt ashamed. Worse than that, he wanted to avoid the society of someone as unhappy and as despairing as the doctor must be. But he made no attempt to do so. A policeman must confront everything or take some other job (retrain, in ES parlance). It was a maxim he had first uttered to himself some thirty years before.

'How are you, doctor?'

Akande shook his head. 'I've been visiting a patient who's only two years short of a hundred,' he said. 'Even she asked me if I had any news. They're

171

very kind, very good. I tell myself it would be worse if they stopped asking.'

Wexford could think of nothing to say.

'I keep thinking about what Melanie might have done, where she went, all that. It's as if I don't think of anything else. It goes round and round in my head. I've even started wondering if we'll ever have her body. I never could understand that, those people who lost sons in war and craved their – their remains. Or just wanted to know where they were buried. I used to think, what does it matter? It's the person you want, the living creature you loved, not the – the outer casing. I understand now.'

His voice had broken on the word 'love' as unhappy people's voices do break on that particular trigger. He said, 'You must excuse me, I try to keep going,' and walked off, as if blindly. Wexford watched him fumbling with the key at his car door and guessed his eyes were thick with tears.

'Poor man,' said Karen, making Wexford wonder if this was the first time she had ever uttered that adjective and that noun in conjunction before.

'Yes.'

'Where are we going now, sir?'

'To Ladyhall Avenue.' He was silent for a moment. Then he said, 'Ingrid Pamber told us something that seems to have got lost in the general shock-horror over Snow's behaviour. Do you know what I'm talking about?'

'Something about Snow?'

'Of course it may not be true. She's a liar and an embroiderer too, I daresay.'

'Do you mean about his wife having some relation living opposite Ladyhall Court?'

Wexford nodded. They turned out of Queens Gardens where Wendy Stowlap lived and passed the corner shop where Ingrid had bought Annette's groceries. A man was banging furiously on the glass side of the phone box in which a woman talked on, unheeding.

A blind woman let them into the house. Her eyeballs, in their baskets of wrinkles, were like glass that has been crazed from too much handling. Wexford spoke gently.

'Chief Inspector Wexford, Kingsmarkham CID, and this is Detective Sergeant Malahyde.'

'She's a young lady, isn't she?' said Mrs Prior, staring into the middle distance.

Karen admitted it.

'I can smell you. Very nice too. Roma, isn't it?'

'Yes, it is. Clever of you.'

'Oh, I know 'em all, all the perfumes, it's how I know one woman from the next. It's no good you showing me those cards of yours, I can't see them, and I don't suppose *they* smell.' Gladys Prior giggled at her own wit. She led them to the staircase and they followed her up. 'What's happened to that young chap B,U,R,D,E,N?' It was evidently some kind of 'in' joke and it made her laugh again.

'He's busy somewhere else today,' said Wexford.

Percy Hammond wasn't looking out of his window. He was asleep. But the light sleep of the very old was easily broken when they came into the room. Wexford wondered what he had looked like when he was young. There was nothing in that creased, pouchy, stretched, puckered face to indicate the lineaments of middle age, still less youth. It was scarcely human any more. Only the white, rosy-gummed dentures, displayed when he smiled, hinted at real teeth, lost fifty years before.

He was dressed in a striped suit with waistcoat and collarless shirt. The knees held up the grey worsted as a frame with sharp metal angles might, and the hands which rested on them were like a pigeon's claws. 'Do you want me to attend an identity parade?' he asked. 'Pick him out from a line of them?'

Wexford didn't. While mentally congratulating Mr Hammond on his quick-witted assumption, he could only tell him out loud that there was no doubt about who had robbed Annette's flat. They already had someone helping them with their enquiries into this matter.

'You couldn't have gone anyway,' said Mrs Prior. 'Not in your state.' She addressed Karen, to whom she seemed to have taken a fancy. 'He's ninety-two, you know.'

'Ninety-three,' said Mr Hammond, thus confirming Wexford's Law that it is only when under fifteen and over ninety that people wish to add years to their true age. 'Ninety-three next week, and I could have. I haven't tried going out for four years, so how do you know I couldn't have?'

'An intelligent guess,' said Gladys Prior with a giggle in Karen's direction.

'Mr Hammond,' Wexford began, 'you've already told Inspector Burden what you saw across the way very early last Thursday morning. Were you looking out of your window on the previous evening?'

'I'm always looking out. Unless I'm asleep or it's dark. Even in the dark sometimes – you can see with the street lights if you turn the light off in here.'

'And do you turn the light off, Mr Hammond?' asked Karen.

'I have to think about the electric bills, missy. My lights were off last Wednesday evening, if that's what you want to know. You want to hear what I saw? I've been thinking about it, going back over it. I knew you'd come back.'

174

He was blest in such a witness, Wexford thought thankfully. 'Tell me what you saw, will you, sir?'

'I always watch them come home from work. Mind you, a few of them have gone away on holiday. Most of them ignore me but that chap Harris, he always gives me a wave. He got home about twenty past five and ten minutes after a girl came. She had a car and she parked it outside. There's a yellow line there that means you're not supposed to park till six-thirty but she took no notice of that. I'd never seen her before. Pretty girl she was, about eighteen.'

Ingrid would be flattered, for what it was worth. By the time you reach ninety-three, Wexford thought, people of fifty look thirty to you and those in their twenties seem children. 'She went into the flats?'

'And came out after five minutes. Well, seven minutes, it was. I'm no good at guessing time but I timed her, I don't know why. Gives me something to do. I do that sometimes, it's a game I play, I bet on it. I say to myself, ten bob on it, Percy, she comes out before ten minutes are up.'

'The young lady doesn't know what ten bob is, Percy. You're not living in the real world, you aren't. Fifty pee to you, dear, it's twenty years and more since the changeover but it's like yesterday to him.'

Wexford interrupted, 'What happened next?'

'Nothing happened. If you mean by that, did any strangers go in. Mrs Harris came out and came back with an evening paper. I had my meal then, bit of bread and butter and a glass of Guinness, the same as I always have. I saw the car come that takes Gladys to her blind club.'

'Seven sharp,' said Mrs Prior. 'And I was back at half-past nine.'

175

'While you were eating, Mr Hammond,' said Wexford, 'did you sit at the table over there? Did you watch any television?'

The old man shook his head. He pointed at the window.

'That's my telly.'

'Don't get much sex and violence on it, though, do you, Percy?' Gladys Prior became convulsed with laughter.

'So you went on watching, did you, Mr Hammond? What happened after Mrs Prior had gone out?'

Percy Hammond screwed up his already screwed-up face. 'Nothing much, I'm sorry to say.' He gave Wexford a shrewd glance. 'What do you *want* me to have seen?'

'Only what you did see,' said Karen.

'It's around eight I'm interested in, Mr Hammond,' said Wexford. 'I don't want to put ideas into your head, but did you see a man go into Ladyhall Court between five to and a quarter past eight?'

'Only that chap with his dog. There's a man whose name I don't know and Gladys doesn't know, he's got a spaniel. He always takes it out in the evening. I saw *him*. I'd think something was wrong if I didn't see him.'

Something *was* wrong, thought Wexford, something was very wrong. 'No one else?'

'No one at all.'

'Not a man or a woman? You saw no one go in at about eight and come out at between ten and ten-thirty?'

'I said I'm no good with times. But I didn't see another soul until the young chap I told Mr What's-his-name about.'

'B,U,R,D,E,N,' said Mrs Prior with a gale of giggles.

'And it was dark then. I was in bed, I'd been asleep, but I got up – why did I get up, Gladys?'

'Don't ask me, Percy. To spend a penny, I dare say.'

'I put the light on for a minute but it was so bright, I turned it off, and I looked out of the window and I saw this young chap come out with a big box in his arms – or was that later?'

Karen said gently, 'That was in the morning, Mr Hammond. You saw him in the morning, don't you remember? That's the one you asked us about, if you'd have to pick him out in an identity parade?'

'So it was. I told you I wasn't much good with time . . .'

'I think we've tired you out, Mr Hammond,' said Wexford. 'You've been a great help but we'll only ask you one more thing. You and Mrs Prior. Is either of you related to some people called Snow of Harrow Road, Kingsmarksham?'

Two disappointed old faces turned towards him. Both liked excitement, both hated having to deny knowledge. 'Never heard of them,' said Mrs Prior gruffly.

'I suppose you know everyone . . . er, down this street, do you?' Wexford asked her as they were going down the stairs.

'You were going to say "by sight", weren't you? Bless you, I wouldn't have minded. Though it'd be nearer the mark to say "by smell".' She waited till she got to the foot of the staircase before letting her laughter escape. 'There's a lot of old folks down here, the houses are old, you see, and some of them have lived in them for forty years, fifty. Would they be

177

young or old, this person that's related to Mrs What-d'you-call-her?'

'I don't know,' said Wexford. 'I don't know at all.'

Chapter Twelve

The house was new, just finished, the last coat of paint applied perhaps no more than a week ago. But it still made him feel in a time warp. Not that he saw Mynford New Hall as old but rather that he had gone back two hundred years and, finding himself a character in, say, *Northanger Abbey*, had been brought here to view a brand-new mansion.

It was Georgian, with a pillared portico and a balustrade along the shallow roof, a big house, ivory-white, the windows perfectly proportioned sashes, the columns fluted. In alcoves on either side of the front door stood stone vases hung with stone drapery and with living ivy and maidenhair fern. A gravel sweep would have been better but the carriage drive was paved. The tubs and troughs clustered on it held bay trees and yellow cypress, red fuchsias in full bloom, orange and cream arbutus, pink pelargoniums. By contrast, the flowerbeds were bare, turned earth without a weed showing.

'Give them a chance,' Dora whispered. 'They've only been here five minutes. They must have hired those tubs for the occasion.'

'Where were they before, then?'

'In that place down the hill, the dower house.'

The hill was a gentle slope of green lawns descending towards a wooded valley. A grey roof could just be made out among the trees. Wexford remembered the old hall on the hilltop, a mid-

Victorian stucco pile, not old enough or distinctive enough to be listed for preservation. Presumably, the Khooris had encountered no planning difficulties in pulling it down and setting the new hall up.

Their guests thronged the big lawn. In the middle of it stood a large striped marquee. Wexford had referred to it laconically as 'the tea tent', a term Dora obscurely felt to be irreverent or even *lèse majesté*. Her husband hadn't wanted to come. She told him not altogether truthfully that he had promised, then that it would do him good, take him out of himself. In the end he had come for her sake because she had said she wouldn't go if he didn't.

'Do you know anybody here? Because if you don't we might as well go for a walk. I wouldn't mind having a look at the old dower house.'

'No, ssh. Here's our hostess and homing on you if I'm not mistaken.'

Anouk Khoori was a protean creature. He held in his mind the image of her in her tracksuit, her face *au naturel*, hair in a bouncy ponytail; and that other image, the champagne social worker, the ardent campaigner and political aspirant, power-dressed, up on high heels, her jewellery and solitary solitaire.

It was on her hand now but with many companions, flashing white and blue from her fingers as she walked towards them. And she was different again, not simply altered as women always are by change of dress and hairstyle, but altogether unrecognizable. If he had met her off her home ground, if Dora hadn't been there to identify her, he doubted if he would have known Anouk Khoori. This time she was the chatelaine in yellow chiffon and a big straw hat piled with daisies, golden tendrils curling on her forehead and escaping to hang to her shoulders.

'Mr Wexford, I *knew* you would come but I'm

180

delighted just the same. And this is Mrs Wexford? How do you do? Aren't we lucky to have this glorious day? You must meet my husband.' She looked about her, then scanned the horizon. 'I don't seem to be able to see him just at the moment. But come, let me introduce you to some very dear friends of ours that I know you'll love.' As one of those women who never bother much with women, she turned her full gaze on Wexford and her fullest smile, a radiant beaming from lips painted geranium with a fine brush and teeth capped to Wedgwood whiteness. 'And who will love *you*,' she added.

The very dear friends turned out to be an aged man, wrinkled and shrunken, with the face of an ancient guru but dressed in denim and Western boots, and a girl some fifty years younger. Anouk Khoori, a genius at picking up and remembering names and one who swiftly dispensed with surnames, said, 'Reg and Dora, I've been longing for you to meet Alexander and Cookie Dix. Cookie, darling, this is Reg Wexford who is a terribly important police chief.'

Cookie? How on earth did anyone get a name like that? She was getting on for a foot taller than her husband, dressed like the Princess of Wales at Ascot, but with waist-length black hair. 'Is that sort of like a sherriff?' she said.

Anouk Khoori gave a long thrilling peal of laughter and on this laughter, as to a cue provided by herself, floated away. Wexford had astonished himself by his reaction to her, one of physical repulsion. But why should this be? She was beautiful, or many would say so, healthy and strong, extravagantly clean, deodorized, powdered, perfumed. Yet the touch of her hand made him shrink and her scent near him was like a foetid breath.

Dora was making an effort to talk to Cookie Dix.

Did she live nearby? What did she think of the neighbourhood? He could make small talk as well as anyone but he could no longer see the point. The shrunken old man stood silent and faintly scowling. He reminded Wexford of a horror film he'd watched one night when he couldn't sleep. There had been a mummy in it which the experimenter had unwrapped, succeeded up to a point in reanimating, and brought along to just such a garden party as this one.

'Have you seen Anouk's diamonds?' Cookie said suddenly.

Dora, who had been talking gently about the weather in July, how it never really got warm in England until July, was surprised into silence.

'The ones she's wearing *now* cost a hundred grand alone. Can you believe that? There's ten times that in the house.'

'Goodness,' said Dora.

'You may well say goodness.' She bent forwards, necessarily stooping in order to push her face close to Dora's, but instead of whispering spoke in her usual clear tones. 'The house is hideous. Don't you think so? Pitiful, really, they think it's based on some Nash design for a house that was never built, but it's not, is it, sweetness?'

The mummy barked. It was exactly what had happened in the horror film, only at this point people had dispersed screaming.

'My husband is a very famous architect,' said Cookie. She extended her neck and pushed her face at Wexford. 'If we were people in a book, me telling you about the diamonds would be a *clue*, there'd be a robbery while we're out here, and you'd have to question all these people. There are five hundred people here, did you know that?'

Wexford laughed. He rather liked Cookie Dix, her

182

naive manner and her metre-long legs. 'At least, I'd say. Still, I doubt if they've left the house un-guarded.'

'They have but for Juana and Rosenda.'

Unexpectedly, the mummy began to sing in a cracked tenor, to a tune from the *Mikado*, 'Two little maids from the Philippines, one of them hardly out of her teens . . . '

'I'd have thought they'd have a staff,' Dora said faintly.

'They used to have another one, as a matter of fact she was the sister of our one, but the rich are so mean, haven't you noticed? Well, darling Alexander isn't and God knows he's loaded.' The mummy's face cracked. At just such a ghastly smile the women in the movie had started screaming. 'Mostly they have caterers in,' said Cookie. 'Their servants don't stay. Well, these two do. The money's rotten but they need it to send home.' For some reason Cookie dropped her voice. 'Filipinos do.'

'Filipin*as*,' said the mummy.

'Thank you, sweet. You're such a stickler. I call him my stickler sometimes. Shall we go and have some tea?'

Together they walked down the green slope, deflected from the prospect of tea by the kind of sideshows considered suitable for this type of charity benefit function. A good-looking dark woman in a kind of ankle-length white sweater was conducting a raffle for Fortnum and Mason hampers. A young man in a smock with an easel and palette was doing instant portraits for a fiver a time. Under a long yellow banner with CIBACT on it in black, a man had his twin daughters on display, little fair-haired girls in white frilled organdie and black patent leather shoes with instep straps. Punters were invited to guess the age of Phyllida and Fenella and whoever came nearest to the correct birth date got the child-size white teddy bear that sat on the counter between them.

'Vulgar, you see,' said Cookie. 'That's their trouble. They don't know the difference.'

Dora glanced at the docile children. 'You mean the raffle is all right and perhaps the artist but not the teddy bear thing?'

'Exactly. That's exactly what I mean. Sad, really, when you've got everything.'

At last Alexander Dix expressed himself, otherwise than in song. Wexford thought his voice what a French speaker's would be if he had lived till the age of thirty in, say, Casablanca, and the rest of his life in Aberdeen. 'Nothing else is to be expected when you are a child of the gutters of Alexandria.'

Presumably he was referring to Wael Khoori. Interested, Wexford was about to ask for more when something happened that always happens at parties. A couple appeared from nowhere and bore down upon the Dixes with cries of astonishment and greeting, and as also is always true, their former companions were forgotten. Wexford and Dora were abandoned, still standing in front of Phyllida, Fenella and the teddy bear.

'Better do something for CIBACT, I suppose,' Wexford said, producing a ten pound note. 'What do you say? I'll guess they're five and their birthday was June the first.'

'I don't like to look too closely. They're not animals at Smithfield or something. I see what that Cookie meant. Oh, all right, I'll say they're five but they'll be six in September, September the fifth.'

'Older,' said a voice from behind Dora. 'Six already. Probably six-and-a-half.'

Wexford turned round to see Swithun Riding. His wife looked very small beside him. There was a

184

greater disparity in their heights than that between Wexford and Dora or, come to that, between Cookie Dix and the diminutive architect.

Susan said, 'Do you know my husband?'

Introductions were made. Unlike his son, Swithun Riding responded. He smiled and uttered the usual archaism that was once an enquiry as to another's health.

'How do you do?'

Wexford handed his money to the twins' father and repeated his estimate of their age.

'Oh, nonsense,' said Riding. 'Have you no children yourself?'

The question was uttered in a tone both indignant and arrogant. Good manners had swiftly fallen away. Riding seemed to imply the discovery in Wexford of a wanton and antisocial partiality to total contraception.

'He's got two,' said Dora rather sharply. 'Two *girls. And* he's got a good memory.'

'Well, Swithun's a paediatrician, after all,' said Swithun's wife in mild reproach.

Her husband ignored her. A twenty pound note was handed over, no doubt as a sign of social and perhaps parental superiority, and Swithun Riding offered his estimate as six-and-a-half.

'They were six on February the twelfth,' he hazarded but in so firm a voice as to suggest that whatever might be Phyllida and Fenella's official birthday, this was what their natural birthday should be.

The Ridings, joined by the burly Christopher in shorts and polo shirt and a fair-haired girl of about ten, set off in the direction of a plant stall. This was enough to turn Dora in the opposite direction towards the tea tent. Tea was a lavish affair, twenty different kinds of sandwiches, scones with raspberry

185

jam and clotted cream, chocolate cake, coffee and walnut cake, passion cake, pecan pie, eclairs, cream slices, brandy snaps, strawberries and cream.

'Just the kind of thing I like,' said Wexford, joining the queue.

It was a very long queue, a serpent of guests that wound round the inside perimeter of the yellow and white striped tent, and it was the kind of queue seldom seen, as different as could be from a line of dispirited ill-dressed people waiting for a bus or worse, as Wexford had seen recently in Myringham, at a dossers' soup kitchen. The tea tent at Glyndebourne was probably the nearest you'd get to this one. He'd been there once and, uncomfortable in a dinner jacket at four in the afternoon, had lined up for smoked salmon sandwiches just as he was doing now. But there a good many like himself had dressed themselves in ancient evening clothes, dinner jackets just post-war, old women in black lace from the forties, while here it was as if a *Vogue* centrefold had turned into a video. Dora said the woman in front of them was wearing a suit from Lacroix while Caroline Charles dresses were thick on the ground. She added abstractedly,

'Don't eat the clotted cream, Reg.'

'I wasn't going to,' he lied. 'I suppose I can have a bit of pecan pie? And a couple of strawberries?'

'Of course you can but you know what Dr Akande said.'

'Poor devil's got more on his mind at the moment than my cholesterol count.'

All the tables in the marquee were occupied. As he had predicted, the Chief Constable was here, sitting at a table with his thin red-headed wife and two friends. Wexford quickly dodged out of the line of sight and he and Dora took their trays outside. They found themselves reduced to a low wall for seats and the top of a balustrade for a table, and were setting out the food when a voice behind Wexford said, 'I thought it was you! I'm so pleased to see you because we don't know anyone here.'

Ingrid Pamber. Behind her was the wild-haired Jeremy Lang, carrying a tray that sagged under its load of sandwiches, cake and strawberries.

'I know what you're thinking,' said Ingrid. 'You're thinking what on earth are that pair doing here up among the nobs.'

Fortunately, she didn't know what he was thinking. If he hadn't made it a rule long ago never to admire other women while accompanied by his wife, never to do this even in his own thoughts, he would have been dwelling appreciatively on her pink and white skin, that hair as satiny as a racehorse's coat, that figure and the charming tilt to her mouth. As it was, he told himself she was ten times prettier in her white top and cotton skirt than Anouk Khoori or Cookie Dix or the woman who ran the hamper raffle. Then he banished covert admiration and said that though this hadn't been the enquiry he had in mind, how did she in fact come to be there?

'Jerry's uncle's a pal of Mr Khoori. They live next door to each other in London.'

The uncle. So the uncle was real. 'I see.' Since Khoori's London was unlikely to be too far distant from Mayfair, Belgravia or Hampstead, the uncle must be a rich man.

Up to a little more thought-reading but this time with greater accuracy, Ingrid said, 'Eaton Square,' and then, 'May we join you? It's great to have someone to talk to.'

He introduced Dora, who said graciously, 'Share our wall.'

Ingrid began chatting about the happiness of having a fortnight off work, all the places she and

Jeremy had been to, some rock concert, the theatre at Chichester. While she talked she managed to mop up a great deal of food. How did the thin eat so much and get away with it? Girls like Ingrid, boys like this bony Jeremy shovelling in scones plastered with their own thickness in clotted cream. They never seemed to think about it, they just ate it.

Better for him anyway to contemplate food and dwell on its effects than about this charming girl who was now with abundant grace and courtesy complimenting Dora on her dress. This afternoon her eyes seemed a brighter blue than ever, almost the colour of a kingfisher's plumage. She wanted to know if they had gone in for guessing the twins' age. Jeremy had said it was silly but she had made him have a go because she did so want to win the teddy bear.

She laid her white hand on Wexford's sleeve. 'I'm mad about cuddly toys. I can't remember – did we go into the bedroom when you came to the flat?'

The serpent uncoiling in the garden, that was what it was like. Graceful and courteous she might be, but poison was there too, a tiny sac of it under her tongue. Dora was looking surprised but no more than that. Jeremy, taking the second plate of passion cake, said, 'Of course he didn't go into the bedroom, Ing. Why would he have? There's not room to swing a cat in there.'

'Or a teddy bear.' Ingrid giggled. 'I've got a golden spaniel my dad bought me in Paris when I was ten and a pink pig and a dinosaur that came from Florida. The dinosaur doesn't sound cuddly but he is, maybe the most cuddly, isn't he, Jerry?'

'Not as cuddly as me, though,' said Jeremy and he helped himself to a brandy snap. 'You met my uncle Wael yet?'

'Not yet. We spoke to Mrs Khoori.'

'I suppose I still call him uncle. Don't know really.

Until the other day I hadn't spoken to him since I was eighteen. I'll introduce you if you want.'

Neither Wexford nor Dora did much want but could hardly say so. Jeremy brushed crumbs off his jeans and got up. 'You stay there, Ing,' he said kindly, 'and finish up the eclairs. You know how you love eclairs.'

Finding Wael Khoori took a long time and involved walking all the way round the outside of Mynford New Hall. Wexford spotted the Chief Constable, this time heading in the direction of some rather sophisticated coconut shies. It seemed likely that he might avoid an encounter. Jeremy said that when they arrived that afternoon he had expected a house that looked like one of his uncle Wael's Crescent supermarkets with what he called 'minaret things' or else something like Abu Dhabi airport. Instead there was this boring Georgian place. Had Mr and Mrs Wexford ever seen Abu Dhabi airport? While Dora listened to a description of this Arabian Nights extravaganza and tourist snare, Wexford glanced up at the windows of the new house with a vague idea in mind of seeing the face of either Juana or Rosenda looking out.

It was a big house for two young women to manage. Mrs Khoori didn't look the sort of woman to make her own bed or wash up the breakfast things. There must be twenty bedrooms and no doubt bathrooms to go with them. What must it be like to be obliged to travel half across the world in order to feed your children?

The sky was beginning to cloud over and above the downs had dulled to a threatening purple. A little breeze whistled out of the woodland as they began to descend the slope. Wexford disliked the idea of climbing it again, he was growing weary of this hunting for a host who by rights should have sought them out. And he was thinking of saying so, though in politer terms, when Jeremy suddenly looked round and waved to the people behind them.

Three men, two of them walking arm-in-arm. It would have looked less odd, Wexford thought, if each had been in a burnous and galabeah, but all were in western clothes and one was unmistakeably Anglo-Saxon, pink-skinned, fairish, bald. The others were both overweight and tall, taller even than Wexford. Each had the handsome Semite's face, hook-nosed, narrow-lipped, the eyes close-set. Plainly they were brothers, the younger man with a badly pock-marked brown skin, but the other's was no darker than an Englishman's with a tan while his hair, copious and rather long, was white as snow. He seemed about ten years older than his wife but she on the other hand might be older than she looked.

The last thing Wael Khoori wanted at this moment, in the midst perhaps of some business discussion, was to be accosted by this nephew-by-courtesy and introduced to people he didn't want to meet. This was clear from his abstracted and then mildly irritated expression. One thing, he knew Jeremy well, there had been no exaggeration there, though Wexford wouldn't have been surprised if there had been. He called him 'dear boy' like some Victorian godparent.

They were presented to Khoori as 'Reg and Dora Wexford, friends of Ingrid's', which Dora said afterwards she thought a bit much. Khoori behaved as the Royal Family are said to do when meeting strangers. But his manner as he asked his banal questions was impatient rather than gracious, he was in a hurry to get on.

'Have you come far?'

'We live here,' Wexford said.

'Like it, do you? Pretty place, very green. Had tea yet? Have some tea, my wife tells me it's tip-top.'

190

'Right,' said Jeremy, 'I might have some more.'

'You do that, dear boy. Kind regards to your uncle when you see him.' To Wexford and Dora, he trotted out the old formula, 'Nice to have met you. Come again.'

Linking arms with both companions, neither of whom had been introduced, he steered them away into a shrubbery as dense as a maze. Jeremy said confidingly as they walked back to the marquee, 'Got a funny voice, hasn't he? Did you notice? Estuary English, I suppose, and a hint of cockney.'

'It can't be, though.'

'Well, it can actually. His brother that's called Ismail talks the same. They had an English nanny and *he* says she came from Whitechapel.'

'So he didn't grow up in the gutters of Alexandria?' said Dora.

'Where did you get that idea? His parents were quite aristocratic, Uncle William says, his dad was a Bey or a Khalifa or one of those things, and it was Riyadh. Hi, Ing, sorry we've been so long.'

'They gave the result of the competition,' Ingrid said, 'and I didn't get the bear and nor did you. It was 368 got it. Well, they didn't get it, because no one came up with the ticket. Why do people go in for things and then not look to see if they've won?'

Dora said they must be going and, varying Khoori's formula, that she was very glad they had met. Wexford said goodbye.

'We should have offered them a lift, you know. Jeremy told me they hadn't got their car with them, it's in for repairs.'

'I bet he did,' Wexford said.

That would be a fine thing, driving them back to Kingsmarkham, perhaps be invited in for a cup of tea and then have Dora in her innocence ask them round next week to spend the evening. 'You must meet my

191

daughter Sylvia . . . ' He could imagine it all. He took his wife's arm affectionately. She had got out her ticket and was looking at it as they passed the twins' stall, from which the children had disappeared, though their father – and the teddy bear – remained.

'Three-six-seven,' she said. 'Missed it by one.' She turned to look at Wexford. 'Reg, you must either have three-six-six or three-six-eight.'

He had the winning ticket, of course he had. By some kind of awful intuition he had known it since Ingrid's announcement. The correct answer to the question of the twins' ages was 1 June, on which date Phyllida had been born five years before at two minutes to midnight, and 2 June, birth date of Fenella at ten minutes past. No one had come up with that and Wexford was nearest with 1 June.

'Let me give it back. You can raffle it for the cause.'

'Oh, no, you don't,' said the twins' father nastily. 'I've had as much of that bloody thing as I can stand. You take it or else I chuck it in the river and pollute the environment.'

Wexford took it. The teddy bear was as big as a child of two. He knew what he would have to do with it, wanted to do this and didn't want to. Dora said, 'You could . . . '

'Yes, I know. I will.'

They were eating again, taking Khoori's advice and having some more tea. Most people were leaving, so they had acquired the best table, outside the marquee, under the shade of a mulberry tree. Wexford set the teddy bear on the empty chair between them. Ingrid's brilliant eyes were wide, covetous, yearning. How could eyes which absorbed light and never gave it off produce a beam of peacock blue? Or was it of deep ice?

'He's yours if you want him.'

'You don't mean it!'

She had sprung to her feet. 'Oh, you're wonderful! You're so kind! I shall call her Christabel!'

Whoever heard of a female teddy bear? He knew what would happen next. It did – before he could get away. She threw her arms round his neck and kissed him. Dora watched enigmatically. Jeremy continued eating coffee walnut cake. Ingrid's body, which was delightfully and distressingly plump and slim at the same time, clung a little too long and a little too close to his own. He took her hands, removed them gently from his neck and said,

'I'm glad you're pleased.'

Since it wasn't in the nature of things that she should be attracted to him – he wasn't rich like Alexander Dix, young like Jeremy or handsome like Peter Stanton – and nymphomania was a myth, only one possibility remained. She was a flirt. A flirt with the world's bluest glance. 'An hundred years should go to praise thine eyes, and on thy forehead gaze . . . ' He would *not* offer her a lift.

'Maybe he can be a boy after all,' said Ingrid. 'I know – your first name's Reg, isn't it?'

Wexford laughed. He said goodbye again, and over his shoulder, 'It's not available for christening teddy bears.'

A second possibility remained. He thought of it now. She was a liar, he knew that: was she also a murderer? Was she nice to him, or what she thought of as being nice, to get him on her side? They were coming into the field that was a car park, before Dora said anything. The first drops of rain had begun to fall. The breeze had become a serious wind and a woman in front of them in cartwheel hat and diaphanous dress was having to hold her skirts down.

'She was all over you, that girl,' said Dora.

'Yes.'

'Who is she, anyway?'

'A suspect in a murder.' He never told her more than that about his cases. She looked at him quite cheerfully.

'Really?'

'Really. Let's get in the car, shall we? Your hat'll get wet.'

There was a queue to get out but not a long one. The line of cars had to pass through a farm gateway and since Rollses, Bentleys and Jaguars predominated, progress was slow. Only two cars remained ahead of him to squeeze between the gate-posts, when his phone started ringing. He picked up the receiver and it was Karen's voice he heard.

'Yes,' he said, 'yes,' and, 'I see.'

Dora could hear Karen's voice but not distinguish words. The car slipped and bumped through the narrow gap. Wexford said, 'Where did you say?' And then he said, 'I'll take my wife home and come straight there.'

'What is it, Reg? Oh, Reg, it's not Melanie Akande?'

'Sounds like it. I'm afraid it is.'

'Is she dead?'

'Oh, yes,' he said, 'she's dead.'

Chapter Thirteen

Kingsmarkham lies in that part of Sussex that was once the land of a Celtic tribe the Romans called the Regnenses. To its colonists it was simply a desirable place to live, pleasant to look at and not too cold, the indigenous population regarded only as a source of slave labour. Numerous remains of female infants unearthed by archaeologists near Pomfret Monachorum suggest that the Romans practised infanticide among the Regnenses with a view to maintaining a male work force.

As well as this grisly discovery, treasure was found. No one knew how this huge cache of gold coins, figurines and jewellery came to be buried on farmland a mile or two from Cheriton but there was evidence that a Roman villa had once stood there. A rather romantic suggestion was made that early in the fifth century the family who lived there, being forced to flee, had buried their valuables in the hope of coming back one day to retrieve them. But the Romans had never come back and the Dark Ages began.

This treasure was found by the farmer himself, digging up a small piece of land, hitherto part of fields on which sheep grazed, with the intention of growing maize on it for fattening pheasants. It was valued at something over two million pounds, most of which he received. He gave up farming and went to live in Florida. The gold statuette he found of a suckling lioness and twin cubs and the two gold bracelets, one chased with a design of a boar hunt, the other of a stag at bay, can now be seen in the British Museum, where they are known as the Framhurst Hoard.

The result was to encourage prospectors. Looking from a distance as if slowly scouring the heathland and the green valley with vacuum cleaners, they came with their metal detectors and worked patiently and in silence for long hours at a time. Farmers had no objection – there was little arable farming in the area – and so long as they damaged nothing and did not frighten the sheep, they were not only harmless but might possibly be a source of untold wealth. Any successful prospector would be obliged to render up half his loot to the landowner.

So far there had been no more. The cache of which the lioness and the bracelets had been part appeared to have been a one-off. But the treasure-seekers went on coming and it was one of these wandering somewhat outside the favoured area, passing and re-passing his detector across an area of chalky scree, who had come upon firstly a coin, then the body of a girl.

It was where the downland began, between Cheriton and Myfleet. A narrow white road, without fence, wall or hedge, ran between the foothills, and it was some twenty yards to the left of it, where the woodland began, on the edge of a wood, that she had been buried. While Colin Broadley was plying his metal detector the weather had been fine, the soil fairly damp from recent rains but not wet. The conditions had been ideal for digging and Broadley, once he had found the coin which had so excited his detector, went on with his excavations.

'When you realized what you'd found,' Wexford said to him, 'why didn't you stop digging?'

Broadley, in his forties, a heavy man with a beer gut, shrugged and looked shifty. He was no archaeologist but an unemployed plumber actuated by greed and hope. It was not he that had called the police but a passer-by who, seeing the extensive excavation in progress and thinking it suspicious, had parked his car and gone to look. This public-spirited citizen, James Ranger of Myringham, was paying for his social conscience by being kept at the scene, seated in his car, where he had been for the past two hours.

'It was a strange thing to do, wasn't it?' Wexford persisted.

'She had to *be* dug up,' Broadley said at last. 'Someone was going to have to do it.'

'That was a job for the police,' Wexford said, and it was true that the police had finished the job. Of course he knew very well what Broadley had been up to. Having found the coin and not being a sensitive or squeamish man, he had dug down, hoping for more money and perhaps for jewellery on what lay beneath.

There had been none. The body was naked. Nor was it possible to say, at this stage, whether or not there was any connection between it and the coin. In the eyes of Broadley, this coin had been the first sample of a Roman treasure, but a closer look told Wexford it was a Victorian halfpenny, bearing the head of the young queen. The hair was done in a style vaguely suggestive of actresses taking part in Ancient Rome movies. Wexford sent Broadley off with Pemberton to sit in one of the police cars.

It was raining steadily. They had put a tarpaulin up over the grave and the trees provided some shelter. Under here the pathologist was currently examining the body. Not Sir Hilary Tremlett nor Wexford's *bête noire* Dr Basil Sumner-Quist, both of whom were

197

away on their holiday, but an assistant or surrogate who had introduced himself as Mr Mavrikiev. Wexford, under an umbrella – there were ten umbrellas at the scene, under the dripping trees – held the coin inside a plastic bag. Not that there was likely to be such a thing as a fingerprint on it after its interment in that fine, chalky, abrasive soil, grains of which clogged the indentations on its surface. Once Mavrikiev was out of there and they had taken the photographs, he was going to have to do what he dreaded: make his way to Ollerton Avenue and tell the Akandes.

He must do it himself, he knew that. He couldn't send Vine or even Burden to do the job for him. Since Melanie had been reported missing he had gone daily to see the doctor and his wife, had missed only the day he had met Akande by chance in the street. He had turned himself into their friend and he knew he had done this because they were black. Their race and their colour merited his special attention, yet this was not as it should be. Ideally, if he truly practised what being unprejudiced was all about, he would have treated them the same as any other parents of a missing child. Later that day the reckoning was coming for him.

Mavrikiev lifted a flap of the tarpaulin and came out. There was some assistant of his at hand to hold an umbrella over him. It was incredible, Wexford could hardly believe his eyes, but the pathologist was going to say nothing to him, was making straight for his waiting Jaguar.

'Dr Mavrikiev!' he said.

The man was quite young, fair, with a washed-out Nordic look. Forbears from the Ukraine probably, Wexford guessed, as he turned round and said,

'Mister. Mister Mavrikiev.'

Wexford swallowed his wrath. Why were they

always so rude? This one was the worst of the lot. 'Can you give me an idea when she died?'

Mavrikiev looked as if he might ask for Wexford's credentials. He pushed out his lips and scowled. 'Ten days. Maybe more. I'm not a magician.'

No, you're a real bastard . . . 'And the cause of death?'

'Nobody shot her. She wasn't strangled. She wasn't buried alive.'

He ducked into his car and slammed the door. Didn't like being called out on a wet Saturday night, no doubt. Who did? Wouldn't like doing a postmortem on a Sunday either, but that was too bad. Burden came stumbling across the slippery wet scrub, his coat collar turned up, his hair dripping, no umbrella for him.

'Have you seen her?'

Wexford shook his head. He didn't feel anything any more about looking on the dead who have met their death by violence, not even on the decomposing dead. He was used to it and you can get used to anything. In some ways fortunately, his sense of smell wasn't what it had once been. He ducked under the tarpaulin and looked at her. No one had covered her, she wasn't even decently covered with a sheet, but lay sprawled on her back, still in a reasonable state of preservation. The face, particularly, was very nearly intact. Even in death, after days of death and interment, she looked very young.

The black patches on her dark skin, notably the sticky black mass on the side of her hair, might have been decay or they might have been bruises. He didn't know but Mavrikiev would. One of her arms lay at an odd angle and he wondered if it could have been broken before death. Out in the rain again he drew a long breath.

'He said ten days or more,' said Burden. 'That would be about right.'

'Yes.'

'Back to Tuesday week's eleven days. If whoever brought her here came in a car they didn't bring the car in here off the road. Of course she may have been alive when she got here. He may have killed her here. Want me to attend the postmortem? He says nine in the morning. I will if you like. I just shan't speak to Mavri-whatsit unless he speaks to me.'

'Thanks, Mike,' said Wexford. 'I'd rather go to the PM than do what I've got to do tonight.'

Ten minutes to nine and still light in that grim hopeless way only a wet summer evening in England can be. It was hard to tell whether it was rain falling or just water dripping from the trees. The air was still and heavy and the humidity hung as a cold whitish vapour. No lights were on in the house but that meant nothing. Dusk had barely come. Wexford rang the bell and almost immediately a light came on in the hall and another in the porch above his head. The boy who opened the door he recognized at once as the Akandes' son who had been in the photograph with Melanie.

Wexford introduced himself. The boy being there made things worse, he thought, but better perhaps for the parents. One child was left to comfort them.

'I'm Patrick. My mother and father are in the back, we're finishing supper as a matter of fact. I only got home today and I've been sleeping. I didn't wake up till an hour ago.'

To forewarn him or not? 'I'm afraid the news is bad.'

'Oh.' Patrick looked at him, then away. 'Yes, well, you must see my parents.'

At the sound of their voices Raymond Akande had risen from the table and was standing there, looking towards the door, but Laurette remained where she was, sitting very upright, both hands lying on the cloth on either side of a plate with orange segments on it. Neither of them said anything.

'I have bad news for you, Dr Akande, Mrs Akande.'

The doctor drew in his breath. His wife silently turned her head in Wexford's direction.

'Will you sit down, please, doctor? I expect you can guess what I've come to tell you.'

The tiny tremor of Akande's head signified a nod.

'Melanie's body has been found,' Wexford said. 'That is, we are as certain as we can be without a positive identification that this is Melanie.'

Laurette beckoned her son. 'Come and sit down again, Patrick.' Her voice was quite steady. She said to Wexford, 'Where was she found?'

How much he had hoped they wouldn't ask! 'In Framhurst Woods.'

Leave it there, don't ask any more. 'Was her body buried?' Laurette asked relentlessly. 'How did they know where to dig?'

Patrick put his hand on his mother's arm. 'Mum, don't.'

'How did they know where to dig?'

'People go up there with metal detectors looking for treasure like the Framhurst Hoard. One of them found her.'

He thought of the bruises and the broken arm, the matted blackness on the skull, but she didn't ask the question so he had had no need to lie. Instead, 'We knew she must be dead,' she said. 'Now we really know. What's the difference?'

There was a difference and it lay in the presence of hope and its absence. Everyone in the room knew that. Wexford pulled out the fourth chair from the table and sat down on it. He said, 'It is probably no more than a formality but I must ask you to come and

201

make an identification of the body. You'd be the best person, doctor.'

Akande nodded. He spoke for the first time and his voice was unrecognizable. 'Yes. All right.' He went over to his wife and stood by her chair but he didn't touch her.

'Where?' he said, 'And what time?'

Now? Let them try to get a night's sleep first. Mavrikiev would want to do the postmortem early but it might take a long time. 'We'll send a car for you. Say one-thirty?'

'I should like to see her,' said Laurette.

You would no more say to this woman that it was better not, that it was an anguish no mother should be put through, than you'd say it to Medea or Lady Macbeth. 'Just as you wish.'

She said nothing more to him but turned her face towards Patrick, who must have read there some rare sign of weakness or sensed an early warning that her control would break. He put his arms round his mother and held her tightly. Wexford left the room and let himself out of the house.

If those stripped raw features had been less unmistakeable, he would have failed to recognize the pathologist. And this had nothing to do with the grisly disguise supplied by a green rubber gown and cap. Mavrikiev was a changed man. Such violent mood swings are rare in normal people and Wexford wondered what cataclysmic event had so soured him the evening before or piece of good fortune recently cheered him up. One of the oddest things was that he behaved at first as if he had never encountered either policeman before.

'Good morning, good morning. Andy Mavrikiev. How d'you do? I'm not anticipating this being a long job.'

He got to work. Wexford wasn't inclined to watch closely. The sound of the saw on a skull, the sight of the removal of organs, though not sickening to him, were not particularly interesting. Burden watched everything, as he had watched Sir Hilary Tremlett's operations on Annette Bystock, and asked a stream of questions, all of which Mavrikiev seemed happy to answer. Mavrikiev talked all the time and not only about the remains on the table.

Although he scarcely offered it as an explanation of his contrast in mood, it *was* an explanation. At five on the previous morning his wife had gone into labour with their first child. A difficult delivery was expected and Mavrikiev had hoped to be with her throughout, but the call to Framhurst Heath had come just as the question was being debated: continue to wait and hope for a normal delivery or perform a caesarean?

'I wasn't best pleased, as you can imagine. Still, I was back in time to see Harriet made comfortable with an epidural and a healthy baby delivered.'

'Congratulations,' said Wexford. 'What was it?'

'A nice little girl. Well, a nice big girl, nearly ten pounds. You see this? Know what it is? It's a ruptured spleen, that's what it is.'

When he had finished, the body on the slab – or rather the face, for the poor empty body was now entirely concealed under plastic sheeting – looked a good deal better than when first unearthed. It even appeared as if decomposition was less advanced, for Mavrikiev had done an undertaker's job as well as a pathologist's. The dreadful confrontation awaiting the Akandes would be less harrowing.

He pulled off his gloves. 'I'll revise what I said last night. I said ten days or a bit more, didn't I? I can do better than that. Twelve days at least.'

Wexford nodded, not surprised. 'What did she die of?'

203

'I told you her spleen was ruptured. There's a fracture of the ulna and a fracture of the radius on the left side – that's the arm, the left arm. She didn't die of that. She was very thin. Could have been a bulimic. Contusions all over her body. And a massive cerebral embolism – bloodclot in the brain to you. I'd say the chap beat her to death. I don't think an instrument was used, just his fists and maybe his feet.'

'You can kill someone with your fists?' said Burden.

'Sure. If you're a big strong guy. Think of boxers. And then think of a boxer doing to a woman what he does to an opponent, only without gloves. See what I mean?'

'Oh, yes.'

'She was just a kid,' said Mavrikiev. 'Late teens?'

'Older than that,' said Wexford. 'Twenty-two.'

'Really? You surprise me. Well, I must get out of this gear and be on my way as I've a luncheon date with Harriet and Zenobia Helena. It was nice meeting you gentlemen. You'll get my report pronto and soonest.'

Burden said when he had gone, 'Zenobia Helena Mavrikiev. What does it sound like?'

The question was rhetorical but Wexford answered it. 'A maidservant in one of Tolstoy's stories.' He cast up his eyes. 'Bit better than last night, wasn't he, but what an insensitive bugger! My God, it got up my nose a bit, him on about *his* daughter and the Akandes' daughter's ruptured spleen all in the same breath.'

'At least he doesn't make sick jokes like Sumner-Quist.'

Wexford found himself incapable of eating any lunch. This departure of appetite, rare for him, seemed to please Dora who was always trying by subtle or direct means to make him eat less. But it excited wondering comment from Sylvia and her family who had invited themselves to lunch, as was increasingly their habit on a Sunday. Today he could have done without their company.

Now that the novelty of being, so to speak, the family's breadwinner was starting to wear off, Sylvia had fallen into the irritating habit of pointing out one thing after another on the table and various objects in the room, such as flowers and books, as being beyond the means of those living on seventy-four pounds a week. This was the sum total of UB and IS granted the Fairfaxes by the Employment Service and the Department of Social Security. How quickly she had seized upon that weapon of the disadvantaged most calculated to wound the sensibilities of the better off! Her father sometimes wondered where she had picked up such a catalogue of maddening habits.

A tinkly laugh preceded most of these comments. 'That's clotted cream, Robin, to put on your raspberries. Make the most of it. You're not likely to get it at home.'

Robin, of course, said it was no problem. '*Koi gull knee.*'

'I shouldn't have any more wine, Neil. Drinking is just a habit and it's not a habit you can afford the way things are.'

'If it isn't there I can't drink it, can I? But it *is here* and I'm making the most of it like you told the boys to do with the clotted cream. Right?'

'*Mafesh,*' said Robin in a heartfelt way.

Wexford felt he was spending his life escaping from things, uncomfortable situations, people's misery, unhappy occasions. It was raining again. He drove himself down to the mortuary, having resisted a masochistic temptation to fetch the Akandes himself.

The car brought them, both of them, at ten past two. Masterful for once, Akande said to his wife, 'I'll go in first. I'll *do* it.'

'All right.'

Laurette was hollow-eyed. Her features seemed to have got bigger and her face smaller. But her glossy hair was still carefully dressed, coiled and pinned to the back of her head. And she was still well dressed. In the black suit and black blouse, she looked as if she was going to a funeral. Raymond Akande's face had been grey for a long while now and he had been losing weight steadily since his daughter first disappeared. That fortnight had made him ten pounds lighter.

Wexford took him into the mortuary, the chilly abode now shared by the bodies of two dead women. He lifted the edge of the sheet in both hands and exposed the face. Akande hesitated a moment, then came forward. He bent over, looked at the face and sprang back.

'That's not my daughter! That's not Melanie!'

Wexford's mouth went dry. 'Dr Akande, are you sure? Look again, please.'

'Of course I'm sure. That's not my daughter. Do you think a man doesn't know his own child?'

Chapter Fourteen

Shock suspends everything. There is no thought, only automatic reaction, movement, mechanical speech. Wexford followed Akande out of the mortuary, his mind a blank, his body obeying motor instructions.

Laurette had her back to them. She had been talking, or doing her best to talk, to Karen Malahyde. At the sound of their footsteps she got up, but slowly. Her husband went up to her. His walk was a little unsteady and when he put out his hand to her he seemed to clutch her arm for support.

'Letty,' he said, 'it isn't Melanie.'

'*What*?'

'It isn't her, Letty.' His voice shook. 'I don't know who it is but it isn't Melanie.'

'What are you saying?'

'Letty, it's not Melanie.'

He was very close to her. He bowed his head against her shoulder. She put her arms round him and held him, she held his head against her breast and stared at Wexford over his shoulder.

'I don't understand.' She was cold as stone. 'We gave you a photograph.'

The enormity of what had happened, realization of that enormity, was beginning to take over from shock. Wexford said, 'Yes,' and 'Yes, that's right.'

Her voice began to rise. 'This dead girl, she's black?'

'Yes.'

Karen Malahyde, who had seen Wexford's face, said, 'Mrs Akande, if you'd just . . . '

Softly, as if it was a baby she held, so as not to disturb the baby, Laurette Akande whispered, 'How dare you do that to us!'

'Mrs Akande,' said Wexford, 'I am extremely sorry this has happened.' He added, with what must have been a lie, 'No one regrets it more than I do.'

'How dare you do that to us?' Laurette screamed at Wexford. She forgot the baby at her breast. Her hands had ceased to nurse him. 'How dare you treat us like that? You're just a damned racist like the rest of them. Coming to our house patronizing us, the great white man condescending to us, so magnanimous, so liberal . . . !'

'Letty, don't,' Akande begged her. 'Please don't.'

She ignored him. She took a step towards Wexford, both fists up now. 'It was because she was black, wasn't it? I haven't seen her but I know, I can see it all. One black girl's just the same as another to you, isn't she? A *negress*. A *nigger*, a *darkie* . . . '

'Mrs Akande, I'm sorry. I am deeply sorry.'

'*You* regret it. You damned hypocrite! You don't have prejudice, do you? Oh, no, you're not a racist, black and white are all equal in your eyes. But when you find a dead black girl it's got to be *our* girl because we're black!'

Akande was shaking his head. 'Not a bit like her,' he said. 'Not a bit.'

'Black, though. Black, isn't she?'

'That's the only way she's like her, Letty. She's black.'

'So we don't get a wink of sleep all night. Our son sits up all night and what's he doing? He's crying. For hours and hours. He hasn't cried for ten years but he cried last night. And we tell the neighbours, the

208

nice white liberal neighbours who are big-hearted enough to feel sorry for parents whose daughter's been murdered, *even though she was only one of those coloured girls, one of those blacks.*'

'Believe me, Mrs Akande,' Wexford said. 'it's a mistake that's been made many times before and the dead have been white.' It was true but still she was right, he knew she was right. 'I can only apologize again. I'm very sorry this has happened.'

'We'll go home now,' Akande said to his wife.

She looked at Wexford as if she would have liked to spit at him. She didn't do this. The tears she hadn't shed when she thought the body in there was her daughter's now streamed down her cheeks. Sobbing, she hung on to her husband's arm with both hands and he led her out to the waiting car.

A salutary lesson. We think we know ourselves but we don't, and self-discovery of this particular kind of ignorance is bitter. What he had said to Laurette Akande about a similar confusion sometimes occurring between the bodies of white people was factually accurate. It was scarcely true in spirit. He *had* assumed a black girl's body was that of a missing black girl and he had done so *because she was black*. The photograph he had of Melanie Akande had not been referred to. The known heights of the missing girl and the dead girl had not been compared. With a wince, he remembered how only that morning, only about three hours before, Mavrikiev had expressed surprise that the age of the body on the table was twenty-two and not eighteen or nineteen. Now he recalled something learned long ago from a forensic report, that certain important bones in the female anatomy have fused by the age of twenty-two. . . .

The worst thing for him was that it had shown him he was wrong about himself. This error had occurred through prejudice, through racism, through making an assumption he could never have made if the missing girl were white and the body white. In such a case he would merely have thought it likely the lost girl had been found, but he would have done a lot more rigorous research into appearance and statistics before summoning the parents to make an identification. Laurette's reproaches were valid, if violent.

Well, it was a lesson and that was how it must be viewed. There was no question of ceasing his visits to the Akandes. The first one, but only the first one, would be uncomfortable for all of them. Unless, of course, they saw to it that the first was the last. He had apologized, and more humbly than he usually did to anyone. He wouldn't say he was sorry again. It came to him, and brought him a wry amusement, that the lesson was having its results already, for from tomorrow he was going to begin treating the Akandes not as members of the disadvantaged minority worthy of special consideration, he was going to treat them as ordinary human beings.

But since the dead girl wasn't Melanie, who was she?

A black girl was missing and a black girl's body had been found but there was no apparent connection between the two.

Burden, untroubled by Wexford's scruples and sensibilities, said it ought to be easy enough to identify her now that the police had a national register for missing persons. It would be easier because she was black. Whatever might be the situation in London or Bradford few black people lived in this part of southern England and still fewer went missing. By this time, however, halfway through Monday, he had already discovered that nowhere in the area of the Mid-Sussex Constabulary had the police a missing person approximating to this girl's description on their computer.

'There's a Tamil woman been missing since February. She and her husband had the Kandy Palace restaurant in Myringham. But she's thirty and though I suppose technically she's black, they're very dark those Tamils . . . '

'Let's not get into that one again,' said Wexford.

'I'll get on to the national register,' Burden said. 'I suppose she could have been brought here, dead or alive, from some place like South London where I've no doubt girls go missing every day. And what happens now to our theory that Annette was killed because of something Melanie told her?'

'Nothing happens to it,' Wexford said slowly. 'Finding this girl has nothing to do with Melanie. It's irrelevant, it's something else. We still have the *status quo*. Melanie does something or says something her killer doesn't want known and he kills Annette because Annette, and presumably Annette alone, has been told what that is. After all, this girl being dead doesn't mean Melanie's alive. Melanie is dead too and we just haven't yet found her body.'

'You don't think this girl – what shall we call her? We'd better give her a name.'

'Yes, OK, but for God's sake don't come up with something from *Uncle Tom's Cabin*.'

Puzzled, Burden said, 'I've never read it.'

'Sojourner, we'll call her,' Wexford said, 'after Sojourner Truth, the "Ain't I a woman?" poet. And maybe . . . well, I somehow see her as impermanent, homeless, alone. "I am a stranger with thee and a sojourner", you know.'

Burden didn't know. He wore his deeply suspicious uneasy look. 'Sodgernah?'

'That's right. What were you going to say. You said that this girl . . . ?'

211

'Oh, yes. You don't think *this* girl – I mean what's-her-name, Sojourner – you don't think *she* said something significant to Annette?'

Wexford looked interested. 'At the Benefit Office, d'you mean?'

'If we don't have a clue who she is she's just as likely to be signing on or be a new claimant as not. It's a way of identifying her, see if they've got someone answering her description among their claimants.'

'Annette was killed on Wednesday the seventh, Sojourner certainly before that, maybe on the fifth or sixth. It fits, Mike. It's a good idea. Clever of you.'

Burden looked pleased. 'We can also check what immigrants are registered with us. I'll go down to the Benefit Office myself. Take Barry with me. By the way, where is Barry?'

Sergeant Vine tapped on the door and was in the room before Wexford had time to answer. He had been in Stowerton, talking to James Ranger. Ranger was retired, a widower, a solitary man, who had been on his way to spend Saturday evening baby-sitting his grandsons when from his car he spotted Broadley digging up a grave.

'He says he won't do that again,' said Vine. 'Apparently, his daughter and her husband missed their dinner dance. He says next time he sees some peasant, I quote, desecrating the environment he's going to accelerate and drive right on past. D'you know what he thought Broadley was up to? You won't believe this. He thought he was digging up orchids! Apparently there's some rare orchid grows up there and he's its self-appointed guardian.'

'Ranger by name and ranger by nature,' said Wexford. 'Bit unusual, though, wasn't it, quiet elderly chap like him, champion of endangered species, baby-sitter, owner of a ten-year-old but immaculate 2CV, bit odd him having a carphone, isn't it? What does he have it *for*? To call the botanical police when he sees someone pick a primrose?'

'I asked him that. He said it was as well he *did* have it, so he could ring us.'

'Not an answer to your question, though.'

'No. When pressed, he said – wait for it – it was in case he broke down on the motorway at night.'

Vine laughed. 'I've got him high on my suspect list. I was coming away from his place, had to park the car half a mile away as usual, when who do I see coming out of that block of flats in the High Street, Something Court, Clifton Court, but Kimberley Pearson.'

'Did you speak to her?'

'I asked her how she was getting on in her new home. She had Clint with her all dressed up in a brand-new baby tracksuit sitting in a very smart buggy. She'd tarted herself up a good bit too, red leggings and one of those bustier things and shoes with heels like that.' Vine held up thumb and forefinger five inches apart. 'A changed woman. She'd told me she was moving into the home of her late grandma. It didn't seem that sort of place. I mean, quite a smart block of newish flats.'

Burden gave Wexford a sidelong look. 'That'll set your mind at rest,' he said not very pleasantly. 'You were getting worried about their fate.'

' "Worried" is a strong word, Inspector Burden,' Wexford snapped. 'Most people not entirely callous would be concerned for a child living in those circumstances.'

There was a short uncomfortable silence. Then Vine said, 'She seems to be getting on all right without Zack. Glad to see the back of him, I expect.'

Wexford said nothing. He had another date with the Snows. Did the death of Sojourner affect his

213

approach to them? Did it perhaps entirely change his attitude? He felt suddenly as if lost in a dark wood. Why had he bitten Mike's head off like that? He picked up the phone and asked Bruce Snow to come to the police station at five.

'I shan't be done here till half-past.'

'Five, please, Mr Snow. And I want your wife here too.'

'You'll be lucky,' Snow said. 'She's going away tonight, taking the kids and going to Malta or Elba or somewhere.'

'No, she isn't,' said Wexford. He dialled the number of the house in Harrow Avenue and a young girl's voice answered.

'Mrs Snow, please.'

'This is her daughter. Who wants her?'

'Chief Inspector Wexford, Kingsmarkham CID.'

'Oh, right. Hang on.'

He had to hang on a long time and felt his temper rising. When she finally came to the phone she had regained her coolness. The ice maiden was back in occupation.

'Yes, what is it?'

'I'd like you to come down to the police station at five, please, Mrs Snow.'

'Sorry, but that won't be convenient. My flight to Marseille is at ten to five.'

'It will be leaving without you. Have you forgotten I asked you not to go anywhere?'

'No, I haven't, but I didn't take it seriously. It's so absurd – what has all this to do with me? I'm the injured party. I'm taking my poor children away from it all. Their father's behaviour has broken their hearts.'

'Their hearts can wait a few days to be mended, Mrs Snow. I don't suppose you'd like to find yourself on a charge of obstructing police enquiries, would you?'

He knew better than to believe he could understand people. Why, for instance, did this woman need to lie? She was, as she had just told him, the injured party. Deceiving a wife with a mistress over a period of *nine years* was to do her a serious injury, for it humiliated as well as hurt her, it made her feel a fool. As for Snow, Wexford knew he would never understand the man's conduct. He would hardly have believed it had someone told him that here, in England, in the nineties, a man could enjoy a woman's sexual favours for years on end without paying her, without giving her presents or taking her out, without the use of a hotel room or even a bed, in his office, on the floor, so as to be within reach of his wife's voice on the phone.

And if he couldn't understand that, why should he understand any other aspects of Snow's behaviour? It seemed absurd to him that the man might have killed Sojourner because, say, Annette had told her about their affair. But *all* Snow's transactions were incomprehensible to him. So might he have beaten her to death and buried her out there in Framhurst Woods? Kill Annette, kill the woman Annette had told, and all to stop it reaching his wife's ears? Well, they all now knew what happened when it did reach his wife's ears. . . . Sojourner could have been blackmailing him. Perhaps only in a small way. It wouldn't hurt him to give her a bit of money from time to time to keep her from telling his wife. And then she asked for more money, perhaps for a lump sum. Wexford found he disliked thinking this way. Somewhere in his mind, not quite consciously, he had made Sojourner into a good person. Sojourner was the innocent victim of wicked men who exploited and abused her, while she was herself virtuous and gentle, a keeper not a betrayer of secrets, a fearful, simple, trusting soul.

Of course he was sentimentalizing her. Where now was the lesson he should have learned and thought he had learned from that business with the Akandes? He knew nothing about the girl, not her real name, her country of origin, her family if any, not even her age. And Mavrikiev's forensic report, when it came, would tell him very little of that. He didn't even know if she had ever so much as set foot in the Benefit Office.

Bruce Snow sat in Interview Room One with Burden. His wife was with Wexford in Interview Room Two. Putting them in the same room last time had resulted in the slanging match Wexford didn't want to see repeated. He faced a sulky Carolyn Snow across the table, Karen Malahyde standing behind her and wearing a look of unconcealed distaste – for everything concerned with Mrs Snow, Wexford guessed, her lifestyle, her status as wife without a job or personal income and, unfortunately, her new position as a betrayed, deceived woman.

'I'd like to put it on record,' Carolyn was saying, 'that I think it outrageous I'm being stopped from going on holiday. It's an unjustified interference with my liberty. And my poor children – what have they done?'

'It's not what they've done but what you've done, Mrs Snow. Or, rather, not done. You can put what you like on record. For all your boasts that you don't tell lies, you haven't been truthful with me.'

In the other room Burden was asking Bruce Snow if he would like to amend his statement at all or add to it in any way. Would he, for instance, care to tell

Burden what he was doing during the evening of the seventh of July?

'I was at home. I was just at home. Reading, maybe, I don't remember. Sitting with my wife. I watched television. But it's no use asking me what I watched, I don't remember.'

'Have you ever seen this girl, Mr Snow?'

Burden showed him a photograph of Sojourner's twelve-days-dead face. It had been skilfully taken but still it looked like the picture of a dead face and a battered one too. Snow recoiled.

'Is that Akande's daughter?'

That mistake again. . . . But Burden wasn't going to let it pass. 'What makes you say that?'

'Oh, for God's sake. I've never seen her before anyway.'

Her eyes as tragic as if she had suffered a bereavement, Carolyn Snow was asking Wexford to let her go on holiday. Her trip had been booked six months before. When it was made Snow would have been going too but his elder daughter had agreed to take his place. The hotel wouldn't be able to take them next week, there would be no places on flights, the travel agent's fee wasn't refundable.

'You should have thought of all that before,' said Wexford, and he showed her the picture of Sojourner, the closed eyes, the bruised skin, the bare patches on the forehead and temples where the hair had begun to fall. 'Do you know her?'

'I've never seen her before in my life.' Instead of flinching, Carolyn peered more closely. 'Is she coloured? I don't know any coloured people. Look, I've missed my plane but the travel agent says she thinks she could get us on the one tomorrow morning that goes at ten-fifteen.'

'Really? Amazing, isn't it, how much more

217

accommodating to passengers' needs air services have become?'

'You make me bloody sick! You're just a sadist. You're enjoying this, aren't you?'

'There's considerable job satisfaction attached to what I do,' said Wexford, wondering if the Employment Service would make 'job satisfaction' all one word. 'I have to get something out of it.' He looked at his watch. 'All these long hours, unpaid overtime. I'd rather be at home with my wife than stuck in here trying to get the truth out of you.'

'Have a good marriage, do you, Chief Inspector? All this has wrecked mine, I hope you know that.'

'Your husband has done that, Mrs Snow. Revenge yourself on him if you like. You won't get revenge on us.'

'What do you mean, revenge?'

Wexford drew his chair closer and put his elbows on the table. 'Isn't that what you're doing? You're revenging yourself on him for his affairs with two women. Deny he was at home that evening, insist he went out at eight and was out two and a half hours, and maybe you won't only get your house and a big chunk of his income out of him, you'll have the added satisfaction of seeing him on a murder charge.'

He had got it exactly right, he could see it in her eyes.

'Was she blackmailing you, Mr Snow?' said Burden on the other side of the wall.

'Forget it. I've never seen her.'

'We know what happens when your wife finds out about your infidelity. We've seen. She's not a forgiving woman, is she? I think you'd have willingly paid up to keep her from finding out and perhaps paid over a long period.' Overstepping the bounds once

218

more, he said, 'What on earth did Annette Bystock have to make you go on and on with it?' There was no answer, only a scowl. 'Still, you did go on. Did you get tired of paying? Did you see there'd never be an end to paying, even if you ended things with Annette? Was killing your blackmailer the only way?'

Beyond the partition, Carolyn Snow said, 'Everything I've said was true but, yes, I'd like to see him come to grief – why not? I'd like to see him pay for those two women with years in prison.'

'That's frank,' said Wexford. 'And what about yourself, Mrs Snow? Do you fancy paying for your revenge?'

'I don't know what you mean.'

'You seem to be looking at things upside-down. You've supposed throughout that we've been questioning you to confirm or deny what your husband says were his movements. That it is your *husband* who is the suspect, your *husband* who is the only possible candidate for Annette Bystock's killer. But you're quite wrong. There is yourself.'

She said it again, but anxiously this time. 'I don't know what you mean.'

'We have only your word for it that you knew nothing about Annette's role in your husband's life until after she was dead. I think we know what your word is worth, Mrs Snow. You had a better motive than he for killing her, you had a better motive than anyone.'

She stood up. She had gone quite white. 'Of course I didn't kill her! Are you mad? Of course I didn't!'

Wexford smiled. 'That's what they all say.'

'I swear to you I didn't kill her!'

'You had motive. You had means. You have no alibi for that Wednesday evening.'

'I didn't kill her! I didn't know her!'

'Perhaps you'd like to make a statement now, Mrs Snow. With your permission we'll record your statement. And then I can go home.'

She sat down again. She was breathing in short fast gasps, her forehead furrowed, her mouth puckered. Clenching her fists and digging the nails into her palms brought back some of her control. She began to tell the recording machine what had happened, how she had been alone in Harrow Avenue but for her son upstairs, how her husband had gone out at eight and returned at ten-thirty, but she broke off and spoke directly to Wexford.

'Can I go away tomorrow now?'

'I'm afraid not. I don't want you leaving the country. You can have a few days in Eastbourne, I've no objection to that.'

Carolyn Snow began to cry.

Tuesday, 20 July
In the past Sergeant Vine had spent many a long hour sitting at one of these desks in the area at the back, trying to look like an administrative assistant while he waited for a certain person to show up and sign on. Someone he was after for a spot of petty crime, it usually was, and this was a sure way of running him to earth. Whatever their income from theft, from bag-snatching, receiving, shoplifting, they all wanted their UB as well.

So while Wexford and Burden were as newcomers to the Benefit Office, it was familiar territory to Vine. No one got on well with Cyril Leyton while Osman Messaoud was generally unapproachable, but he had an easy relationship with Stanton and the women. Burden, closeted with Leyton and the security officer, left him to get on with it. Waiting till Wendy Stowlap was temporarily free, he surveyed the waiting claimants and spotted two he knew. One of them was Broadley, the discoverer of Sojourner's body, the other Wexford's elder daughter. He was still trying to think of her name, it must begin with a letter between A and G, when Wendy Stowlap's client moved away from the desk.

She looked up. 'All these foreign people coming in here, Italians, Spanish, I don't know what. Why should we keep them on our taxes? The European Union's got a lot to answer for.'

'Surely you don't have a lot of black claimants, though, do you?' he said to her. 'I mean, not out in this neck of the woods.'

'Out here in the boondocks, is that what you're saying?' Wendy was a native of Kingsmarkham and fiercely proprietorial of her home town. 'If you don't like it here why don't you go back to Berkshire or wherever you come from that's so lively and sophisticated?'

'OK, sorry, but do you?'

'Have claimants who are coloured people? You'd be surprised. We've more than we did two years ago. Well, we've got more *claimants* than we had two years ago, a lot more. The recession may be ending but unemployment's still very serious.'

'So you wouldn't specially notice a black girl?'

'Woman,' Wendy corrected him. 'I don't call you a boy.'

'I should be so lucky,' said Sergeant Vine.

'Anyway, I never noticed any black *woman* speaking specially to Annette. I never noticed that Melanie, as you know. Frankly, I've got enough on my plate here on the counter without watching what everyone else is doing.' Wendy pressed the switch that made the next neon number come up. 'So if you'll excuse me I can't keep my clients waiting any longer.'

Peter Stanton wanted to know if Sojourner was

221

good looking. He said frankly that he often fancied black women, they had such fantastic long legs. He liked their long necks, like black swans, and narrow hands. And the way they walked, as if they carried a heavy jar on their heads.

'I only saw her when she was dead,' said Vine.

'If she made a claim – that is, if she completed an ES 461 – we can find her for you. What's her name?'

Hayley Gordon also asked Sojourner's name. The two supervisors asked a lot of pointless questions about whether she was claiming UB or Income Support, had she ever worked, and what kind of job was she looking for. Osman Messaoud, off the counter this week and doing his stint at the very desk where Vine had been used to sit and wait, said he closed his mind and sometimes his eyes to young women claimants. If he caught sight of them he forced himself not to look.

'Your wife doesn't trust you as far as she can throw you, is that it?'

'It is proper for a woman to be possessive,' said Osman.

'That's a matter of opinion.' An idea came to Vine. He felt around it, trying to put the question delicately. 'Is your wife . . . er, Indian like yourself?'

'I am a British citizen,' said Osman very coldly.

'Oh, sorry. And where's your wife from?'

'Bristol.'

The man was really enjoying this, Vine thought. 'And where did her family come from?'

'I am asking myself what all this can be leading up to. Am I perhaps a suspect in the murder of Miss Bystock? Or perhaps my wife is.'

'I only want to know . . . ' Vine gave up and said brutally, 'if she's coloured too.'

Messaoud smiled with pleasure at the corner into which he had driven the sergeant. 'Coloured? What an interesting term. Red perhaps or blue? My wife, Detective Sergeant Vine, is an Afro-Caribbean lady from Trinidad. But she is not on the dole and she has never set foot in this office.'

Eventually Vine was able to extract from the combined Benefit Office staff, at the sacrifice of political correctness on everyone's part, that a total of four of their claimants were black. They were two men and two women and all of them were over thirty years old.

Chapter Fifteen

Did he know, Sheila asked on the phone, that the BNP had put up a candidate for the Kingsmarkham borough by-election?

'But that's next week,' Wexford said, trying to remember who or what the BNP were.

'I know. But I've only just heard about it. They've already got one borough council seat.'

Memory returned. The BNP were the British National Party, committed to a white Britain for the white man. 'That's in East London,' he said. 'It's a bit different out here. It'll be a Tory walkover.'

'Racist attacks in Sussex increased sevenfold last year, Pop. That's fact. You can't dispute statistics.'

'All right, Sheila. You don't suppose I want a bunch of fascists getting on the council, do you?'

'Then you'd better cast your vote for the Liberal Democrat – or Mrs Khoori.'

'She's standing, is she?'

'As an Independent Conservative.'

Wexford told her about his encounters with Anouk Khoori and about the garden party. She wanted to know how Sylvia and Neil were getting on. For the first time for many years Sheila was without a man in her life. This lack seemed to have made her a calmer, sadder woman. She was to be Nora in an Edinburgh Festival production of *A Doll's House*. Would he and Mother think about coming? Wexford thought about Annette and Sojourner and the missing Melanie and said he was afraid not, he was very much afraid not.

Visiting the Akandes for the first time since that scene in the mortuary, he told himself not to be a coward, to face them, he had acted in good faith if carelessly, but for all that he couldn't eat any breakfast. Coffee he could manage but nothing more. Some lines from Montaigne came into his mind: 'There is an old Greek saying that men are tormented not by things themselves but by what they think about them.' Who could tell if he was thinking in the right way?

After the storms of the weekend, warmer less stuffy weather had come back and it was hot today, the air glass-clear, the sky a bright hard blue. Pink and white lilies had opened in the Akandes' front garden. He had been able to smell their funereal scent before he even reached the gate. Laurette Akande came to the door. Wexford said, 'Good morning,' and waited to have it slammed in his face.

Instead, she opened it wider and asked him to come in, though not very graciously. She seemed chastened. The house was quiet. No doubt the son Patrick wasn't up yet – it was only just after eight. The doctor was in the kitchen, standing up by the table, drinking tea out of a mug. He put the mug down, came up to Wexford and for some reason shook hands with him.

'I'm sorry about what happened on Sunday,' he said. 'Obviously it was a genuine mistake on your part. We hoped it wouldn't mean you'd not come and see us any more, didn't we, Letty?'

Laurette Akande shrugged and looked away. Wexford thought he might make it one of his laws – he had a mental catalogue of Wexford's first law, second law, and so on – that if after the first two or three expressions of regret you stop apologizing to someone you have offended, they will soon start apologizing to *you*.

'As a matter of fact,' said Akande, 'oddly enough, it's rather cheered us up. It's given us hope. The fact that this girl wasn't Melanie has really given us grounds for hope that Melanie's still alive. Perhaps you think that's foolish?'

He did, but he wasn't going to say so. They were in the worst position parents could be in, worse than that of those whose child is dead, worse than Sojourner's parents, if she had any. They were the parents whose child has disappeared and who may never know what her end was, what torment she suffered and what was the nature of her death.

'I can only tell you I've no more idea of what may have happened to Melanie than I had two weeks ago. We shall continue to look for her. We shall never give up looking. As for hope . . .'

'A waste of time and energy,' said Laurette harshly. 'Excuse me, I have to go to my work now. Patients don't stop needing nursing just because Sister Akande's lost her daughter.'

'You mustn't mind my wife,' the doctor said after she had left. 'All this is a terrible strain on her.'

'I know.'

'I'm just thankful I've got this quite illogical feeling that Melanie's alive. It may be ridiculous but I could almost say I *know* I'll come home from my rounds one afternoon and find her sitting in there. And she'll have a perfectly reasonable explanation for where she's been.'

Such as what? 'It would be wrong of me to encourage you to hope,' said Wexford, remembering his resolve to treat the Akandes just like anyone else. 'We've no grounds for believing Melanie is still alive.'

226

Akande shook his head. 'Do you know who the . . . the other girl is, the one you thought might be Melanie? I suppose I shouldn't ask, any more than you'd ask me about a patient.'

'I was about to ask you. I was going to ask if you'd ever seen her before.'

'You didn't have much chance, did you? We should have been relieved but we were only angry. I'd never seen her before. Surely it won't be hard to find who she is? After all, there aren't many people like us down here. Only one of my patients is black.'

Whether they were connected or not, this second death inevitably meant that all the possible witnesses in the first case must be questioned again in reference to the second. If one of them had seen Sojourner in any connection, recognized her face, remembered her however tenuously, this might provide the link they were looking for. It might go some way to establishing her identity. The worst scenario he could construct was the one in which Sojourner's body had been brought by car hundreds of miles, perhaps from some northern place where inner-city prostitutes were as likely to be black as white, had no past, certainly no future, and whose disappearance might pass unnoticed.

He found he was once more thinking of her tenderly and the forensic report did nothing to mitigate his tenderness. Mavrikiev established her age as no more than seventeen. Her injuries were frightful. As well as the arm, two ribs were fractured. Bruising to the inner thighs, old, healed lacerations of the genitals indicated some previous violent sexual assault and on more than one occasion. The pathologist calculated that a violent blow of the fist had sent her sprawling and that in her fall she had struck her head on some hard, sharp object. This it was that had caused her death.

Fibres found in the head wound had gone to the lab for analysis. Mavrikiev expressed his opinion that these were wool from a sweater, not from a carpet, but would commit himself no further on this subject which was not his speciality. Wexford read a lab report which confirmed this. The fibres were Shetland wool and mohair, typical components of a knitting yarn. More of this mixture had been found under her fingernails, along with grains of the soil in which she had been buried. But there was no blood under the nails. She had scratched no one in putting up a fight for her life.

Embassies, High Commissions, African countries all had those. It was a line of enquiry and he put Pemberton on to it. Karen Malahyde set up enquiries at the places of education, many of them closed by now, so that meant contacting head teachers, school administrators, college principals and accommodation officers. If Sojourner was only seventeen she might have been still at school. The chances of her having stayed in an hotel immediately prior to her death were slight, but enquiries had to be made at all of them, from the Olive and Dove at one end of the scale to the Glebe Road humblest bed-and-breakfast at the other.

Annette had told her cousin that she had something she ought to tell the police, and Wexford asked himself why she hadn't said those same words to Bruce Snow when he phoned her that same Tuesday evening, the evening before her death. He thought of the relative in Ladyhall Avenue whose existence both Snows denied. And he wondered what a girl as young, as vulnerable and, it seemed, as unwanted as Sojourner could have done to make someone beat her to death. Could he be looking at things back to front? Could the case be, not that Annette had been killed because of what she was told, but that

228

Sojourner was killed because of what Annette said to *her*? Was Annette herself the repository of some secret, unknown to Snow or Jane Winster or Ingrid Pamber?

Meeting Burden outside the Nawab, he said, 'I couldn't face breakfast this morning and now I'm feeling that not unpleasant emptiness which is the silent luncheon gong of the soul.'

'That's P. G. Wodehouse.'

Wexford didn't say anything. This must have been the first time Burden had ever guessed the source of one of his quotations. It was a heart-warming experience, over which the Inspector immediately poured a stream of cold water. He said in the crabbed voice he sometimes used, 'Messaoud's got a West Indian wife.'

'I've got an English wife,' said Wexford inside the restaurant, 'but that doesn't mean she knew Annette Bystock.'

'It's different. You know it's different.'

Wexford hesitated, took a piece of *nan* from the plate in front of him. 'OK, yes, I do know. It is different. I'm sorry. And, incidentally, I'm sorry about yesterday. I shouldn't have spoken to you like that.'

'Forget it.'

'Not in front of Barry I shouldn't. I'm sorry.' Wexford remembered his new law and changed the subject. 'I like Indian breads, don't you?'

'Better than Indians. Sorry, but that fellow Messaoud is really bad news. But I'll go and talk to his wife, shall I?'

The businessman's special they had ordered, the 'Quickie Thali', arrived quite quickly. It consisted of practically everything you thought of as Indian food put round the edge of a big plate with a pile of rice in the middle and a *poppadom* on the side. Wexford poured himself a glass of water.

'I wish that picture we've got didn't make her look so dead, so *long dead*, but it can't be helped. It won't do any harm to show it around in Ladyhall Avenue. We shall try it on the shopkeepers in the High Street and the shopping centres, the supermarket checkouts.'

'The station,' said Burden, and the bus station. Churches?'

'Black people go to church more than white people, so yes – why not?'

'Stowerton Industrial Estate? They'd be glad to have someone go missing up there – wouldn't have to make them redundant. Sorry, a sick joke. It's worth trying, isn't it?'

'Everything's worth trying, Mike.'

Wexford sighed. By 'everything' he hadn't meant talking to every black resident of the British Isles. He had really meant proceeding as they would have if Sojourner had been a white schoolgirl. But he knew suddenly that he couldn't do that, that this wasn't the way, however apparently ethical.

A quick glance at the fax from Myringham Police awaiting him on his desk told him none of the descriptions matched Sojourner's details. The missing women were categorized according to their ethnic origin, but wasn't such classification inevitable in a case such as this? He remembered a conversation he had once had with Superintendent Hanlon of Myringham CID on the subject of political correctness.

'As far as I'm concerned,' Hanlon had said, 'PC means police constable.'

Four women whose forebears were from the Indian sub-continent and an African were on the list. Myringham, with its industry, though now depleted, had attracted far more immigrants than

Kingsmarkham or Stowerton, and its two universities were attended by students from all parts of the world. Melanie Akande was not the only alumna of the former Myringham Polytechnic to have gone missing. Here on the list was Demsie Olish from the Gambia, a sociology student, whose home was in a place call Yarbotendo. One of the Indians, Laxmi Rao, was a graduate student at the University of the South. There had been no sign of her since Christmas but it was known she had not returned home. The Sri Lankan Burden had already mentioned to him as the missing restaurateur. The Pakistani, Naseem Kamar, a widow, had been employed as a seamstress in a garment factory until the company which owned it went into receivership in April. With the loss of her job Mrs Kamar disappeared. Darshan Kumari, Myringham Police were nearly sure, had run off with the son of her husband's best friend. They suspected that Surinder Begh had been killed by her father and uncles for refusing to marry the man of their choice, but they had no evidence to support this theory.

These women's next-of-kin would have to be fetched to the mortuary and try to make an identification. Well, not Mrs Kamar's. She was thirty-six. And the age of Laxmi Rao, twenty-two, was an unpleasant reminder of the mistake he had already made. The most likely candidate was Demsie Olish. She was nineteen, had gone home to the Gambia in April and returned, had been seen by her landlady, by the two other students living in the house, by numerous students in her year at Myringham – and then, after 4 May, was seen no more. It was a week before she was reported as missing. Everyone who knew her thought she must be somewhere else. The drawback to her being Sojourner was her height, which was given as five feet five. Once these women had been eliminated, they would spread the net further afield. . . .

He called a conference at five for a pooling of discoveries and offered up Demsie Olish himself. A girl who had been her friend and whose home was in Yorkshire was coming to look at the body next day. To be on the safe side, if no identification was made, Dilip Kumari would be asked to attempt it. His wife was only eighteen.

Claudine Messaoud had been as helpful as her husband was obstructive. It sounded as if Burden had liked her, which was something of a triumph for race relations. Though she knew of no black woman between sixteen and twenty who might have gone missing, she put Burden on to the church she attended and which was also attended by other black people. These were the Kingsmarkham Baptists. The minister told Burden that most of Kingsmarkham's black families had a representative there, usually a middle-aged woman. Even so, they were few.

'Laurette Akande goes there too,' he said. 'So that only leaves four families. I've seen one of them but they're young and their children are only two and four. I thought Karen might feel like talking to the rest.'

'Karen?' said Wexford, turning to her.

'Sure. I'll do that tonight. But I suspect I've already seen two of them, that is the ones that have kids at the Comprehensive. Two girls of sixteen and a boy of eighteen, all currently at home and available and seen by me.'

'That will leave the Lings, I should think,' said Burden. 'Mark and Mhonum, M,H,O,N,U,M, in Blakeney Road. He's from Hong Kong, runs the Moonflower restaurant, she's black, and the age of their kids isn't known, or if they have any. She's the one who is Dr Akande's only black patient.'

Pemberton had talked to someone at the Gambian High Commission. They were aware of the

232

disappearance of their national, Demsie Olish, and were 'keeping a close eye'. The numerous other African embassies had even less to offer him. He had narrowed down the women on the national register who came closest to matching Sojourner's description to five. Next-of-kin and, failing that – that often did fail – friends, would have to be fetched to Kingsmarkham for the weary work of attempting identification.

Wexford had calculated that, as far as he could tell, eighteen black people lived in Kingsmarkham, perhaps half a dozen more in Pomfret, Stowerton and the villages. That number included the three Akandes, Mhonum Ling, nine people comprising three of the church-going families, the two male clients at the Benefit Office, a mother and son who were the other Kingsmarkham Baptists, Melanie Akande who was one of their female clients, and the sister of one of the Baptists who was the other.

The Epsons, who lived in Stowerton, were the family whose children Sylvia had taken into care. He was black, she was white. A year ago they had gone on holiday to Tenerife, leaving their nine-year-old in charge of their five-year-old. Now it appeared they were away again but when Karen phoned, a child-minder answered. The woman sounded jittery and harassed but knew of no missing black girl aged seventeen.

'Those boys, young men, that hang about outside all the time, I don't suppose it's always the same lot, but the day I went there after we found Annette's body, one of them was black. Dreadlocks and a big knitted cap. We seem to be locating and pigeon-holing every black person in Kingsmarkham, I don't like it but no doubt it has to be, so what about him? Where does he fit in?'

'He wasn't there today,' said Barry, and to Archbold, 'He wasn't there, was he, Ian?'

'I didn't see him. You've got a mother and son on the list – he may be the son.'

'He's probably my eighteen-year-old,' said Karen.

'Not if yours is still at school, he isn't. Not unless he's a full-time truant. He'll have to be found.' Wexford glanced from one to the other, suddenly feeling ages older than any of them. The rest of what he was going to say was on the tip of his tongue, but he said it to himself. It's not so easy, is it? Not all their mothers go to church. Most of them don't stay on at school or go on to further education. As for embassies, we forget, we always forget, that most of these people are British, are in the law as British as we are. They aren't on record, they have no dossiers, no cards of identity. And they slip through the net.

She was very young and though dark, with an olive skin and long black hair, looked fragile. This was Demsie Olish's college friend, Yasmin Gavilon from Harrogate, who seemed uncertain what was expected of her, whose shyness was extreme. Wexford would have preferred someone else to take her in there, but this was a task he couldn't delegate. Still fresh in his mind was what had happened last time. And this girl looked so young, looked far less then her twenty years.

He had explained three times now that what she was to see might not be Demsie, was even very probably not Demsie. She must only look and tell him the truth. But looking down into her trusting puzzled face, so seemingly innocent, so untouched by experience, he very nearly told her to go home, get the next train back, and he would find someone else to look at Sojourner's body.

The smell of formaldehyde was like a gas. The plastic cover was folded back, the sheet withdrawn. Yasmin looked. The expression on her face changed

234

no more than it had done when she was brought into Wexford's office and introduced to him. Then she had murmured, 'Hallo,' and now she murmured, 'No. No, it isn't.' The tone was the same.

Wexford escorted her out. He asked her again. 'No,' she said. 'No, that isn't Demsie,' and then, 'I'm glad it isn't.' She tried to smile, but her face had taken on a greenish pallor, and she said quickly, 'I want to go to the toilet, please.'

When she had been given hot sweet tea and taken away in a car to the station, Dilip Kumari arrived. If Wexford had seen him in the street, had not been told his name or heard his voice, he would have taken him for a Spaniard. Kumari spoke in the sing-song Welsh-sounding but perfect English of the Indian who is Indian-born. He was the assistant manager of the NatWest Bank in Stowerton High Street and he looked all of forty.

'Your wife is very young,' said Wexford.

'Too young for me? Is that what you are saying? You are right. But it didn't seem so at the time.' He was philosophical, fatalistic, almost jaunty. It was quickly apparent he was as certain as he could be, without having seen her, that Sojourner was not Darshan Kumari. 'To the best of my belief, she has run off with a boy of twenty. Of course, if this is she, which I doubt extremely, I will not have the trouble and expense of divorcing her.'

He laughed, perhaps to show Wexford he was not entirely serious. They went inside and Sojourner was once more exhibited. 'No,' he said. 'No, indeed,' and outside once more, 'Better luck next time. Do you happen to know if you can divorce a woman you can't find? Perhaps only after five years, alas and alack. I wonder what the law is on this matter? I shall have to find out.'

Which particular net had she slipped through? The

same one perhaps as the boy with dreadlocks in the coloured cap who wasn't outside the Benefit Office when Wexford got down there ten minutes later. The shaven-headed boy was there, this time in a tee-shirt so faded that the dinosaur on it was a ghost of its former self, and the ponytailed boy in tracksuit pants, chain smoking. And with them was a very short stout boy with golden curls backcombed to make him look taller and a nondescript spotty boy in shorts. But the black boy with dreadlocks wasn't there.

Two sat on the chipped, stained, rough-surfaced balustrade on the right side and two on the left where there was also a small rubbish tip of empty, caved-in coke cans and crushed cigarette packets. The pony-tailed boy was smoking a cigarette he had rolled himself. The spotty boy sat with his feet in a sprawl of cigarette stubs, his toes in the black canvas lace-up boots desultorily making a pattern of circles and loops in the ash. He was chewing the cuticles round his fingernails. His opposite neighbour with the pale dinosaur on his chest, just as Wexford approached, hit on the diverting idea of throwing pieces of gravel, of which he had a handful, at the stack of cans, his aim perhaps being to dislodge the top one and send it rolling into the area below.

He took no notice of Wexford. None of them did. He had to say who he was twice before getting anyone's attention, and then it was the short boy who looked up at him, possibly because he was the only one not otherwise occupied.

'Where's your friend?'

'You what?'

'Where's your friend? The one in the striped hat?' That was one way of not having to identify him by ethnic origin. Wexford told himself for God's sake to stop being needlessly sensitive. 'The black one with the plaits?'

'Don't know what you're talking about.'

'He means Raffy.' A stone found its target, the can wobbled and fell. 'He has to mean Raffy.'

'OK, I do. D'you know where he is?'

No one answered. The smoker smoked, concentrating as if it was a study he was engaged in, involving memory and even powers of deduction. The cuticle-biter bit his cuticles and made more rings with his toes in the smoker's ash. The stone-thrower threw his handful of gravel over his shoulder and produced a packet from which he took a cigarette. Having given Wexford the kind of look one might give a dangerous dog, at present quiescent, the fat golden-haired boy got off the wall and went into the Benefit Office.

'I asked you if you know where he is?'

'Might do,' said the stone-thrower in the dinosaur tee-shirt.

'So?'

'Might know where his mum is.'

'That'll do for a start.'

It was the cuticle-biter who gave him the information. He spoke as if only a madman, living in a self-created world of schizophrenic fantasy, could be ignorant of this fact. 'She sees the little kids across at Thomas Proctor, don't she?'

This sentence, though seemingly obscure, immediately told Wexford, without his having to pause and decipher, that Raffy's mother was the lollipop lady who, at 9.00 am and 3.30 pm, conducted the children who attended the Thomas Proctor Primary School across the road.

He asked the stone-thrower, 'Has he a sister?'

The thin shoulders rose and dropped again.

'A girlfriend?'

They looked at each other and started laughing. The golden-haired boy came out and the cuticle-biter

237

whispered something to him. He too laughed and
the infectious laughter soon had them all convulsed.
Wexford shook his head and walked off the way he
had come.

Chapter Sixteen

A full moon loomed behind the distorted branches of a cherry tree on which the blossoms were an improbable shade of bright pink. This picture, painted on a bamboo scroll, was repeated all round the walls of the Moonflower Takeaway's waiting room. It was the only place he'd ever been to, Wexford had once said, where they kept the radio and the television on at the same time. The clientele, waiting for their fried rice and lemon chicken, never looked at the moon and cherry blossom pictures and they only looked at the television when sport was on.

This lunch time the radio was playing Michelle Wright singing 'Baby, Don't Start With Me', and the television was showing a re-run of *South Pacific*. Karen Malahyde walked into the Moonflower just as Mitzi Gaynor, the fierce competition with the country singer, had started to wash that man right out of her hair. Karen went up to the counter where a woman was dispensing orders as they came through from the back.

It was a semi-open plan arrangement and Mark Ling could be seen in the gleaming steel kitchen as he conjured with half a dozen woks, while his brother stood talking to him and decanting a sack of rice.

Mhonum Ling was a small sturdy woman whose skin was the colour of a coffee bean and whose straightened hair, still faintly crinkled, had the glitter of a seam of coal. Wearing a white coat like a doctor's, she was dispensing foil containers of chow mein and sweet and sour pork to customers whose numbers came up in red neon above her head. It was a bit like a happier version of the Benefit Office, though the Moonflower's clients sat on cane chairs, reading *Today* and *Sporting Life*.

When Karen told her what she wanted, Mhonum Ling beckoned rather peremptorily to her brother-in-law and cocked her head in the direction of the counter. He came at once.

She looked at the picture. 'Who's this?'

'You don't know? You've never seen her before?'

'No way. What she done?'

'Nothing,' said Karen carefully. 'She's done nothing. She's dead. You've not seen anything about it on TV?'

'We got work to do,' said Mhonum Ling proudly. 'We've no time for watching that.' With a long plum-red fingernail, she prodded her brother-in-law, who was gossiping with a customer and had failed to see an order of fried rice and bamboo shoots come up behind him. She gave the clients a severe glance. 'No time for reading papers either.'

'OK, so you don't know her. There's a boy, maybe eighteen, with Rasta hair, always wears one of those floppy cap things, he's the only person that looks like that round here, he's not your son, is he?'

For a moment Karen thought Mhonum was going to say she'd had no time for having children. But, 'Raffy?' she said. 'That sounds like Raffy. Don't forget the fortune cookies, Johnny. They don't like going without their fortune cookies.'

'Is he a relative, then?'

'Raffy?' she said. 'Raffy's my nephew, my sister's son. He left school two years ago but he's never had work. He never will, there aren't the jobs. My sister Oni, she wanted Mark to give him a job here, just a job helping in the kitchen she said, you could do with another pair of hands, but what's the use? We don't need no other two hands and we're not in the charity business, we're not aid workers in Africa.'

Karen asked where Mhonum's sister lived and was given an address. 'But she won't be home, she'll be working. *She's* got work.'

On the chance of finding Raffy at home, Karen went round to Castlegate, Kingsmarkham's only tower block, where Oni and Raffy Johnson lived at number twenty-four. It wasn't much of a tower, a mere eight storeys high, local authority housing which the borough council would have liked to sell off to its tenants, if those tenants had been prepared to buy. Wexford had predicted that soon they would have no option but to pull it down and start afresh. Twenty-four was on the sixth floor and the lift was, as usual, out of order. By the time she got up there Karen was sure Raffy wouldn't be at home. She was right.

What made Wexford think this Raffy could help them? He had no grounds to go on, not the least evidence, just a hunch. You could call it intuition and sometimes, she knew, he intuited spectacularly. She had to have faith and tell herself that if Wexford thought Raffy was worth hunting down because the answer lay with Raffy, it quite possibly did. Sojourner – somehow, in some perhaps tenuous way – was connected to this boy his aunt spoke of so contemptuously.

She got back just as Kashyapa Begh's Jaguar swept on to the forecourt in front of the police station and Wexford asked her to take him into the mortuary. Kashyapa Begh was a shrivelled elderly man with white hair who wore a pinstriped suit and snow-white shirt. The pin in his red silk tie was a large ruby and two small diamonds. He put Karen's back up by asking her why he was being escorted on this serious business by a woman. She said nothing, remembering that in all likelihood this man and his male relatives had murdered a girl to stop her marrying the man of her choice. Glancing at the body with no attempt to conceal his distaste, Kashyapa Begh said in an outraged tone,

'That was a complete waste of my time.'

'I'm sorry about that, Mr Begh. We have to work on a process of elimination.'

'Process of folly,' said Kashyapa Begh and strutted off towards his car.

It was scarcely out of sight before a police car brought Festus Smith, a young Glaswegian, whose seventeen-year-old sister had been missing since March. His reaction to the body was much the same as Begh's, though he didn't say travelling 400 miles to see it had been a waste of his time. After him came Mary Sheerman from Nottingham, mother of a missing daughter. Carina Sheerman had disappeared on her way home from work on a Friday in June. She was sixteen and she had gone missing once before just before her fourteenth birthday, but she wasn't the dead girl in the mortuary.

On his way to see Carolyn Snow, Wexford told himself that Sojourner was a local girl, she had lived within the town or its environs. It was not that she had slipped through a net but that her disappearance had never been reported. Because it wasn't known? Or because whoever would know wanted to keep her absence concealed, as they had once wanted to conceal her existence?

Carolyn Snow was in the back garden, sitting on a striped sun lounger and reading just the sort of example of modern fiction from which, he had told Burden, her knowledge of obscenities derived. It was

Joel who took him out there. Wexford thought it a long time since he had seen such a look of desperate bewildered misery on an adolescent's face.

Carolyn Snow barely looked up. 'Yes?' she said. 'What is it now?'

'I thought I would give you an opportunity to tell the truth at last, Mrs Snow.'

'I don't know what you're talking about.'

Another of Wexford's laws was that no truthful person ever makes this remark. It is exclusively the province of liars.

'I, however, know very well that you weren't telling me the truth when you said your husband went out in the evening on July the seventh. I know he was here all the evening. But you told me he went out and, moreover, you encouraged your son, a boy of fourteen, to support you in this lie.'

She laid the book face down on the seat beside her. Wexford remained standing. She looked up at him and a faint flush came into her face. The twitch of her lips was almost a smile.

'Well, Mrs Snow?'

'Oh, so what?' she said. 'To hell with it. I've given him a few sleepless nights, haven't I? I've punished him. Of course he was at home that evening. It was just a joke saying he wasn't, and it was pretty easy too to fool everyone. I told Joel all the details of what he'd done *and* I told him about that Diana, and he would have done anything to support me. There are *some* people who care about me, you know.' Her smile was a real one this time, a broad, sunny, slightly mad, smile. 'He's in an awful state, he really thinks he could be done for murdering that bitch.'

'He won't be,' said Wexford. 'It's you I'll be charging with wasting police time.'

He had made himself Australian and already had a

marked Australian accent. Vine had scarcely shaken hands with him, had said no more than, 'Good morning, Mr Colegate,' before the man was off on a diatribe against the Royal Family and the virtues of republicanism.

His mother, whose house in Pomfret this was, put her head round the door to ask Vine if he would like tea. Stephen Colegate said, not tea, please, what was wrong with coffee, for God's sake?

'Nothing for me,' said Vine.

Two children hurtled into the room with a Scottie dog at their heels. They jumped on to the sofa, arms up, screaming. Colegate looked at them with satisfaction. 'My daughters,' he said. 'I got married again in Melbourne. Wife couldn't come, she's got a high-powered job. But I'd made a promise to my mother I'd make it to the UK this year and when I say something I stick to it. Take the doggie in the yard, Bonita.'

'So you didn't come over for your former wife's funeral?'

'Good God, no. When I got shut of Annette that was for keeps.' He gave a loud laugh. 'In life, in death and beyond the grave.'

It occurred to Vine that Annette Bystock had had an unfortunate taste in men. The two little girls leapt off the sofa and fled, the younger aiming a kick at the dog as they passed it.

'When did you arrive in this country, Mr Colegate?'

'Now why the hell would *I* kill Annette?'

'If you would just tell me when you got here, sir.'

'Oh, sure. I've nothing to hide. It was last Saturday. I came on Qantas, wouldn't touch a Pom airline with a six-foot pole, rented a car at Heathrow, the kids slept all the way. I can prove all this. You want to see my air ticket?'

'That won't be necessary,' said Vine and he showed him Sojourner's picture but it was clear from the indifferent glance Colegate gave it that he had never seen her before. The coffee came, brought by an apprehensive woman who was unused to making it.

Stephen Colegate said, 'I never got here till Saturday, did I, Mum?'

'More's the pity. You told me you were coming on the sixth, I still don't know why you changed your mind.'

'I *told* you. Something came up and I couldn't get away. If you say that sort of thing he'll think I came over earlier and hid out somewhere so as I could throttle Annette.'

Mrs Colegate gave a little shrill scream. 'Oh, Stevie!' She drew breath while her son, wrinkling his nose, skimmed floating grains off the surface of the thin brown liquid in his cup. 'I know it's wrong speaking ill of the dead,' she said, and was still doing so, dismembering Annette's character and, by extension, that of her parents, when Vine quietly took his leave.

It was far from usual practice in Kingsmarkham local elections to display posters with photographs of the candidate on them. That's because they're so ugly, Dora had said uncharitably, and Wexford had to agree. The bull-necked, red-faced representative of the British National Party, with his head of grey stubble and small piggy eyes, was no beauty, and the vulture-faced Lib Dem with beaky nose and hooded eyes not much better. Anouk Khoori, on the other hand, in most people's opinion, would be an ornament to any office she might hold and her poster the best advertisement she could have contrived for herself.

Wexford paused to look at the one displayed on a hoarding in Glebe Road. It was all photograph but for her name and her political status. She smiled down at him and judicious air-brushing had removed the lines such smiling must have created. For the photograph her hair had been done in the ringleted mode. Her eyes were limpid, sincere, earnest. The Thomas Proctor School would be a polling station next week, and this poster was just near enough to it for that face to linger in the mind.

He was early, but cars were already parked at the pavement, waiting to pick up departing children. It was said to be a good school, the choice of certain affluent parents more likely to have opted for private education. His quarry came round from the side of the school, carrying her stop sign. She was evidently also Karen Malahyde's quarry. By some different route from his, Karen must have been led to this school and this crossing, for he suddenly saw her leave a car he had at first taken for that of a Thomas Proctor parent and begin walking towards the woman who had reached the pavement.

She turned when she saw him. 'Great minds, sir,' she said.

'I hope the great minds think wisely as well as alike, Karen. Her son's called Raffy. Do you know the surname?'

'Johnson. She's Oni Johnson.' She risked asking the question. 'Why do you think Raffy might identify her?'

He shrugged. 'We've no more reasons to think Raffy knew her than that old villian Begh did. Or Dr Akande, come to that. It may be because I think of them both as . . . well, outcasts. Expendable people that no one cares much about.'

'And it's our last chance?'

'There's no such thing as a last chance in our work, Karen.'

The school doors opened and the children started coming out. Most of them were carrying bags and packages as well as satchels. It was their last day until school started again in September. Oni Johnson was a stocky black woman, about forty, her navy skirt tight on her, wearing a day-glo yellow jacket over her white blouse and a navy peaked cap on her head. She stood at the pavement edge like a shepherd who must gather in her flock without a dog to help her. But the children were obedient sheep, they had done this before, they had done it every day.

She looked to the right, to the left, to the right again, and then she marched into the road, holding up her stop sign. The children streamed after her. Wexford noted the youngest Riding child, the girl who had been at the garden party with her brother. Further up the pavement a black-haired girl with gold earrings was hauled into a car driven by a woman that Wexford thought might be Claudine Messaoud. He was seeing black people everywhere these days. That was always the way. This time it was a boy of eight or nine opening the door of a car he recognized as the Epsons' but driven by someone whose face he couldn't see. Not exactly black this child, though, light brown with light brown curly hair, black only in the world's uncompromising categorization.

Oni Johnson held up her hand at the fresh throng of children waiting on the pavement. She walked back to them, taking slow deliberate steps, and back on the kerb, beckoned to the traffic to proceed. The Riding girl jumped into her parents' Range Rover. The car that might have been the Messaouds' passed southwards and a stream of traffic followed it. Wexford went up to Oni Johnson, showed her his warrant card.

'Nothing to worry about, Mrs Johnson. Just

routine. We'd like to talk to your son. Will you be going home when you've finished here?'

Alarm flashed in her eyes. 'My Raffy – what's he done?'

'Nothing, so far as I know. We want to talk to him about something else, some information he may have.'

'All right. I don't know when he be home. He come in for his tea. I be going straight there when I'm done here.' She let a car pass and then, holding up her stop sign, she marched into the road, but this time, Wexford thought, less confidently.

The first of the cars that waited while she shepherded the children over was, he saw, being driven by Jane Winster. She looked at him and looked away. The child sitting next to her was all of sixteen and must have been fetched from some other school, the Comprehensive probably.

He wasn't far from home. A quick cup of tea in his own house, he thought, and then he'd meet Karen at Castlegate. The last car to pass was a Rolls Royce driven by Wael Khoori.

Sylvia was there with her sons, sitting round the kitchen table with Dora. For Ben and Robin this too was the last day of term. 'I'm thinking of doing a training course. It's to be a counsellor in a medical centre.'

'Enlighten me,' said her father.

'They have one at Akande's, Reg.' said Dora. 'Haven't you seen "Counsellor" on the door when you go down the passage to his surgery?'

Robin was temporarily distracted from his video game. 'A counsellor is what they call lawyers in America.'

'Yes, well, it isn't here. I'll have patients referred to me for counselling as a better option than handing

248

out tranquillizers, that's the idea. And don't try to say something else clever, Robin. Just get on with your puzzle.'

'*Ko se wahala*,' said Robin.

Long ago the members of his family had stopped asking Robin any questions about his 'no problems'. Sylvia's theory was that if ignored, he would grow out of it. As phases went, this one had lasted a long time and showed no sign of coming to an end. It was months since parents, grandparents and brother had laughed or commented or enquired but now Wexford said, 'What language is that, Robin?'

'Yoruba.'

'Where do they speak it?'

'In Nigeria,' said Robin. 'Sounds good, don't you think? *Ko se wahala*. Better than *nao problema*, that's practically the same as English.'

'Did you get it from someone at school?' Wexford asked, hopeful but of what he hardly knew.

'Yep. I got it from Oni.' Robin seemed very pleased to have been asked. 'Oni George. She's next to me on the register.'

So Oni was a Nigerian name . . . Raymond Akande was Nigerian. He was suddenly sure, for no good reason but instinct, that Sojourner was too. The other Oni, Oni Johnson, had said she would be home by five. He had a strong feeling, an almost excited intuition that he was on the brink of finding it all out, of finding who Sojourner was, what connection there was between her and Annette and why they had both been killed. The boy was the answer, the boy called Raffy in the coloured cap, who had nothing to do all day but observe, notice, record – or go blindly through his empty days?

Karen was waiting for him when he got to Castlegate at five past. The hoarding outside the block was covered with posters of Anouk Khoori, no fewer than ten of them, pasted up side by side. He and Karen picked their way across the broken concrete forecourt. A dog, or fox, or even, these days, a human being, had torn open one of the black plastic rubbish bags piled by the front entrance and left behind a scattering of chicken bones, takeaway containers, frozen vegetable packets. It had become a lot warmer as the day went on and an almost chemical smell of decay emanated from the bags.

Wexford could remember when a Victorian Gothic house with turrets and crenellations had stood on this spot, not very beautiful, grotesque rather, but interesting. And its garden had been an arboretum of rare trees. All of it went in the sixties and, in spite of universal disapproval, petitions and even a demonstration, Castlegate had been built on the site. Even those who would otherwise have been homeless disliked it. Wexford pushed open the entrance doors and the cracked glass in them rattled.

'The lift's not working,' said Karen.

'Now she tells me. How many flights up is it? If the boy's not home we may as well wait for him here.'

'It's only six flights, sir. But if you'd like me to go up and find out I . . . '

'No, no, of course not. Where are the stairs?'

The walls were concrete, painted cream and peeling, the floor laid with grey composition tiles, crazed by wear to the colour of coal dust. A graffitist had spray-painted 'Gary is a scumbag' on the wall that contained the broken lift.

'They're going to pull the place down,' Karen said as if it was her responsibility to apologize for the shortcomings of Castlegate, for its Inner London-style sleaze and dilapidation. 'Everyone's been rehoused but the Johnsons and one other family. Round here, sir. The stairs are on the left.'

She checked a cry. Her hand flew to her mouth. A split second and Wexford too saw what she had seen.

At the foot of the concrete staircase a woman, or a woman's body, lay spread on the tiles. Her head was in a pool of blood. Oni Johnson had never reached home.

Chapter Seventeen

In the Intensive Care Unit at Stowerton Royal Infirmary, Oni Johnson lay all night between life and death. In that small world she was the responsibility of Sister Laurette Akande, who had been in charge of this ward for the past year. Not all Oni's injuries came from falling downstairs, though it seemed she had fallen and rolled down all six flights. A bruise on her head was on the left side while it was the right which had struck the floor, so there was a policeman stationed outside her door day and night and Wexford was treating the case as one of attempted murder.

Murder, if she died. Laurette Akande told him she doubted if Oni Johnson would survive her injuries. Both legs were broken and the left ankle, there was a fracture of the pelvis, of three ribs and the right radius, but the most serious injury was a depressed skull fracture. Cranial surgery was essential if her life was to be saved and an operation was performed by Mr Algernon Cozens, the neurosurgeon, on Friday afternoon. The boy who had sat by her bed for hours on end, who had sat there staring, unchecked tears trickling down his face, had signed the form of consent with slow deliberation like a robot whose mechanism is wearing out.

'But why was the attack just before we got there?' Karen asked Wexford.

He shook his head.

'Do we know what the weapon was?'

'Bare hands perhaps. Whoever did this waited round the corner at the top of the stairs and when she appeared, struck her a blow in the face with his fist which sent her rolling down those stairs. All he had to do was run down after her, kick her down probably, and make his escape ten minutes before we got there.'

'Bare hands were used on Sojourner,' said Burden. 'I'll never forget that, Mavrikiev telling me how to kill with your fists.'

'Yes. It's the only link we have and it's not much of one.'

'Where was the boy?'

'When all this happened? He never seems to know where he is at any given time. One thing, he wasn't at Castlegate. That crowd that hang about outside the Benefit Office say he was with them for part of the afternoon but they don't know which part. They wouldn't. He drifts about. He begs.'

'He *begs*?'

'They all do, Mike, if they see a likely benefactor. That's what he took me for. I suppose I should be flattered. We were looking for him – remember? – when his mother was taken to hospital and I met him coming along Queen Street towards Castlegate. He stuck out his hand and said, "Got the price of a cup of tea, mate?" When I told him who I was and what had happened I thought he was going to faint.'

Three hours after that he and Raffy Johnson had had their talk. But Raffy had never seen any black girls in Kingsmarkham. 'Only old women,' he told Wexford. How about Melanie Akande, Wexford asked, had he ever seen her?

A curious look, part humiliation, part scorn, came into Raffy's face, and Wexford understood before he spoke that these children of immigrants were already

253

infected with the English disease. Their blackness had not saved them.

'It's like, she's a different class, in't she?' said Raffy. 'Her dad's a doctor and all that.'

Race and poverty and a hierarchical system had condemned him to a lonely celibacy, for it seemed never to have crossed his mind to speak to, let alone try to befriend, a white girl.

'Your mother is from Nigeria, isn't she?'

'Right.'

He looked blankly at Wexford. Raffy had apparently never asked his mother about her native land and no information had been given him unasked. He knew only that she had come here with her sister when they were very young and after her sister had married a Chinese man. Wexford had no interest in the identity of Raffy's father, if indeed the boy knew it. He seemed to know so little, to be without interests or skills, ambition or hope, but to live from day to day, his only wish to stay alive to wander the streets of the town that had given him nothing.

'I asked him,' Wexford said, 'if he knew why anyone would try to kill his mother. I expected indignation, I expected shock. What I didn't expect was a sort of nervous smile. He looked at me as if I was having him on. He was almost embarrassed.'

'But he takes it seriously now?'

'I don't know. I tried to make him understand that someone had attempted to murder his mother. God knows, he must see murder on television every day of his life, but for him telly is fantasy and life is reality – just what they're supposed to be, only we're always being told that young people confuse the two.'

Karen said tentatively, 'The perpetrator couldn't have been confused, could he? Mistaken Oni Johnson for Raffy? It wasn't very light up there.'

'Even if it was dark no one could mistake Oni for her son. He's six inches taller, for one thing. He's as skinny as a rake and she's rather plump. No, it was Oni our killer meant to attack and I haven't the faintest idea why.'

The only other people who lived in Castlegate, a married couple, had been at work at the time. No one had been about in the empty parking areas which surrounded the block. It was as if it had already been abandoned to the demolition squad, the fact that four people still lived in it almost forgotten. Oni Johnson's attacker could hardly have found a more propitious place to attempt a silent secret murder.

Karen's suggestion had its final dismissal next day when someone made a second attempt on Oni Johnson's life.

Archbold was outside her door all night and Pemberton took over from him in the morning. Nobody could have gone in without being seen by them but they had seen only the hospital staff, doctors, nurses, technicians, and Raffy.

It was the staff nurse who told Wexford, a young woman called Stacey Martin. He came into the ward at nine and she met him when he reached the door of Oni's room where Pemberton was already waiting.

'Would you come in here, please?'

She took him into the office with 'Sister' on the door. 'I came on at eight this morning,' she said. 'The night to day changeover is at eight. Sister had already come on. I went straight in to look at Oni and I thought it was funny, the sheet was pulled up over her hand.'

'I don't follow you,' said Wexford.

'It's hot in here, as I expect you've noticed. We keep it hot so patients don't need bedclothes over them. The sheet was covering the back of her hand

255

where the IV line goes in. Well, I pulled it back and the line wasn't going in. It had been taken out and a clip put on to stop it leaking all over the bed.'

He looked at her and saw shock still on her face. 'You say "someone" took it out. Could she have done it herself?'

'Hardly. I mean, I suppose it's just possible . . . but why would she?'

Before he could answer, if he could have answered, the door opened and Laurette Akande came in. She eyed him like a headmistress with a troublesome pupil. He realized for the first time how deeply she disliked him.

'Mr Wexford,' she said in frosty tones. 'Can I help you?'

'You can tell me what goes through the . . . er, drip on Oni's arm?'

'The intravenous line? Drugs. Quite a cocktail of medication. Why do you want to know that? Oh, I see. Staff Nurse Martin's been passing on her ridiculous suspicions, has she?'

'But the line was pulled out, wasn't it, Mrs Akande?'

'Sister. Unfortunately, it was. That is, it *came* out. No harm was done, there was no setback in Mrs Johnson's condition . . . ' She changed her tune abruptly, sending a beaming smile in Stacey Martin's direction, 'thanks to Staff Martin's prompt action.' The tone became mildly satirical. 'We must all be very very grateful to her. Come along now, I'll take you in to see Mrs Johnson.'

She was alone in the room, wearing a white gown, covered only to the waist by a sheet and propped up, not lying flat. One of Raffy's comics was on the bed table but Raffy wasn't there.

'Is she conscious?' Wexford asked. 'Can she talk?'

'She's asleep,' said Laurette Akande.

'Could the boy have done it?'

'Nobody did it, Mr Wexford. Nothing has been done. The IV line came out. It was an unfortunate accident but no harm was done. All right?'

There would be a hospital enquiry, he thought, if he told anyone else of this, if Staff Martin did. It was clear Sister Akande had no intention of telling anyone, for her job would be on the line. And what was the point now?

'I would like to stay here,' he said. 'Inside this room.'

'You can't do that. You've an officer outside, that's the usual procedure.'

'I'll be the best judge of the usual procedure,' he said. 'There are curtains round that bed. If there are things to be done it would be improper for me to see, you can draw the curtains.'

'I've never in all my years of nursing heard of a policeman sitting inside a room in an ICU.'

'There's always a first time,' said Wexford. He forgot about being polite, sensitive to this woman's feelings, he even forgot his terrible blunder in the mortuary. 'I shall create a precedent. If you don't like it you'll have to lump it or I go to Mr Cozens for permission.'

She compressed her lips. She folded her arms and looked down at them, controlling the temper of which he had had a previous sample. Then she advanced a step to the bed and peered closely at Oni Johnson. She agitated the IV line for a second or two, eyed the monitor on the wall and stalked out without looking at him again.

Either he or Burden must stay there, he thought. Barry Vine, perhaps, and Karen Malahyde. No one else. Until she talked and told them what it was she knew she must never be left on her own. He sat down on the uncomfortable chair and after half an hour a nurse he hadn't seen before, a Thai or Malaysian woman, brought him a cup of tea. They drew the curtains round Oni in the late morning and at one o'clock Algernon Cozens came in with a retinue of housemen, registrars, Staff Nurse Martin and Sister Akande.

No one took any notice of Wexford. Laurette Akande must have given some prior explanation for his presence but he would have betted anyone anything it wasn't the correct one. He called Burden on his cellphone and at three the inspector came in to take over, entering the room simultaneously with a very smartly dressed Mhonum Ling. Her tight high-heeled shoes gave her an added four inches and, with her hair elaborately piled on the top of her head, she had become quite a tall woman.

In time-honoured fashion, she had brought grapes, useless to Oni who was still fed intra-venously. She seemed glad to see Burden, it was someone to talk to and share the grapes with, though Burden shook his head when they were offered.

She had no idea, she said, why anyone would want to kill her sister. Like Raffy, she seemed embarrassed by the question, and glossed over it as soon as she could to begin on a catalogue of Oni's misfortunes and mistakes, how ill-luck had dogged her since their arrival in Britain, how she always seemed one of life's victims. She didn't know how her sister managed always to stay so cheerful. Mhonum had no children and perhaps this was why she cited Raffy as the chief of her sister's troubles, a problem since the day he was born – since *before* he was born, since his father disappeared as soon as Oni told him she was pregnant. Raffy had been hopeless at school, had been a chronic truant. He could do nothing, could barely write his name. He would never have a job, would live on benefit all his life. The hard-working and prosperous Mhonum shook her head over Raffy, remarking that the only good thing she could say about him was that he wouldn't hurt a fly.

'Does your sister have any enemies?' Burden asked, rephrasing his question.

Mhonum popped a grape into her mouth. 'Enemies? Oni? She don't even have friends.' She glanced over her shoulder at the sedated woman as she spoke. 'There's only Mark and me and we're busy people. We've a business to run, right?' Her voice went down to a whisper. 'Oni had this boy-friend but he was soon gone, she scared him off. Oh, she was so possessive, you wouldn't believe, want to own him, right? But he run off like Raffy's daddy, it's the same old story all over again.'

'Can you think of any reason why anyone would want to kill Mrs Johnson?'

She licked the tips of her fingers delicately. Burden observed her clothes, what he calculated was five hundred pounds' worth of turquoise silk trouser suit and cream-coloured Bruno Magli shoes. 'No one want to kill her,' she said. 'They just *kill*, a person like that. They're made that way. She was there and they kill, that's all.'

As if he didn't know, as if he needed instruction in that particular field.

Barry Vine took over from Burden in the evening. He brought with him a computer game belonging to his son and a Spanish exercise book. He was learning Spanish when he managed to make it to the evening class. In response to a peremptory summons Wexford drove himself to Stowerton to see the Chief Constable. The traffic was at its worst in the early evening and he found himself in a slow line approaching the roundabout. In his rear mirror he saw the Epsons' pink car behind him but no more than a pale glimmer of the driver's face. It took him all of a further fifteen minutes to get to Freeborn's house.

He had described it to Burden as the only even moderately attractive house in ugly little Stowerton. Once it had been the rectory, a sprawling place with several acres of garden.

'How long is this going to go on, Reg?' Freeborn wanted to know. 'Two girls dead and now this woman at death's door.'

'Oni Johnson is recovering,' Wexford said.

'More by luck than your activities. Come to think of it, she's only in the state she is because of your activities.'

Wexford thought that hard. He could have rejoined that if he and Karen had been less prompt she would soon have died, lying there in her own blood on Castlegate's concrete floor. He didn't. A quite arbitrary date came into his head and he said he would have worked the whole thing out by the end of next week. Just give him a week.

'No one been taking any more mugshots of you, I trust?' Freeborn laughed unpleasantly. 'I'm scared to look in the paper these days.'

Barry sat all night in Oni's room and Wexford took over from him in the morning. Sitting there, he watched a doctor come in and draw the bed curtains, a new staff nurse shake the I V line. How could he tell who meant harm to Oni? How would he know if the injection administered by the surgical registrar was beneficial to Oni – or lethal? All he could do was *be* there and hope the time would soon come when she could talk to him.

Raffy came in at mid-morning, as usual wearing his knitted cap, though it was a hot day and hotter in the ward. He looked at the pictures in his comic, got out his cigarettes and, perhaps realizing smoking would be the ultimate solecism, put them away again. He sat there for half an hour before creeping out. Wexford heard him running down the corridor outside. Karen took over in the afternoon, her arrival timing with Raffy's return. He walked in eating chips out of a greasy paper bag.

'If she comes round, if she talks, let me know at once.'

'Of course I will, sir,' Karen said.

It happened on Sunday while Vine was in the ward. Raffy was the first person Oni's opening eyes alighted on. She put out her hand, secured his and held it. Wexford found them like that, the boy looking puzzled and somewhat at a loss, Oni clutching his long fingers in her plump stubby ones. She smiled at Wexford and she started talking.

Once she had begun, she spoke a lot, about the room she was in, the nurses, the doctors, she spoke to Raffy about the chances of getting a job as a hospital porter. Of what had happened to her at the top of the stairs in Castlegate she had no memory at all.

It was only what he had expected. The mind is kind to the body and allows it to heal without the setbacks painful and terrible memories may induce. But he dared not leave her until she had told him everything she knew. If only she knew what it was she knew! God help her if what she knew seemed to her trivial or insignificant or, worse, she had forgotten it. She had emerged as a cheerful and co-operative woman, willing to talk about herself and her life and her son but whose memory now held two segments of recollections, those of the hospital that went back to her waking in the ward on Saturday, and those of her previous life which ended abruptly

261

as she entered Castlegate on Thursday afternoon, walked past the dysfunctional lift and began to climb the stairs.

'That lift always out of order,' Oni said. 'But, you know, I always hope. Always I say to myself, Oni, I say, maybe today they mend it and up you go, sailing up like a bird. But no way and I have to go on my own two feet. These things are sent to try us, I'm telling myself, and then all go black and the floor come up in my face and I wake up in here.'

'Before you went into the building, can you remember seeing anyone about? Was there anyone about outside?'

'Not a soul. He was up there, wasn't he, waiting to bop me with his great boxer fist.'

'And you've no idea who "he" might be?'

She shook her head under its thick white bandage. Her own phrase 'great boxer fist', which she had used several times, always made her laugh. She had that curious habit, common to Africans and Afro-Caribbeans too but almost incomprehensible to Europeans, of laughing merrily at tragic or terrifying events. Her laughter shook the bed and Wexford looked round, anxious not to alert a nurse who might take Oni's excitement as a sign to terminate their talk for another day.

'Has anyone threatened you? Have you quarrelled with anyone?' His questions elicited giggles, then a casting up of eyes. She looked as her son had looked when asked who would want to kill his mother: embarrassed, suspicious of mockery, determined to treat the situation lightly. Sudden inspiration made Wexford ask,

'Have you had any quarrel or argument with a car driver, someone you've stopped on the crossing?'

It was mad to think of attempting to kill for such a reason, or he would once have thought it mad. Now

262

he knew people did such things. Sane-looking, ordinary men drove the streets of this town and any other, who if reproved by a traffic warden would think nothing of taking savage revenge – especially if it was a woman who had dared upbraid them. Especially if it was a black woman. But there had apparently been no such violent paranoiac in Oni Johnson's past.

Like her sister, she said, 'He's a killer, right? Don't have to have no reason. He kill, he made that way.' And her brisk summing up of man's senseless iniquity brought so much fresh cause for laughter that this time the nurse did come over and say that was quite enough for today.

It was possibly quite enough for ever. Leaving Barry Vine in the ward and walking back to the lift down the corridor, Wexford asked himself if there was anything more to be got out of Oni, or if she and Mhonum Ling could be right and this was a virtually unmotivated attack by some psychopath; someone who took against black residents or women or mothers or dwellers in tower blocks or even just other people. Perhaps it had nothing to do with Raffy, nothing to do with the Benefit Office and Annette, perhaps there was no connection between Oni and Annette or, come to that, Oni and Melanie Akande. Perhaps Raffy had plucked the IV line out himself because it frightened him or he thought Oni was hurt by it or he was merely trying to shake it the way he had seen done by the hospital staff. Weren't most killings, after all, committed from motives incomprehensible to ordinary men or from no apparent motive at all?

He had been so deep in thought that he missed his way but, finding a staircase ahead of him, walked down it. Here, however, he was really lost, in a part of the hospital he had never been before. He had just registered the words, Department of Paediatrics and Diseases of Children, lettered above the open double doors ahead of him, when a door opened on his left and Swithun Riding, his white coat open over a fawn fuzzy sweater, came out of it with a baby in his arms.

Wexford expected to be ignored, but Riding instead gave him a cordial smile and remarked that he was glad to see him, he had intended, next time he did see him, to congratulate him on guessing the correct age of those twins at the garden party.

'My wife told me. So much for *my* expertise, she said. What do you do with the teddy bear, have a childhood regression and cuddle up to it at night?'

Wexford was too interested in Riding's manner with the baby to think up a clever rejoinder. He said merely, 'I gave it away,' and marvelled at the tender way the paediatrician held the child, with such delicacy for one so big, with such gentle firmness, each of his huge hands large enough to contain it like a cradle. And Riding's expression, normally so elevated and arrogant, the lofty look of the proud possessor of superior intellect and physique, grew soft and almost feminine as he looked down into the tiny round face, the wide blue eyes.

'Nothing wrong with him, I hope?' Wexford hazarded.

'Nothing worse than an umbilical hernia and we've seen to that. Not a him, by the way. A lovely little lady. Don't you adore them? Aren't they gorgeous?'

It might have been a woman talking, and the words, uttered in a strong baritone, which should have been grotesque, sounded only charming. Riding was transformed, he was for a moment a 'nice' man. And Wexford felt it would be possible to ask the way out without risking some crushing put-down.

'Oh, back the way you've come and turn left,' said the paediatrician. 'And now I must take this little sweetheart back to Mother or she'll be fretting and no wonder.'

Telling Dora about it later, Wexford was rather surprised to hear it was no surprise to her.

'Sylvia was referred to him with Ben, don't you remember? When Ben broke his arm and had those complications. Oh, it must have been three years ago, soon after the Ridings came here.'

'One judges people on the strength of a single unfortunate encounter. It's a pity but there it is.'

'She said he was wonderful with Ben and Ben had quite a crush on him.'

Three years ago when Sylvia had a job and Neil had a job and Dora complained they never saw them. 'We're not expecting them tonight, I hope. I mean, any of them.'

'No. We're not *expecting* them, for what that's worth. We oughtn't to talk about our child like that, ought we? It's wrong of us. I always think I'm tempting Providence and something awful will happen and then think of the guilt I'll feel.'

Wexford was starting to say that Providence had been tempted enough times by now to have learned how to resist, when the doorbell rang. Sylvia had a key but she also had the sensitivity not to use it when she came unexpectedly. 'I'll go,' he said, thinking on his way to the door of another evening of counsellor-training, job club and polyglot 'no problems'.

But it wasn't Sylvia and family. It was Anouk Khoori.

Again he had to look twice to be sure it was she. Her blonde hair was severely drawn back, her make-up light and she wore the female politician's favoured pearl ear studs. The skirt of her dark blue linen dress came well below the knee. Her manner was simple and disarming. At first it appeared the best, the least pompous technique a woman of her sort and her appearance could have used. She stepped inside without waiting to be asked. 'You'll have guessed. I've come to ask you to vote for me.'

He had guessed but only a matter of seconds before. She reminded him suddenly of Ingrid Pamber, a sophisticated and highly accomplished version of Ingrid. And this was strange because she was far from attractive to him, while Ingrid . . . To his surprise, to his distaste, Anouk Khoori tucked her arm into his and led him through his own house unerringly to where Dora was.

'Now Dora, my dear,' she said. 'I've the whole of this street to do tonight and all the next one – politics is *hard* work – but I've come to you first, the very first, because I feel we three have something special, we're what everyone but the English calls *sympathetic*.'

The look on his wife's face he knew well, the smile, the rapid blinking of her eyes, and then only the smile with lips closed, the lifted head. Pretentiousness evoked it and an assumption of intimacy on the part of virtual strangers. Anouk Khoori's hand on his arm, a beige-coloured hand with purple vein branches, purple varnish on the long nails, lay there, in his fancy like some exotic crustacean. It was as if his arm, immersed in water, had come up with this thing attached to it, this pentapod or tentacled actinia. If he had indeed attracted such a creature while swimming he could have shaken it off. No such recourse was open to him here and his earlier aversion from this woman, his senseless repulsion, returned to him with a shudder.

But she had to sit down and this she could hardly do while clamped to him. Dora offered her a drink, a cup of tea if she preferred. Anouk Khoori, refusing with a smile and an inordinate show of gratitude, launched into her appeal. At first it seemed an exclusively defensive campaign. The idea of fascism, which these days meant racism, coming to a place like Kingsmarkham was horrible in the extreme. She herself was a relative newcomer to the borough but she felt so at home here that it was almost as if she was a natural Kingsmarkhamian, so profound was her sympathy with the hopes and fears of its residents. Racism appalled her and any ideas which might be prevalent of aiming at a white Kingsmarkham. The British Nationalist must be kept off the council at all costs.

'I wouldn't call electing you an action to take "at all costs", Mrs Khoori,' Dora said smoothly. 'I was going to vote for you anyway.'

'I knew it! I knew you'd feel that way. In fact, I said to myself as I came to your door – before going to anyone else, if you remember – I said to myself, I'm wasting my time, they don't need this, they're my supporters already, and then I thought, but *I* need their boost and *they* need . . . well, just to see me! Just to know that I appreciate them and I *care*.'

She turned the full radiance of her smile on Wexford and, unable to resist the flirtatious gesture, lifted one hand and smoothed her sleek sweep of hair. In spite of what she had said, her raised eyebrows and enquiring tilt of the head implied the expectation of a like support from him. But Wexford had no intention of committing himself. The poll was secret and his vote private. He asked her what positive moves she had in mind should she be elected and was rather amused by signs of ignorance.

'Don't worry,' she said. 'The first thing I shall work for will be the demolition of that terrible Castlegate where that poor woman was attacked. And then we shall build good new local authority housing on the site from the proceeds of private sales.'

267

Wexford corrected her gently. 'Local councils' assets from private sales are frozen and look like being so for some time to come.'

'Oh, I ought to know that, I do know it really.' She was not a whit put out. 'I can see I've a lot of homework to do. But the great thing is to get me there first, don't you agree?'

This Wexford refused to do. Pressed – the hand was back on his arm as he showed her out – he said that he was sure she also really knew his vote was a private matter between himself and his conscience. She entirely agreed, but she was tenacious, she was confrontational, her husband said, it was part of her nature not to shirk the truth, however unpalatable. By this time, Wexford had no idea what she meant but he managed a fairly gracious goodbye with the usual rider of its having been delightful to see her.

Later on she must have given a similar treatment to the Akandes, for when Wexford called on them next morning, Laurette so far unbent as to complain about the candidate's remarking that black people were her special friends and asserting her affinity with them.

'Do you know what she said to me? "My skin is white," she said, "but oh, my soul is black." You've got a nerve, I thought.'

Wexford couldn't help laughing but it was discreet gentle laughter. Mirth had no place in that house. But Laurette seemed to have forgotten their altercation in the matter of the IV line. She was more cordial than he had ever known her, for the first time offering him something to drink. Would he like coffee? Or she could easily make tea.

'Mrs Khoori won't get very far if that's her manifesto,' said the doctor. 'There can't be more than half a dozen of us in the place.'

'Eighteen precisely,' said Wexford. 'That's not families, that's individuals.'

*

He drove himself to the Infirmary and parked his car in the only available space, next to the library van. The car on the other side was a curious purplish colour and this brought to mind the Epsons' car. Suddenly Wexford understood what had been teasing the back of his mind since driving to the Chief Constable's house. The pink car behind him was being driven by a white man. He hadn't been able to see his face but he had seen that the man was white. The Epsons were a mixed-race couple – no doubt candidates for Laurette Akande's disapproval – but it was *Fiona Epson who was white and her husband black*. Did that mean anything? Was it significant? He had often remarked that everything was significant in a murder case. . . .

The library service was a private concern run by volunteers and last year Dora had persuaded him to donate to it a dozen of his books which she called 'superfluous'. To his surprise he saw Cookie Dix step down from the driving seat of the library van. It was rather more astonishing that she recognized him.

'Hallo,' she said. 'How are you? Wasn't that a wonderful party at the Khooris? Darling Alexander adored it, he's been quite bearable to live with ever since.'

She spoke as if they were old, intimate friends, and all the details of her no doubt problematic married life common knowledge between them. Wexford asked her if he could help her load the books on to her trolley. Though nearly as tall as he, she looked fragile with her stick limbs, fairy face and stream of black hair.

'You're terribly kind.' She stood back to let Wexford lift the trolley out from the back of the van. 'I hate Monday and Saturday mornings, I really do, but these are the only good works I ever do and if I give

269

them up my life will be one of pure unbridled hedonism.'

Wexford smiled and asked her where she lived. 'Oh, don't you know? I thought everyone knew the house that Dix built. The glass palace with the trees inside? The top of Ashley Grove?'

One of the town's monstrosities, one of the places all the visitors stared at and asked about. He helped her load books on to the trolley, enquired where they came from and who selected them. Oh, she did, all her friends gave her books. He should bear her in mind when next he had a clear-out.

'Everyone thinks of romances and detective stories,' she said as he parted from her inside the entrance, 'but I find horror the most popular.' She gave him a beaming smile. 'Mutilation and cannibalism actually. That's the stuff if you're feeling really low.'

Vine had been with Oni Johnson all night. She was sleeping now and the curtains were drawn round her bed. Wexford said quietly,

'I know you're going off duty but there's just one thing. Three times now Carolyn Snow has told me Snow's former girlfriend was called Diana. If it rings any bells with you, think about it, will you?'

Half an hour after he had taken Vine's place Raffy came in, gave his mother a kiss which woke her up and sat down to look at the pictures in his comic. Today must have been Laurette Akande's day off and the ICU sister was a red-haired Irishwoman. She brought tea which Raffy looked at suspiciously and asked if he could have a coke.

'My goodness, you go down and fetch that for yourself out of the machine, young man. Whatever next!'

'I like him here beside me,' said Oni when Raffy had gone outside, having first helped himself to coins from her purse on the bedside table. 'I like to know what he's doing.' But Wexford remembered her sister's words about Oni's possessiveness. 'What we going to talk about today?'

'You're looking a lot better,' Wexford said. 'I see you've got a smaller bandage.'

'Small bandage for a small brain, huh? Maybe my brain smaller now that doctor been cutting it around?'

'Mrs Johnson, I'll tell you what we're going to talk about today. I want you to think back a few weeks, say three weeks, before last Thursday, and tell me of anything strange that may have happened.'

She looked at him without speaking.

'Anything odd or different at home, at work, anything about your son, any new person you met. Don't hurry, just think about it. Go back to the beginning of July and try to remember any unusual thing.'

Raffy came back with a can of coke. Someone had switched on the television and he moved his chair closer to it. Oni couldn't reach his hand. She let hers rest on his arm. She said to Wexford, 'You mean, like someone talking to me at the crossing? Like coming to the front door? Like seeing a stranger?'

'All that,' said Wexford. 'Anything.'

'There was someone draw a thing on our door but Raffy clean it off. Like a cross with turning corners.'

'A swastika.'

'That was the day the Job Centre had a job for Raffy and he go for the interview but it was no go. Then Mhonum, my sister, she had her birthday, she forty-two, though she don't look it, and we go to Moonflower for birthday dinner. I got another job – you know that? School cleaner, three times a week. There was one day I'm cleaning and I find a ten pound note, they get lot of pocket money these kids, and I hand it in to the teacher. Thought I might get a reward but no way. These things are sent to try us, you know? This the kind of thing you want?'

'Exactly the kind of thing,' said Wexford, though he had hoped for something more illuminating.

'This is all the start of July, right? On Sunday the lady come to the door, lady with long blonde hair, saying you vote for me in council elections, but I say maybe, I don't know, I think about it. Though maybe that was the next Sunday. It was a Monday the day after, I know that, what was the date of the first Monday?'

'July the fifth?'

Raffy was laughing at something on the television. He put his empty coke can on the floor. His mother said, 'Come here, Raffy. I like to hold your hand.' The boy shifted his chair a fraction without taking his eyes from the screen. Oni made a grab for his hand and gripped it, though this meant stretching her arm to its fullest extent.

'What happened on that Monday?' said Wexford.

'Not so much. The only one thing was in the afternoon and I am at the crossing. Maybe not that Monday but the next. All I am sure is the day after the election lady come. I thought, pity Raffy not here. He take you there, poor girl, you won't lose your way if Raffy take you.'

Wexford was lost. 'I don't quite follow you, Mrs Johnson.'

'I'm telling you, I stand at the crossing before the children come out of school, I just stand there, and a girl come along and stop in front of me, right on the pavement, right in front of me, and she talk to me in Yoruba. I am so surprise you could knock me over with a feather. I never hear Yoruba in twenty years but from my sister and she too proud for it. But this girl is from Nigeria and she say to me in Yoruba, what way is it to where they give you jobs? *Mo fé mò ibit'ó gbé wà* I want to know where it is.'

272

Chapter Eighteen

Four hours of deep sleep and Barry Vine was up, had taken a cold shower and phoned Wexford. The Chief Inspector said something incomprehensible to him in an African language. The translation was enough to send him straight off to the Benefit Office.

Ingrid Pamber's holiday was over and she had been back at work for two days, at the desk between Osman Messaoud and Hayley Gordon. She turned the blue beam of her eyes on Vine and smiled at him as if he were a departed lover returned from the wars. Deadpan, he showed her the photograph of Sojourner's dead face and a photograph of Oni Johnson that Raffy had managed to produce from the flat in Castlegate. Sojourner meant nothing to her; Oni she recognized.

Vine's indifference to her charms and smiles made her petulant. 'The lollipop lady, isn't she? I'd know her face anywhere. I think she's got it in for me. I only have to be late for work coming down Glebe Road and she's bound to stick that lollipop sign of hers up in front of me.'

'Did Annette know her?'

'Annette? How should I know?'

Ingrid alone of the Benefit Office staff failed to ask what had happened to Oni and why he wanted to know. On the other hand, she was the only one who recognized her. No one, to the best of their recollection, had ever seen Sojourner before. It was Valerie

273

Parker, one of the supervisors, who voiced what the others perhaps had hesitated to express in words.

'I'm afraid all black people look much alike to me.'

Osman Messaoud, passing her on his way to one of the computers, said nastily, 'How peculiar. All whiteys look alike to black people.'

'I wasn't talking to you,' said Valerie.

'No, I don't suppose you were. You keep your racist remarks for like-minded individuals.'

A momentary hesitation – should he stand up and be counted? Should he hotly deny the imputation? – and Vine had left them to an argument that was developing into a low-voiced hissing match. Niall Clark, the other supervisor, a would-be sociologist, said, 'I don't think white people do know black people in a society like this. I mean, in a place like Kingsmarkham, a country town. After all, up until about ten years ago there weren't any black people here. You'd turn round and stare if you saw one in the street. When I was at school there weren't any black pupils. I doubt if we've got more than three or four blacks signing on here now.'

Valerie Parker, routed by Messaoud and rather pink in the face, said, 'What was her name?'

'I wish I knew.'

'I mean we could try checking with the computer if we knew her name. I mean, there are probably hundreds with the same name but we could . . . '

'I don't know her name,' Vine said, and he had a feeling he was never going to find out.

Even without a name, it should be easy to identify and locate a lost black girl in a town like Kingsmarkham where whites overwhelmingly predominated, but it wasn't. She had been directed to this place, presumably she started on her way to this place, but somewhere along the line she had vanished. Or she had reached here but no one had noticed her. Privately, Vine thought she had never got here, he would want to know more from Oni Johnson before he pursued this line. On his way to the door he passed the booth where Peter Stanton was advising a new claimant and he saw that the claimant was Diana Graddon.

Until now he hadn't made up his mind whether to talk to her or not. It seemed unnecessary, even prurient. Of course Wexford's remark had rung a bell and of course he had thought about it, before falling asleep and from the moment he awoke. But what was it to him, or to any of them, if this woman had once been Snow's girlfriend, and been superseded by Annette Bystock? What was its relevance to this case of two murders and one attempted murder? But now he had seen her Vine sat down on one of the grey chairs next to a plastic pot with its plastic peperomia and waited.

What sort of an impression did that Stanton make on women, eyeing them like that, his eyes rolling? Of course Diana Graddon was quite attractive but Vine had the feeling that all that would ever matter to Stanton was that she was youngish and a woman. He pulled a leaflet called 'Income Support, See If You Are Entitled' out of the rack and read it to pass the time.

It took Burden no more than twenty minutes to arrive at the Infirmary with the photograph of Sojourner. Oni Johnson recognized her at once.

'That's her. That's the girl spoke to me outside Thomas Proctor.'

It must have been July the fifth, Wexford thought. She was dead by the evening. Mavrikiev had said she died at least twelve days before she was found on the seventeenth. Oni Johnson had spoken to her a matter of hours before she died.

275

'I don't suppose she told you her name?' Burden asked.

'She never said her name. Why should she? Never said where she come from, no way. She say to me where she going, to the Job Centre, to get a job. That all she say. *Mo fé mò ibit'ó gbé wà?*

'Can you describe her?'

'Someone been beating her, that I do know. I seen *that* before. Her lip's been cut and her eye, you don't get no bruises like that walking into doors, no way. So I tell her where ESJ is, down the road and right and right again, between Nationwide and Marks and Spencers, and then I say to her, who been beating you?'

'You said that in English or in Yoruba?'

'In Yoruba. And she say to me, *bí ojú kò bá kán ẹ ni, m̀ bá là òràn náà yé ẹ.* I tell you what that mean. "If you are not in a hurry, I would like to explain to you." '

Wexford's heart did a little bounce. 'And did she?'

Oni shook her head vigorously. 'I say, yes, I have the time, the children not coming out for five minutes, ten minutes, yet, but then, when I am saying this, a car pull up right by where I stand, a mother driving a car, right? She come to fetch her child and I say to her, no, you can't park here, you go further down road, and when I am done with all this I turn round but that young girl, she gone.'

'What, gone out of sight?'

'I could see her, long way away, long way off down the road.'

'Tell me what she was wearing.'

'Had a cloth round her head, a kind of a blue cloth. A dress with flowers, white with pink flowers, and shoes like Raffy wear.'

Both policemen looked at Raffy's feet, twisted round the chair legs. Black canvas lace-up half-boots with rubber welt and soles, perhaps the cheapest

276

footwear obtainable in Kingsmarkham's most down-market shoe shop.

'Can you remember which direction she came from, Mrs Johnson?'

'I never see her till she's there, talking in my ear. I don't see her coming from the High Street, so maybe she come from other end. Maybe she come from Glebe Lane end where there's fields. Maybe she drop from helicopter into field, huh?'

'She talked to you in Yoruba,' said Wexford. 'But she could speak English?'

'Oh, sure. Little bit. Like me when I come here. I say to her, you go down there, long way down, and you in High Street, you turn right and after little way right again and there's ESJ between Nationwide and Marks and Spencers. It all English words so I say it in English. And she nods her head like this . . . ' Oni Johnson nodded her bandaged head vigorously, 'and say what I say, down here and right and right again, and here it is between Nationwide and Marks and Spencers. And then I ask her who been beating her.'

'Mrs Johnson, can you remember anything about her manner? The way she was? Was she out of breath? Had she been running? Was she happy or sad? Was she nervous?'

The smile which had come back into Oni's face slowly faded. She frowned a little and nodded again, but less energetically. 'It was like someone is after her,' she said, 'someone chasing after her. She was frightened. But after she gone I watch and the place empty, no one is after her, no one chasing. But I can tell you, she very frightened.'

'We can discount being dropped from a helicopter,' Wexford said in the car. 'Though the idea does have its attractions. She came from somewhere in the neighbourhood, Glebe Road, Glebe Lane, Lichfield Road, Belper Road . . . ' He considered, seeing the topography in his mind's eye, 'Harrow Avenue, Wantage Avenue, Ashley Grove . . . '

'Or across the fields beyond Glebe End.'

'What – from Sewingbury or Mynford?'

'Why not? Neither of them are that far.' Burden considered. 'Bruce Snow lives in Harrow Avenue, or he used to. He was living there on July the fifth.'

'Yes. But if you can think of some reason for Bruce or Carolyn Snow to be chasing a terrified black girl down Glebe Road at three-thirty in the afternoon, you're a better scenario-maker than I am. Mike, this isn't a very big place even now. She could have come from anywhere north of the High Street and that includes your house and mine.'

'And the Akandes,' said Burden.

'Those shoes – is there any point in asking around the shoe shops to see if a black woman bought those sort of shoes recently?'

'It can't do any harm,' said Wexford, 'though she's not likely to have left her name and address on their mailing list, is she?'

'Meanwhile, we've got all this new stuff but we're no nearer knowing who she was, are we?'

'We probably are but we don't know it yet. For instance we know the motive behind the attack on Oni. Someone wanted to stop us getting that information about Sojourner out of her.'

'Then why not do it two weeks ago?' Burden objected.

'Very likely because although he, whoever he is, knew Oni Johnson had that information, he never supposed we would run her to earth. He never imagined we'd get to speak to someone whose tenuous connection with Sojourner was merely that she happened by chance to ask her the way in the street. But last Thursday he realized he was wrong. *He saw Karen and me talking to Oni outside the Thomas Proctor.'*

'He?'

'He or she, or let's say, his or her agent. Someone in the know saw us. The rest was guesswork and he had just about an hour in which to get to Castlegate and wait at the top of those stairs. We're going to do a house-to-house, Mike. We're going to question every householder in Kingsmarkham north of the High Street.'

At the Benefit Office they found themselves asking the same questions that Barry Vine had asked an hour before. But Barry had only conjectured that Sojourner had been there without knowing when; Wexford was almost positive that she had come into the building on Monday, 5 July, no later than four o'clock in the afternoon.

'Looking for work,' he said to Ingrid.

'Aren't they all?' Ingrid turned the blue beam of her eyes on him and lightly lifted her shoulders. 'I *wish* I'd seen her, I really do.' The implication was that she wished it for his sake, so that she could please him. 'But I *would* remember on account of seeing Melanie Akande next day. I'd have thought when I saw Melanie, wow, look at that, how odd, another black girl I've never seen in here before.' She gave him a rueful smile. 'But I didn't see her.'

'She may have lived near you,' Wexford persisted. 'In Glebe Lane or at Glebe End. If you didn't see her in here that day, do you think you ever saw her near where you live? In the street? Looking out of a window? In a shop?'

She looked as if she pitied him. He had this onerous task to perform, this quest to make, this job to do, and she was so sorry . . . If only she could

279

help, if only there was something she could do to make his burden lighter. Her head was a little on one side, a characteristic gesture. He thought how it would be if he were, say, twenty-five again, and there was this girl that he was obliged to keep meeting, a girl who was spoken for in a way, but only in a way, and he wondered how he would have gone about cutting Jeremy Lang out. Not 'if' but 'how', for he was sure he would have attempted it, if only for the bluest eyes on earth. . . .

'I've never seen her in all my life,' Ingrid said and, suddenly brisk again, she pressed the buttons on her machine that would light up the next client's number above their heads.

Deep in thought, Wexford made his way back through the Job Centre area and the free-standing advertising on which potential employers offered what situations were vacant. Most of them gave no names and no locations, stating only pitifully low wages and curious trades, some of which he had never before heard of. He was momentarily distracted and let his eye run down the ranks of cards. In fact, there were few jobs here that anyone, however desperate, would want to apply for and a phrase came into his mind: 'needy nothing trimmed in jollity. . . . ' Inadequate salaries were offered to those willing to care full time for three children under four or combine twenty hours a week assisting in a boarding kennels with keeping house for a family of five.

He didn't know why an advertisement for a children's nanny (no previous experience required) while the parents were abroad on business seemed to ring a bell in his mind. But he knew his intuition was usually sound and he was searching back in his memory, trying to find a link, when he went outside to find Burden.

The boys sitting on the wall outside had already been shown Sojourner's photograph by Barry Vine. 'That other one', was how the short boy with the golden hair described him. The boy with the ponytail seemed to be doing his best to get through his packet of twenty cigarettes by lunchtime, for eleven stubs lay in the ash round his feet. Burden pinned his hopes on their ability now to be more specific.

'On a Monday afternoon,' he said. 'The first Monday of July. At about four.'

The shaven-headed boy with the range of tee-shirts – he was in a faded red one today with Michael Jackson's face on it – looked at the photograph and, armed with these new details, said as if squeezing the statement out, as if it was the result of tremendous intellectual effort, 'I might've.'

'You might have seen her? You might have seen her go into the Benefit Office?'

'The other one asked me that. I don't mean that. I said I never see her go in there.'

Wexford said quickly, 'But you did see her.'

A glance at ponytail and, 'What d'you reckon, Danny? It's a long time back.'

'I never seen her, man,' said Danny, stubbing out his cigarette and coughing. With nothing to do with his hands, he began picking at the skin round his fingernails.

The boy with the golden hair said, 'I never seen her neither. D'you reckon you saw her, Rossy?'

'I might've,' said the one in the tee-shirt. 'I might've seen her across the road. Standing over there looking. There was me and Danny and Gary and a couple of other kids, don't know what they call them, we was all on the steps like now, only more of us, and she was over there looking.'

He had said so before. Burden remembered now. In the early days of the hunt for Melanie Akande, he had mentioned seeing a black girl on the Monday. 'And that was on July the fifth in the afternoon?' he asked, full of hope.

But if it had been that Monday he had now forgotten. 'Don't know about that, don't know the day or the *time*. It was hot, I do know that. I took me top off to get a bit of sun and this old bat come along and says to me, that's the way to get skin cancer, young man. I told her what she could do, silly old cow.'

'The girl on the other side, do you think she wanted to go into the Benefit Office?'

Danny spoke while still picking bits of his cuticles, 'If she'd wanted to, why'd she never cross the road? She'd only to cross the road.'

'But you didn't see her, did you?' Burden asked.

'Me? No, I never see her. But it stands to reason, she'd only to cross the road.'

'She never did,' said Rossy, and losing interest, 'Give us one of your fags, Dan.'

Half an hour before, standing on the same spot, Diana Graddon had said to Vine, 'Do you mind if I smoke?' They were about to get into his car.

'I'd rather you waited till we've got you home.'

She shrugged and compressed her lips. He was fascinated by her resemblance to Annette Bystock. They might have been sisters. This woman was the younger by a few years and she was slimmer than Annette, less voluptuous, but they had the same dark curly hair, similar bold features, big mouth, strong nose and round dark eyes, only Annette's had been brown and this woman's were a bluish-grey.

Asked about Snow, she had made no attempt to deny the relationship, though she showed considerable surprise. 'It was ten years ago!'

'D'you mind telling me if it was you introduced him to Annette Bystock?'

282

Surprise was renewed. She was incredulous. 'How could you possibly know?'

Vine, of course, was well-practised in parrying such enquiries. 'The relationship hadn't lasted long, I'd guess.'

'A year,' said Diana Graddon. 'I found out he'd got children. The youngest was only three. Funny, how it all comes back. I haven't thought about any of this for years.'

'But you didn't split up then?'

'We started having rows. Look, I was only twenty-five and I didn't see why I should settle for him sneaking round for an hour in the evening and then not hearing a word for a week and then a phone call and another bang-bang, thank you very much, sir. He did take me out but only once in a blue moon. I didn't want him permanently either, I mean I wasn't thinking marriage or anything like that. I was young but I wasn't daft. I could just envisage what that'd be, living with a guy who'd got three kids and a wife to keep and a possessive wife by all accounts.' She drew breath and Vine, drawing up outside the house in Ladyhall Road, was wondering how much more of this he wanted to hear when she said, 'He came round one evening when Annette was there. Oh, I knew he'd come, he always phoned first, but I thought, so what? We'll have a *social* evening for once, we'll actually manage to meet without having sex, see what he thinks about that, though I could imagine. Funny how it all comes back, isn't it? Annette didn't know who he was or . . . well, what we were to each other, if you see what I mean.' An unpleasant thought seemed to strike her. 'You don't mean you think he did it? Killed her, I mean?'

Vine smiled. 'Can we go into the house, Miss Graddon?'

'Oh, yes, sure.' She unlocked the door. Helen

Ringstead appeared not to be at home. They went into the living room. 'I mean,' she said, 'he and Annette, they hardly knew each other. I don't suppose they ever met again.'

So she didn't know . . . he was amused. Odious though Snow might be, you had to hand it to him, he had it all worked out. Vine was going to ask another question but he didn't have to.

'He broke things off soon after that. He told me his wife had found out. Someone she knew had seen us together in a restaurant on one of the *rare* occasions he gave me dinner. This woman had heard him call me Diana. He confessed it all to her, threw himself on her mercy, or so he said.'

'Was it about then that you told Annette there was a flat for sale opposite?'

'It must have been. She'd got divorced a little bit before that. We were still friends then.' Diana Graddon lit the cigarette Vine had denied her in the car. She drew in a long inhalation. 'The fact is, I don't know why we stopped being friends. You'd think we'd have been in and out of each other's houses, living more or less opposite, but we sort of drifted apart, and I think it was her doing. She sort of withdrew into herself. And what's more, I don't think she's had a boyfriend since she split up with Stephen. But I'm just amazed when you say you suspect Bruce.'

He hadn't said it. Vine marvelled at Snow's structure of deceit and double-dealing. However much as a human being he deplored Snow's behaviour, as a man he could not fail to admire his chicanery. He had kept his affair with Diana a secret from Annette and his affair with Annette a secret from Diana, and if he had not succeeded in keeping Diana a secret from his wife he had lulled Carolyn for nine years into the belief that her marriage was inviolable. Had Annette's move to Ladyhall Gardens, opposite Diana, dismayed him? Or had it rather given him the perfect reason for his new relationship to remain on the level of a simple sexual transaction, continually repeated? It was obviously unwise to entertain a girlfriend in a restaurant and indiscreet to go to her home, so he was protected against closer involvement.

What had he said to Annette? Don't be too friendly with Diana, she knows my wife? Or even, she's quite capable of getting in touch with my wife? The best liars stick as close to the truth as mendacity allows.

'I mean, Bruce would have had to know her,' Diana persisted. 'He'd have had to have a motive, wouldn't he? Believe me, I'd have seen him if he'd ever been to see her here and I never did. I mean, I saw everyone Annette knew, I must have seen everyone who ever called there.' She hesitated, coughed a little. The cigarette trembled in her fingers. 'It's funny, but I was sort of fascinated by her. I wonder why that was? I don't know why I'm asking you, you're not a psychologist, but I wonder if a psychologist would say it was because she . . . well, she rejected me really, didn't she?'

Vine, who knew Wexford's methods, waited in silence. He might not be a psychologist but he knew what psychotherapists did. They put the patient or client or whatever on a couch and they listened. A word uttered at the wrong time might be fatal. He would listen, though he didn't know what he was listening for. Nor did Freud, he thought.

'I suppose I resented that. I used to say to myself, who does she think she is, giving me the cold shoulder? I saw her come in with that pretty girl sometimes, the one from the employment office that she worked with, and she was a bit pally with Edwina What's-her-name. But, d'you know, that

285

was all. Well, I saw her cousin there once or twice, a Mrs Winster, I can't remember her first name. Joan, Jean, Jane. No man ever set foot in the place, it was like a nunnery. I mean, the idea of Bruce going in there, it's a laugh really.' She smiled a little at the absurdity of the notion. 'Old Bruce,' she said. 'What's he up to these days? Apart from murdering women he doesn't know?' The smile split into laughter.

Disappointment slumped Vine's shoulders. She had nothing to tell him. It was all over. He thought of revealing all to her in the hope that disbelief, the slow dawning of enlightenment, the subsequent rage, would bring forth revelations. But if there were no revelations to deliver? He said idly, preparing to go,

'You told me you last saw her on the Monday evening?'

'Yes, I was going away to stay with my boyfriend in Pomfret.' She gave a sidelong smile, glad of the opportunity to tell him Snow had a successor. 'It was always a bit awkward, you can imagine, Annette and me, we sort of avoided each other, but we happened to look across the road at the same time. She said hallo and I said hallo and then I remembered I'd left a sweater I wanted behind, so I went back.

'When I came out again – oh, it was no more than two minutes, if that – she'd gone into the flats and there was this girl standing outside the door, the front door of Ladyhall Court, I mean. Well, Annette must have gone straight into her livingroom to open the window. She leaned out and saw the girl and the girl – she was a black girl, incidentally – she went over to the window and said something and that . . . well, that was the last time I ever saw Annette.'

Chapter Nineteen

Which way is it to find work? She had asked Oni Johnson this in an obscure language because there was something about Oni that told her this woman was Nigerian too.

And Sojourner had done what she was told and walked on, southwards to the High Street, fearful of some pursuer, but reaching there unscathed, reaching the Benefit Office too. Instead of going in, she had waited on the other side of the street, staring. Why hadn't she crossed the road, as Rossy suggested, and gone in?

'Men,' said Wexford. 'She was scared of men. Yes, OK, I know Rossy and Danny and Co don't seem very intimidating to us, but neither you nor I is a seventeen-year-old and, I suspect, extremely unsophisticated black girl. She's got an inbuilt fear and distrust of whites anyway. Some man had been beating her and she was going to tell Oni about it but just at that moment those kids had to come out of school.

'Men are more frightening to women than other women are. Yes, they are, Mike, whether you like it or not. And here are this lot, one of them stripped down to nothing but his jeans, sitting there, more of less barring the door. And to crown it all, when a woman comes along and speaks to one of them he shouts at her, gives her some obscene instruction, calls her a silly old cow – or worse. That's what he tells *you* he calls her.'

The house-to-house enquiries had begun. With a street plan of north Kingsmarkham in front of him, Wexford was beginning to see how the town had expanded since first he came there. Estates as big as villages had been built on the northern outskirts. In the inner areas old houses had been pulled down, as in Ladyhill Avenue, and each one replaced by a dozen small ones and yet another block of flats. The ward in which he would vote in the council election had once comprised the whole town; now it was a small section of it. He looked up from the map as Burden said,

'So Sojourner hangs about on the opposite pavement – what for? Just in the hope that they'll go away?'

'Or that someone will come out. She'll have seen clients go in and come out again but no one after about three-thirty, remember. No one signs-on on a Monday and the New Claims Advisers have their last appointment at three-fifteen. So anyone who comes out at four-thirty is going to have to be working there.'

'You're saying she followed Annette home?'

'Why not?'

'You mean it was just chance she picked Annette?'

'Not quite,' said Wexford. 'Most of the other people that work there have cars parked in the car park at the back. They wouldn't come out the front way.'

'Stanton doesn't take his car to work,' Burden objected. 'And nor does Messaoud. His wife has it in the day.'

'They're men. Sojourner wouldn't have followed a man.'

'All right, she follows Annette across the High Street, down Queen Street over there . . .' as if Wexford hadn't a street plan in front of him, 'along

Manor Road and into Ladyhall Gardens. It's then that Diana Graddon sees her. Or, rather, she sees Annette and when she comes out a second time, she sees Sojourner at the front door of Ladyhall Court.'

'To be precise, she sees Annette leaning out of the window talking to Sojourner. Did Annette let her into the house? Did she want to be let in?'

'Annette must have told her that if she wanted work, or wanted the dole, her only course was to come to the Benefit Office next day, the Tuesday. Maybe she said to ask for her and gave her her name but didn't let her in. She wasn't very free about letting people into her flat.'

'So what did Sojourner say that made Annette wonder if she should tell the police?'

'You think that's what it was? It was Sojourner that told her that, whatever it was? This was twenty-four hours, more than twenty-four hours, before she spoke on the phone to cousin Jane on Tuesday evening.'

'I know, Mike. I'm guessing. But look at it this way. Sojourner said something to Annette that she didn't like or made her suspicious. What it was we don't know, very likely what she was going to tell Oni but never did, something about the man who beat her and maybe where he lived. However, we do know that Sojourner never took the advice Annette presumably gave her, to come to the Benefit Office next day.

'When she didn't come, don't you think it likely that Annette became uneasy? Perhaps she wanted to discuss whatever it was with Sojourner before she took any steps. But by that time Annette was feeling unwell. She went home, went to bed, was ill enough to tell Snow she couldn't see him next day but was still worried enough to pass her worries on to her cousin.

'As to why I think the something the police should know came from Sojourner, well, she *died* that night, didn't she, she was murdered that night. She couldn't go to the Benefit Office because she was dead. And her failure to come must have compounded Annette's fears – only with that virus, believe me, for the time being you're not thinking about anyone but yourself.'

'So on the Monday evening, Annette just sent Sojourner back home, wherever that was?'

'She behaved, no doubt, as anyone would in the circumstances. Probably she didn't give any advice at all beyond telling her to come to the Benefit Office. Unfortunately, tragically, Sojourner had nowhere else to go but home. What happened next we've no idea, but we can make a reasonable guess that someone at home, father, brother, husband even, some male relative, shall we say "punished" her for running away?'

'The person she was afraid was pursuing her?'

'Oh, yes.'

'How did he know about Oni Johnson? How did he know about Annette?'

'She told him, don't you think?'

Burden looked as if he would like to ask why but he didn't. 'You said Sojourner "told him". Told who? Her father? Her brother? Husband? Boyfriend?'

'Husband or boyfriend, it would have to be. We know all the black people here, Mike, we've found them all, we've talked to them. But she may have had a white boyfriend.'

All the while Wexford talked he had been thinking, inescapably, of Dr Akande. It sometimes seemed to him that all roads led back to the Akandes and that, conversely, every route he took he found one or other of the Akandes there. He picked up the phone and asked Pemberton to come up.

'Bill, I want you to get on to Kimberley Pearson's family and find out everything you can about them.'

Pemberton attempted to disguise his incomprehension and failed. 'Zack Nelson's girlfriend,' said Burden.

'Yes. Oh, sure. What, parents, d'you mean? Where are they?'

'I don't know. I haven't the faintest, somewhere within a radius of twenty miles, say. There is, or was, a grandmother. I want to know where she lived and when she died. And Kimberley's not to know. I don't want a hint of this reaching Kimberley.'

With a flash of insight that surprised Wexford and pleased him, Pemberton said, 'Do you reckon Kimberley's life's in danger, sir? Is she the next girl he's after?'

Wexford said slowly, 'Not if we keep away from her. Not if he – or she – thinks we've done with her. I'm going back to the hospital. I want to talk to Oni again.' He added, remembering what Freeborn had accused him of, 'But I'm not even going to drive down Stowerton High Street, I'll go the long way round.'

Mhonum Ling was there. If there were to be a competition for the most over-dressed woman in Kingsmarkham, Wexford thought, it would be hard choosing between Oni's sister and Anouk Khoori. Mhonum's ankle-length pink skirt was just short enough to disclose her jewelled sandals. The tee-shirt she wore was a far cry from Danny's; it had sequins on it. He held Oni's hand for a moment and she gave him one of her tremendous smiles.

'I'm going to take you through all that again,' he said.

She made a face of mock-horror but he thought she enjoyed it really. Raffy walked in, carrying a ghetto-blaster, mercifully not on. Wexford he was used to by now but he gave his aunt the sort of look more likely to be on the face of someone who has seen a lioness on the loose. When Oni repeated the things Sojourner had said in Yoruba, Mhonum shrugged her shoulders and turned her head to look Raffy up and down.

'When she'd gone out of sight,' Wexford said, 'did the children start coming out? Or did a lot of parents arrive before that?'

'Mothers and father, mostly mothers, they start coming five, ten minutes before children come out. That one in the car parked right by my feet, the one I moved on, she was the first. Then all the others start coming.'

'I'd like you to think carefully about this, Mrs Johnson. Did you get the impression she ran away from you because she was afraid of *one of the parents seeing her*?'

Oni Johnson tried to remember. She screwed her eyes tight shut with the effort of concentration. Mhonum Ling said, 'You know her name yet?'

'Not yet, Mrs Ling.'

'What you bring that radio in here for, Raffy?' she said to her nephew and, without waiting for an answer, 'You go down the drinks machine and fetch a Diet Fanta for auntie and one for your mummy.' She produced a handful of change from her pink patent-leather bag. 'And have yourself a coke, good boy, hurry up now.'

Opening her eyes, Oni said, 'No good, I don't know. I never did know. She frightened, she in big hurry, but I don't know what she frightened of.'

He went down the stairs with the silent boy pattering along in front of him. Raffy stopped at the drinks machine, stared hopelessly at the keys and the pictures above them. Diet Coke he could wrest from it. Fanta presented more of a problem. Wexford

292

put out a finger as he passed, tapped the relevant key and walked on out to the car park. At least a hundred cars had arrived since he left his. He was remembering how he had told the Chief Constable and a good many other people besides that he would have this case solved by the end of the week. Early days, though, it was only Tuesday.

Turning out of the hospital gates and into the roundabout, he nearly took the first exit. Then he remembered he had to avoid the High Street and drove round to the third. Perhaps he was being over-scrupulous. No one was following him, the idea was ridiculous, it wasn't as if he intended to stop outside Clifton Court, still less call on Kimberley Pearson, but he took the third exit just the same. He might have saved Oni Johnson's life but he had terribly endangered it first.

This devious route took him along Charteris Road and into Sparta Grove. He hadn't been along that street since the little Epson boys were taken into care, and he had only gone there then to say a few words into the television cameras about parents who went off on holiday and left their children at home unattended. Now he tried to remember which of this three-storey Victorian row was their house. Not a slummy house at all, the Epsons weren't poor, if they didn't want their children with them they could easily have afforded to pay a child-minder.

He was driving slowly. Ahead of him a man came out of one of the houses, closed the front door behind him and got into a pink car parked at the pavement edge. Wexford pulled in and switched off the engine. The man was tall and heavily-built, fair-haired, young, but he had his back to him and Wexford couldn't see his face. He wasn't Epson. He was too young and Epson was black, a Jamaican.

The car moved off, gathering speed very rapidly,

tearing round the corner into Charteris Road. He had seen that man in that car very recently and he had an idea the circumstances were somehow distasteful or that he wanted to avoid thinking about them. That, no doubt, was the reason he couldn't remember.

He sat there for a moment or two but memory had deserted him. His route home took him through the industrial estate, a stark and deserted place, half the factories boarded-up or to let. A narrow country lane led back on to the Kingsmarkham road and ten minutes later he was in his own house.

The answer to things had sometimes in the past come to him, directly or indirectly, from Sheila; from a remark she made or her latest interest or passion, or something she had given him to read. Whatever it was, it had set him on the right road. He needed her now, a word or two from her, a pointer.

But it was his other daughter visiting him this evening with Ben and Robin, having arranged to meet Neil in her parents' house after his job club session. Her indulgent mother had invited them all to stay for supper. Even as he digested this, Wexford thought how much Sylvia would hate being termed, even in his secret mind, his 'other daughter'. No father ever struggled so hard not to show the preference he felt and no father, he thought, so signally failed. As soon as he walked in the door he had realized he must resist phoning Sheila while Sylvia was there, or at least while Sylvia was in earshot.

The evening was warm. They sat outside, a ring of chairs round the sunshade table, and Sylvia's suggestion that they eat there was met, inevitably, by a version of her older son's favourite phrase.

'*Mushk eler.*'

'Well, it's a problem for me,' said Wexford. 'You know I can't stand al fresco eating, all those mosquitos. It's the same with picnics.'

The boys and their grandmother immediately engaged in argument about the merits and demerits of picnics. Sylvia, ignoring them, lay back in her chair, half-closed her eyes, and began to talk about her counselling course, how completely different was the approach from when she did her social sciences degree, how the emphasis here was on people, on human interaction, on enabling and personal interdependence . . . It was ridiculous, Wexford thought, the way he was behaving, afraid to phone Sheila secretly, lest she had her answering machine on and would therefore ring back after an hour or two. How soon would Sylvia and family go? Not for hours. Neil wasn't expected for an hour.

Dora took the boys with her into the house. Robin was to lay the table, she said. The expected response didn't come, presumably because it *was* a problem.

'Wouldn't you like a drink?' he said to Sylvia, as much to stem the tide as because he wanted one.

'Sparkling water. Mostly we'll be dealing with depression and anxiety states. But there's always a lot of domestic violence and you have to bear in mind the secrecy imperative in creating confidence in the client. We shall counsel each other, I mean, of course, initially . . .'

When Wexford came back with her water and his beer she was still talking. She seemed to have reached the physical abuse by strong people of other, weaker people. Her eyes were shut now and she was staring up through her closed lids at the blue summer sky.

'Why do they do it?' said Wexford.

He had interrupted her in mid-flow. She opened her eyes and looked at him. 'Do what?'

'Men beat up their wives, people mistreat their kids.'

'Are you really asking me? Do you really want to know?'

A pang, a guilty wince, was the effect on him of these questions. It was as if she was amazed that he wanted to know anything she could tell him. She would talk, she would assert herself, on and on, relentlessly, but not to entertain or inform. To get back at him, to show him. Now he sounded as if he really wanted to know. Her tone was one of incredulity – you're asking *me*?

What he really wanted was to find a way of escape and phone Sheila. Instead he said, 'I'd like to know.'

She didn't answer directly. 'Have you ever heard of Benjamin Rush?'

'I don't think so.'

'He was the Dean of the Medical School at the University of Pennsylvania. Oh, nearly two hundred years ago. He's known as the father of American psychiatry. Of course there was slavery then in the United States. One of the things Rush maintained was that all crimes are diseases and he thought not believing in God was a mental disease.'

'So what's he got to do with physical abuse?'

'Well, I bet you've never heard of this before, Dad. Rush made up something called a Theory of Negritude. He believed being black was a disease. Black people suffered from congenital leprosy but in such a mild form that pigmentation was its only symptom. Do you see what holding a theory like that means? It justifies sexual segregation and social maltreatment. It means you've got a reason for ill-treating people.'

'Wait a minute,' said Wexford. 'What you're saying is that if someone is an object of pity you're going to want to use physical violence against them? That seems cock-eyed. It's the contrary of everything social morals teach us.'

'No, listen. You *make* someone into an object of – not so much of pity as of weakness, sickness, stupidity, ineffectiveness, do you see what I mean? You hit them for their stupidity and their inability to respond, and when you've hurt them, marked them, they're even more sick and ugly, aren't they? And they're afraid and cringing too. Oh, I know this isn't very pleasant, but you did ask.'

'Go on,' he said.

'So you've got a frightened, stupid, even disabled person, silenced, made ugly, and what can you do with someone like that, someone who's unworthy of being treated well? You treat them badly because that's what they deserve. One thinks of poor little kids that no one can love because they're dirty, covered in snot and shit, and always screaming. So you beat them because they're hateful, they're low, they're *sub-human*. That's all they're good for, being hit, being reduced even further.'

He was silent. She mistook his silence for shock, not at the content of what she had said but because she had said it, and quick to make amends, said, 'Dad, it's horrible, I know, but I do have to know about these things, I have to try to understand something about the doer as well as the done-to.'

'No,' he said, 'It's not that. I know that. I'm a policeman, remember? There was something else you said, it struck a chord. One word. I can't remember . . .'

' "Sub-human"? "Ineffectiveness?" '

'No. It'll come to me.' He got up. 'Thank you, Sylvia. You don't know how you've helped me.' Her look went to his heart. For a moment she looked like her son Ben. He bent over and kissed her forehead. 'I know what it was,' he said, half to himself. 'It's come back to me.'

Upstairs, at his bedside as yet unread, were the leaflets and brochures Sheila had sent him, the literature of her latest passion. He would read them as soon as Sylvia had gone. But he had also remembered something about the man who came out of the Epsons' and had been driving the Epsons' car. He hadn't seen his face. And he hadn't seen the face of whoever was driving that car when a little boy had come out of the Thomas Proctor gates and got into it.

Wexford could see that little boy quite clearly, a brown boy with brown curly hair, who could have been that man's son but only if his mother was black and only if he had fathered him when he was a boy himself.

Was this the man Sojourner had been running to escape a fortnight before?

No, Wexford thought, that wasn't the way it was at all. . . .

Chapter Twenty

The usual call on the Akandes must be postponed. If Wexford's guess was right, he would be in no mood to face them with this at the forefront of his mind. And what was there to say? Even the common pleasantries, weather commentary, enquiries after their health, would come stiltedly. He thought of how he had tried to prepare them, telling them to abandon hope, and he remembered Akande's optimism, flaring one day, dying the next.

He drove himself to work, passing the Akandes' house but keeping his eyes on the road ahead. Reports awaited him on the progress of the house-to-house enquiries but they were negative, they had yielded nothing apart from racism among unlikely householders and an unsuspected liberal attitude where prejudice was most anticipated. When it came to human beings, there was no knowing. Malahyde, Pemberton, Archbold and Donaldson would keep on all day, ringing doorbells, showing the photograph, asking. If Kingsmarkham produced nothing, they would begin on the villages, Mynford, Myfleet, Cheriton.

Wexford took Barry Vine with him to Stowerton. They avoided the High Street and went by way of Waterford Avenue where the Chief Constable's house was. The neighbourhoods changed very quickly in Stowerton and it was a long stone's throw to Sparta Grove. Wexford smiled to himself as they passed the house, thinking how near Freeborn had been to it all, this . . . well, conspiracy, wasn't it? – going on under his nose.

The pink car was parked in the road, back where he had first seen it the night before. In the broad daylight of a sunny morning it looked very dirty. A finger graffitist had written 'Clean me now' in the dust on its boot lid. Not a window in the house was open. It seemed empty – but the car was there.

The doorbell wasn't working. Vine banged smartly on the knocker and remarked, looking up at the closed windows, that nine in the morning was early for some people. He knocked again and was about to bellow through the letter box when the sash of an upstairs window was raised and the man whose back Wexford had seen the evening before and had been unable to identify, put his head out. It was Christopher Riding.

'Police,' said Wexford. 'Remember me?'

'Should I?'

'Chief Inspector Wexford, Kingsmarkham CID. Come down and let us in, please.'

They waited a long time. Scuffling noises came from inside and the sound of something made of glass being dropped and broken. A string of muffled curses was followed by a dull thump. Vine suggested wistfully that it would be a good idea to kick the door down.

'No, here he comes.'

The door was opened cautiously. A child of about four put his head round it and giggled. He was peremptorily pulled back and the man whose face had appeared at the window stood there. He wore shorts and a heavy, very dirty, Aran sweater. His legs and feet were bare.

'What d'you want?'

'To come in.'

'You'll need a warrant for that,' said Christopher Riding. 'You're not coming in here without one. It's not my property.'

'No, it's the property of Mr and Mrs Epson. Where are they this time? Lanzarote?'

He was a little disconcerted, enough to step back. Wexford, who had the edge on him as far as height went, if not youth, gave him a shove with his elbow and pushed past him into the house. Vine followed, shaking off Riding's detaining hand. The child began to wail.

It was a house of numerous little rooms, a steep staircase climbing up its centre. In the middle of the staircase stood an older child, a grubby soft toy trailing from one hand. It was the brown boy with brown curly hair Wexford had seen come out of Thomas Proctor. When he saw Wexford he turned tail and fled upstairs. The sound of a radio came from behind a closed door. Wexford opened it quietly. On all-fours on the floor, a girl was picking up broken glass – no doubt the remains of the object which they had heard dropped – and putting the pieces on to a folded newspaper. She turned her head at the sound of his careful cough, sprang to her feet and let out a cry.

'Good morning,' Wexford said. 'Melanie Akande, I presume?'

His coolness belied his true feelings. Extreme relief at finding her alive and well and living in Stowerton fought in his mind with anger and a kind of appalled fear for her parents. Suppose Sheila had done this? How would he have felt if his daughter had done this?

Christopher Riding leant against the fireplace, a cynical half-amused expression on his face. Having looked at first as if she was going to cry, Melanie had

301

controlled her tears and now sat in an attitude of despair. In her surprise she had cut her finger on one of the pieces of glass and it bled unheeded. Blood trickled on to her bare feet. From upstairs one of the Epson children began to wail.

'Go and see what he wants, will you?' Melanie spoke to Riding as if they had been married for years and not too happily.

'Christ.'

Riding shrugged his shoulders with great drama. The younger boy got hold of his jeans and hung on, burying his face in the back of the man's knees. Christopher walked off, dragging the child behind him, and banged the door.

'Where are Mr and Mrs Epson?' Wexford said.

'Sicily. They're coming back tonight.'

'And what were you planning to do?'

She sighed. 'I don't know.' The sight of her finger brought the tears back once more to her eyes. She started wrapping a tissue round it. 'See if they'll keep me on, I suppose. I don't know, God knows, sleep on the streets.'

She was dressed exactly as, according to the missing person description, she had been on the day she vanished, in jeans, a white shirt and a long embroidered waistcoat. The look on her face was one of utter disenchantment with the life she found herself in.

'Do you want to tell me about it here or shall we go to the police station?'

'I can't leave the kids, can I?'

Wexford thought about it. There was a funny side which he might come to see later on. Of course she couldn't leave the kids. The Epson children were on the Social Services register and had been since their parents were given suspended prison sentences for leaving them in the house alone for a week. But he didn't fancy fetching out a child care officer, getting a care order made, setting the whole machinery in motion for the sake of removing Melanie Akande for one day. No doubt the Epsons, considerably frightened by what had happened last time, had more or less properly engaged her to look after their two sons.

'What did you do? Answer an ad in the Job Centre?'

Melanie nodded. 'Mrs Epson, she said to call her Fiona, she was in there. I'd been talking to the New Claims Officer and when I was done I sort of wandered over into the jobs part and there was this woman standing by the board that advertises jobs for nannies and minders and whatever. I'd never thought of that sort of work but I was looking at it and she said did I want to come and work for her for three weeks.

'Well, I knew you weren't supposed to go with people who offer you jobs like that but a woman seemed different. I mean, it's because of sexual harassment, isn't it? She said, why not come and see, so I went with her. She had a car in the car park and we went out the side door – that car you saw outside.'

'That's why those boys outside never saw you leave,' said Vine.

'Maybe.' A thought struck her. 'Have my parents been looking for me?'

'The whole country's been looking for you,' said Vine. 'Didn't you see the papers? Didn't you see the telly?'

'The TV broke down and we didn't know who to get to come and see to it. I never saw a paper.'

'Your mother thought at first you were with Euan Sinclair,' said Wexford. 'She *feared* it was possible. Then she thought you were dead. Mrs Epson brought you here, then? Just like that? She didn't ask if you wanted to go home first, if you wanted to fetch your things?'

'They were going away the next day. They'd more or less decided they'd have to take the kids. I can understand they didn't want to. They're *awful* kids.'

'Not surprising, is it?' said Vine, the conscientious father.

Melanie lifted her shoulders. 'I said to Fiona that I could stay if she wanted. I'd got my things with me, you see . . . well, I'd got enough on account of I'd been going to Laurel's. But I didn't want to go there. I had a date with Euan first but I didn't want to meet him, I didn't want to hear any more of his lies. This house and being here was just what I wanted. Anyway, I thought so. I'd earn some money that wasn't a grant or *pocket money* from Dad. I thought I'd be alone and that was what I wanted, to be alone for a bit. But you're not alone with kids.'

'Christopher Riding wasn't with you all the time?'

'I don't know where he was. I didn't know him very well – not then. It was – it was after I'd been here about a week. I was nearly giving up, those kids are so terrible, I had to drive the big one to school, that's why they left me the car, and Chris saw me, he recognized me, and then he – he followed me back here.'

After she had been there about a week, Wexford thought. That would have been the day or the day after he had talked to Christopher Riding and asked him about Melanie. At least he had been telling the truth then.

'He thought it was funny,' Melanie said. 'I mean, the whole set-up. It sort of fascinated him. He stayed a bit.' She looked away. 'I mean, he came and he went. He helped me with the kids. They *are* awful kids.'

'And were you an awful kid, Melanie?' said Vine.

'It's a pretty awful daughter, isn't it, that goes off, disappears, without a word to her parents? Lets them think she's dead? She's been murdered?'

'They couldn't have thought that!'

'Of course they did. What stopped you making one phone call?'

She was silent, looking down at the blood-soaked tissue on her finger. Wexford thought of all the people who must have seen her and who did nothing about it, who did nothing because she was always with two black children they took to be her children. Or saw her with Riding, that they took to be the father of the children with them. Wexford had thought a missing black girl should be easy to find because black people were rare here, but the reverse was true. It was for that very reason that she had failed to be recognized.

'They wouldn't have let me stay here,' Melanie said in a voice not much above a whisper. Christopher, who had come back into the room, got a sidelong unhappy look. 'My mother would have called it being a servant. My father would have come and fetched me home.' Her voice rose and there was a hysterical edge to it. 'You don't know what it's like at home. No one knows.' She gave Christopher a bitter look. 'And I can't get away if I haven't got a job and a–a roof.' She said to Wexford, picking him for some reason, 'Can I talk to you alone? Just for a minute?'

A shattering scream split the air. It came from upstairs but it might have been in the same room. The scream was followed by a violent crash. Melanie shouted, 'Oh God!' and 'Go and see what he's doing, Chris, *please*.'

'Go yourself,' said Christopher, laughing.

'I *can't* go. They want me here.'

'For Christ's sake, I've had enough of this. I don't know what the attraction was in the first place.'

'I do!'

'It's wearing thin now at any rate.'

'I will go,' said Barry Vine in stern admonitory tones.

Wexford said to Melanie, 'We'll go into one of the other rooms.'

A bleak place that no one seemed to use with a dining table and chairs round it and a bicycle in one corner. A green window blind was pulled down to its fullest extent. Wexford motioned the girl to a chair and sat down opposite her.

'What did you want to say to me?'

'I thought of having a baby,' she said, 'just so that the council would give me a place.'

'More likely put you up in one of their famous bed and breakfasts.'

'That would be better than Ollerton Avenue.'

'Really? What's so bad about it?'

She relaxed quite suddenly. She put her elbows on the table and gave him a look that was conspiratorial, secrets-sharing. Her wry smile made her enormously attractive. She was at once pretty and charming. 'You don't know,' she said. 'You don't know what they're really like. You just see the hard-working kindly GP and his beautiful efficient wife. They're fanatics, those two, they're obsessed.'

'In what respect?'

'They're probably better educated than almost anyone in this place. That's for a start. My mother got a science degree before she started nursing and she's just about everything you can be as a nurse, she's got qualifications in *everything*. Medical and psychiatric, you name it, she's got it. When we were kids, Patrick and me, we never saw her, she was off all the time getting more certificates. Our gran and our aunties looked after us. My father may be just a GP but he's a surgeon too, he's a Fellow of the Royal College of

306

Surgeons, he can do all sorts of surgery, not just take out an appendix. He could easily be as good as Chris's dad.'

'So they were ambitious for you?'

'Are you kidding?' said Melanie. 'You know what they call people like them? The Ebony Elite. The black *crème de la crème*. Our futures were all mapped out for us before we were ten. Patrick was to be the great consultant surgeon, a brain surgeon probably – yes, really, that's not funny to them. And it's all right for him, that's what he wants, he's heading that way. But me? I'm not all that bright, I'm just average. I like singing and dancing, so I did my degree in that, but my parents *hated* it because it's what successful black women do, you see. They were glad when I couldn't get a job, they wanted me to go back to college so long as I could live at home. Or I'd be permitted to get office work and study for business management in the evenings *from home*. They talk about careers and training and degrees and promotion *all the time*. And they're too civilized to actually say it, but they're both bursting with pride because they found out that the people who wouldn't live next door to us both left school at sixteen.

'If I got away they thought I'd get back with Euan or someone like him.' She twisted her mouth into a bitter shape. 'And maybe I will now. I can't have a baby if I haven't got a man, can I? I wouldn't let Chris go that far, though that's what he came for, whatever he says. He only fancies me because I'm black. Charming, isn't it? I've had to fight him off.'

'Your parents shouldn't be kept in ignorance any longer. Not for an hour. They've been through a lot. Nothing they've done could justify that. They've suffered intensely, your father has lost weight, he looks an old man, but they've carried on with their work . . .'

'They would.'

'I'll tell them you're safe and then you must see them. Bring the children with you, you haven't much choice.' He thought of the waste of police time and resources, the cost of it all, the misery and pain and abuse, her brother's recall from his Asian journey, his own shame and self-justification. But he relented. Mawkish and sentimental it might be, but he was sorry for her. 'When do the Epsons get home?'

'She said nine or ten.'

'We'll send a car for you at six.' He got up, preparing to leave, but remembered something. 'One good turn deserves another. I'll want to talk to you again. All right?'

'Yes.'

'I suppose it was you talked to my officer on the phone when we rang up to enquire about the dead girl?'

She nodded. 'It gave me a fright. I thought that was *it*.'

'You'd better see to that finger. Have you any plasters in the house?'

'Thousands. That's top priority. Those kids are always wounding themselves and each other.'

Two reports from Pemberton were on his desk waiting for him. The first told him that the Kingsmarkham shoe shop which sold black cloth and rubber half-boots kept close records of their sales. In the past six months four pairs had been sold. An assistant remembered selling one pair to John Ling. She knew him because he was one of only two Chinese men in the town. Another pair had gone to someone she described as a 'bag lady', who had come into the shop carrying two bulging carrier bags and looked as if she slept on the street. The purchasers of the other pairs she couldn't remember.

Wexford gave the second report a quick glance and said, 'I want Pemberton here too.'

The phone in his hand, Burden said, 'You've gone quite red in the face.'

'I know. It's excitement. Listen to this. Kimberley Pearson's grandmother did die at the beginning of June but she didn't leave any money, still less any property. She'd been living in one of those council bungalows in Fontaine Road, Stowerton. Mrs Pearson, who was her daughter-in-law, knows nothing about any money coming to Kimberley, not family money that is, there *is* no family money, they're all as poor as church mice.

'Clifton Court, where Kimberley moved after Zack was put on remand, is a block of rented flats – or apartments, as Pemberton mysteriously calls them. And who do you think the company is who owns the freehold of the block?'

'Just cut the suspense and tell me.'

'None other than Crescent Comestibles, or in other words, Wael Khoori, his brother and our local council candidate, his wife.'

Pemberton came in. 'You can rent those flats with an option to buy,' he said. 'Forty pounds a week and they claim that when the transfer's made mortgage repayments will amount to the same. Of course, I haven't talked to Kimberley, I asked her mother not to say a word about any of this. Her mother says she went over to Clifton Court the minute Zack was banged-up, put down a deposit and fixed up to move in next day. She's bought a whole lot of furniture since then.'

'Is she going to buy?'

'According to mother, she's already got a solicitor doing the conveyancing. They were squatting in that cottage at Glebe End, by the way, only nobody cared. It's no use to the owner, is it? It needs fifty thousand spent on it before anyone would buy it.'

'And Crescent Comestibles own that block of flats?'

'So the managing agents told me. It's no secret. They're building all over Stowerton, wherever there's a bit of land going or an old house knocked down. It's the same process everywhere. The flats are cheap by today's standards. You pay rent while you're waiting for your mortgage to come through and the mortgage is a hundred per cent with no deposit. Your mortgage repayments are the same as your rent.'

'In accordance with Mrs Khoori's own political standpoint,' said Wexford slowly. 'Help the disadvantaged to help themselves. Don't give it to them but give them the chance to be independent. Not a bad philosophy, I suppose. I wonder if the day will come when someone starts a political party called Conservative Socialists.'

The doctor was told between seeing patients at the medical centre, his wife called to the phone in Intensive Care. Wexford came to the house as Dr Akande arrived home and the pain in his face was as bad as when he thought his daughter was dead. It would be worse if she were dead, immeasurably worse, but this was very bad. To learn that your child is prepared to put you through this, is indifferent as to whether you go through it or not, that is made bearable only when filtered through anger and Raymond Akande wasn't angry. He was humiliated.

'I thought she loved us.'

'She acted impulsively, Dr Akande.' He hadn't said anything about Christopher Riding. Melanie could do that.

'She was in Stowerton all the time?'

'It looks like it.'

310

'Her mother works just down the road. I was there making my rounds.'

'The Epsons left them a car to do the shopping and take the child to school. I don't suppose she went out much on foot.'

'I ought to be down on my knees thanking heaven for all its mercies, I ought to be in a seventh heaven – is that what you're thinking?'

'No,' said Wexford, and boldly, 'I know how you feel.'

'Where did we go wrong?'

Before he could answer – if he had felt able or inclined to answer – Laurette Akande walked in. Wexford's first thought was that she looked ten years younger, his second that she was brimming with happiness and his third that she was the angriest woman he had seen in years.

'Where is she?'

'A car will bring her at six. She'll have the children with her. It was either that or making some care arrangement and since the Epsons return tonight . . .'

'Where did we go wrong, Laurette?'

'Don't be silly. We didn't go wrong. Who is this woman, this Mrs Epson, who leaves her children in the care of a totally unqualified person? I hope someone's going to prosecute her, she should be prosecuted. I am so angry I could kill her. Not Mrs Epson, Melanie. I could kill her.'

'Oh, don't, Letty,' said the doctor. 'We thought someone *had* killed her.'

The car brought Melanie and the boisterous Epson boys a couple of minutes after six. She walked defiantly into the room, her head held high. Her parents, who were sitting down, remained seated, but after a moment or two of silence her father got up and came towards her. He put out a hand and took hers. He pulled her a little towards him and kissed her cheek tentatively. Rather than responding, Melanie allowed this.

'I'll leave you,' Wexford said. 'I'll see you here tomorrow, Melanie, nine in the morning.'

None of them took any notice of him. He got up and went towards the door. Laurette found a strong determined voice. She no longer seemed angry but only decisive.

'Well, Melanie, we'll hear your explanation and then we'll say no more about it. I think you'd better apply to do a degree in business studies. You might get in in October if you're quick about it. The University of the South do a good course and that would mean you can live at home. I'll send away for the forms for you tomorrow and meanwhile Dad might let you temp for the receptionist at the. . . .'

The younger Epson boy began screaming. Wexford let himself out.

Chapter Twenty-One

In the seclusion of the booth he made a cross on his voting paper. There were three names: Burton K.J., British National Party; Khoori A.D., Independent Conservative and Sugden M., Liberal Democrat. Sheila said the Lib-Dem didn't stand a chance and the only way to keep out the BNP was by drumming up big support for Anouk Khoori.

But Wexford now had serious reasons against voting for Mrs Khoori and he made his cross next to the name of Malcolm Sugden. Maybe it was a wasted vote but he couldn't help that. He folded his paper in half, turned round and dropped it through the slot in the ballot box.

Since he went into the Thomas Proctor Primary School some five minutes before, Anouk Khoori had arrived in a car driven by her husband, a gold-coloured Rolls Royce. Burton of the BNP was already there, standing on the asphalt forecourt, surrounded by ladies in silk dresses and straw hats, the former vanguard of the Conservatives, seduced away by the attractions of the far right. He was smoking a cigar, the fumes of which hung heavily and reached distantly, on this warm still morning. Mrs Khoori stepped from the car like a royal personage. She was dressed like one, but of the younger set, in a very short white skirt, emerald green silk shirt, white jacket. Her hair hung like a yellow veil from under her white hat brim. When she saw Wexford she put out both hands to him.

'I knew I should find you here!'

He marvelled at the confidence which enables someone who is almost a stranger to speak in the tones of a lover.

'I knew *you* would be among the first to vote.'

Her husband materialized behind her, smiled a big broad studied smile and thrust his hand in Wexford's direction. The thrust was strong, like he imagined a boxer's might be, but the handshake was limp and it was as if his own hand held a wilted lily. He withdrew it and remarked that they had a fine day for the poll.

'So English,' said Mrs Khoori, 'but that's what I love. Now I want you to promise me something, Reg.'

'What would that be?' he said, and even in his own ears his voice sounded off-puttingly grave.

She was quite undeterred. 'Now that County Councils are disappearing, this authority of ours is going to expand and become very important. I am going to need an adviser on crime prevention, on public relations, on my approach to the *people* of this sleepy old town – right? You will be that adviser, won't you, Reg? You'll help me? You'll give me the support I'm going to need more than I've ever needed support all my life. What do you say?'

Wael Khoori was grinning all over his face, as well he might, but this was a genial empty smile directed at whoever passed. Wexford said, 'You'll have to get in first, Mrs Khoori.'

'Anouk, *please*. But I am going to get in, I know it, and when I'm there you'll help me?'

It was absurd. He smiled but said nothing, avoiding the direct snub. The time was five to nine and Raymond Akande's morning surgery started at eight-thirty. Laurette would have left in time to start the day shift at eight. In the five minutes it took him

314

to drive to Ollerton Avenue, Wexford thought of all those visits he had paid to this house, the doctor's misery, the boy's tears. He remembered taking those parents to the mortuary and Laurette's hysterical rage. There was nothing to be done about all that. He could hardly charge any more people with wasting police time as that itself was a waste of police time.

The chances were he would never come here again. This was his last visit. Even after yesterday, after identification and explanation, it was a shock to see the photographed face, the dead face, alive. She opened the door to him and for a moment he was silenced by the very fact of her, her existence.

'There's no one here but me,' she said.

'Christopher would hardly be welcome, I suppose?'

'He's gone back home. I don't ever want to see him again. It was his sister that was my friend, it was Sophie, not him.'

Wexford followed the girl into the living room whose walls had heard her parents ask if there was any hope of her being alive. She smiled at him, tentatively at first, then serenely.

'I'm feeling happy, I don't know why. It must be getting shut of the Epson kids.'

'How much did they pay you?'

'A hundred. Half before they left and the other half last night.'

Wexford showed her the photograph of the dead Sojourner.

'Have you ever seen her?'

'I don't think so.'

This expression, of course, means no, but a not entirely unqualified no.

'Sure?'

'I've never seen her. Are you allowed to take photographs of dead people and show them around?'

315

'What alternative would you suggest?'

'Well, records kept of everyone with photos and fingerprints and DNA and whatever, a central computer with details of everyone in the country on it.'

'Our job would be a lot easier if we kept records like that but we don't. Tell me what you did the day before you went to the Benefit Office and met Mrs Epson.'

'What do you mean, what I did?'

'How you spent the day. Your mother said you went for a run.'

'I go for a run every day. Well, I couldn't when I had those kids to look after.'

'All right. You went for a run – where?'

'My mother doesn't know everything, you know. I don't always go the same way. Sometimes I go up Harrow Avenue and along Winchester Drive and sometimes I take Marlborough Road.'

'Christopher and Sophie Riding live in Winchester Drive.'

'Do they? I've never been to their house. I've told you, I'd only seen him a couple of times before he followed me back to the Epsons'. I knew Sophie at college.'

If she had been happy five minutes before, she now looked disproportionately distressed. He wondered what would become of her, if the bullying tactics of that domineering mother would drive her to seek out Euan Sinclair again. He eased the subject back to the route she had taken while out running.

'So which was it that day?'

Melanie seemed pleased to cross him. 'I didn't go there at all that day. I went across the fields to Mynford. By the footpaths.'

He was disappointed, though he hardly knew why. By asking these questions, whose significance

316

he felt rather than knew, he had hoped to intuit something.

She fixed her eyes on him the way her father did. 'I went nearly to Mynford New Hall. It gave me a bit of a shock, seeing the house. I didn't know I was so near it.' Her gaze bored into him mesmerically. 'That was the day I went to the Benefit Office. You are talking about that, aren't you?'

'It's the day before you went to the Benefit Office I want to know about.' He tried to keep his patience. 'The Monday.'

'Oh, the Monday. I'll have to think. I went along the Pomfret road on Saturday, and then on Sunday – it was the same Sunday and Monday, along Ashley Grove, up Harrow Avenue, along Winchester Drive and into Marlborough Road. It's nice up there, nice air, and you can look down and see the river.'

'While you were out on these runs you never saw this girl?'

He had the photograph out again and she looked at it again, but quite dispassionately this time.

'My mother said you got them to identify a corpse as me, only it wasn't me. Was it her?'

'Yes.'

'Wow. Anyway, I never saw her. I hardly ever saw anyone on foot. People don't walk, do they? They go in cars. I bet you'd be suspicious, wouldn't you, if you saw someone walking up there? You'd stop them and ask what they are doing.'

'It hasn't come to that yet,' said Wexford. 'You never saw her face at a window? Or saw her in a garden?'

'I've told you, I never saw her.'

It was hard to remember Melanie Akande was twenty-two. Sojourner at seventeen, he was sure, would have seemed older. But Sojourner, of course, had suffered, had been through the mill. The

317

Akandes had kept their daughter a child by treating her as an irresponsible person, fit only to be controlled and directed by others. It made him shudder to think of her having a baby in order to escape.

The house-to-house was over. Nothing had come out of it, so when he said that they were off to Ashley Grove, Burden wanted to know what was the point of that.

'We are going to pay a visit to an architect,' he said to Burden when he had told him of the interview with Melanie. 'Or perhaps an architect's wife before she goes out doing good works in the parish.'

But this was not Cookie Dix's day for taking reading matter to the sick. She was at home with her husband, though it was neither of them that admitted Wexford and Burden to the house.

And what a house! The hall, which was circular and from which a white staircase arced up, bulging like the prow of a sailing ship, had a marble floor on which lemon trees in pots flowered and fruited simultaneously. Other trees grew in the soil itself, of which beds had been created, ficus with rustling leaves and feather-leaved alders, pen-thin cypresses and silver willows with distorted trunks, all reaching up to the light from the glass dome high above them. The maid, black-haired, black-eyed and sallow, kept them waiting under the trees while she went away to announce their presence. She was back within thirty seconds and led them through a pair of double doors – Wexford had to duck under a branch – through a kind of ante-room, stark black and white, and another pair of doors, into a yellow and white sun-flooded dining room where Cookie and Alexander Dix sat eating their breakfast.

In a reversal of the usual order of things, Cookie got to her feet while her husband remained seated.

He had *The Times* in one hand and a piece of croissant in the other. In response to their good morning he said nothing but called out to the departing servant, 'Margarita, bring some more coffee for our guests, will you?'

'We are rather late getting started this morning,' said Cookie. If she had been questioned the day before by Pemberton or Archbold she said nothing about it. She was wearing a dark green satin garment, more like a dressing gown than anything else but not much like one, being extremely short and tied round the waist with a jewelled cummerbund. Her long black hair was fastened on to the top of her head where it sprouted in fronds rather like the top of a frost-blackened carrot. 'Do sit down.' She waved a vague hand at the other eight chairs ranged round the glass-topped table with its verdigris encrusted legs. 'We were out on the toot last night . . . well, at a party. It was the small hours – the tiniest of hours – when we got home, wasn't it, darling?'

Dix turned the page and started reading Bernard Levin. Something made him laugh. His laughter was the sound sappy wood makes when burning, a crackling and spitting. He looked up, still smiling, watched Wexford sit down, then he watched Burden, and when they were in chairs opposite each other, said, 'What can we do for you gentlemen?'

'Mr and Mrs Khoori are friends of yours, I believe?' Wexford said.

Cookie glanced at her husband. 'We know them.'

'You were at their garden party.'

'So were you,' said Cookie. 'What about them, anyway?'

'At that party you said Mrs Khoori had a maid who had recently left her and that she was the sister of your maid.'

'Of Margarita, yes.'

Wexford felt a pang of disappointment. Before he could say any more Margarita came back with the coffee on a tray and two cups. It was impossible to imagine her and Sojourner being related, still less sisters. Cookie, who was very quick off the mark, said something to her in rapid fluent Spanish and the answer came back in that language.

'Margarita's sister went home to the Philippines in May,' Cookie said. 'She wasn't happy here. She didn't get on with the other two maids.'

Having poured the coffee and held out the milk jug and sugar basin to each of them in turn, Margarita stood passively, her eyes downcast.

'They came over together?' Wexford asked and at Cookie's nod said, 'On the six months' stay allowance or for twelve months because their employers were living here?'

'Twelve months. That's renewable – I mean, the Home Office – is it, darling? They'll – what will they do, Alexander?'

'She will apply to have her stay extended by successive periods of twelve months and after four years, if she wants to remain longer, she can apply to stay indefinitely.'

'How did you and the Khooris come to have sisters working for you?'

'Anouk went to an agency and told me. There's this agency that recruits women in the Philippines.' She said something in Spanish and Margarita nodded. 'She can speak English quite well if you want to talk to her. And she can read it. When she and her sister came into this country they had to be interviewed by the entry clearance officer and they were given a leaflet explaining her rights as a – what is it, darling?'

'Domestic entering the United Kingdom under the Home Office Immigration Act 1971,' said Dix without looking up from Levin.

Overnight Wexford had read it all up from Sheila's literature. He said to the waiting woman, 'Was there anyone else working with your sister apart from . . .?'

'Juana and Rosenda,' said Margarita. 'Those two not nice to Corazon. She cry for her children in Manila and they laugh.'

'But no one else?'

'No one. I go now?'

'Yes, you can go, Margarita. Thank you.'

Cookie sat down and helped herself to coffee from the new pot. 'My head's a bit rough this morning.' Wexford would never have guessed it. 'Corazon has four children and an unemployed husband at home. That's why she came to work here, for money to send home. Margarita hasn't children and she isn't married. I think she came . . . well, to see the world, don't you, darling?'

Dix's laughter might have derived from her rather inane enquiry or from the article he was reading. He reached over and patted her hand with a scaly claw of the kind usually seen in the Natural History Museum. Cookie shrugged her green satin shoulders.

'She gets around a bit, has herself some fun. I think she's found a boyfriend, hasn't she, darling? We don't exactly keep her locked up like some do.'

There was a pause. 'Such as the Khooris,' said Alexander Dix with devastating timing.

Burden set his coffee cup back in its saucer. 'Mr and Mrs Khoori keep their servants locked up?'

'Darling Alexander does exaggerate, but yes, you could call them rather restrictive. I mean, if you live at Mynford Old Whatsit, you can't drive and there's no one to drive you – *ever* – and you've got the whole of that huge house to keep spick and span – what on earth do those words mean, I wonder, "spick" and "span"? – never mind, we all get the sense of it. If you live like that, what can you do if you *are* let out, but walk across the fields into the outermost reaches of Kingsmarkham?'

Involuntarily Burden glanced at Wexford and Wexford glanced at him. Their eyes met for an instant. 'They've had no other servants?'

'Not so far as I know,' Cookie said, wavering.

'Margarita would know,' said Dix, 'and she says not.'

'But Margarita never actually went there, darling.' Cookie pursed her lips and gave a silent whistle. 'Are you looking for someone shut up in the house? A sort of madwoman in the attic?'

'Not quite that,' said Wexford and he said it sadly.

Dix must have picked up the note in his voice, for he said in a hospitable way, 'Is there anything else we can get you?' He surveyed the table and found it wanting. 'A biscuit? Some fruit?'

'No, thank you.'

'In that case, perhaps you'll excuse me. I have work to do.' Dix got up, a very small diplodocus on its hind legs. He made a small bow to each of them, then to his wife. He would perhaps have clicked heels had he not been wearing sandals. 'Gentlemen,' he said, and, 'Cornelia,' thus answering one of Wexford's unspoken questions.

Cookie said confidingly when he was out of earshot, 'Darling Alexander is so excited, he's starting a new business. He says we're about to see the dawn of a new Renaissance in building in this country. He's found this marvellous young man who's going into partnership with him. He advertised and this brilliant person answered just out of the blue like that.' She smiled happily. 'Well, I do hope I've been of help.' Wexford marvelled at her disconcerting habit of seeming to read his thoughts.

'You won't find Anouk at home today, you know. She'll be riding about on a float, *exhorting* the populace to vote for her.'

From the front drive they looked back at the house, an intricate arrangement of glass panels, black marble panels and sheets of what looked like wafer-thin alabaster.

'You can't see in,' said Burden, 'you can only see out. Don't you think that's claustrophobic?'

'It would be if it was the other way about.'

Burden got into the driving seat. 'That woman, Margarita I mean, she seemed happy in her work.'

'Sure. There's no objection to people employing servants if they treat them properly and pay them what they're worth. The labourer is worthy of his hire. And the Act's all right, Mike, as far as it goes. In fact, on the surface it looks very good, it looks as if it deals with all contingencies. But it's open to terrible abuse. Domestic workers coming into the country aren't given immigration status independent of the household they work for. *They may not leave and they may not take up any other form of work*. That's what we're looking for, something of that sort.'

Instead of Anouk Khoori, it was the BNP's float which passed them as they came back into the High Street. Ken Burton, the candidate, unselfconscious in black jeans and a black shirt – was its significance largely lost on observers? – rode standing up where the passenger seat should have been, blasting out his manifesto through a megaphone. He might be of the *British* Nationalists but, with some subtlety, it was England for the *English* that he was promoting in this sweet warm corner of Sussex.

Posters plastered over the back of the van not only exhorted the electorate to vote for Burton but also to join the march of the unemployed which was

323

scheduled to take place from Stowerton to Kings-markham on the following day.

'Did you know about that?' Burden asked.

'I've heard rumours. The uniformed branch have it sewn up.'

'You mean they're expecting trouble? Here? *Here*?'

'In this green and pleasant land? Well, Mike, there *are* a lot of people out of work. It's much higher than the national average in Stowerton, about twelve per cent. And tempers do run high.'

'It's time to pay a visit to Mynford New Hall, I think.'

'She won't be there, sir. She's out drumming up defaulters.'

'So much the better,' said Wexford.

'You mean we talk to the servants?'

'It's not a servant we're looking for, Mike,' Wexford said. 'We're looking for a slave.'

Chapter Twenty-Two

This was the long way round, by the road that took in Pomfret and Cheriton. You could walk it across the fields from Kingsmarkham in forty minutes or run it in twenty-five, it was only about two miles, but seven this way. Burden, who was driving, had never seen Mynford New Hall before. He asked if it was as old as it looked but, on hearing building had barely been completed at the time of the garden party, lost interest.

Wexford had expected election posters, even though Mynford was outside the ward for which Mrs Khoori was standing. But there was nothing on the gateposts and nothing in the windows of the mock-Georgian house. Someone had planted full-grown, fully-blooming geraniums in the beds that had been bare a fortnight ago. A bell-pull had been added since his first visit and a pair of the biggest and most elaborate carriage lamps he had ever seen.

But he doubted if the bell-pull was connected, either that or there really was no one at home. It was Burden who looked up and saw the face looking down at them, a pale oval face and head whose black hair was invisible in the blackness behind it. Wexford, who had rung that bell four times, called out,

'Come down and let us in, please.'

Obedience was not prompt. Juana or Rosenda continued to stare impassively for some moments.

Then she gave a little nod, a bob of the head, and disappeared. And when the door was finally opened it was not she who opened it but a woman with brown skin and Mongolian features. Wexford had not exactly expected a uniform but he was surprised by the pink velour tracksuit.

It was very cold in the house, with the same feel that you get when entering the chilled food area in a supermarket. Perhaps they had the same air conditioning system as that installed in the perishable food departments of Crescent Stores. He and Burden produced their warrant cards. The woman looked at them with interest, apparently deriving some amusement from a comparison between photographs and the living men.

'You got old since this one,' she said to Wexford with a scream of laughter.

'What's your name, please?'

The laughter was switched off and she looked at him as if he had said something very impertinent.

'Why you want to know?'

'Just give us your name, please. Are you Juana or Rosenda?'

The change from affront to sullenness was rapid. 'Rosenda Lopez. That one Juana.'

The woman whose face had stared down at them had come silently into the hall. Like Rosenda she wore white trainers but her tracksuit was blue. Her accent was the same as Rosenda's but her English was better. She was younger and might almost have given justification to Dix's *Mikado* parody that the Khooris' maids were barely out of their teens.

'Mr and Mrs Khoori are not at home.' Her next words sounded like a phone answering machine. 'Please leave a message if you would like to.'

'Juana what?' said Burden.

'Gonzalez. Now you go. Thank you.'

'Ms Lopez,' said Wexford, 'Ms Gonzalez, you have a choice. You may either talk to us here and now or else come with us back to Kingsmarkham to the police station. Do you understand what I'm saying?'

It was necessary to repeat this several times, for him to repeat it and for Burden to put it into slightly different words, before there was any sort of response. Both women were mistresses of the art of silent insolence. But when Juana suddenly said something in what he took for Tagalog and both broke into giggles, Wexford thought he could understand the misery of Margarita's sister Corazon who had been laughed at for missing her children.

Juana repeated the incomprehensible words, then apparently translated them. 'No problem.'

'OK. All right,' said Rosenda. 'You sit down now.'

There seemed no need to penetrate further into the house. The hall was a vast chamber, pillared, arched, alcoved, the walls panelled and with recessed colums, very much the kind of room guests must have been welcomed into at a Pemberley or a Northanger Abbey. Only this was new, all new, barely finished. And even in the early nineteenth century, even in winter, no great house would have been as cold inside as this one. He sat down on a pale blue chair with spindly gold legs but Burden remained standing as did the two women, side by side, enjoying themselves.

'Did you work for Mr and Mrs Khoori when they were in the Dower House?'

Burden had to take them to a window and point out the woods in the valley, the invisible roofs. Nods encouraged him.

'And again, of course, when they came here in June?' More nods. He remembered what Cookie Dix had said about shutting people up. 'Do you go out much?'

'Go out?'

'Into town. Go and see friends. Meet people. Go to the cinema. Do you go out?'

From the vertical, their heads moved horizontally. Juana said, 'Don't drive car. Mrs Khoori go shopping and we don't want cinema, have TV.'

'Was Corazon with you at the Dower House?'

His very anglicized pronunciation of the name had them in giggles again and the way he said it repeated by each of them. Then, 'She was cook,' said Juana.

Memory returned. The medical centre and a woman who broke the no smoking rule. 'She had to have the doctor? She was ill?'

'Always ill she was. Homesick. She went home.'

'And that left the two of you,' Wexford said. 'But there was another servant, at the same time as Corazon or perhaps after?'

It was hard to tell if they were blank or wary. He sought political correctness, saying carefully, 'A young girl, seventeen or eighteen, from Africa.'

Almost shivering from the cold, Burden showed them the photograph. The effect was to stimulate more laughter. But before Wexford could decide whether they were laughing from race prejudice, simple wonder that anyone could suspect them of an ability to identify this girl or from a kind of pleasurable horror – Sojourner's face seemed to look more deeply dead each time he produced the photograph – the front door opened and Anouk Khoori came in, immediately followed by her husband, Jeremy Lang and Ingrid Pamber.

'Reg,' she said, not a bit discomposed, 'how lovely! I had a feeling I might find you here.' She held out both hands to him, one of them holding a cigarette. 'But why didn't you let me know you were coming?'

Wael Khoori said nothing. His was invariably the

manner of the highly successful millionaire business-man who puts on a genial, smiling, silent front, while seeming to be quite elsewhere, preoccupied by distant things, high finance, perhaps the Hang Seng index. He smiled, he was patient. He stood waiting.

'We have come home for lunch,' said Mrs Khoori. 'Electioneering is very hard work, I can tell you, and I'm famished. Isn't it lovely and cool in here? Of course you must stay to lunch, Reg, and you too, Mr . . .?' She addressed Rosenda in exactly the same friendly rather breathless way, 'I do hope you can put on something delicious and *quick*, please, as I have to get back to the *fray*.'

Khoori spoke. He ignored everything his wife had said. She might not have said a word. 'I'm quite aware of what you're here for.'

'Really, sir?' said Wexford. 'We'll talk about it then, shall we?'

'Yes, of course, after lunch,' said Anouk. 'Come along, into the dining room everyone, and quickly because Ingrid has to go back to work.'

Again she was ignored. Khoori simply stood his ground while she swept up Jeremy and Ingrid, an arm round each of them, and propelled them across the hall. Ingrid, pinched and pale in her sleeveless dress, nevertheless turned to give him one of her flirtatious looks, arch, tantalizing. But she was changed, the blue glance had lost its power. Her eyes had lost their colour and for a moment he wondered if he had imagined that brilliant azure, but only for a moment, for Khoori was saying,

'Come with me. In here.'

It was a library but a quick glance round showed him it was not of the kind one would use for reference or wish to spend much time in. The Khooris had perhaps said to a firm of interior decorators, put shelves all over the walls and fill them with suitable books, old ones with handsome bindings. So *The Natural History of the Pyrenees* in seven volumes had been supplied and Hakluyt's *Voyages* and Mommsen on Rome and Motley on the Dutch Republic. Khoori sat down at a reproduction desk. Its green leather inlay had been made to look as if quill pens on parchment had been scratching at it for centuries.

'You don't seem surprised to see us, Mr Khoori,' said Wexford.

'No, I'm not, Mr Reg. Annoyed but not surprised.'

Wexford looked at him. This was very different from Bruce Snow's assumption that they were traffic police. 'What do you suppose this is about?'

'I suppose, I *know*, that those women or one of them have not applied to the Home Office for an extension of their stay. This, despite their extreme desire to stay and my having had the applications typed for them. And their knowledge that they can only stay under the provisions of the Immigration Act of 1971. All they have to do is sign the letter and take it to the post. I know because this is what happened last time, when they first came to us and had been granted an initial stay of six months. You have to keep a constant eye on these people and I haven't the time to be as vigilant as I should be. So, very well, that's that. What do we do to put matters right?'

A little subterfuge would do no harm, Wexford thought. 'Simply reapply, Mr Khoori. A mistake was made but made in good faith, apparently.'

'So I reapply and this time make sure the application gets to its destination?'

'Right,' said Burden, transforming himself into an Immigration official. He began inventing with a facility Wexford could only admire. 'Now, this woman Corazon, we understand she wanted to change her employment, which is of course illegal. Under the provisions of the Act she's only permitted to work for the employer whose name is on the stamp in her passport.'

'There was some story about the other servants ill-treating her . . . well, being unkind to her. She was always in tears.' Khoori shrugged. 'It wasn't very pleasant for myself and my wife.'

'So, understanding she wasn't permitted to work elsewhere, she went home? When would that have been?'

Khoori put up one hand and smoothed his casque of white hair. It fitted him like a wig but it plainly was not a wig. The hand was long, brown, exquisitely kept. He frowned a little while he thought. 'About a month ago, maybe less.'

And it was exactly four weeks to the day since Wexford had first encountered Anouk Khoori at the medical centre. She still had a cook then, a servant who had perhaps fallen ill through homesickness and the cruelty of others.

'Would you mind telling me, sir,' Wexford said, 'where the money came from for her return flight?'

'I paid, Mr Reg. I paid.'

'Very generous of you. Just one other thing. I'd like you to set me right on this question. Would you say it was true that in the Gulf States the labour laws don't recognize domestics as workers but treat them as family members?'

Suspicion that this might be a trap flicked in Khoori's eyes. 'I'm not a lawyer.'

'But you're a Kuwaiti national, aren't you? You must be aware if this is so or not, if it is in fact taken for granted.'

'Broadly speaking, I suppose it's so, yes.'

'So that families from the Gulf States do bring in servants *as family members or friends*, having no status as domestics and therefore no protection from abuse? And although it's clear they are coming in not on holiday but to work they are allowed to stay as visitors.'

'Possibly. I've no experience of it.'

'But you know it happens? And that it happens because refusing entry to domestics either as workers tied to one employer and restricted to twelve-month stays, or as family members or friends and ostensible visitors, might discourage wealthy investors like yourself from coming here at all?'

Khoori gave a loud braying laugh. 'I'm damned if I'd be here if I had to wash my own dishes.'

'But you have never personally brought anyone in under those special circumstances?'

'No, Mr Reg, I have not. You can ask my wife. Come to that, you can ask Juana and Rosenda.'

He led them into a vast cold dining room with ten windows down one wall and a painted ceiling. Some ten feet under the depicted cherubs, cornucopias and lovers' knots Anouk, Jeremy and Ingrid sat at a mahogany table big enough for twenty-four, eating smoked salmon and drinking champagne.

'We are celebrating my victory in advance, Reg,' said Anouk. 'Do you think that a very foolhardy thing to do?'

Her husband whispered something to her. It evoked a tinkle of laughter, not however a happy sound. The repulsion she held for Wexford came back and he turned instinctively to look at Ingrid, beautiful fresh young Ingrid whose hair was still crisp and smooth and skin glowing with health but whose eyes had become as dull as stones. As he looked she took a pair of glasses from her bag and perched them on her nose.

If she had changed, it was nothing to the change that had come over Anouk Khoori. Under the make-up she had gone bright red and her features seemed to knot up with tension.

'It's that girl who was murdered, isn't it? That black girl? We've never seen her.' Her carefully modulated voice grew shrill. 'We know nothing about her. We've never had anyone working for us here but Juana and Rosenda and that Corazon who left and went home. I think it's awful this happening today. I will not have anything like this happening to spoil my chances!'

As her voice rose on to a high note of panic, Juana and Rosenda both came into the room, the former with a carafe of water on a tray, the latter carrying a fresh plate of brown bread and butter. Their employer's vexation, the sudden angry distress that Wexford at any rate had never witnessed before, caused them a mirth they could barely conceal. Juana had to hold her hand tightly over her mouth while Rosenda's lips twitched as she stood staring.

Wexford had scarcely anticipated her inspired guesswork. Or was it less guesswork than genuine guilt?

'You tell them,' Anouk shouted, 'you tell them, you two. We never had anyone here like that, did we? You love it here, don't you? No one ever hurt you, you tell them.'

Juana's laughter broke free. She was beyond controlling it. 'He crazy,' she said, gasping. 'We never see no one like that, do we, Rosa?'

'No, we never see no one, no way.'

'No way we don't. Here your bread and butter. You want more lemon?'

'All right,' Wexford said. 'Thank you. That's all.'

Evidently remembering that he had already voted, Anouk shouted at him, 'You can get out of my house! Now! Both of you, get out!'

With a little gasp, Ingrid had got up, clutching her

333

napkin. 'I shall have to go. I must get back to the office.'

Rosenda was holding the dining room door open, murmuring, 'Come on, come on, you got to go now.'

'You'll give me a lift, won't you?' Ingrid said to Wexford.

It was Burden who answered. 'I'm afraid not.'

'Oh, but, surely . . .'

'We're not a taxi service.'

Behind them in the dining room Anouk had given way to a crisis of nerves, uttering little staccato cries. Khoori said to no one in particular that it might help to bring the brandy. Wexford and Burden made their way across that desert of a hall to the front door, escorted by both giggling women. The heat outside met them in a wave, a positive sensuous pleasure. They were barely in the car when Ingrid came out followed by Khoori who handed her into the car they had arrived in.

'I'll bet that's the first time a Rolls like that has ever brought anyone to the Benefit Office,' said Burden, starting the engine. 'Looks a bit different without her contact lenses, doesn't she?'

'You mean that blue was *lenses*?'

'What else? I suppose she got allergic and had to leave them off.'

Perhaps it was from the scent of his after-shave, but Gladys Prior knew it was Burden before he spoke. She even spelt his name out before he spoke, persisting with the joke that afforded her so much amusement. Wexford's enquiry brought fresh gales of laughter.

'Is he in? Bless you, he hasn't set foot outside in four years.'

Percy Hammond was at his Mizpah, looking out across his Plain of Syria. Without turning round, identifying them by their voices and their footsteps, he asked, 'When are you going to catch him, then?'

Wexford said, earning a surprised and perhaps admonitory glance from Burden, 'Tomorrow, I should think, Mr Hammond. Yes, we'll catch . . . er, them, tomorrow.'

'Who's going to have that flat opposite?' said Mrs Prior unexpectedly.

'What, Annette Bystock's flat?'

'That's the one. Who's going to have it?'

'I've no idea,' said Burden. 'It'll probably go to the next-of-kin. Now, Mr Hammond, we'd like a little more help from you . . .'

'If you're going to catch him tomorrow, eh?'

Burden's expression showed all too plainly what he thought of Wexford's wild boast. 'What we want you to do, sir, is go back over what you saw from this window on July the eighth.'

'And, more importantly,' said Wexford, 'what you saw on July the seventh.'

It would have been unprecedented, he would never have done it, not actually done it, but Burden *nearly* corrected Wexford. It was on the tip of his tongue to murmur, you don't mean that, not the seventh, he saw no one on the seventh but that girl with the blue lenses and Edwina Harris and a man with a spaniel. It was all in the report. Instead of saying it, he coughed, he cleared his throat just a little. Wexford took no notice.

'On the Thursday morning, very early, you saw this young chap who looked a bit like Mr Burden here come out of the house with a big box in his arms.'

Percy Hammond nodded vigorously, 'About four-thirty it was, a.m.'

'Right. Now on the previous night, the Wednesday night, you went to bed and to sleep but you woke up after a while and got up . . .'

'To spend a penny,' said Gladys Prior.

'And naturally you looked out of your window – and you saw someone come out of Ladyhall Court? You saw a young man come out?'

The old wrinkled face was distorted even more by the effort of remembering. He clenched his hands.

'Did I say that?'

'You said it, Mr Hammond, and then you thought you'd made a mistake because you definitely saw him in the morning and you couldn't have seen him twice.'

'But I did see him twice . . .' Percy Hammond said, his voice dropping to a whisper. 'I *did*.'

Wexford took it gently, moving with care. 'You saw him twice? In the morning – and the night before?'

'That's right. I knew I did, whatever they said. I saw him twice. And the first time, he saw *me*.'

'How do you know?'

'He wasn't carrying a box that first time, he wasn't carrying anything. He came to the gate and he looked up and looked straight at me.'

It was the last visit he would pay to Oni Johnson. She had nothing more to tell him. By her openness she had saved herself and next day she would leave Intensive Care for a room to be shared with three other women in Rufford Ward.

Laurette Akande came out to meet him. She looked at him and spoke as if the past month had never been. She had never lost a daughter and he hadn't found that daughter, there had been no anguish, no suffering and no joyful reunion. He might have been a sympathetic stranger. Her manner was light, her voice brisk.

'I wish someone could get that boy of hers to have a wash. His clothes and his hair smell, not to mention the rest of him.'

336

'He'll be gone when his mother goes,' said Wexford.

'It can't be soon enough for me.'

Oni looked pretty, sitting up in bed wearing a pink satin quilted bedjacket over the bandages, much too hot for the temperature, the obvious gift of Mhonum Ling. Mhonum was on one side of the bed, Raffy on the other. It was true that he smelt unpleasant, his curious hamburger and tobacco odour battling, and winning the battle, against his aunt's Giorgio eau-de-toilette.

'When you going to catch him then?' said Oni.

He was fated, it seemed, to be that afternoon the butt of eveyone's laughter. Oni laughed and then Mhonum laughed and Raffy joined in with a sheepish snigger.

'Tomorrow.'

'Are you kidding?' said Mhonum.

'I hope not.'

It was developing into a pattern. Sylvia drove the children and Neil into Kingsmarkham, Neil went to his job club, promising to meet them later, and Sylvia homed on her parents. Or, more often, her mother. Wexford never asked how long she had been there by the time he got home, he didn't want to know, though later Dora sometimes told him, always qualifying these grumbles with a prefatory 'I really shouldn't talk like this about my own child . . .'

'I don't suppose you've any objection,' Sylvia said when he walked in, 'if I take part in the unemployed march tomorrow?'

He was surprised to be asked – and just a little touched. 'It won't be the kind of event in which arrests are made. There'll be no setting fire to property and no overturning of cars.'

'I thought I ought to ask you,' she said in a tone that implied long-suffering dutifulness.

'Do as you like as long as you don't frighten the horses.'

'Will there be *horses*, grandad?'

Wexford laughed. He thought he was due for a spot of laughter whose meaning eluded the others. The doorbell rang suddenly. No one ever came to their door and rang it in the Colonel Bogey mode: da-da-di-di-di-pom-POM. Such jauntiness was wholly unexpected. Wexford went to answer it. His son-in-law was on the doorstep, grinning widely, insisting on shaking hands with him.

'Can I have a drink? I need one.'

'Of course.'

'Whisky, please. I've had a wonderful afternoon.'

'I can see that.'

Neil took a swig of his drink. 'I've got a job. And in my own line. I'm going into partnership with this old architect, terribly distinguished man, and he's funding it, I'm . . .'

'I do think,' said Sylvia, 'that it's outrageous you coming out with that in front of everyone instead of telling me first.'

Her father was inclined to agree but he said nothing. He had a drink too. 'Alexander Dix,' he said, when the whisky struck home.

Neil had taken his younger son on his knee. 'That's right. The one offer I answered that was taken up. How did you know?'

'I doubt if there's more than one rich old distinguished architect in Kingsmarkham.'

'We're starting with a rather ambitious plan for the Castlegate site. A shopping mall, if that isn't to degrade what it will ultimately be. A thing of beauty, an asset to the town centre, crystal and gold, with a Crescent supermarket as the pivot of the whole thing.' He caught his father-in-law's eye and misinterpreted the gleam he saw there. 'Oh, without the

338

moons and minarets, don't worry. It's part of this new government policy to restore commerce to town centres.' He said laconically to Sylvia, 'You can stop signing on as from Tuesday.'

'Thanks very much. That's for me to decide, I think.'

'You might say you're pleased.'

'I don't specially want to be part of the kind of society where the woman is indoors and the man comes home and says he's got a lucrative new job, so she says, Oh goody, can I have a pearl necklace and a fur coat now?'

'You shouldn't wear fur,' said Ben.

'I don't, I can't afford it, and never will be able to.'

'*Walang problema*,' said Wexford in Tagalog.

Robin, in his headset, looked up at him pityingly from the screen in his hand. 'I don't do that any more, grandad,' he said. 'I'm into first day covers with celebrity autographs now. Do you think you could get me Anouk Khoori's?'

Chapter Twenty-Three

The march of the unemployed was due to begin at
eleven in the morning, the marchers asked to
assemble in Stowerton marketplace with their
banners and the column would form up from the
steps of the old Corn Exchange. It was going to be
even hotter, but with rain later and the chance of
thunder. The local news, that Wexford watched
intermittently while getting dressed, told him all
this, but it was Dora, who had got it from Sylvia, who
supplied the details of the route. The march would
proceed through Stowerton to the roundabout, pass
along the bleak streets of the industrial estate, rejoin
the Kingsmarkham road and enter the town by the
Kingsbrook Bridge. Its final destination was Kingsmarkham Town Hall.

He had to go back to the news for results in the
council election. Voting, however, had been so close
between the Liberal Democrat and the Independent
Conservative that a recount was taking place. Ken
Burton was out, having secured a mere fifty-eight
votes. Wexford wondered whether to phone Sheila
and tell her the news, but decided against it. She
probably had her own means of knowing, anyway.

'Guess what,' said Dora. '*We're* invited to Sylvia's
for Sunday lunch.'

But Wexford only said obscurely, 'I hope it's all
right,' and added, 'Neil's job, I mean.'

The day was still and sultry, heat hanging under a

sky of veiled blue. It was like the beginning of the month when he had been reading by the open french windows and Dr Akande had phoned with the first mention of Melanie. The air this morning had a scalding feel, and Burden said he'd known cooler steam come out of a kettle. Inside the car the air conditioning was as efficient as that at Mynford New Hall and Wexford told Donaldson to turn it off and open a window.

'We're very quick to dismiss old people's statements of fact, aren't we?' Wexford said. 'If there's the slightest doubt we immediately assume they're senile or their memories are useless or even that they're no longer quite sane. Whereas with a younger person we'd at least listen and even encourage while they sort things out.

'Percy Hammond said he went to bed on that Wednesday evening, went to sleep, but woke up, got up and "put the light on for a minute". He turned if off "because it was so bright". I think we all know that feeling. He looked out of the window and saw "this young chap come out with a box in his arms". "Or was that later?" he said.

'We didn't ask him to think about it, we didn't say "think carefully, try and remember the times", Karen just confirmed that it must have been later, this was in the morning, he saw the "young chap" in the morning. I was just as much to blame, I let it go too. But, Mike, the fact was that the old man *saw Zack Nelson twice.*'

Burden looked at him. 'What d'you mean?'

'He saw him at eleven-thirty or thereabouts on Wednesday and he saw him *again* at four-thirty the following morning. There was no real doubt in his mind about that. The only doubt was whether Zack was carrying the "box" at night or in the morning. And that first time, on the Wednesday night, Zack

341

saw *him*. He saw a face looking at him from the window. D'you see what that means?'

'I think so,' Burden said slowly. 'Annette died after 10.00 pm on the Wednesday and before 1.00 am on the Thursday. If Percy Hammond saw him for the first time at . . . But that means Zack killed Annette.'

'Yes, of course. The doors were open. Zack went in at, say, eleven-thirty, and found Annette asleep in bed. She was weak, she was ill, she was probably running a temperature. He looked around for something with which to do the deed. Perhaps he had something with him, a scarf, a cord. But the lamp lead was better. He pulled it out of the lamp, strangled Annette – who was too feeble to put up much of a fight – took nothing and left. There's not a light on anywhere but a street lamp, there's no one to see him, he's in the clear – until he looks across the road and sees, pressed against the glass, old Percy Hammond's face staring out at him.'

'But then surely, the last thing he'd do would be to go back five hours later?'

'Are you sure of that?'

'The last thing he'd want was to draw attention to himself.'

'No, that's exactly what he did want. He wanted to draw attention to himself or someone else wanted him to. This is what I think happened. It's guesswork but it's the only possible answer. Zack was scared stiff. The possessor of what is, after all, putting it brutally, quite a frightening face, had seen him, had stared long and hard at him. He panics, he needs advice. He realizes fully the enormity of what has happened.

'Who can advise him? Obviously, only one person, the man or woman who has put him up to this, the instigator whose paid hitman he is. It's the middle of the night but never mind that. He's doubtless been

342

told never to contact this person, but never mind that either. He makes his way down the road to the corner shop, outside which is a phone box. He makes his call and the advice comes back from a far cleverer perpetrator than Zack could ever be: go back, steal something, make sure you're seen. Make sure you're seen a second time.'

'But why? I don't get it.'

'He, whoever he is, must have said, They will know the time she died. If you go back at four or later *they will know she must have been dead before you got there*. You will be in the clear as far as murder goes. Of course you'll go to prison for the theft but not for long and it's worth it, isn't it? It was an elderly person saw you, you say? They'll take it for granted an elderly person was confused about the time.'

'We did,' Burden said. 'We did take it for granted.'

'We all do it. We all patronize the old, and worse. We treat them as if they were small children. And we'll be on the receiving end of that one day, Mike. Unless the world changes.'

The place was strangely like the interior of the cottage at Glebe End. Kimberley had transported all her possessions in cardboard boxes and plastic carriers and in these containers they remained. They were still to her what cupboards and drawers are to other people. But she had bought furniture: a huge pneumatic three-piece suite of purple and grey tapestry with gold braid and gold swags, a crimson table inlaid with gilt, a television set in a white and gold cabinet. There was no carpet, there were no curtains. Clint, who had learned to walk since Burden had last seen him, staggered about the room, wiping the chocolate biscuit he had sucked on any tapestry surface he came into contact with. Kimberley was dressed in black leggings, stiletto heeled white shoes and a strapless red bustier. She gave Burden a belligerent look and said she didn't know what he meant.

'Where did it all come from, Kimberley? All this? Three weeks ago you were wondering what'd become of you if you lost that cottage.'

She maintained her sullen glare, but taking her eyes from his face, gazing down at her own feet, her toes turned in.

'It came from Zack, didn't it? It didn't come from your grandmother.'

She said to her feet, 'My nan did die.'

'Sure she did but she didn't leave you anything, she'd nothing to leave. What was it, paid to Zack in cash, was it? Or did he open a bank account for you and him and have it paid in there?'

'I don't know nothing about this, you know. It don't mean nothing to me.'

'Kimberley,' said Wexford. 'He murdered Annette Bystock. He didn't just steal her TV and her video. He murdered her.'

'He never!' She looked up and sideways, her shoulder hunched, as if trying to protect her face from a coming onslaught. 'He nicked her things, that's all he done.' The child, back at his favourite occupation of removing articles from one cardboard box and putting them into another, now fished out an unopened packet of teabags and trotted over to his mother with his find in his hands. She snatched him up and set him on her lap. It was as if she made him into a shield for herself. 'He told me, he just nicked her telly and stuff. If he's got money in the bank, why shouldn't he have? OK, it was his family it come from, not mine. He said to say my nan, on account of she died. But it was his family it come from. His dad's got money. Don't tear that open, Clint, you'll have the tea all out.'

The child took no notice. He had torn the cardboard and found the teabags. He was immensely content. Kimberley held him tightly, her arm clamped round his waist. Her voice was fierce, 'He never done no murder. Not Zack. He never would.'

She was telling the truth, Wexford thought, insofar as she knew it. He was almost sure she didn't know. 'Zack told you there'd be money in the bank, did he, before he went away?'

She nodded vigorously. 'In *my* account. He put it in there for me.'

Clint had a teabag gripped in both hands, his face growing red with the effort of tugging at it.

'Why this flat, Kimberley?' said Burden.

'It's nice, in't it? I liked it, I fancied it, in't that enough for you?'

'Wasn't it because you didn't have to make any effort? It belongs to Crescent Comestibles, doesn't it, and that's Mr Khoori? You didn't have to do a thing. Mr Khoori put you in here and gave you the money to get what you wanted.'

It was plain to Wexford that she had no idea what Burden meant. She was no actress. She was simply ignorant and these names signified nothing to her. The child on her lap had succeeded in his endeavour, had split open the teabag and was scattering tea over her leggings and the floor. But she was oblivious to it. She stared in bewilderment and said at last, 'You what?'

Wexford saw no point in explaining. 'What did happen, Kimberley?'

She brushed the blackish grains off her legs and gave Clint a half-hearted shake. 'I was walking down the High Street here with him in the buggy and I saw that written up about flats and mortgages and whatever and I thought why not, there's all that money Zack says is mine now, and I went in and saw

345

this feller and said I got the money, I could give him the cash or a cheque and when could I move in. And that's what I done, moved in. And I don't know nothing about any Mr Coo-what you said, I've never heard of him.'

Of course, she must know that the source of this unexpected accession of cash was suspect. Legitimately earned money, no doubt many thousand pounds, does not find its way miraculously into the bank accounts of such as Zack Nelson. Families such as the Nelsons have no private fortunes, set up no trusts, to assist their humbler scions. She knew that as well as they did. But Wexford was aware she would never come out with it, she would never say she knew this gain must be ill-gotten but her desire for better accommodation was so great that she conveniently overlooked that fact. She would only come up with wilder explanations and excuses.

The main thing,' he said to Burden when they were outside in Stowerton High Street, 'is that she doesn't know where it came from. Zack Nelson, in his wisdom, never told her. Or, rather, he told her a lie which he knew she would know was a lie but would accept. He meant her to be safe and she is safe. We needn't have made detours to avoid the High Street.'

'*He* knows, though.'

Wexford shrugged. 'And do you think he'll say? At this stage? OK, we can go along to the remand centre and ask him and he'll trot out all that stuff about Percy Hammond being senile and Annette being dead long before he ever went into Ladyhall Court. And that's what we can't prove, Mike. We'll never prove Percy Hammond saw Zack twice. If Zack keeps his mouth shut now, and he will, the worst that can happen to him is he'll go down for six months for burglary.'

They were walking along the street, just walking and quite aimlessly, the heat making for slow idle steps, yet they were at the Market Cross almost before they knew it. Banks are always together in whatever part of a town is given over to them and passing first the Midland, then the Natwest, made Burden say,

'This bank account Zack opened. He must have done that before killing Annette. As soon as he agreed to do it, on the Tuesday or the Wednesday at the latest. We can find out whose cheque or banker's draft or whatever was paid in to that a couple of days later.'

'Can we, Mike?' Wexford said it almost wistfully. 'On what grounds are we going to take a look at a bank account in Kimberley Pearson's name? She hasn't done anything. She hasn't even been charged with anything. She doesn't know where the money came from but she's probably convinced herself by now that it came from Zack's rich old grandad. She's innocent in the eyes of the law and no bank is going to let us breach her right to privacy.'

'It beats me why Zack Nelson drew attention to himself by having Bob Mole sell that radio in full public view like that, in the market that we make a point of keeping our eye on.'

Wexford laughed. 'Just for that, Mike. For that reason. It was the same as when he went into Annette's flat, the same drawing attention to himself. That's what he wanted to do, to get it over, get himself charged with theft and banged-up, out of harm's way. He even chose the most easily identified item among the stolen goods, that radio with the red stain on it.'

They stopped in the square and were about to turn round and retrace their steps, as people do who have been walking aimlessly, when Wexford's attention was caught by the crowd which had gathered outside the Corn Exchange. It was a Victorian building, its pillared entrance approached by a flight of steps. These steps some of the people who were waiting treated like seats in an amphitheatre, sitting or lounging on them. Up by the entrance half a dozen seemed to be working on a banner, which suddenly unfurled and stretched out read, 'Give Us the Right to Work'.

'It's the start of the unemployed march,' said Burden. 'Who would have thought that could ever happen here? I mean, you could imagine it in Liverpool, say, or Glasgow. But here?'

'Who could imagine slavery would ever happen here? But Sojourner was a slave.'

'Not exactly that, surely.'

'If someone works without wages, or without accessible wages, cannot leave her employment, is not allowed out, is beaten and abused, what is she but a slave? "Slaves cannot breathe in England, if their lungs Receive our air, that moment they are free; They touch our country and their shackles fall." I got that out of a book, I don't suppose it'll stay in my memory for long. The point is, it may have been true once, it isn't any more.' Wexford took a piece of paper from his pocket. 'I copied this down. It's a case history and it didn't happen in the eighteenth century or the nineteenth but six years ago.

' "Roseline," ' he read, ' "is from Southern Nigeria. At the ago of about fifteen she was 'bought' for £2 from her impoverished father who was led to believe he would be paid that sum regularly every month to help feed his other five children. Roseline, he was told by the couple, was to stay as their guest and be taught domestic science. They brought her to Sheffield where the husband worked as a doctor. She was kept as a servant, not allowed out, slept on the

348

floor, and was made to kneel on the floor for two hours if she fell asleep before being allowed to go to bed. Her working day started at 5.30 am and lasted for eighteen hours. She cleaned and washed for her employers and their five children. She was caned and kept short of food. On one occasion, in desperation, she wrote a note intended for the next-door neighbour offering sex for a sandwich. The note was discovered and she was further punished. In September 1988, while her abusers were away for a week, she gathered enough courage and spoke to a regular passer-by who had often seen her staring out of the window, and beckoned to her. This neighbour helped her to escape, and she took her former employers to court. She was awarded £20,000 in damages. However, she had only been given leave to stay for three months, and her employers had kept her for over three years. She was an illegal overstayer and thus liable to immediate deportation." '

Burden was silent for a moment. Then he said, 'Sojourner tried to escape and was further punished – is that what you're saying?'

'They went too far with their punishment. No doubt, they were afraid of the publicity and of having damages awarded against them. They made sure that wouldn't happen. They made very thoroughly sure by killing Annette, who perhaps had it in her power to reveal their identity and whereabouts, and tried – twice – to kill Oni who might have been told where they lived.'

'You think she was allowed in like this Roseline as a visitor? She was allowed three months or six months but overstayed?'

'Who's to know if she's never allowed out and no one sees her? If visitors to the house never see her? In fact, an employer has only to say to her that if she's discovered she'll be deported to wherever it is, the

Gulf probably, for her to collude in this breaking of the law.'

'If conditions are that bad for her wouldn't she want to be deported?'

'That depends on what awaits her. There are a good many parts of the world where all that's left for a homeless destitute woman is prostitution. In any case, Sojourner only colluded so far. She is supposed to have been told her rights *before* she left to come here, she's supposed to have been given the pamphlet to read, explaining the Immigration Rules Concession and what to do if she's ill-treated. But that's good only so far as it goes. If, as I think, Sojourner came in as a visitor with the family, as a *guest*, she wouldn't have any rights and, for all we know, she can't read. She very likely can't read English, anyway.

'Probably she knew very little about the outside world, this England, Kingsmarkham. She was black but she never saw another black person. And then, one day, looking out of a window, she saw Melanie Akande out running . . .'

'Reg, that's pure fantasy.'

'It's intelligent conjecture,' Wexford retorted. 'She saw Melanie. Not once only but many times. Nearly every day from the middle of June onwards. She saw a black girl like herself out there, a Nigerian like herself, and maybe she sensed Melanie's African origins.'

'Allowing that that's true, which I'm not sure I can, so what?'

'I think it gave her confidence, Mike. It showed her that escape might be possible and the world wouldn't be entirely alien. So she ran away, in the dark, knowing nothing else . . .'

'No, that won't do,' Burden said. 'That can't be so. She *knew about the ESJ*. She knew it was where you

went to find work or get money if there was no work
. . . Look . . . the march is starting.'

A hundred of them? Like most people, Wexford wasn't much good at calculating numbers from a rapid glance. He would have to see them in sets of four or eight before he could tell. They were forming up now, four abreast, with a chosen two in the vanguard, holding the banner, both men and both middle-aged. Burden thought he recognized one of them from frequent visits to the Benefit Office. It was then that he had his first sight of the two officers from the uniformed branch, two of whom had suddenly appeared on the Corn Exchange steps.

They were a procession now and they began to move. What signal set them off was hard to know. A whispered word perhaps, travelling down the line from one to another, or the banner suddenly up-raised. The two officers on the steps went back to their car, parked on the market square flagstones, a white Ford with the scarlet stripe and eagle crest of the Mid-Sussex Constabulary.

'We'll follow them too,' said Wexford.

They stood back to let the column pass. Marching was rather slow, as it always is at the start. Speed would pick up when they came out into the main road to Kingsmarkham. Nearly everyone wore jeans, a shirt or tee-shirt, trainers on the feet, the ubiquitous uniform. The oldest person there was a man well into his sixties who could not have hoped for work and must be marching out of public-spiritedness or altruism or even for the fun of it. The youngest was a baby girl in a pushchair, her mother a twin of Kimberley Pearson before she came into a fortune.

A second banner brought up the rear: ' Jobs for All. Is It Too Much to Ask?' Two women carried it, a pair who looked so much alike they must have been mother and daughter. The column proceeded up the

High Street, the police car crawling behind it. Wexford and Burden got back into their car and Donaldson moved out behind the white Ford.

'Someone must have told her,' said Wexford stubbornly, answering Burden's rebuttal as if there had been no break in their conversation. 'There must have been someone who went there or someone she met who told her the ESJ was the place.'

'Like who?' Burden was very sure of his ground. 'And if so, why didn't this person tell her where it was? Help her to escape, come to that? Tell her how to have recourse to the law?'

'I don't know.'

'If this person told her about jobs and benefit and how to get away, why hasn't he or she come to us?'

'These are minor things, Mike. These questions will be answered. At the moment we don't know where this beating up happened, where her death happened. But we do know why. Because, getting no help from Annette, she had no choice but to go home. Where else could she go?'

The column turned left into Angel Street and, picking up speed, came to the roundabout. The first exit was for Sewingbury, the second for Kingsmarkham, the third led to the industrial estate where Wexford had been two days before. After passing between the factory sites, it would rejoin the Kingsmarkham road at the pub called the Halfway House.

'Not much point in that,' said Burden. 'Half the industry's closed down.'

'I expect that is the point,' Wexford said.

The sun which had shone quite brightly while they were in Stowerton marketplace had gone in, retreating behind a thin veil of cloud. It had grown white and distant, a mere puddle of light, and the cloud was breaking, the little clouds were edged with darkness. But the heat remained, the heat even increased, and two of the young men among the marchers shed their shirts and tied them round their waists.

Reinforcements awaited them on the corner of Southern Drive, half a dozen men and a young woman with a banner of their own, obscurely proclaiming: 'Yes to Euro-Work'. There is perhaps no more dismal sight in social terms than a row of empty factories. Boarded-up shops have nothing on it. The factories, two of them brand new, had their windows all closed in the heat, their front doors padlocked, and signs either offering the buildings to let or for sale planted in lawns on which untended grass grew long. The members of the column, again at some signal, turned their heads as one to acknowledge these monuments to joblessness as they passed, like a regiment honouring a cenotaph.

Not all the factories were closed. One that manu-factured machine parts had remained open and another producing herbal cosmetics seemed to be flourishing, while Burden remarked that the printers on the corner of Southern Drive and Sussex Mile had reopened and its presses were once more operating. It was a good sign, a sign of recession ending and prosperity returning, he added. Wexford said nothing. He was thinking, and not just about economic problems. In accordance with its previous behaviour, the column should have cheered but it kept silence. Its members seemed not to share Burden's optimism. Up the long shallow hill the column went. The distance was a mile, at least a mile, and Wexford would have asked Donaldson to pass and go on ahead but passing was impossible. The road became a narrow country lane, a white pathway between high hedges and giant trees.

They met only one car before they reached the turn

into the Kingsmarkham road. It stopped and the white Ford stopped too. But before the officer had his door open, the column's members had shifted, had converted themselves into a single line, the banners held back flat against the hedge. Slowly the car came on and as its occupants came into focus Wexford saw that the driver was Dr Akande, his son beside him in the passenger seat. Akande nodded and raised one hand in the classic gesture of thanks. The hand went down before he saw Wexford, or it might have been that he didn't see him. The boy next to him had a sullen injured expression. That was a family who would never forgive him for warning them to prepare for a daughter's, a sister's, death.

Traffic on the Kingsmarkham road wasn't at its heaviest at Friday lunchtime but it wasn't light either. The white Ford went past the marchers and took up its new position at the head of the column. More joined at the point where the Forby road turned in and they stopped to let a dozen cars coming this way from Kingsmarkham pass by. It was close on a hundred and fifty people now, Wexford calculated. A good many seemed to have decided that this stretch was the place to attach themselves to the marchers, whole families who had abandoned their cars on the grass verges, women with three or four children who looked on this as a fine day out, boys in their teens that Burden said could only be there because they were looking for trouble.

'We'll see. Maybe not.'

'I meant to tell you. All this slavery stuff put it out of my head. Annette did make a will and who do you think she left her flat to?'

'Bruce Snow,' said Wexford.

'How did *you* know? That's too bad, I was going to astound you.'

'I didn't know. I guessed. You wouldn't have been

354

so dramatic if it had been the ex-husband or Jane Winster. I hope he's grateful. He'll have somewhere to live after his wife's taken him to the cleaners. Won't be very comfortable with Diana Graddon on the other side of the street.'

The column was coming up to the outskirts of Kingsmarkham. Like most English country towns, it was approached by roads lined by big houses dating from the mid- and late-nineteenth century, 'villas' with high hedges and old-fashioned gardens, a subtly different atmosphere from Winchester Avenue and Ashley Grove. Wealth hid inside the walls of these houses instead of flaunting itself, concealed under an indifference that almost amounted to shabbiness.

A woman came running out of one of the houses, down a long flagged path, to join the march. She might have been employer, employee or employed, it was impossible to tell from her jeans and sleeveless shirt. Would Sylvia stay at home now the need had gone? Or would she join the march, generously campaigning for others? Burden, who had been lost in thought, suddenly said,

'That case history of yours, does it give the nationality of the employer?'

'No. Presumably, the family were British.'

'They might be, but Nigerian too.' Burden was struggling and Wexford didn't help him. 'I mean they might have been Nigerian *before* they were British.' He gave up. 'Were they black?'

'It's PC, it doesn't say.'

Up ahead of them the bridge over the Kingsbrook had come into sight. A massive resistance to the introduction of roundabouts had kept Kingsmarkham town centre, at least to a superficial eye, much as it had always been. But the bottleneck caused by the narrow bridge had resulted in so many

355

traffic hold-ups that the bridge had been widened two years before. It was no longer the shallow stone arch featured on many postcards, but an uncompromising affair of grey-painted steel, overlooked by the motel extension to the Olive and Dove Hotel. The trees were mostly still there, the alders and willows and giant horse chestnuts.

It was the favoured beat of teenage boys who ran among traffic stopped by a red light to clean windscreens. The boys were there today but they gave up their thankless and often unwelcome labours to join the march. This side of the bridge a knot of people, perhaps a dozen, joined the tail of the column. Among them was Sophie Riding, the girl with the long corn-coloured hair Wexford had first seen waiting her turn in the Benefit Office and whose name he had learned from Melanie Akande. She and a woman with her were carrying a red silk banner, skilfully made and with the words 'Give Graduates a Chance' cut out in white and stitched to the silk.

The column waited. The policeman on duty waved on the three cars waiting at the lights and when they had passed beckoned the marchers on to the bridge. Wexford saw the drinkers at the tables outside the Olive get to their feet and crane their necks to see the lengthening procession go by. Burden said, 'By the way, something else I forget to say, Mrs Khoori got in.'

'Nobody ever tells me anything,' said Wexford.

'With a majority of seven. What you might call a close-run thing.'

'D'you want me to follow them, sir?' Donaldson asked.

The marchers intended to turn into Brook Road. The banner-carriers at the head of the column stopped on the far side of the bridge and one of them held up his hand, pointing to the left. Some

356

consensus of opinion, an invisible wave, must have passed along the quadruple line of people, for the message reached him and the column turned, snaking to the left like a train negotiating a sharp curve in the rails.

'Park opposite the Benefit Office,' Wexford said.

Ahead of them, the marked police car did this too. On the walls between which the steps ran up sat Rossy, Danny and Nige, and Raffy with them. Raffy, without his hat for once, displayed the huge helmet of dreadlocks that crowned his head and tumbled in a cascade down his back. As the procession approached and came to a straggling halt, Danny got down off the wall and stubbed out his cigarette.

'What happens now?' Burden said.

'Some gesture will be made.'

As Wexford spoke, Sophie Riding gave up her end of the 'Give Graduates a Chance' banner to the man next her. She detached herself from the column and walked up the steps. In her hand she held a sheet of paper, a petition perhaps or statement. Rossy, Danny, Raffy and Nige stared after her as she disappeared into the Benefit Office.

She was inside no more than fifteen seconds. The paper had been handed over and a point had been made. Within moments of her absorption back into the column, the double doors of the Benefit Office opened and Cyril Leyton appeared. He looked from left to right, then directly at the column, which was no longer a column, which had lost its shape and become an amorphous scattered crowd. Leyton scowled. He seemed about to say something and perhaps would have done if he had not, in that moment, caught sight of the police car on the opposite side of the road.

The door swung and swung again behind him as he went in. It was the kind that is made, no doubt wisely in the circumstances, to be unslammable. Apparently at no word of command, like a flock of birds whose leader directs them by silent unknown means, the crowd formed into fours once more, swung round – those in the vanguard had no intention of giving up pride of place – and headed back the way it had come.

The boys from the wall joined on the end. Sophie Riding took up one end of her banner and the woman with her the other end. As the column turned into the High Street, the clock on St Peter's church began striking noon.

Chapter Twenty-Four

The heat was like the inside of a rain forest now, or like a sauna. There was no breath of wind. The sun was lost under banks of frothy whiteness that overlaid a sky of dark grey cloud. Thunder had begun to roll but so distantly that its rumblings were lost behind the throb and beat of traffic noise.

The march occupied the left-hand lane of Kingsmarkham High Street. Here the High Street was fairly wide and there was room for Stowerton-bound cars to creep past, but those heading for Stowerton were diverted into Queen Street and the long serpentine southern route. The column passed St Peter's church as the final note of the midday clock chimes died away, and proceeded northwards close to the churchyard wall. At the point where the diversion began two police officers, a man and a woman, cleared space for the column to pass. It had picked up more people at the churchyard gate and, outside the biggest of the High Street supermarkets, a man and a girl who had taken a trolley from the rank on the forecourt abandoned it and tagged on to the end of the procession instead.

The police car with the stripe down its side and the crest on its door had turned back and been replaced by an unmarked Vauxhall, driven by PC Stafford from the uniformed branch with PC Rowlands beside him. Wexford and Burden had left theirs on a vacant meter outside the offices of Hawkins and

Steele where Bruce Snow worked, but when Stafford put his head out and offered a lift, Wexford shook his head and said they would follow the column on foot. Sophie Riding, who had handed in the petition at the Benefit Office, was two people ahead of them. They were sandwiched between her and her banner and the unmarked police car. That was how they came to witness so entirely what was about to happen.

The Range Rover was parked on the right-hand side and facing right on a broken yellow band fifty yards or so ahead of them outside Woolworths. It was an inconvenient place to have parked on this morning of all mornings but its positioning broke no traffic rule. Wexford didn't recognize the Range Rover, any more than he did the white van behind it and the car in front of it, but he did note the behaviour of its driver and the behaviour of the other drivers in leaving vehicles on that particular spot as antisocial. He noted too its olive green colour and a memory came into his mind of the Women, Aware! meeting and a note passed to him. More interesting at that moment was the sight, far ahead, only accessible to someone as tall as he, of Anouk Khoori crossing the greensward outside the council offices, her arms outspread. She wore a loose flowing garment and she was holding out her arms like a royal personage returning from a goodwill tour, greeting the children from whom she has been parted for a month.

Wexford was remarking to Burden that he wondered if she would tell the marchers that she knew they would come, she had had a feeling they would, when the nearside door of the Range Rover opened and Christopher Riding stepped down on to the pavement. The Range Rover was now no more than a car-length ahead of where Wexford and Burden were. Its offside door opened and

Christopher's father got out. Things happened very quickly then.

Christopher edged round the front of the Range Rover as his sister Sophie came alongside. He and Swithun Riding in a concerted swift movement seized her by the arms and she dropped the banner with a cry. They lifted her off her feet, threw back the car door and slung her inside. Both tall and powerful, with big hands and muscular arms, they swung her in the air, her bright swatch of corn-gold hair flying out, before throwing her into the back seat.

The marchers in the immediate vicinity fell back, fanning out. A woman screamed. Someone picked up the banner. The column ahead of the girl marched on, unaware of what had happened, but those at its tail stopped to stare. Now Swithun Riding was back in the driver's seat, his son squeezing himself between the bonnet of the Range Rover and the car in front of it. There must have been a central locking system, for Sophie couldn't unlock the door and escape. She was beating her fists against the window, she began to scream.

Wexford looked back at the unmarked Vauxhall and cocked his head at Stafford. He lunged forward and grabbed the rear door handle, but finding the door locked as he expected, hammered on the glass. Stafford and Rowlands had both left the Vauxhall. This was not what they had expected, this was unprecedented, this in *Kingsmarkham*?

The driver of the car ahead of the Range Rover, knowingly or unwittingly, now reversed an inch or two. It was a dangerous move and made Christopher let out a bellow of rage and fear. The reversing car nearly crushed him, but the driver had braked just in time. Christopher found himself trapped between its rear bumper and the Range Rover's front fender. The two vehicles made a man trap which pinned his legs.

361

He stood struggling, waving his arms and shouting, 'Go forward, go forward, you bastard!'

The front of the column, still unaware of the fracas at the rear, marched on, unperturbed. Like a pantomime horse whose hind legs have given up the game, it broke into an ungainly trot for the last final hundred yards of its progress. The rearguard had scattered into a crowd of fascinated spectators. Burden, with a quick nod to Wexford, slipped round the back of the Range Rover and in front of the white van behind it, walked past the imprisoned screaming girl, and wrenched open the passenger door Riding had unlocked for his son.

'Go back, go back!' the boy was yelling now.

Riding started the engine and had begun to move the shift when Burden put his foot on the step and climbed into the passenger seat. Riding had never seen him before and must have taken him for an interfering member of the public. Without hestitation, he did at once the utterly unexpected, drawing back his right arm like a discus thrower and letting fly with a savage punch to Burden's jaw.

The passenger door swung open. Burden reeled backwards through the empty space. He broke his fall by clutching at the door frame but still half-tumbled to the pavement. The girl screamed more loudly. His passenger door swinging, Riding reversed into the white van, hitting it with a reverberating crash. Then he saw the uniformed policemen. He saw Wexford.

Wexford said, 'Open that door.'

Riding only stared at him. Half the crowd had moved round the Woolworths side of the van. Someone picked Burden up. He staggered, dazed, put a hand up to his head and sat down heavily on the low wall in front of the store. Wexford pushed the boy out of the way and, moving between the Range

Rover and the car ahead, stepped up inside the swinging door.

'Don't try the same thing with me, will you?' he said.

He unlocked the nearside rear door and helped the girl out. Her face was awash with tears. She held on to him, her hands gripping his sleeves. A stream of invective pouring from Riding made her tremble. He thrust his face at the open door, shouting in Burden's direction, 'What's it to you if I stop my own daughter making a foul exhibition of herself? What business is it of yours, for Christ's sake?'

The girl shook. Her teeth had begun to chatter. Christopher, now free and rubbing his crushed legs, stood up and put out one hand to her in a gesture of appeasement. She screamed at him, 'Get away from me!'

Wexford said, 'All of you are coming to the police station *now*.'

Blood was running down Burden's face. He mouthed something, while holding on to his head. The howling siren of an ambulance, summoned by Stafford, sent the crowd falling back, splitting now into two distinct groups, one solidly behind Burden, the rest spectators by the churchyard wall. The ambulance came out of York Street and blocked the road, parking where the column had marched. Ahead the marchers had gone out of sight and with the appearance of the paramedics, two of them with a stretcher Burden scowled at, the first drops of rain began to fall.

Riding had unlocked his driver's door. His face dark red, he stepped down and said to Wexford. 'Look, what I did was entirely justifiable. I told my daughter I'd stop her if she joined the march, she knew what was coming to her. That chap seemed to think he was making some sort of citizen's arrest . . .'

363

'That chap is a police officer,' Wexford said.

'O God, I didn't. . .'

'If you'll get into the car we'll go to the police station. You can do your explaining there.'

The girl was tall and strong and straight. She looked what she was, the product of twenty-two or -three years of top-grade feeding, fresh air, care and attention, the best of schools. Wexford didn't know when he had seen a more vulnerable face. There was no bruising on it but still it looked bruised. The skin was soft beyond belief, almost transparent, the eyes puffy, the lips chapped and that in high summer. Her hair, the colour of the ripe barley they had been cutting in the fields up at Mynford, looked unnatural framing that suffering face, it looked like false hair worn by an actress miscast for her part.

She said to Karen Malahyde, 'I can go home if they're not there.'

'Well,' said Karen, but she said it kindly, 'just at the moment you aren't going anywhere. Would you like a cup of tea?'

Sophie Riding said she would. Carefully, Wexford said to her, 'We won't go in the interview room. They aren't very pleasant places. We'll go up to my office.' Suddenly, he thought of Joel Snow and he knew Karen was thinking of him too. This was different, of course it was – wasn't it? Joel too had been unwilling while this girl knew it was the only way. He said to her in the lift, 'It won't take long.'

'What do you want me to do?'

'Something I wish I'd been able to ask you to do two weeks ago.'

They went into his office. The rain was heavy enough to blind the windows and make it dark. Karen put on lights and the sky outside the window turned to a streaming twilight. She gave Sophie a chair.

364

Wexford sat down behind his desk. 'It was you sent me that question about a rapist at the Women, Aware! meeting?'

She was eager to talk but she was afraid too. 'Oh, yes! I wanted to come round afterwards, like you said. I would have done if I could, I hope you believe me.'

Suddenly, preceding the thunder by seconds, a brilliant zig-zag of lightning expelled everything, seeming to hold the streaming water suspended, making the dark sky invisible, until the crash came and the world went on. Sophie shuddered and made a little sound, like a protest. There was a tap at the door and Pemberton came in with tea. She covered her face with her hands for a moment, then took them away to show the tears flowing down her cheeks. Karen pushed the box of tissues at her.

'I believe you,' Wexford said. 'I understand what stopped you coming to me.'

Sophie took a tissue. 'Thanks.' She said to Wexford, 'What do you want me to do?'

'Make a statement. Tell us about it. It won't be difficult, practically speaking. It may be difficult emotionally.'

'Well,' she said, 'I can't go on like I have been. It has to stop. I can't go another day, not another minute.'

He said fairly, 'There are other ways. We'll manage without your statement. You don't have to do it. But if you don't, I'm afraid . . . well, there may be more . . .'

Karen said into the recording device, 'Sophie Riding at Kingsmarkham Police Station on Friday, July twenty-ninth. The time is 12.43pm. DCI Wexford and DS Malahyde are present . . .'

When it was over and he had heard it all, Wexford

365

went downstairs to where Sophie's father sat in Interview Room One with DC Pemberton. He looked chastened. His face had resumed its normal colour. The twenty minutes he had waited down here had no doubt brought him to regret his hasty behaviour. A man who has hit another man is always aghast to discover that the other is a policeman.

He got up when Wexford came in and began to apologize. His reasons for behaving as he had came out with easy fluency and they were the excuses of the man who has always been able to buy or talk his way out of trouble.

'Mr Wexford, I can't tell you how sorry I am about all this. Needless to say I wouldn't have struck your officer if I'd had any idea. I took him for a member of the public.'

'Yes, I expect you did.'

'This doesn't have to go any further, does it? If my daughter had been reasonable and got into the car – after all, she'd completed the best part of that damn fool march – if she'd done that none of this would have happened. I'm not a harsh father, I adore my children . . .'

'Your treatment of your children isn't in question,' Wexford said. 'Before you say any more I should warn you that anything you do say will be taken down and may be given in evidence . . .'

Interrupting, Riding shouted, 'You're not charging me with hitting that chap!'

'No,' said Wexford. 'I'm charging you with murder, incitement to murder and attempted murder. And when I have done that I shall go into the room next door and charge your son with rape and attempted murder.'

'Without Sophie Riding's statement,' Wexford said, 'I doubt if anything could have been made to stick.

366

We have no evidence and no proof, no more than conjecture.'

Burden's face was swollen like a Victorian cartoonist's image of a man with toothache. 'Assault on a police officer is the least of his worries, I suppose. Odd, isn't it, I was the one most impressed by what Mavrikiev said about killing someone with your fists and it was me who really had it brought home to me.

'It's a funny thing, you see these characters in films, westerns and that sort of thing, they knock each other around but it never seems to have any effect, they get a great swinging blow to the jaw but they're up again in a flash and hammering away at the other one. And you see them in the next scene with not a mark on them, all spruced up with a girl on their arm, taking her out for a night on the town.'

'Hurts, does it?'

'It's not so much that it hurts. It feels so enormous. And it doesn't feel as if it'll ever *work* again. At any rate he left me all my teeth. So, are you going to tell me about it?'

'Freeborn'll be here in half an hour and I'll have to tell *him*.'

'Well, you can tell me first,' said Burden.

Wexford sighed. 'I'll play you the tape of Sophie Riding's statement. You realize, of course, that Sojourner knew of the existence of the Benefit Office through Sophie. She'd heard Sophie talking about it, about going there and signing on and so forth, though she didn't know where it was.'

'What, talking about it to her parents?'

'And her brothers and her little sister, no doubt. Sojourner waited on them, she'd always have been in and out, though never out of the house.'

'How did they get her into the country in the first place?'

'Sophie doesn't know. She wasn't there, she was

367

already at Myringham Polytechnic that's now Myringham University and before that she'd been at boarding school here. But she'd seen Sojourner at their home in Kuwait when she was there in the holidays and she remembers when Sojourner first came. Her idea is that she was brought here as the boy's girlfriend. In a hideous kind of way, she *was*, if "girlfriend" is one definition of the woman you have forcible sexual intercourse with.'

'*That* was going on?'

'Oh yes. The father too, I daresay, though I don't know – yet. Listen to Sophie.'

Wexford wound the tape on, pressed 'play', reversed and got the point in the statement he wanted. The girl's voice was soft and plaintive, yet outraged too. It came over as a cry for help, yet there was no appeal in it.

My mother told me a Kuwaiti man bought her from her father in Calabar, Nigeria, for five pounds. He meant to educate her and treat her like a daughter but he died and she had to be a servant. My mother talked as if we'd done her a great favour, as if it was the best thing in the world for her finding a 'good home' with us. 'Good home' is the expression they use about dogs that get rescued, isn't it? I think she was about fifteen then.

I never thought much about it. I know I should have but I wasn't at home with them very much. I liked it here in England, I was always longing to get back to England. When the Gulf War started they came home. It wasn't a problem for my father, he could work anywhere, he's a brilliant paediatric surgeon. I don't like saying it, I wish I didn't have to, but it's true. He loves babies, you should see him with a baby, and he loves all of us, his family, his children. But we're different, as far

368

as he is concerned, we're what he calls the upper crust. He says some people are destined to be hewers of wood and drawers of water. I think that comes from the Bible. For him some people are born to be slaves and wait on others.

I must have been very naive. I didn't know what the bruises on her were . . . well, the bruises and cuts and all the other marks. In Kuwait I'd thought she was pretty to look at but she wasn't pretty in England. I'd graduated and I was home all the time and it was all a mystery to me. I never saw anyone hit her but I could tell she was frightened of my father and my brother. And my other brother David when he was at home, though mostly he wasn't, mostly he's away at college in America. The bad part – for me, that is – the bad part was that I thought she was stupid and clumsy, I could even see what my mother meant when she said she wasn't fit to sleep in a proper bedroom.

The machine on pause, Wexford went on, 'Psychologists say that someone ugly and dirty is a ready candidate for abuse. That your own abuse has resulted in the ugliness makes no difference. The reasoning behind it seems to be that ugliness deserves punishment and dirt and neglect of personal hygiene even more so. It got to a point where Sojourner was being beaten and struck for every small fault. She worked twelve or fourteen hours a day but that wasn't enough. Susan Riding told me herself they had six bedrooms in that house but that didn't mean they had one for Sojourner. She slept in a small room off the kitchen. All the rooms on the ground floor at the back have bars at the windows, to keep out burglars no doubt, but very convenient if you want to prevent someone escaping.

'I've just been to the house, I've seen it. It used to be a dogs' room and they've got a dog in there now. Susan Riding says it was more "appropriate", her word, for Sojourner to be in there, "in case they wanted her to do anything for them in the night." The mattress on the floor was apparently "what she'd been used to", she "wouldn't know what to do with a bed." Here's Sophie again.'

The girl's voice sounded clearer and more confident this time.

I needed a job, so I did the obvious thing, I went to the Job Centre and I signed on, only it wasn't the obvious thing to my parents. My father said it was a disgrace, that was for the working classes. He was quite prepared to keep me. Education wasn't *for* anything, he said, it was to make you a finer, better person. He'd make me an allowance. Hadn't he always kept me? My mother actually said they would keep me *until I got married*. We argued about this a lot and that poor girl overheard. Her English was never brilliant but she'd have understood that. She'd have known there was a place nearby you could go to and ask them to find you work and if there wasn't any work they'd give you money.

It was the beginning of July, the first or the second, when my brother Christopher asked her to wash his running shoes for him . . . well, told her to. They were white trainers. She made a mess of it, I don't know what she did, but she was terrified. Anyway, he beat her up for it. That was when I first realized what went on. It sounds absurd, I know, that I didn't know before, but I suppose I just didn't want to believe that of my own brother. I love my brother, or I did love him, he's my twin, you know.

I saw Christopher go into her room and come out again after about twenty minutes. I'd have

370

gone in but she didn't make a sound, not through all that beating she never made a sound.

But when I saw her next day I knew. I asked my brother and he denied it. She was clumsy, he said, I should know that, she always had been, she wasn't really fit to live in a civilized house. He made a lot of remarks about mud huts and he said she couldn't cope with furniture, she was always knocking into furniture. Well, I wasn't satisfied, I told my father but all that happened was he flew into a rage. If you haven't seen him in a rage you can't know what I mean. He's terrifying. He accused me of being disloyal to my family, he wanted to know where I'd 'picked up these ideas' and was it from my 'Marxist' friends I'd met at the Job Centre.

I know I should have done more. I have a lot of guilt about that. Somehow, then, I knew what I'd been hiding from myself all this time, that Christopher had raped her too, over and over, there had been all the signs I pretended not to see. All I did was send you that question at the meeting and that was worse than useless.

On the Monday after the beating she disappeared. My father was at the hospital and Christopher was in London at a job interview of all things. I guessed she'd run away and my mother thought she had, but we didn't know what to do, and in the evening my mother had to go out to a committee preparing for that Women, Aware! meeting. She left a note for my father. I said we ought to tell the police but my mother got into a panic at that. Of course I can understand why now. I had a date and when I got in at about eleven-thirty my mother was in bed and Christopher was out but my father was there. He said he didn't know what we were in a flap about, he'd told my mother. He'd sent the girl home, she was worse than useless and it made him sick seeing her about the house. He said he'd sent her back to Banjul on British Airways but there isn't a BA flight to Banjul on a Monday, the only flights are on Sunday and Fridays, I checked. My brother was out all evening and my father told me and my mother he was driving her to Heathrow but he can't have been because there wasn't a flight.

I didn't believe any of it. For some reason I thought she'd be in her room. They'd have beaten her up when she came back and she'd be in there lying on her mattress. I tried the door but it was locked. Well, you know, in a house like ours – a house like *theirs* – all the inside keys fit all the locks. I got another key and unlocked the door and everything was gone. She hadn't got much, just the two dresses that were my mother's cast-offs from years back and those awful black lace-up canvas boot things my mother bought her, the cheapest you can get. But it was all gone, all but the mattress and her headcloth. I don't know why they didn't find it when they cleaned the blood up but they didn't. It was on the mattress and the mattress was sort of red and blue. Well, the cloth was blue and red – red with the blood on it.

I've kept it. It was like a kind of madness, keeping it. I longed to throw it away but I couldn't. Even then it didn't occur to me that she might be dead. My brother was out that night for hours. I heard him come in, it must have been two-thirty or three, and he went off on his holiday to Spain next morning, so I never had a chance to talk to him. Anyway, I was afraid to talk to him, this wasn't my brother, this wasn't Chris that had been closer to me than anyone. Then I found his sweater in the wash with blood all over it.

I thought maybe my father had got her taken to

hospital secretly because my brother had gone too far. My father has a lot of influence, I don't know if he could do that, but I thought he could. All I could think of then was my brother raping her, my brother raping *anyone*. I didn't blame my father much then, I thought maybe he was just protecting his own son, I went to the Women, Aware! meeting with him and I wrote that question to you on an impulse. My father didn't see what I'd asked. I told him I'd asked whether it was legal to carry a CS gas canister. But I couldn't come up afterwards and explain, I couldn't get away from him.

Chief Constable Freeborn seemed to have forgotten about Wexford's 'carousing' picture in the paper. If the three weeks it had taken to catch the murderer of the two women still rankled, he gave no sign of it. He was all affability. To the old 'snug', a tiny room containing a table and three chairs, in the deepest recesses of the Olive and Dove, a barmaid brought the three beers he had ordered. Wexford sat down in the chair with the arms. He thought he deserved it.

'You have to remember,' he began, 'that she knew nothing about what rights she had under the Immigration Act, she didn't know there *was* an Immigration Act. She knew she wasn't allowed to work, but "work", it had been explained to her long ago, was what you got paid for and she was never paid, she was simply given "a good home". Susan Riding called her the "au pair" – or that's what she called her to me after Sojourner was dead. To do Mrs Riding justice, and I suppose everyone merits justice, I don't think she knew much about Sojourner's fate. She let her sleep on a mattress on the floor in the "dog's room" because she's that sort of woman, the kind that used to talk about the poor keeping coal in the bath if you gave them bathrooms. In buying Sojourner the cheapest footwear she could get, she probably thought she was being very bountiful. I wonder what she'd say if she knew the shop assistant put her down as a bag lady who slept on the street?

'But she knew nothing about the rape or the violent assaults, and if she suspected she shut her eyes to it, told herself not to let her imagination run wild. That evening when she came home from the committee meeting, her husband told her he'd sent the girl home and Christopher was out driving her to the airport. According to Mrs Riding, Sojourner had become "dirty and lazy" and was worse than useless. Except that she needed help in the house, she was glad to see the back of her.

'What had in fact happened was that Sojourner ran away on the Monday afternoon. Riding was out, the boy Christopher was in London and the young sister was at school. She didn't know where to go, she had never been out before, not out of their grounds, that is, but she knew there was a place where you went to find a job. She must have reasoned that anywhere she could find work couldn't be worse than what she'd left behind.'

Freeborn interrupted. 'You say she didn't know where to go. Winchester Avenue's a good way from the – what-d'you-call-it – ESJ, how did she know the way?'

'She didn't, sir. Perhaps she followed the river. You can see the Kingsbrook if you look down from there over the gardens. Melanie Akande liked to look at it while she was out running. Maybe some instinct led Sojourner towards the river, downhill, maybe she knew a town is often on a river. Her instinct led her to Glebe Road and she encountered Oni Johnson who directed her to the Benefit Office. The rest you know, how she followed Annette home and, failing to get the help she wanted from her, she had no choice but to return to where she had come from.'

374

'Pity this Annette didn't send her to us,' said Freeborn.

The understatement of all time, Wexford thought, but of course he didn't say so. 'She doesn't seem to have gone home at once or perhaps it took her a while to find her way back. At any rate, she didn't get there until Susan Riding and Sophie had gone out. Let us take it that she went in the back way and into her room where Swithun Riding found her.

'I don't say he meant to kill her. There seems no reason why he would. He asked her where she had been and when she told him he asked if she had spoken to anyone. Yes, the woman who takes the children across the road and this woman from the place where they give you jobs or they give you money. What's her name and where does she live? She tells him and it all comes out. Riding's daughter has described his rages. He flew into one then and set about her with his fists. Mike knows what his fist feels like and she was a young girl, thin and frail. They fed her pretty badly. Even so, she didn't die from his fists but from striking her head against the steel frame round the window bars. When you're in that room you can see how it happened.'

'So he got his son to help him dispose of her,' said Burden. 'Young Christopher took the body to Framhurst Woods and buried it, did he?'

'That was when he was supposed to be driving their erstwhile slave to Heathrow. I doubt if he knew where to do the deed, just drove out into the country until he found somewhere suitable. The road isn't busy and he'd have waited till dark.'

'And after that Riding had to make up his mind what to do about Annette and Oni.'

'I don't think he meant to do anything about Oni. After all, the Oni connection was a bit tenuous. Oni wouldn't go to the police, she had nothing to go *with*,

375

but Annette was different. He must have gone nearly mad wondering what Sojourner had told Annette. He wouldn't have got much sleep that night. Just after Annette made her phone call to the Benefit Office next day a man phoned and asked for her. Ingrid Pamber thought it was Snow but it wasn't, it was Riding. And he got an answer that gave him a little breathing space. Annette was at home ill in bed.'

'How did he know her name?' Freeborn wanted to know.

'Sojourner got it off the plate above the bell at Ladyhall Court. His next move was to get hold of Zack Nelson. Nelson owed him one, you see. It was Riding who performed the operation on Zack's son when the child was found to have some kind of heart malformation at a few weeks old. No doubt, Nelson had made extravagant promises at the time – "Anything in the world I can do for you, doc, any time, you only have to ask," – you can imagine the kind of thing.

'Zack needed money too. He needed somewhere for his girl friend and their child to live. But Zack botched it up, he let Percy Hammond see his face and he had to go back on Riding's instructions for a somewhat less venal offence – burglary. He knew he'd go down for that, he *wanted* to go down for that, so he got Riding to pay the blood money into an account he opened for Kimberley Pearson.

'So it looked as if Riding and his son were in the clear, until that is our treasure-seeking plumber dug up the body. Even then it must have been clear to Riding no one had the faintest idea who Sojourner was. The real fear started when he was picking up his younger daughter from the Thomas Proctor School and he saw me homing on Oni Johnson.

'I saw the Range Rover pull away from outside the

Thomas Proctor the day of the attack on Oni but of course I didn't make the connection. I thought it was her son Raffy we wanted to talk to, not Oni. Riding easily got to Castlegate before she got home – or else his son went: Christopher may also have seen me, for he was there in the Epsons' pink Escort, picking up the Epsons' older child. By the way, unpleasant though it is to contemplate, I think Christopher followed Melanie to Stowerton on that previous occasion because he had acquired a taste for black girls, it was black girls he fancied. Luckily for her, Melanie didn't fancy *him* and he was no doubt afraid to attempt the rape of a free and independent young woman.

'I don't yet know which of them made the attempt on Oni's life. We shall find out. I do know that it was Riding who went into the Intensive Care Ward next day and – with very little time or privacy at his disposal – pulled the IV line out from Oni's arm. It didn't work but it was worth a try.'

'Who picked the Riding child up from school the day Sojourner ran away?' Burden speculated. 'Not Riding or his wife obviously. A friend probably, they very likely had a rota system. Because if he'd done it or his wife had done it they'd have caught Sojourner before she got to Annette or Oni and none of it would have happened. I wonder if he thinks of that now?'

Freeborn, who had finished his drink in one single long swig, said irritably, 'Why do you call her that? What does it mean?'

'I didn't fancy Miss X. We hadn't a name for her.'

'Well, you know it now, presumably?'

'Oh, yes.' said Wexford. 'I know it now. If she ever had a surname no one seems to remember it. Sophie never forgot the first name she gave them when she was handed over from the man who died, but the others had forgotten it. She was called Simisola.' He got up. 'Shall we go?'

Acknowledgement

The author is grateful to Bridget Anderson for permission to quote in this novel passages from her book *Britain's Secret Slaves* published by Anti-Slavery International and Kalayaan.